W9-CDL-658

SECOND EDITION

Healthy Foundations
in Child Care

Barbara Pimento
George Brown College

Deborah Kernested
R.N.

Nelson
Thomson Learning™

Australia • Canada • Denmark • Japan • Mexico • New Zealand • Philippines
Puerto Rico • Singapore • South Africa • Spain • United Kingdom • United States

1120 Birchmount Road
Scarborough, Ontario M1K 5G4
www.nelson.com
www.thomson.com

For permission to use material from this text or product, contact us by
• Web: www.thomsonrights.com
• Phone: 1-800-730-2214
• Fax: 1-800-730-2215

Canadian Cataloguing in Publication Data

Pimento, Barbara
      Healthy foundations in child care

2nd ed.
Includes bibliographical references and index.
ISBN 0-17-616580-0

1. Day care centers – Health aspects – Canada. 2. Family day care – Health aspects – Canada. 3. Children – Health and hygiene – Canada. I. Kernested, Deborah, 1957– . II. Title.

HQ778.7.C3P55 1999 362.71'2 C99-932295-8

Acquisitions Editor	Joanna Cotton
Marketing Manager	Kevin Smulan
Project Editor	Jenny Anttila
Production Editor, Copy Editor	Bob Kohlmeier
Proofreader	Matthew Kudelka
Art Director	Angela Cluer
Cover Design	Suzanne Peden
Cover Image	Nicholas Wilton
Production Coordinator	Hedy Later
Typesetter	Barb Bannerman
Printer	Webcom

Printed and bound in Canada
1   2   3   4   03 02 01 00

Contents

▶ **Unit 3   Illness Prevention and Management   117**

▶ Unit 5   Safety Promotion   299

▶ Unit 6   Child Abuse Prevention   395

▶ Unit 7   Supporting Children's Development   453

▶ List of Exhibits and Appendixes

Before You Begin

Health is a complex subject that is interesting, challenging, thought-provoking, sometimes complex, and includes a wide range of perspectives. We are confident that this new edition *of Healthy Foundations in Child Care,* like the first one, reflects all of these attributes and, in addition, addresses more fully those issues that are of greater concern now than they were when the first edition appeared. As the title of this textbook implies, health is a cornerstone in ensuring high-quality child care. Learning through play is fostered and supported when children are healthy and able to participate fully in child-centred curriculum. Health is integrated with children's development, and each of this book's units reflects this belief.

In collaboration with families, caregivers have an integral role in maintaining or improving children's overall health status. This role requires an anti-bias attitude, respect, and sensitivity to diverse ethno-cultural and family health beliefs and practices. Each of us has a responsibility for our own health status, yet we can't dismiss the responsibility of our communities and society.

Healthy Foundations in Child Care, Second Edition, reflects a national perspective while recognizing differences among the provinces' and territories' child care regulations. As a result, the authors have selected a number of terms that are used through the textbook.

CAREGIVER

Regardless of the formal definition used in a particular province or territory, people working in the field often prefer to use a different title to describe their profession, such as the following:

- educator
- educarer
- facilitator
- teacher
- caregiver

- child care worker
- child care provider
- child care practitioner
- early childhood educator
- child care professional

At the national level there is ongoing discussion about selecting one term that can be used to designate each person who has formal early childhood education training, one term that reflects the complexity of roles in working with children and their families in child care programs. Two suggestions are "early childhood educator" and "early childhood care and education teacher." No consensus has been reached on this important issue. Further complicating the discussion is the fact that in most literature the term "early childhood" spans the ages between birth and 8 years, thus excluding those working with school-agers between the ages of 9 and 12. For readability the term "caregiver" has been selected for this textbook. It is not our intention to offend or negate the complex roles and responsibilities of those working in child care programs. The authors recognize that trained, qualified professionals who work in child care programs care, support, facilitate, and educate. Yet when we look at children's health, one of the primary roles is providing care; thus, "caregiver" is an appropriate term.

Director

The daily operation of a centre is often determined by the number of children enrolled and the organization's management style. As a result, in some situations the director is responsible for both the centre's overall administration and for the supervision of staff and sometimes works with children. In other situations, the director oversees the finances and policy and staffing decisions and also takes primary responsibility for networking in the community and formally representing the centre. In addition, one or more supervisors oversees the staff and works directly with children and families for all or part of each day. The term "director" refers to the individual who has primary responsibility for supervising caregivers and managing day-to-day operations. Centres that operate as cooperatives do not have directors. In these programs, "director" refers to the collective that makes decisions.

Centre

The term "centre" refers to child care centres that are licensed by the province or territory. Some of the content of this book could be used by staff working in other types of facilities—drop-in centres, resource centres, family day care homes, and nursery school programs. However, the content was not written with those programs in mind.

Parent

The term "parent" refers to any adult who has primary responsibility for the child. For the sake of clarity, the term encompasses legal guardians and foster parents. The authors recognize that the child's immediate family may be far more diverse than simply biological or adoptive parents, and we hope that the term "parent" reflects inclusiveness.

Child Care Office

The term "child care office" refers to the office or agency primarily responsible for licensing centres in individual provinces and territories. When we refer to child care regulations, we mean those that apply to your province or territory.

Age Groups of Children
- infants: birth to 12 months
- toddlers: 12 to 24 months
- preschoolers: 2 to 5 years
- school-agers: 6 to 12 years

Classifications for age groups vary with child care regulations. We use these definitions throughout the textbook.

The second edition of *Well Beings* (1996), by the Canadian Paediatric Society, provides the Canadian child care community with a current and comprehensive health resource manual. The book's audience extends beyond centre directors and caregivers to include child care office personnel, public health staff, physicians, and early childhood education instructors and students. It was important that this new edition of *Healthy Foundations in Child Care* reflect the consensus reached in recommendations for standards of care and practice. Thus, we refer to *Well Beings* and use selected material from it throughout this textbook. *Healthy Foundations in Child Care*, Second Edition, provides you with entry-level knowledge and skills and introduces you to *Well Beings*, Second Edition, which you will use as a resource manual on graduation to expand your knowledge and skills.

The emphasis in this textbook is on the overall health needs of all children. We have not included discussion on physical, cognitive, or socio-emotional challenges and long-term medical conditions such as epilepsy or diabetes. In most, if not all, early childhood education training programs, students are required to complete a course on children with special needs and working effectively with families and others involved in their care. Students then combine the knowledge, skills, and attitudes that they learn in their courses and centre placements to meet the physical, emotional, and social needs of each child. Most training institutions also offer post-diploma education in this area.

New to the Second Edition

Along with updated information and statistics in all units, significant additions to the second edition include:

- expanded coverage of adult health issues, including dimensions of wellness and Health Canada's Physical Activity Guide in Unit 2
- discussion on current concerns about antibiotic misuse and asthma management in Unit 3
- more detailed discussion of playground safety and CSA guidelines, as well as a new section on environmental contaminants in Unit 5
- reorganization of Unit 6, Child Abuse Prevention, to better reflect caregivers' day-to-day responsibilities. The revised unit includes clarification on the controversy over the use of corporal punishment as well as new guidelines on personal safety programs for children.
- a discussion of self-regulation in Unit 7 that reflects current research and suggestions for caregivers to support children's self-regulation

Learning Outcomes

Educational reform and initiatives across Canada, such as prior learning assessment, standards, and outcomes, are catalysts for some educational institutions to embark on the process of establishing learning outcomes. These are clear, broad statements that embody the necessary and significant knowledge, skills, and attitudes that learners are expected to demonstrate to successfully complete each course or program.

The authors have examined this textbook for significant learning statements. On completion of this textbook in conjunction with studies in health, it is expected that students will have demonstrated the ability to

1. represent the holistic nature of health through examining its physical, emotional, and social dimensions
2. identify the scope and limits of the caregiver's roles with regard to health in early childhood education, recognizing the importance of sensitivity and respect for the primary role of parents and family
3. apply principles of a health promotion philosophy to their lives as well as to their work with children
4. promote children's health based on knowledge of child development and observation
5. assimilate the importance of collaborating and networking with other professionals and agencies on an ongoing basis to enhance health in child care programs
6. transfer the principles of essential health policies and practices to new situations in child care

Acknowledgments

The knowledge I gain continually through my relationships with family, friends, colleagues, and students is more meaningful to me than I can put to paper. Michael is wonderful, always there to listen, share ideas, and offer his wisdom and support in countless ways. Taryn's and Taylor's love for life and budding passion for health issues that affect all of us give me strength and make me proud.

Thanks to my George Brown College colleagues, who are incredible individuals and have contributed so much. In particular, thanks to Lynn Wilson, Pam Doyle, and Marie Goulet for editing and writing, and to Gail Hunter, Rita Barron, Connie Winder, and Jane Bertrand for their encouragement.

Now that Deborah and I are a province apart, I appreciate her many strengths even more this time around. When we work together, it's magic!

—Barbara Pimento

To my mother, Rhoda, my sister Carla, and Anastasia, Erik, and Greg, along with my friends, thank you all for your love and encouragement. Separated geographically during the writing of this second edition, Barb and I have had to meet some unique challenges. Thank you, Barb, for your commitment, dedication, and tenacity in making the second edition a reality. I've said this before, but I couldn't have asked for a better writing partner and friend.

—Deborah Kernested

There are many we would like to thank for sharing during the development of *Healthy Foundations in Child Care*, Second Edition. Here are a few: Marie Goulet, Lynn Wilson, and Pam Doyle, for their significant editing and writing in Unit 7; Drs. Lee Ford-Jones and Susan Skull of the Hospital for Sick Children, for their consultation in Unit 3; Malak Sidky from Safe Kids Canada, for her review of Unit 5; and Sue Hunter from the Toronto Child Abuse Centre, for her thorough review and edit of Unit 6. To our production editor at Nelson, Thomson Learning, Bob Kohlmeier, whose commitment to this book along with his guidance and expertise are gratefully appreciated by both of us, thank you, Bob. Thanks also to the many others at Nelson whose hard work helped make this book possible.

A textbook is not complete without its photographs. Thank you so much to the children, families, and staff at the five centres who generously welcomed us into their wonderful programs. Some of the photographs in this book are courtesy of Lynn Wilson, Toronto; Carla Kernested, Winnipeg; the Patterson-Reynolds family, Toronto; Marie Goulet, Toronto; George Brown College, Child Care Programs, Toronto; Sister Celeste, Fort Norman, N.W.T.; the Manitoba Child Care Association, Winnipeg; FoodShare, Toronto; Joanna Cotton, Nelson, Thomson Learning; and Health Canada.

Unit 1

Health Promotion

Unit 1: Health Promotion

CONTENTS

Promoting the health of children and families in child care programs is one of the most important roles of staff. So much of what caregivers do involves health. In this introductory unit, we explore what health is, and we look at what determines our health. We then provide you with a basis for understanding how Canada's health care system is organized. We explore health promotion and our changing attitudes toward health. The unit closes with an introduction to the health promotion action plan blueprint and how it can be incorporated into child care programs. The action plan is revisited in the subsequent units.

What Is Health?

▶ **OBJECTIVE** To learn the World Health Organization's definition of health.

The most influential definition of health in the 20th century was introduced by the World Health Organization (WHO) in 1947. Health, said the WHO, is "a state of complete physical, mental, and social well-being and not merely the absence of disease and infirmity." The definition has been criticized over the years because of, among other reasons, its use of the word "state" rather than "process" and for the impossibility of achieving a "complete" state of health. Yet there is no doubt that this definition paved the way for a social model of health and health promotion in Canada, broadening the concept of health from a medical one to one that encompasses quality of life. Quality of life refers to the degree to which an individual enjoys the important dimensions of her or his life, including the fulfilment of physical and emotional needs, social belonging, and the realization of goals, hopes, and aspirations. Quality of life is relevant to all humans, at any time and from their own perspectives (Brown et al. 1998, 4).

In 1984 the World Health Organization revised its definition of health to:

> the extent to which an individual or group is able, on the one hand, to realize aspirations and satisfy needs; and, on the other hand, to change or cope with the environment. Health is therefore seen as a resource for everyday life, not the objective for living; it is a positive concept emphasizing social and personal resources, as well as physical capacity.

The ever-changing nature of our health means that our adaptability to change is an important lifelong attribute and influences our health. Also, health is enhanced by reasonable lifestyles and the equitable use of public and private resources that permit people to use their initiative individually and collectively to maintain and improve their own well-being, however they may define it (Rootman and Raeburn in Pedersen et al. 1994, 69).

Determinants of Health

 OBJECTIVES To describe community and individual responsibility in determining health.
To identify and explain four aspects of our lives that affect our health.

Health is a basic human right, so why are some of us more likely to enjoy good health than others? To answer this question, we first need to consider health determinants. There are no guarantees of good health and many aspects of our lives affect our health status. Maintaining our health is the combined responsibility of each of us, the community, and society.

Individual and Community Roles

From the time we are conceived, heredity and environmental factors are always interacting. They affect all aspects of our health—physical, emotional, and social.

 The way we react to a life event (environment) such as losing a job is affected somewhat by our temperament (heredity).

Each of us is born with a unique genetic background that affects our strengths and challenges in the physical, emotional, and social self. Just as your genetic makeup determines your body type and eye colour, so it may predispose you to a particular medical condition (e.g., you may have a family history of allergies, heart disease, diabetes, or some other physical or emotional condition).

Heredity is only one determinant of health. Awareness of your family history, and an understanding of the risk factors that contribute to a particular disease, can help to prevent the disease or to reduce its effects.

 Frank has a family history of lung cancer but continues to smoke, which increases his likelihood of developing a serious and perhaps fatal lung disease.

People's attitudes and knowledge affect their behaviour. *Canada's Health Promotion Survey* concluded that people's decisions about their health contribute significantly to their health status, either positively or negatively (Stevens and Fowler Graham 1993, 308). Yet individual decisions are not made in isolation from society.

The community plays an equally important role in the health status of its members. Clean water, clean air, and an adequate sewage system are key factors in preventing widespread illness. A community also provides an economic infrastructure that supports employment opportunities and social, educational, emergency, and health services. Social attitudes, legislation, and policies affect our well-being and quality of life.

 Many young girls believe that they must diet to achieve society's unrealistic notion of the ideal female body image. They may also smoke—believing this will help reduce their appetite. Young girls are bombarded by unattainable images of women in television, magazines, and movies. A young girl's decision to diet is influenced by complex realities (e.g., family situations, media influences, issues around personal control).

Many aspects of our lives affect whether our basic physical, emotional, and social needs are being met. Each of these requirements includes a role for both individual and community (or societal) responsibility. Although Canadians focus attention on the health care system, in reality the most significant determinants of health are in fact social and economic. These include:

► income/social status
► healthy child development
► freedom from discrimination
► communication and life skills

INCOME/SOCIAL STATUS

We have known for some time that the better off people are in terms of income, social status, social networks, sense of control over their lives, self-esteem, and education, the healthier they are likely to be. The wealthiest Canadians can expect to live four years longer than the poorest Canadians, and non-Aboriginal Canadians can expect to live seven years longer than Aboriginal Canadians. (National Forum on Health 1997, vol. I, 15)

The National Forum on Health acknowledges that health improves with each step up the income and social status ladder, and not only because of the obvious fact that the more income one makes, the better the services one can afford. It is also true that having choices and control over many of the decisions in one's life contributes to one's well-being, and a degree of control is enjoyed by most wealthier Canadians. It follows, then, that poverty, unemployment, and cuts in social supports have a dramatic impact on the health of many Canadians. A standard of living that fosters well-being is achieved when adults have the opportunity to work at meaningful jobs and have access to quality child care and education for their children.

Although Canada takes pride in its international reputation for fairness and compassion and is considered one of the best countries in the world in which to live, the United Nations Human Poverty Index (HPI) ranked Canada tenth in its treatment of the poor. The HPI measures levels of functional illiteracy, the number of poor people, and the level of social exclusion indicated by long-term unemployment (Campaign 2000 1998, 11).

A significant measure of the health and strength of a society is the well-being of its children and families. By that measure, Canada is failing. One in five children in Canada lives in poverty. A large and growing proportion of children are living in conditions of economic hardship that are heightening risks and limiting their chances to become healthy, involved citizens. (Campaign 2000 1998, 2)

Campaign 2000 is a national, nonpartisan movement to build awareness and support for the 1989 all-party House of Commons resolution to eliminate child poverty. The fact that Canada, rather than moving forward in eliminating poverty since this resolution, has moved backward, is unacceptable and requires immediate action.

The situation of Canada's Aboriginal peoples highlights Canada's failure in addressing social and economic determinants of health. The Royal Commission on Aboriginal Peoples (1996, 3–4) reported that:

▶ Aboriginal Peoples have higher unemployment rates.
▶ The incidence of violence, physical and sexual abuse, and suicide is higher among Aboriginal peoples.
▶ Children in Aboriginal communities have the highest rates of injury and death of all Canadian children.
▶ Many Aboriginal communities have higher rates of infectious diseases (e.g., tuberculosis, AIDS) than non-Aboriginal communities.

FIGURE 1.1   CHILD POVERTY: WHAT HAS HAPPENED SINCE 1989?

The number of —

Poor children	up 60%
Children in families with incomes less than $20,000 (in constant 1996 dollars)	up 65%
Children in families experiencing long-term unemployment	up 33%
Children in working poor families	up 45%
Children in families needing social assistance	up 51%

Change between 1989 and 1997

Children living in unaffordable rental housing	up 91%
Poor children in two-parent families	up 43%
Poor children in lone-parent families	up 92%

Source: Reprinted with permission from Campaign 2000, *Family Poverty in Canada: Report Card* (Toronto: Family Service Association of Toronto, 1998), 2.

FIGURE 1.2   PERCENTAGE OF CHILDREN LIVING IN POVERTY

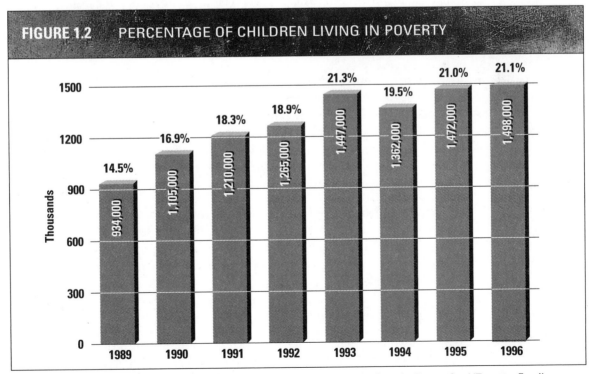

Source: Reprinted with permission from Campaign 2000, *Family Poverty in Canada: Report Card* (Toronto: Family Service Association of Toronto, 1998), 3.

"Canada's Aboriginal people have contributed a rich heritage to the country, but they have not shared fully in its social and economic development" (Health and Welfare Canada 1992, 3). The serious health inequalities that Aboriginal children and families suffer must be addressed. In many cases, important traditional cultural values and the traditional way of life have been lost or weakened. Aboriginal people are demanding change, and their work must be financially and justly supported by the various levels of government and by Canadian society.

A family's income determines whether a child lives in poverty. That an adult in a household is employed does not guarantee that the income earned provides the basic necessities or a standard of living above the poverty level. Many families depend on two wages to provide basic needs, and even the two combined may be insufficient. Between 1981 and 1991, families with two or more earners were one of the groups that had an increased proportion of poverty (Ross et al. 1994, 61). The gap between poor and well-off families in Canada has been widening since 1973. This is mainly due to the lack of access to jobs that can support families. Most of the jobs that have been created are part-time, low-wage, contract, or seasonal, with few or no benefits. Furthermore, in recessionary times, people who have been gainfully employed for years may lose their jobs, putting them in short- or long-term poverty situations. A growing number of families are being excluded from participation in the economic and social life of their communities. This undermines the connectedness that communities need to maintain and build public support for social programs (Campaign 2000 1998, 5, 7).

The likelihood that families with children have two incomes is particularly unrealistic. Consider:

▶ the number of single-parent families, most of them led by women earning an average of 70 cents on the dollar to men (Ross et al. 1994, 61).

▶ the lack of affordable quality child care, which for parents who want to work results in one of the salaries barely or not even covering child care costs.

▶ in households where one of the adults is physically or emotionally challenged, the possibility that he or she may be unable to find employment that provides an adequate income—or to find any employment at all.

Evidence strongly suggests that poverty is the greatest barrier (or threat) to health—people living in poverty are much more likely to develop health problems, including chronic illnesses such as heart or lung disease, and to die at an earlier age than people living above the poverty level. Research shows that people with lower incomes have a higher incidence of high blood pressure, obesity, smoking, and lack of exercise, all of which are risk factors for cardiovascular disease (Wilkins 1988, 16–18).

Poverty also adversely affects children's well-being:

▶ Children who live in poverty have about twice the infant death rate, are more likely to die from injuries, and are hospitalized significantly more than children from families with adequate incomes (Canadian Institute of Child Health 1994, 128).

► Education positively influences life chances, yet poor children often lose out. "Although the drop-out rate has declined considerably for both groups since 1981, 16- and 17-year-old children in poor families dropped out of school in 1991 at more than twice the rate of their nonpoor counterparts" (Ross et al. 1994, 67).

Combine these facts with the ongoing stress that comes from living in poverty. It is not surprising that children who are poor are not likely to enjoy the same level of self-esteem or quality of life as their more financially stable peers (e.g., they are less likely to participate in sports or other physical activities because of high costs).

In conclusion, poverty, particularly as it affects children and families, must be addressed in order to improve health. The *Child Poverty Report Card* (1998, 13) proposes the following policy options for the federal government to implement:

► Uphold its commitment to spend at least 50% of budget surplus on valued social programs.
► Make children the focus of the federal budget.
► Launch the National Children's Agenda and provide opportunities for community input.
► Establish a National Millennium Fund for Early Childhood Care and Education as the key federal initiative of the National Children's Agenda.
► Develop concrete proposals for enhanced maternity/parental leave, safe, affordable housing, and the creation of good jobs.

HEALTHY CHILD DEVELOPMENT

Healthy child development is now known to be a key determinant of long-term health (Hertzman 1998, S14). A healthy start in life has a great impact on the well-being of children and throughout life, providing children with opportunities to develop the attributes and resilience needed to mature into healthy adults in our complex society. "Childhood is the most vulnerable period of human development, and by far the most influential. If the experiences of children support healthy development, they will be more likely to fulfil their potential as adults" (Guy 1997, xix).

Our Promise to Children (Guy 1997) is the culmination of a nationwide collaborative effort that brings together the findings of extensive research in order to focus on the future of Canada's children. It clearly explains why and how to invest in children. Neuroscience tells us about brain development while the social sciences are able to predict the kinds of environments that foster or hinder that development.

We are beginning to understand how social determinants affect the body through biological pathways. We now know that, although the brain has all its areas and neurons at birth, it is far from fully developed. Wiring essentially takes place during the first few years of life and ends around age 10. The neuron connections are made as a result of care and nurturing, and these depend on the quality of relationships with adults in the early years.

During this investment phase, children develop language skills, the ability to learn, to cope with stress, to have healthy relationships with others, and to have a sense of self.... Failure to provide optimum conditions for a child's development during this time makes the developing brain physically different from the brain of children who have been well nurtured, and these differences can have lifelong differences. (Hertzman in Guy 1997, 6)

Since the central nervous system communicates with all the systems in the body (e.g., immune, hormone, gastrointestinal), it follows that brain development affects long-term functioning of the body, hence the incidence of disease (Hertzman 1998, S16).

Research shows that the following determinants of health will help children to achieve optimal development:

1. protection (from harm and neglect)
2. relationships (children's developmental potential is supported or diminished by the care and attention received from parents, friends, relatives, neighbours, teachers, and other caring adults)
3. opportunity and hope (enabling children to build self-esteem and sustain hope for the future)
4. community (families need support networks around them, and in times of change the quality of the communities to which we belong is of tremendous importance)

When these determinants are in place for children, they are more likely to grow up healthy and happy. For many children in Canada, however, these needs are not met. Some are able to overcome the odds and flourish, but the more risks in a child's life, the less likely that he or she will be able to develop the flexibility and self-confidence to surmount the obstacles and live up to potential (Guy 1997, xvii). Childhood poverty, for example, has so many negative influences on lifelong development that "the preferred long term strategy is not to build resilience in poor children, but to eliminate child poverty" (Guy 1997, 21).

The "family time famine" that is a reality in many homes due to economic pressures that require two working parents, or a full-time working lone parent, can also affect children's development. Parents are working long hours to make ends meet. This is problematic, because families need time together to nurture relationships and enhance their members' sense of security, belonging, and competence. Schools, workplaces, and governments need to create family-friendly policies that are supportive to the changing demands, dynamics, and composition of families. "We have a collective responsibility to create the kinds of social and physical environments that enable children to thrive" (Guy 1997, 21).

Freedom from Discrimination

Freedom from discrimination as a result of an individual's race, religion, first language or ethno-culture, physical or emotional limitations, gender, age, social class, sexual orientation, physical size, or any other reason is important for well-being. When one is a victim of racism, classism, or any other form of discrimination, the effects on one's physical, emotional, and social well-being can be substantial.

Members of a minority group experience the frustration of being judged according to a stereotype and having limited options and opportunities.

Students looking for housing may have experienced subtle or not-so-subtle prejudice from landlords who stereotype students as unreliable renters. Consequently students may be limited to housing that doesn't feel as safe, is overpriced, or is farther from school. This situation may affect their physical, emotional, and social well-being:

▷ Money that is spent on high rent is not available for food.
▷ Emotional stress comes from feeling physically unsafe in the neighbourhood.
▷ Students from a minority ethnic group or who are single parents may face even further discrimination.

On the other hand, if you feel pride in who you are, and are accepted and respected by others, your health and quality of life are positively affected. Individuals have a responsibility to respect others. Society has a responsibility not to tolerate discrimination and to continue to find ways to educate people about the importance of tolerance and to include them in plans to improve their health and welfare.

COMMUNICATION AND LIFE SKILLS

Communication skills include the ability to speak and be understood as well as literacy. In Canada, literacy is defined as being able to read and write in one or both of our official languages, English and French. "Two national surveys, one by the Southam newspaper chain and another by Statistics Canada, have found that 38% of Canadians have limited or no skills in reading and writing in English or French" (Morgan 1993, 1197). Although individuals may be literate in their first language (e.g., Mandarin, Italian, Cree) but not in English or French, statistically they are not considered literate and are at a disadvantage in the larger community. Illiteracy often results in poorer health because the individual cannot read printed information about health. People who do not speak or understand one of the official languages well are at a disadvantage, since they may not seek out information or must depend on someone else's interpretation of it. When a person who is illiterate is unable to access an interpreter, that person may be unable to make effective use of health or social services.

► A person may not adequately understand the physician's or pharmacist's instructions.
► In a centre, when the parents and caregivers are not sufficiently fluent in the same language, the parents won't understand when they are asked to bring in their child's immunization record.
► Parents who are illiterate may not tell you that they can't read the centre's parent handbook outlining the health policies.

To improve readability, many public materials are now written in plain and simple language. In large cities, or areas where many people speak, read, and write in languages other than English or French, municipal governments often publish pamphlets and other documents in other languages. This service has a positive effect on the well-being of people in the community.

Health, social services, and educational departments continue to find ways to increase the number of informational resources accessible to those who do not speak, read, and write English or French. As well, individuals and their cultural/ethnic communities have a responsibility to access language and literacy programs in English or French to enable themselves to use the available resources.

We depend on communication skills in our day-to-day activities—interpersonal skills, coping skills, problem-solving skills. A person who is socially isolated is not likely living up to potential. Individuals who adopt a problem-solving approach to life, who interact effectively with family and community, become responsible in a social context. All communication skills play a significant role in the individual's level of participation in the labour force, training opportunities, and social/community activities.

Knowledge and skills in personal hygiene, sanitation, nutrition, food preparation and storage, basic health care, budgeting, and so on have positive effects on healthy behaviour. Learning life skills enables individuals to participate in society. Community resources must be available to answer individual questions.

A parent recognized that the family's current eating habits were not as healthy as they could be and contacted the public health nurse for information on buying and preparing food. The parent is more likely to buy a variety of fresh vegetables and grains when she knows how to cook and serve them.

What determines how healthy an individual is, then, is a complex combination of hereditary and environmental factors. Figure 1.3 provides a model that connects all the risk factors and conditions for poor health status.

FIGURE 1.3   THE SOCIOENVIRONMENTAL APPROACH TO HEALTH

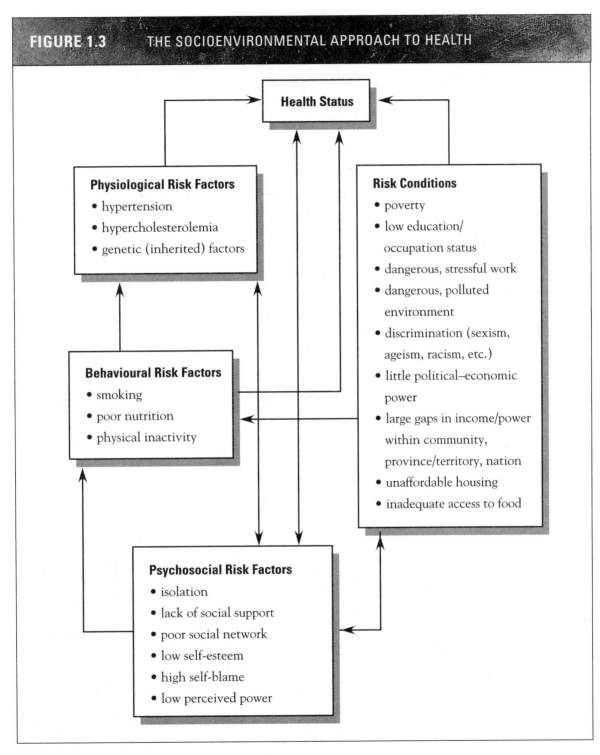

Source: Reprinted with permission from R. Labonté, *Health Promotion: Theory and Practice Background Material #1* (Centre for Health Promotion, University of Toronto, 1993), 30.

Canada's Health Care System

▶ **OBJECTIVES**   To list and define the five principles of medicare.
To differentiate between the roles of the personal and public health
care systems.

Where does Canada's health care system fit in this picture? As discussed earlier, social and economic factors have a greater impact on our health than does health care, and improvement in health for populations is strongly linked to policies and programs that address inequities. However, the quality of that health care also influences our health, in both prevention and management of disease and injury.

> Medicine is better than ever. And we live longer than ever before. But there's a problem. People put these two facts together and wind up assuming a cause-and-effect relationship between them that simply doesn't exist.... How we live—how we eat, how we work, how we love, and how we take our minds off our troubles—has far more impact on our health than the efforts of hospitals and doctors. (Rachlis and Kushner 1992, 162–63)

In Canada we are fortunate to have a system of universal medical and hospital insurance, one that tries to provide all citizens with equal access to health care. Canada has made the right to health care one of the priorities on its political agenda. We are treated by doctors and are hospitalized when necessary.

Over the past decade the health care system has reached a crisis point. Every few days you hear a news story about balancing the budget, spiralling health care costs, hospital closures, staff layoffs, cuts in health care services, and reductions in the quality of care. Canada and the provinces are paying more than they can afford in health services but they are not seeing the anticipated return in overall health. Health care reform has proved to be a immense task in Canada. Health care reform—rethinking and restructuring—is being taken on worldwide.

In late 1994 the National Forum on Health was launched by the federal government to involve and inform Canadians and advise the federal government on innovative ways to improve our health care system and the health of Canada's people. What the working groups found was that the basic principles of medicare set generations ago still reflect people's values of equity, compassion, collective responsibility, individual responsibility, respect for others, efficiency, and effectiveness (National Forum on Health 1997, vol. I, 2).

The somewhat rigid structure of the health care system has not provided the flexibility needed to meet the diverse needs of a rapidly changing society. For example, technological and therapeutic improvements should have made it possible to shift away from institutional-based health care (National Forum on Health 1997 vol. I, 12).

If our health care system were being established today, the system would rely less on hospitals and doctors and provide a broader range of community-based services (National Forum on Health, vol. II, 12). A high standard of care remains essential, but simply doing more of the same with less won't work.

All levels of government in Canada are calling for a more community- and home-based approach to health care, yet some of these governments are also cutting social services that are needed in an infrastructure for an integrated and comprehensive system. Simply sending patients home from hospital earlier without adequate support for care at home doesn't address the problem and certainly doesn't contribute to modernizing medicare for the 21st century (Kirkey 1998, 11).

Despite the criticisms, there is little doubt that most people living in Canada have benefited from our social medicare system. How did this system evolve?

Medicare's History: In Brief

THE EVOLUTION OF CANADA'S MEDICARE SYSTEM

1867	The British North America Act (BNA) proclaimed Canada's Confederation, which granted provinces jurisdiction over hospitals. Most hospitals were run by voluntary, charitable, or municipal organizations. Those who could afford to pay for services (fee-for-service), did so.
1935–1945	The federal government made two attempts at establishing a national health insurance program, but both attempts failed because the provinces viewed the program as an intrusion on their jurisdiction.
1947	Saskatchewan Premier Tommy Douglas introduced the first hospitalization plan in Canada, for all Saskatchewan residents. British Columbia, Alberta, and Newfoundland and Labrador soon followed with similar plans.
1957 and 1967	With the passage of the federal Hospital Insurance and Diagnostic Services Act (HIDS) and the Medical Care Act (medicare), respectively, the provinces recognized the advantage of a cost-sharing agreement with the federal government.
1972	All the provinces had now entered into this provincial–federal agreement. Health care for the Territories and Aboriginal communities (Native reserves) is primarily the responsibility of the federal government. Transfer payments are made to each province, but each plan must comply with the five principles of medicare.
1984	The Canada Health Act abolished extra billing and user charges to ensure that all Canadians had equal access to necessary medical services.

The Five Principles of Medicare

▶ Universality:

Medicare is available to all Canadians.

▶ Comprehensiveness:

Medicare covers all necessary medical procedures.

▶ Portability:

Medical coverage in one province is accepted in the others and pays for a limited number of medical costs outside Canada.

▶ Publicly administered:

A public authority is accountable to its provincial government.

▶ Accessibility:

All Canadians have an equal opportunity to obtain necessary medical services.

Components of Canada's Health Care System

There are two components of the health care system: personal health and public health.

Personal Health Care System

Although health care reform is affecting change, the personal health care system essentially includes conventional medical services available to people who want to maintain their health and seek cures for illness. General practitioners, family physicians, and pediatricians are the physicians that we first contact when seeking medical care or advice. In certain situations, these physicians consult with specialists (e.g., gastroenterologists, cardiologists) and other medical professionals such as physiotherapists, dietitian-nutritionists, and audiologists. Social workers and other relevant professionals are often brought into patients' medical care when non-physical factors affect health (e.g., housing, poverty, substance abuse, child abuse).

Public Health Care System

"The goal of the public health system is to improve the health status of the whole population; it focuses on groups rather than individuals" (Canadian Paediatric Society 1996,

21). In Canada, public health services are provided regionally within each province and territory. Each public health department serves a specific geographic area.

> Usually, each agency is headed by a medical officer of health, who is a physician with specialty training in community medicine. The medical officer of health is given legal powers to prevent health hazards through provincial/territorial public health legislation. (Canadian Paediatric Society 1996, 21)

The public health agency usually provides a variety of services when budgets permit. The medical officer of health designates services to address the public health needs in that geographic area. Large urban communities, for example, have a higher concentration of individuals addicted to drugs or living with AIDS than do rural communities. When a region has a number of child care centres, ideally the public health agency responds to each centre's unique needs for information, consultation, and education.

As an early childhood educator, you will be involved with the public health system. Public health agencies are responsible for inspecting and approving health standards in centres. Many centres, however, also actively seek an ongoing relationship with their public health professionals, to maximize the potential for health promotion. Centre directors commonly seek guidance with infectious disease control, immunization, safety, nutrition, and dental health.

Financial restraints have meant larger workloads for public health personnel. Often the agency's priority for health promotion makes a relationship with a centre mutually beneficial. Directors or caregivers may need to initiate contacts with the designated public health nurse due to great demands on the nurse's time.

Changing Attitudes toward Health Care

▶ **OBJECTIVE**   To discuss a holistic view of health and its effect on Canada's changing health care system.

More people today are questioning the curative approach to conventional medicine and are considering the merits of a holistic approach to health care. The holistic approach encompasses health promotion as a way of reducing health risks to individuals and the community at large. A reduction in health risks would mean less money would be needed for curative treatments and more money could be reallocated to health promotion measures, which include prevention. Many in the medical establishment are resistant to this change in ideology, as the balance of power in decision-making over the health of individuals shifts and the health care delivery system is restructured.

In 1972 the federal government commissioned the Lalonde Report: *A New Perspective on the Health of Canadians*, which looked beyond the curative boundaries of the health care system and focused on the importance of lifestyle, the environment, and biological risk factors in relation to health. The report identified health promotion as playing an essential role in health. It focused on broad concepts but not on strategies for implementation. Critics observed that the report placed overwhelming emphasis on the individual's responsibility for making changes in his or her lifestyle to improve health. The report hardly acknowledged the sociopolitical factors that negatively or positively affect individuals' health and the role that societal changes (e.g., laws) can play in health. In 1986, Jake Epp, then the federal health minister, published *Achieving Health for All: A Framework for Health Promotion*, a report that reaffirmed the conclusions of the *Lalonde Report* but took them one step further.

Epp's report included implementation strategies in order to progress in the aim of achieving health for all. (See Figure 1.4.) The three major strategies include:

▶ fostering public participation, to enable people to take more control over their health

▶ strengthening community health services, to adjust the health care system in ways that give community-based services more responsibility in allocating resources and funds

▶ coordinating healthy public policy, to implement policies that enhance the opportunities for people to make healthy choices

Areas in which the federal government has implemented healthy public policy are restrictions on the sale and advertising of tobacco, publicity to counter impaired driving, and the recent ban on PVC use in plastic mouthing/teething toys. Since the Lalonde Report and Epp's *Achieving Health for All*, we have deepened our understanding of the factors that contribute to better health. At first, government policies focused on lifestyle choices and on healthy public policy. Now, largely because of research on the non-medical determinants of health and on health promotion, the focus has shifted to the societal level, beyond factors that are within the immediate control of individuals and communities (e.g., the creation of good jobs, safe and affordable housing, enhanced maternity/parental leave).

Conventional medical care has become established in Western countries only in the past 200 years. Medical care primarily focuses on treating people after they become sick and on health maintenance rather than on health care based on promotion. Most people seek medical advice only after experiencing symptoms of illness. Physicians evaluate the symptoms, look for a cause, and decide on a treatment. The recommendations can be narrow in focus. Usually they treat the physical symptoms rather than consider the connection among the patient's dimensions of well-being. Treatments commonly include surgery, medication, physical or occupational therapy, and/or a change in nutritional habits, all of which relate to the patient's physical health. This style of medical care is one in which the doctor is in charge and the patient asks few questions. When a patient is hospitalized, other health care professionals, such as dietitian-nutritionists, occupational therapists, and respiratory technicians, see the patient when the doctor requests a consultation.

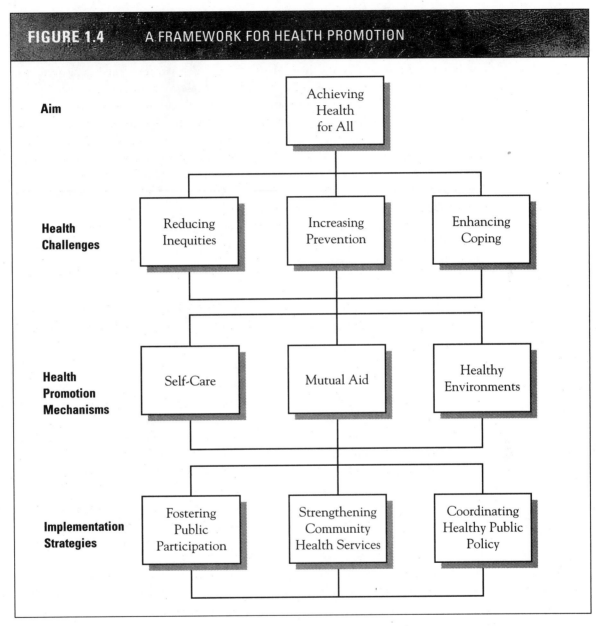

FIGURE 1.4   A FRAMEWORK FOR HEALTH PROMOTION

Achieving Health for All: A Framework for Health Promotion, Health Canada. Reproduced with permission of the Minister of Public Works and Government Services, 1999.

Conventional medicine is extremely expensive, because of its reliance on highly specialized professionals and institutions (hospitals and clinics). More importantly, it does not care for the patient as a whole. It does not routinely use the expertise and skills of a variety of health professionals within a collaborative team approach; rather, it uses them as consultants if the doctor deems their input necessary. Health promotion costs less than curing or treating illness, especially in the management of long-term medical conditions. For both the individual and the community, avoiding illness altogether makes the most sense.

This curative or "health recovery" approach was, and still is to some degree, a widely held approach among many in the medical community and society. Many patients expect doctors to be miracle workers—to cure all their ills without accepting responsibility for unhealthy lifestyles. But another health care delivery system is gaining support, one that takes a holistic or broader view of health. We

are becoming more informed consumers, asking our physicians questions and viewing ourselves as partners or advocates in our health care. Many Canadians are taking more individual control over accessing health professionals—chiropractors, physiotherapists, herbalists—rather than waiting for a doctor's referral.

Traditionally, health care providers have been the main source of information and advice for patients. While this is still largely true, there are patients using the Internet who believe they know more about their conditions than does their physician. However, without the background health knowledge and experience of a physician, the average Canadian is not prepared to make decisions based on Internet information, since so much of this information is unreliable. Nevertheless, the demand by patients for greater involvement in decision-making has made it essential that the public have access to user-friendly information. It also suggests that the role of health care providers will become more interpretative, with a greater focus on the vast amount of information available to the public (National Forum on Health 1997, vol. I, 19).

An Emerging Collaborative Approach in Health Care

Medicine is a business and doctors are having to adapt to the changing attitudes and expectations of consumers. Examples of the changing direction in Canada's health care system include a revamping, on the part of some medical schools, of teaching programs to a community-based model, a movement toward community medicine (e.g., community health centres), and the licensing of midwives.

e.g. ▶ Midwifery has been a legal and legitimate profession in England for over 500 years, but the publication of the Midwifery Act in Ontario on January 1, 1994, was the first legal acknowledgment in Canada of the legitimacy of birthing babies in other than a medical model approach. Pregnancy and childbirth is a natural and low-risk process for most women. Midwives provide continuity of care by supporting the woman and her family throughout the pregnancy, during the birth, and for six weeks after delivery. When there is less of a medical emphasis through the pregnancy and at birth, medical procedures such as cesarean section surgeries are reduced. Tyson's study (1991, 14–18) of 1001 home births in Toronto attended by midwives found that there was a 4 percent cesarean section rate, compared with an average of 18 to 25 percent in Canadian hospitals. Women who use midwives can choose a home or hospital birth. For midwife-attended hospital births, the mother's hospital stay decreases dramatically.

e.g. ▶ Community health centres are another example of this direction. They provide under one roof the services of professionals such as physicians, nurses, public health nurses, nurse practitioners, dietitian-nutritionists, social workers, physical and occupational therapists, health advocates, counsellors, interpreters, massage therapists, and pharmacists. These professionals work together to meet the diverse needs of individuals and their families. The centres refer patients to, and/or work with, other community services or agencies such as job retraining, English-as-a-second-language (ESL), housing and income agencies, legal aid, and so on.

These and other measures benefit patients and the public by reducing overuse and misuse of the system and by providing alternatives that may be more appropriate for the health and well-being of some individuals. Obviously the expertise of doctors is and will always be important to Canada's health care system, but a team approach effectively uses the expertise of many health and health-related professionals.

This change moves away from the doctor's office and hospitals to clinics that provide a variety of services in collaboration. Community health centres also make a statement that health and social services should not be separated. Many people who live in poverty or on the street, or are not fully literate, or have recently immigrated to Canada are unable to obtain the level or quality of health care that others can in the conventional medical care system. Ideally, community health centres are designed and administered by the community to meet its unique needs.

ALTERNATIVE MEDICINE PRACTITIONERS AND PRODUCTS

Historically, alternative (or traditional medicine) practitioners such as homeopaths and naturopaths have been excluded from the conventional medical model in Canada. Many alternative practices and products have not been *scientifically* proven to be effective or safe, so they are unregulated and not covered by medical insurance plans or drug benefit plans. Conversely, critics of conventional medicine question whether some treatments covered by medicare are medically necessary or effective, or at least they question those that are overused (e.g., the high number of ultra-sounds done during healthy pregnancies). One may assume that using an alternative practitioner is a step toward holistic health; that may not always be the case. If an individual chooses to consult an alternative practitioner—or a physician, for that matter—she or he must be a very conscientious consumer. Urgent attention is needed to ensure the safety and effectiveness of alternative and complementary interventions.

> Currently, we have little systematic information to help us determine which interventions are beneficial and which are potentially harmful. With the growing public interest in alternative therapies and treatment choices, it is imperative that assessment and evaluation be undertaken. (National Forum on Health 1997, vol. I, 18)

To respond to increasing demands from Canadian consumers for natural health products such as vitamins, minerals, herbal remedies, and homeopathic products, Health Canada is developing a more efficient product-licensing system to provide access to safe products. *Natural Health Products: A New Vision*, a report by the House of Commons Standing Committee on Health published in November 1998, recommended:

▶ a new federal regulatory authority for natural health products
▶ strict new labelling guidelines that would include information about dosage, storage, side effects, benefits, expiry dates, use for children, and need to consult a doctor. (Walker 1998, A1)

Some families in child care programs use alternative practitioners and medicines. Remedies and medicines may come either from cultural or traditional backgrounds or from a philosophy that differs from the established medical model. It is important to respect health practices different from your own and to be aware of your role in promoting the health of each child in your care. If you question an aspect of the family's health practices, find out more about it before taking action.

In Canada, some practitioners unregulated in the past are receiving provincial government funding under medicare; osteopaths and chiropractors are two examples. Some medical doctors are incorporating alternative practices into their patients' care. These doctors are under increasing scrutiny from their licensing body. In contrast, some European countries have progressed further in recognizing the effectiveness of combining conventional and alternative medical practices, resulting in what is called "complementary medicine." The cost of alternative practices is covered by their medical insurance plans.

Prevention and Health Promotion

▶ **OBJECTIVES:** To learn the World Health Organization's definition of health
promotion.
To define prevention.
To describe how prevention fits into the health promotion approach.

Prevention and health promotion activities have been practised for centuries. In the 1970s a more committed and conscious movement toward healthy living began in Canada.

What Is Prevention?

As one component of health promotion, "prevention involves identifying the factors which cause a condition and then reducing or eliminating them" (Epp 1986, 4). The goal is to have individuals adopt preventive strategies in their daily lives that may lower the risk of occurrence or recurrence of a particular illness or injury. Although lowering a risk doesn't guarantee that a disease is prevented, most people recognize the positive elements of this change.

Here are some examples of prevention strategies:

▶ stop-smoking programs and no-smoking policies for preventing lung cancer and lowering the risk of heart disease and other major diseases
▶ monthly breast self-exams and regular Pap smears for women for early identification of disease
▶ regular dental checkups
▶ hand-washing and immunization programs for children to reduce the spread of infectious diseases
▶ the design of play equipment for safety and appropriateness for the ages and number of children using it
▶ the use of seat belts in cars and bike helmets on bicycles

There is not always evidence to support cause-and-effect relationships between health behaviour and disease. In fact, the many interrelated factors involved in disease make prevention complex. Also, popular opinion often promotes certain preventive lifestyle behaviour. These situations highlight the importance of the informed consumer, one who weighs the pros and cons of specific behaviour. In particular, we cannot assume that every preventive practice recommended for adults can be applied to children.

 Promoting a high-fibre diet is believed to help prevent colon cancer in adults. However, "high intakes of dietary fibre may not be well tolerated by youngsters"

(Network of the Federal/Provincial/Territorial Group on Nutrition & National Institute of Nutrition 1989, 43). There is concern (1989, 43) that a lot of fibre for children has these results:

▷ causes very loose stools in young children
▷ does not allow foods to remain in the digestive system long enough for the needed vitamins and minerals to be absorbed from the food
▷ does not provide enough of the caloric needs of children

This example highlights the importance of consulting with the appropriate health professional, in this case a dietitian-nutritionist, before making decisions that affect someone else's health.

What Is Health Promotion?

Health promotion is "the process of enabling people to increase control over, and to improve their health" (World Health Organization, Health and Welfare Canada, and Canadian Public Health Association 1986, 1).

> Health promotion is concerned with creating living conditions in which people's experience of "health" (well-being) is increased. To an extent, this also requires decreasing their risk of disease. But disease prevention is not the primary goal of health promotion; it is a secondary goal. A health promotion program can improve health (well-being) without necessarily reducing the prevalence of disease, or of specific disease risk factors such as smoking, high fat intake or lack of fitness. (Labonté 1993, 6)

With a holistic view of health, everyone can be involved in promoting health. It is becoming increasingly apparent that people who believe they can control aspects of their lives and have choices are more likely to be action-oriented and self-confident. It is easy to lose hope or view ourselves as ineffective when we believe we have no control over our destiny. In your work with children, you will model and foster feelings of self-confidence and belief in oneself within a realistic framework of what we may or may not be able to control.

Integrating Prevention into a Health Promotion Approach

A *Framework for Health Promotion* identifies health challenges for individuals, communities, and society: reducing inequities, increasing prevention, and enhancing coping—integral parts of the health promotion model. (See Figure 1.4, p. 21.) Prevention is just one of three challenges. You may be saying to yourself, "I have control over most aspects of my life," and that is true to a degree. Many of us didn't succumb to outside influences and start smoking. Perhaps we made other lifestyle decisions based on positive or negative influences. No one can claim, for example,

"Cigarette advertising and peer pressure made me smoke." To focus solely on individuals' lifestyle decisions is to ignore the complex aspects of health behaviour. Nor can society simply blame the victim, absolving itself of its responsibility for coordinating healthy public policy, fostering public participation, and strengthening community health services (Epp 1986, 8). An individual's ability to implement specific prevention strategies and the likelihood of success or failure is directly related to other factors that affect her or his life. To think otherwise is to blame the victim (e.g., "It is the teenage girl's fault that she has anorexia," or "If he had been stronger willed and stopped smoking, he wouldn't have lung cancer," or "She's fat because she eats too much"). This attitude toward prevention is unacceptable and does nothing to enhance our understanding of health and improve our well-being.

e.g. ▶ Tobacco use is Canada's number one public health enemy. Smoking accounts for 55 percent and 51 percent of premature death among males and females, respectively. Tobacco kills approximately nine times as many Canadians prematurely as suicide, traffic collisions, HIV/AIDS, and homicide combined (Villeneuve and Morrison 1994, 102). Sarah quit smoking to reduce her health risks. She can't understand why everyone else can't do the same. For others, quitting smoking is more than withdrawal from addiction to nicotine. Malcolm has tried to quit a few times, but he recently lost his job and smoking helps to reduce his overwhelming feelings of stress. Sarah is probably right when she says Malcolm should find a healthy alternative for relieving his stress, but it is a more complicated issue. Most of Malcolm's friends smoke and their social activities permit them to smoke. Moreover, his father and uncles smoked and lived long lives without developing lung cancer, so he has no firsthand evidence in support of claims made by experts.

A health promotion perspective takes into account the challenges of reducing inequities in Malcolm's life and enhancing his capacity to quit smoking. He enters a job-retraining program that results in meaningful employment. His standard of living improves, as does his self-esteem and outlook on his future. With lowered stress levels, Malcolm is better able to cope with everyday stress by walking to and from work. He now works in a no-smoking workplace. His new friends at work happen to be nonsmokers and he is involved in different social activities. And when you add the high cost of cigarettes, no-smoking legislation in public places, and concerns about second-hand smoke, smokers are feeling society's pressure to stop smoking. Malcolm now has a much better chance of success because so many other factors are in place to support his decision.

▶ By society's standards, Marsha is obese. She has spent years yo-yo dieting and trying to attain a body size that is acceptable to those around her. Whenever she loses weight, even under a physician's care, she quickly regains it. She feels like a failure because she realizes she will never be able to lose the weight that she wants to. Family and strangers joke about Marsha's size, which is hurtful and disrespectful, and which diminishes her self-esteem (e.g., "You would be so pretty if you would only lose weight."). Marsha's anger is understandable—"prejudice to fat" is one of the last forms of discrimination in which disparaging attitudes and comments remain socially acceptable.

Hercilia, a friend of Marsha's, is a large woman yet is much more self-assured. She suggested that Marsha consult with her dietitian-nutritionist, who follows a health promotion model. This is the turning point for Marsha. Two years later, Marsha's body size still does not fit society's standard. However, she has become much more aware of what is important to her and has a quality of life that far surpasses that of her past, when she was always "on hold" until she lost weight. She consistently makes healthy food choices and incorporates physical activity into her daily routine. For the past year, Marsha and her counsellor have worked through her feelings of failure, and that work has improved her self-esteem. The self-help group that she attends provides mutual support in coping with society's prejudice against people who are "fat," their putdowns, and intrusive questions (e.g., a taxi driver asks his passenger, "So how much *do* you weigh?"). Since Marsha has stopped focusing on weight loss and has incorporated a health promotion model, she has more energy than ever before and is slowly losing weight.

The fashion industry creates powerful images of beauty and desirability that affect society's view of women in particular. However, changes in societal attitudes are gradually taking place. Now there is some recognition of a wide range of body sizes and a realization that one type is not better than another. Several clothing stores now specialize in fashionable clothes for larger women and some department stores have added larger sizes. Even fast-food restaurants have started to offer foods that help people make healthier choices. Some physical activity programs are designed for larger people, which helps them feel less self-conscious about exercising in front of others. Women's groups are educating the public and breaking down stereotypes.

In summary, health promotion involves all aspects of a person's life that affect his or her well-being, and prevention focuses on particular risks or behaviour believed to be causal factors in disease or injury.

Health Promotion Action Plan

 OBJECTIVE To identify the four components of a health promotion action plan and describe how they can be implemented.

Health promotion in a broad sense enables individuals and the community to identify health risks and make positive changes at the individual, community, and societal levels.

Action Plan Blueprint

Health promotion activities can be divided into four components:

▶ individual problem-solving and self-reliance
▶ collective self-help
▶ community action
▶ societal change

Optimally, when all four components are at work, the likelihood of significant change is high. Realistically, though, we are not always successful in achieving our original goals. During the process we may need to adjust the vision. Barriers may be impossible to overcome. But even these situations usually have outcomes that contribute to health, such as developing coping skills, increased social supports, networking, and a long-term commitment to work for change.

INDIVIDUAL PROBLEM-SOLVING AND SELF-RELIANCE

As individuals, we solve problems all the time, and many of our behavioural changes occur when we put our mind to it. However, changing our behaviour is easier when we do not have to overcome barriers or when we have the resources to effect change.

▶ When a child's parents provide a variety of nutritious foods, she learns to make healthy food choices. The parents guide their daughter's development of healthy eating habits through modelling. By the time she is of school age, she will have developed the knowledge and decision-making skills to make choices. Then when she becomes influenced by peers and the media and may not always make the healthiest choices, she will at least be aware when she is eating less nutritious foods and can therefore balance choices.
▶ You decide to add more physical activity to your life by regularly walking to work or school.

Societal barriers or influences can either positively or negatively affect our ability to make healthy lifestyle decisions. In the past, smoking was accepted by society. The media depicted smoking as fun, sophisticated, and elegant. Smokers could smoke almost anywhere, and no one was concerned about secondhand smoke or about pregnant women smoking. There were no barriers; in fact, society encouraged people to smoke. Today smoking is recognized as the most serious public health concern, and this has resulted in public education on the risks of smoking, support and products to help stop smoking, legislation on smoke-free environments, taxes on tobacco, strict limitations on advertising, and limitations on availability (e.g., pharmacies do not sell tobacco, and cigarette vending machines have been banned). Long-time smokers are quitting, supported and encouraged by society. People are more comfortable in asking smokers not to smoke in their cars or homes, and many smokers ask permission before lighting up. Smoking in public has been severely restricted. Today public health officials are concerned about the number of teenagers (more girls than boys) who are first-time smokers. From a developmental perspective, it's not surprising that adolescents are exerting control over their lives and may in fact make decisions counter to parental or public opinion. This is complicated by the fact that teenagers and young adults view themselves as invincible.

COLLECTIVE SELF-HELP

When individuals come together as a collective, they pool skills, knowledge, and resources to support one another and work toward change.

A group of tenants in an apartment building has recognized that grocery shopping is difficult because of issues such as these:
▷ their low income
▷ the lack of public transportation to affordable stores
▷ the many single-parent families who have no one to care for their children while parents are grocery shopping
As a collective, the tenants organize a food depot that is open once a week and sells fresh fruit and vegetables. A food produce supplier provides the produce at a reasonable cost.

Collectives don't always have to be large groups of people.

Several neighbours organized an informal baby-sitting system that lets one parent do grocery shopping while another cares for the children. This allows the parents to shop without taking tired, bored, or hungry children with them, which often results in impulse buying and angry parents or frustrated children.

Although this example reflects cooperation, the group is somewhat self-reliant. Often, once groups have worked together in this way, they begin to identify broader social and health issues or concerns (e.g., causes of ill health) and may move toward more of a community action model.

A group of centre directors that meets regularly as a network shares a concern about the food that parents are providing for their school-age children. The directors organize a parent meeting, invite a dietitian-nutritionist and social worker, and provide child care and dinner. At the meeting, participants identify a number of issues:
▷ lack of affordable food
▷ lack of nutrition resources that fit the literacy and interest level of a number of the parents
▷ time constraints for parents and their need for ideas for nutritious lunches that can be easily prepared
▷ children's practice of trading lunch items with peers and a concern that nutritious foods won't be desirable

▷ children's beliefs that foods from their ethno-cultural backgrounds will not be accepted by their peers

These issues call on the resources and agencies in the community. They highlight the importance of looking beyond self-help to a much broader health promotion action.

COMMUNITY ACTION

This health promotion strategy is viewed more and more as an effective way to make change to meet the health needs of the community, particularly where barriers are present. Its aim is to achieve change that will affect the whole group. It happens when groups of people

▶ work together to identify issues and priorities that reflect their needs
▶ develop and implement an action plan, which usually involves communication with a number of agencies and resources
▶ evaluate the strengths and deficiencies of their actions and the extent to which they have realized their goals

In the previous example, on nutrition for school-age children, the collective's work led the participants to develop an action plan that included reaching out into the community for resources. This had benefits not only for the immediate issue but also for long-term well-being. Regular links with the broader community tend to foster an active problem-solving approach to life.

All participants involved have some role in the process, including evaluating whether goals have been met. Parents and staff may have different responsibilities and perspectives, but everyone works toward the same goal. Depending on the ages of the children and the actions being taken, some or all of the children may be involved in the process (e.g., if a community vegetable garden is part of the solution).

 A few people in a neighbourhood are concerned about the quality of the air due to smokestack emissions at a local factory. Together, they go door to door to gain citizen support, meet with public health officials, governmental officials, and the factory management, and develop a plan of action to reduce the emissions.

Depending on the extent of the issue and who is involved, community action can lead to legislative changes locally, provincially, or federally, which affect everyone. If we take this example a step further, stricter government regulations for companies to reduce air pollution levels may emerge from what began as a small community action. (See Appendix 1.1, p. 52.)

SOCIETAL CHANGE

Issues can have a broader impact on everyone through the work of community and lobby groups, agencies, and so on. Societal changes often result from changes in legislation or public health policy. Here are some examples:

▶ air pollution controls
▶ no-smoking policies in public places
▶ drinking-and-driving legislation
▶ changes in advertising guidelines for the tobacco and liquor industries
▶ legislative bans on manufacturing and selling equipment that does not adhere to safety regulations, etc.

Let's take one last look at the example of staff and parents in a school-age program and their concerns about children's nutrition. As a group, they recognize that their experience is not isolated, that the issue and solutions go beyond their own community and into the society at large. Consequently, some participants have joined a lobby group that is trying to ban television advertising of junk food aimed at children, while others are working with a national antipoverty group. As discussed earlier in this unit, a focus on the bigger issue of reducing and eliminating poverty is, ultimately, the most effective health promotion approach. A collective vote is a powerful tool for effecting change. Find out where political candidates stand on various issues and cast your vote accordingly.

Health Promotion in Child Care Centres

▶ **OBJECTIVE**   To discuss student and caregiver strategies to advocate for quality child care.

Promoting health is something we can do to improve the quality of our life and the lives of those around us. How can child care centres be part of this movement?

High-Quality Child Care

Tens of thousands of children in Canada are enrolled in licensed group child care. Consequently, society must acknowledge that child care is an essential service for families, recognize the indicators of high-quality child care, and support the delivery of service through legislative and financial changes. If parents have access to quality child care, they can participate fully in their work or education, which enhances the quality of their lives and the lives of their children.

Child care programs support parents in their role as their children's primary caregivers. High-quality child care has positive long-term health effects for children. Although research on the effects of child care sometimes varies, one thing is certain: quality child care "supports and assists the child's physical, emotional, social and intellectual well-being and development" (Doherty 1993, 1).

Child care legislation in each province and territory establishes regulations for licensed child care programs, including specifications for the following matters, among others:

▶ early childhood training requirements
▶ group size
▶ staff–child ratios
▶ space requirements
▶ program planning
▶ nutrition requirements
▶ management of ill children

Every licensed centre has a copy of the child care regulations. It is important to understand that these regulations ensure that a *minimum* standard of child care is provided in centres. A *minimum* level of care is not high-quality child care. Since child care is a provincial responsibility, regulations vary greatly across Canada. An area of particular concern is the wide variation in levels of early childhood education training required for staff working in child care programs.

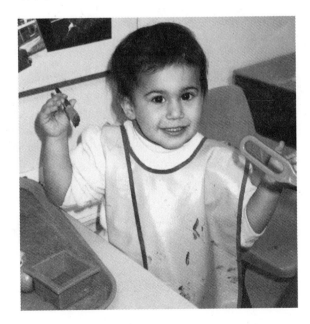

Child Care Sector Study on Quality

Elements of Quality

The elements of quality include both the ways in which child care environments are organized and the nature of interactions supported by that environment—in other words, the structure and process elements. A high-quality child care environment incorporates the following principles:

- Responsible, stable caregiver–child interactions that are sensitive to children's needs, provide support and encouragement, and set consistent behavioural expectations are of primary importance in both home- and centre-based child care.
- Caregiver knowledge of child development (usually indicated by postsecondary education credentials) supports positive adult–child interactions in both family child care and child care centres.
- The caregiver–child ratio and group size, which allows the caregiver to be aware and involved, are important to adult–child interactions in child care centres.
- Low staff turnover creates a stable and consistent caregiver–child relationship. High turnover reduces stability.
- Daily routines, including planned activities and free play, with health and safety provisions, support children's learning and protect their well-being in family care homes and child care centres.
- A child-appropriate physical environment allows children to take part in learning opportunities and encourages increased positive interactions with caregivers.
- A positive organizational climate, which includes opportunities For caregivers to be involved in decision-making, creates a coherent administrative framework to support caregivers in centres. In family child care, support and contact with other caregivers is part of a positive organizational climate.
- In family child care settings, caregiver "intentionality" is associated with better outcomes for children. Intentionality is the conscious commitment to caring for children and the provision of nurturing, stimulating child care.

Ensuring Quality

The elements of quality and the quality of the care provided are affected by factors outside the immediate program setting. The following principles ensure quality:

- In centre-based programs, adult–child interactions are influenced by the caregiver's job satisfaction level, which, in part, is determined by the work environment, including wages and benefits, general working conditions, and administration. Low job satisfaction is associated with higher staff turnover, which reduces the stability of relationships between caregivers and children. Compensation levels and other aspects of the work environment are determined by the level of available funding.
- High-quality child care is more likely to be found in nonprofit than in commercial child care settings. However, there are both low-quality nonprofit centres and high-quality commercial centres.
- The level of government regulation, particularly for caregiver education, caregiver–child ratios, and group size, does influence the quality of care in centre-based settings.
- Quality may be encouraged through professional standards of practice for individual caregivers and for child care settings.

Source: Adapted from Beach, Bertrand, and Cleveland (1998), 32–34.

Your role as a student and entry-level caregiver in providing quality care is crucial in promoting the physical, emotional, and social well-being of the children and families you serve.

ADVOCATING FOR QUALITY CHILD CARE

While many regard child care as a social welfare program rather than a health promotion program, child care has significant implications for children's health. In 1988 the federal government announced a child care support program for working mothers. In the 1980s advocates for a national child care plan agreed on three fundamental principles for a child care system: universal accessibility, comprehensiveness, and high quality. Their continued advocacy for child care indirectly promotes children's health. The legislation was not enacted and was abandoned in 1991; the advocacy movement wasn't.

Advocacy doesn't occur only at the national level. Advocates for quality care are working to improve standards of care in each province and territory by ensuring that revisions made to child care legislation will reflect the indicators of quality child care.

How can centre staff and early childhood education students deliver high-quality child care that encompasses health promotion? Your training provides you with the entry-level knowledge and skills to provide a level of care higher than the minimum set out in the child care regulations. Your training also helps you recognize the importance of delivering a high level of quality care. This commitment to ongoing learning and professional behaviour makes you a "personal" advocate. To

be a public policy advocate, you can be involved in local, provincial, territorial, or federal child care organizations that advocate for access to quality care for families and professional recognition for caregivers. We need to speak with one voice in order to safeguard accomplishments and move forward (Gestwicki and Bertrand 1998, 230–31).

Centre Policies

A centre can ensure that high-quality child care is implemented by having

► a written philosophy that states its ideology about children's care and learning
► policies and procedures that answer the who, what, when, where, and why for each policy
► caregivers who consistently implement the policies and procedures. Caregivers and parents need to understand the rationale behind the policies before they can see the big picture in procedures.

Child care is a cooperative effort shared by the staff and parents. The development of a policy manual is one way to demonstrate that shared commitment. Writing, reviewing, and revising the policy manual annually draws on the expertise of the staff, parents, and professionals in the community (e.g., public health, child abuse prevention, social services). The reviewers evaluate the effectiveness and relevance of the policies and procedures. Health information, circumstances, and priorities change. Staff or parents may raise new issues and concerns.

Health Policies Policy manuals are legal documents that outline the centre's philosophy, the program's goals and objectives, and how the caregivers intend to meet the child care regulations and implement the procedures. Well-written policies combine the child care regulations, ECE training, past experiences, the expertise of other professionals and parents, and the most current health information available. However, child care regulations are only *minimum* requirements based on legislation. Quality child care programs move beyond that foundation to develop fuller, broader, inclusive policies that reflect their knowledge and skills in caring for children on a daily basis. When a policy is well written, its rationale is clearly understood and the stated procedures obviously promote the well-being of children, staff, and families.

Policy manuals could be referred to as living documents. Our knowledge of children's well-being, including health, nutrition, hygiene, safety, growth and development, illness, medical conditions, and physical or emotional challenges, is evolving faster than legislators make or change regulations. In addition, caregivers use past experiences to identify additional policy issues. Policy manuals incorporate the unexpected—"What will we do if this happens?" (For example, the manual outlines the steps to follow if a child's non-custodial parent arrives to take the child from the centre, and how to proceed when a child vomits medication.) An effective policy manual is one that evolves with the changing needs of individual centres.

e.g. An infant centre has an outbreak of diarrhea. The centre's hand-washing and diapering routines should be suspected of causing the spread of the virus or bacteria that are responsible for the gastrointestinal infection. Without the policy manual containing the steps for diapering and hand-washing, staff are not able to evaluate the caregivers' compliance to the routines that would have prevented the spread. Perhaps the policy and procedures are not effective. Perhaps caregivers need retraining in the routines and closer supervision.

Beyond the legal licensing requirement for having a centre manual, policies can have a variety of purposes:

► to conduct staff orientation, in-service training, and job performance appraisals
► to extract the most relevant policies to be developed into parent handbooks
► to define lines of communication and confidentiality
► to contain the administrative and medical/health forms, and to specify who has access to that information
► to contain information sheets and handouts, and routines that can be used for posters such as diapering, toileting, hand-washing, and exclusion criteria
► to identify the names and associations with which the centre networks
► to stay current with early childhood and related research

Each regulation provides centre directors, caregivers, their boards, and parents with the base from which policies and procedures are developed to enhance and capture the nuances of day-to-day child care, the ages of the children, and the location of the centre. The following illustrates a few of the issues that may be included in discussions about developing and revising policies and procedures.

► The medication policy would indicate which medications are permitted and the reason for that decision. Procedures are clearly spelled out and cover administration, storage, and record-keeping; identification and reporting of side effects and medication errors; and managing emergency situations. The centre's expectations of parents regarding medications would also be included. In the event of a medication incident, reviewing the procedures and comparing these with the actions of the caregiver will determine whether precautions were in place and carried out to the best of her or his ability to prevent the error. Perhaps the review will determine that the current medication procedures require revision.
► A child fell from a climbing structure in the winter and broke her arm. On examination, the impact-absorbing surface was found to be covered with a sheet of ice. Does the centre have an outdoor play policy and procedures in place that, when implemented, would prevent children from using a climber when the surface does not meet safety requirements?
► A school-age centre located in an elementary school establishes clear lines of communication with the principal and the children's teachers to ensure the consistent coordination of health policies.

e.g. ▶ When a child gets sick during the day, does the school notify the parents, or is doing so the centre's responsibility?

▶ Are the regular safety checks of the playground and equipment a shared responsibility of the centre staff and the school, or are they solely the school's responsibility? Are the expectations about the use of the playground equipment consistent between centre and school? When issues arise, how are they reported and recorded? Who is responsible for record-keeping?

▶ Do the caregivers and teachers consistently teach and model healthy habits?

▶ When concerns are raised about a child or family by either the caregivers or a teacher, do both parties work together to address the concerns?

HIV is cloaked in emotion, fear, and discrimination. A small number of children and caregivers in centres are HIV-positive. Consequently, some centres have developed an HIV/AIDS policy. We propose that when centres have comprehensive policies and procedures, the issues surrounding HIV/AIDS have *already* been integrated. Policy statements relating to confidentiality, freedom from discrimination, universal precautions, and the management of all blood-borne diseases encompass HIV/AIDS. HIV/AIDS education, not policy, is *the* most effective instrument in changing the attitudes and behaviour of caregivers, parents, and the general public. We send an inappropriate message to staff, parents, and the community when a policy is developed for a specific infection that is not spread through casual contact and has never been reported transmitted in a centre.

PARENT–CAREGIVER PARTNERSHIPS

You share a partnership with parents and other family members in enabling the child to be the best that he or she can be—physically, emotionally, socially. Parents know their child best, and it is important that you respect their values and parenting practices. After all, the child is part of a family for a lifetime but is part of the centre for only a limited time. Parents are the decision-makers about their child's health. Caregivers, however, may be able to provide information such as referrals to agencies, books, articles, and other individuals that helps parents consider new information or another perspective in their decisions. Building relationships with parents on a day-to-day basis benefits everyone involved.

After you graduate as an early childhood educator, you may at times be concerned about the effects of a family's health values, or practices, on the child's well-being. You must determine whether your concern stems from a parenting value or practice that is different from any that you are accustomed to. This difference may reflect sociocultural differences, a term that refers to ethnicity, race, class, religion, or any other aspect of a social group that shapes values and practices. This value or practice may be very different from, or even in conflict with, one that you grew up with. If it is, you must decide whether this value or practice is simply another way of looking at something or is potentially harmful to the child's physical, emotional, or social well-being. You broaden your awareness by learning about other perspectives. You may or may not decide to adopt this value or practice, but it is important that you not judge others solely on the basis of your limited view. Competent caregivers strive to communicate with families and support each family's values as much as possible while maintaining standards of quality child care.

If, on the other hand, you are unsure about the parents' values or practices because of the potential for physical, emotional, or social harm to the child, you have a responsibility to investigate. Effective communication with parents ensures that you understand the value or practice. Ineffective communication often results in assumptions and judgments based on incomplete information. It is possible, often with the help of community resources, to make a more informed decision on

the issue and decide, likely with the director, on a plan of action. Keep in mind that most parents care about their children and believe that their parenting reflects this care. Often this principle is helpful in deciding what to do next.

e.g. You have concerns about the child's eating habits. You talk with the parents about the child's total nutritional intake and any food restrictions. Perhaps a dietitian-nutritionist from the public health department can provide you and the parents with educational material.

In addition to pre-enrollment interviews, parents and caregivers find out more about each other through day-to-day communication and regular parent–caregiver interviews, the parent handbook, bulletin boards, and other communication vehicles. In situations where differences exist between the centre's philosophy and policies and the parents' values and practices, the parents might consider using a centre that better reflects their attitudes. In most situations, however, caregivers and the director will have tried to negotiate a mutually acceptable situation before that happens.

Cultural Diversity in Child Care

"Culture" is a very complex term. What is culture? It is probably best defined by each individual. "Inherited" culture includes one's race, ethnicity, language, religion, and social class. "Personal" culture, on the other hand, is acquired.

You may have become interested in environmental issues, and the way you live is based on a philosophy of care for the environment. Your philosophy may affect the way you eat, the clothes you wear, the way you travel, and so on.

You may define your personal culture primarily by your family structure, your race or ethnic background, the language you speak (e.g., deaf culture), your religion, your sexual orientation (e.g., lesbian), and so on. People usually define their culture by the aspects of their lives that most affect their day-to-day living.

> **Assessing the situation:**
> The staff and parents value dependence differently, so how do they compromise in the best interests of the child?
> Scenario: Your child care program's philosophy places a high value on helping children develop independence. However, one family in the centre places a high value on interdependence (i.e., a long-term commitment to depending on one another, remaining close to family).

"One way, especially if it is your own, may feel [more right] to you" (Gonzalez-Mena 1997, 87). By asking parents informal questions such as "How do you handle this type of situation at home?" you can gain insight into why a child does not respond well to the caregivers' strategy, and you can also acquire another way of looking at the issue. In a program that has an open view to diversity, this would simply be viewed as a different way—a way to be respected. Children can be caught between two value systems. When issues come up around value differences, it is a priority to negotiate a cultural conflict so that neither way is devalued. (See Table 1.1, p. 42.)

Caregivers have a responsibility to find out as much as possible about the child and family's culture and be sensitive and responsive to differences. It is certainly possible for children to move between centre and home culture, where roles, expectations, and interactions may differ considerably, if there is mutual respect and interest by caregivers and parents. A climate of acceptance paves the way for understanding and learning for everyone involved.

A child and his parent believe that the child care environment supports the child's individuality and cultural values, his beliefs and practices, and they feel emotionally secure and comfortable contributing to others' awareness of their values and practices. Children are profoundly influenced by the attitudes of their adult community.

So far, we have defined culture very broadly. The term "ethno-culture" commonly refers to specific ethnic groups—that is, a group of people identified by

themselves and others as sharing racial or national origins sometimes called common heritage or ancestry. People from common ethnic backgrounds may have shared traits (e.g., skin colour, language), customs, and behaviour. How people view health and illness, doctors, medicine, and different approaches to healing may be influenced by their ethnicity. In addition to finding out about these beliefs directly from parents, you can contact agencies that are aware of an ethno-culture's health beliefs and practices. We can't assume from general information, however, that a family has particular health beliefs or practices. Individuals and families are unique in their situations and beliefs—ethnicity is just one aspect of many that shape people's lives.

NETWORKING WITH THE COMMUNITY

Networking within the community contributes to the well-being of children, families, caregivers, and the overall child care program. Caregivers working effectively as a team contribute significantly to the level of quality care provided by the centre. No one works in isolation, and centres are no exception. Staff cannot and should not try to be all things to all people. Centre staff must establish a network with professionals, agencies, and associations in their community. This network allows the staff to grow both personally and professionally, resulting in higher-quality child care. Your ECE training and skills equip you to work as an effective member of the network of professionals concerned with the growth, development, and health of children (e.g., public health departments, child abuse prevention teams, school boards, community health centres). Collaboration with others should have the additional benefit of drawing a number of services together, thus reducing duplication, improving the delivery of service, and lowering costs.

TABLE 1.1   SUGGESTIONS FOR APPROACHING CULTURAL CONFLICTS

Here is a summary of hints to help you deal with the cultural conflicts that can arise in a child care setting:

1. *Take it slow.* Don't expect to resolve each conflict immediately. Building understanding and relationships takes time. Some conflicts won't be resolved; they'll just be managed. You have to learn to cope with differences when there is no common meeting ground or resolution. This coping sounds hard, but it's possible, if you're willing to accept the fact that resolution is not always the outcome of disputes.

2. *Understand yourself.* Become clear about your own values and goals. Know what you believe in. Have a bottom line, but leave space above it to be flexible.

3. *Become sensitive to your own discomfort.* Tune in on those times when something bothers you instead of just ignoring it and hoping it will go away. Work to identify what specific behaviours of others make you uncomfortable. Try to discover exactly what in yourself created this discomfort.

4. *Learn about other cultures.* Books, classes, and workshops help, but watch out for stereotypes and biased information. Your best source of information comes from the parents in your program. Check out what they believe about their cultures, and see if it fits with other information you receive. However, don't ever make one person a representative of his or her culture. Listen to individuals, take in the information they give you, but don't generalize to whole cultures. Keep your mind open as you learn. Check out your point of view. There's a difference between finding and celebrating diversity and explaining deficiencies.

5. *Find out what the parents in your program, individually, want for their children.* What are their goals? What are their caregiving practices? What concerns do they have about their child in your program? Encourage them to talk to you. Encourage them to ask questions. You may find out about cultures this way, or you may just find out about individual or familial differences. All are important.

6. *Be a risk taker.* If you are secure enough, you may feel you can afford to make mistakes. Mistakes are a part of cross-cultural communication. It helps to have a good support system behind you when you take risks and make mistakes.

7. *Communicate, dialogue, negotiate.* If you have a chance to build a relationship before getting into negotiations, you're more likely eventually to reach a mutually satisfying point.

8. *Share power.* Empowerment is an important factor in the dialogue-negotiation process. Although some see empowerment (allowing others to experience their own personal power) as threatening, in reality empowerment creates new forms of power. Some teachers and caregivers fear that empowerment means giving away their own power, but this is not true! No one can give personal power, and no one can take it away. We all have our personal power, though we can be discouraged or prevented from recognizing or using it. Sharing power, or empowerment, enhances everyone's power.

In conclusion, hard as it may be to take the risks involved in cross-cultural encounters, to learn what is needed to understand culturally different people, to gain skills in communication, and to cope when conflicts arise, exposure to more than one culture is a definite asset. As you care for children from various cultural backgrounds, everyone gains. You, the children, and the parents have the opportunity to learn more about and appreciate human diversity.

TABLE 1.2   SOME PRACTICAL STEPS IN NETWORK-BUILDING FOR CAREGIVERS
To Improve the Status of Child Care as a Profession
Actively participate in your local, provincial, or national child care associations.
Improve your own knowledge and skills through continuing education.
Lobby for better working conditions and salaries.
Demand better resource services.
Support improved standards and insist that resources be made available to implement them.
To Build a Local Network

Exchange information with
  • parents
  • members of your board of directors or parent advisory committee
  • co-workers
  • public health nurses
  • physicians
  • other health professionals
  • social workers
  • cultural centre representatives
  • suppliers of goods and services
  • politicians
  • teachers

Seek help and advice from a wide variety of sources, such as universities, colleges, religious institutions, bureaucrats.
Make contact with local schools attended by older children and siblings of younger children.
Open your centre to students in health care, social service, and education who express an interest in learning about child care.
Offer your expertise to community groups.
Present workshops at child care and other meetings.
Share information with other caregivers and interested professionals.
Have open houses at centres.
Write articles for local newspapers and professional journals.
Invite a broad range of people to sit on your board of directors or parent advisory committee.

Source: Reprinted with permission from Canadian Paediatric Society (1996), *Well Beings* (Ottawa: Canadian Paediatric Society), 24.

As students in an early childhood education program, you may be overwhelmed when you think about developing relationships with individuals and groups, but be assured that it doesn't happen overnight. It is important that you see the benefits of working cooperatively, learning from others, and also sharing your expertise. In centres where staff and the director do not work cooperatively, children, families, and staff are at a real disadvantage. No one person or agency can do it all or know it all. Networking increases resources and decreases caregiver stress levels. (See Table 1.2, p. 43; Figure 1.5, p. 45.)

As you can see from our discussion on health promotion, your approach to your work can affect the health and well-being of children and families. For those caregivers who are committed to their profession, what you think (attitude), what you know (knowledge), and what you do (behaviour) are evolving positively through education and experience. We must recognize our strengths and limitations throughout this lifelong learning process and make responsible decisions accordingly. All caregivers and directors need access to resources; a student or recent graduate of an early childhood education program needs to have increased support that is readily available.

Health Promotion Action Plan in the Child Care Program

An action approach to promoting health in centres is positive for a number of reasons:

1. *It fosters partnerships with parents.* Working together for common goals recognizes and builds on people's knowledge and strengths. In addition to getting the job done, you are developing your relationships with parents—a benefit to everyone involved.

2. *An action approach helps people learn to solve problems and experience the value of working cooperatively.* When individuals see results, they are more likely to view themselves as having enough personal and collective power to effect change. When all the players are committed to the issue, there are fewer barriers. Of course, there are times when interactions between employers, administrators, and centre boards, or budget restraints, result in insurmountable obstacles. Although this will be disappointing, it is helpful to view what has been gained through the process. Obviously, in addition to the benefits from the action itself, working cooperatively also models a cooperative approach for children that is crucial for adapting in our ever-changing world.

3. *An action approach increases the individual's and groups' awareness of community resources as well as community agencies' knowledge of community needs.* An action plan will probably include communication with the public health and other municipal departments, community health centres, social service agencies, doctors, and so on. An active approach to promoting health in centres can lead to improved accessibility for children and families to the larger community, as information is shared through family and friends.

FIGURE 1.5   GROUPS AND INDIVIDUALS THAT INTERACT WITH CHILD CARE

Immediate Relationships
Children
Parents
Volunteers
Board of Directors or Parent
    Advisory Committee
Sponsoring Agency
Suppliers

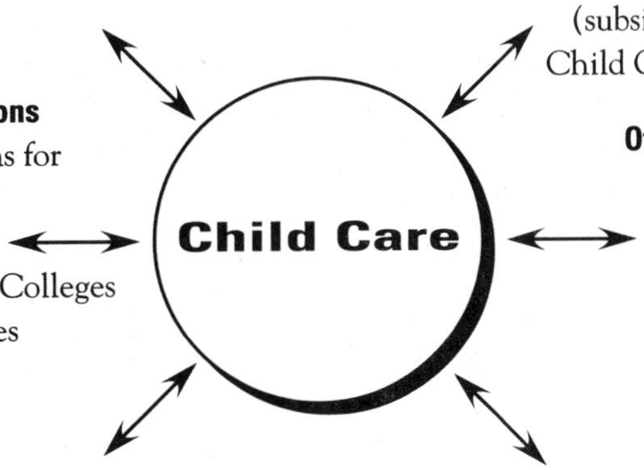

Educational Institutions
Training Programs for
    Child Care
School System
Universities and Colleges
Extension Courses

Fundamental Required Relationships
Licensing Agency
Municipal Government
    • zoning laws
    • fire inspector
    • building inspector
Funding Agency
    (subsidy, grants)
Child Care Resource Centre

Other Community Relationships
Voluntary Organizations
Cultural Associations
Friendship Centres
Second Language Training
    Programs (e.g., ESL)
Religious Organizations
Universities and Colleges

Child Care

Child Care Network
Local Professional Associations
Other Child Care Professionals
Provincial and National Organizations
Labour Unions
Social Workers
Child Protection Workers
Teachers

Professionals
Public Health
    • nurses
    • inspectors
Other Resource People (e.g.,
    nutritionists, dental hygienists)
Personal Health Care
    • paediatricians
    • subspecialists (e.g.,
      rehabilitation, infectious diseases)
    • general practitioners and
      family physicians
    • other health professionals
      (e.g., occupational therapists,
      speech therapists, audiologists,
      child life workers)
Social Workers
Child Protection Workers
Teachers

Source: Reprinted with permission from Canadian Paediatric Society (1996), *Well Beings* (Ottawa: Canadian Paediatric Society), 37.

Conclusion

As caregivers, we can contribute to the health promotion plan. In our daily work with children and families, we can put into practice a health promotion philosophy by

▶ developing and following healthy policies and procedures
▶ modelling healthy habits ourselves
▶ communicating in an ongoing way with the families, demonstrating sensitivity and openness to their health beliefs and practices
▶ networking with the community, realizing that we all benefit through sharing resources

Each of the following units will discuss the health-related practices in the child care program.

Healthy lifestyles, the physical environment, and genetics are significant determinants of health. In order to improve the quality of life for all Canadians, however, action needs to be taken on the social and economic determinants of health in particular, giving priority to the serious problem of unemployment, making investments in children, and promoting communities (National Forum on Health 1997, vol. I, 20).

As Nelson Mandela, former president of the Republic of South Africa, put it (Campaign 2000 1998, 11): "Security for a few is insecurity for us all."

WHAT'S YOUR OPINION?
TO HAVE A HEALTH ADVOCATE OR NOT?

Provincial/territorial occupational health and safety act amendments require employers with more than a specified number of employees (e.g., 7 to 19 in Ontario) to designate one staff member as the health and safety representative. When employers exceed a specified number of employees (e.g., 20 in Ontario), they are required to establish a committee. This representative is responsible for bringing employees' health concerns to management's attention. Her or his role could be expanded to increase the awareness of co-workers, parents, and the community about health promotion in the centre and action for change.

Aronson (1991) suggests that these individuals could be called "health advocates." They would ensure the implementation of health-related tasks such as conducting health checks in the morning, assessing potentially ill children during the day, and regularly evaluating hygiene practices. The health advocate would not necessarily be solely responsible for implementing these practices.

Discuss the pros and cons of centres having health advocates regardless of the labour legislation. Please note: This legislation may not be relevant in your province/territory, and some centres may be exempt.

▶ A S S E S S   Y O U R   L E A R N I N G

Define terms or describe concepts used in this unit.

- health
- health status
- determinants of health
- principles of medicare
- personal health care system
- public health system
- community health centres
- alternative medicine
- health promotion
- prevention
- health promotion action plan
- quality child care
- centre policies
- cultural diversity
- networking

Evaluate your options in each situation.

1. You and your housemate are bored with eating pasta and sauce, burgers, and hot dogs. You're both intrigued by a number of the fruits, vegetables, and grains you've noticed in a new grocery store. You would like to try some, but you don't know where to start.

2. Your doctor hands you a prescription. When you ask him what it is for and whether there are side effects, he replies, "Don't worry about it, dear. Just take these pills and you'll feel better."

3. Classes have been cancelled for the day to allow students to attend a child care rally at the legislature. You are tempted to skip it because you have to study for a test.

4. A parent is angry at pickup time because his daughter's sleeves are damp from water play even though she was wearing a smock. He believes that this is how someone gets a cold. He asks that his daughter never play at the water table again.

5. A safety issue arises at the centre. None of the staff can think of a viable response, and you suggest that consulting with another centre may provide options. The director insists, "We can work this out ourselves," and does not want outside interference.

▶ R E S O U R C E   M A T E R I A L S

Organizations

Campaign 2000, c/o Family Service Association, 355 Church Street, Toronto, ON
   M5B 1Z8. Tel. (416) 595-9230, ext. 244; fax (416) 595-0242
   Web site: www.campaign2000.ca

Canadian Child Care Federation, 100–30 Rosemount Avenue, Ottawa, ON K1Y
   1P4. Tel. (613) 729-5289, fax (613) 729-3159
   Web site: (Child and Family Canada) www.cfc-efc.ca

Canadian Institute of Child Health, 512–885 Meadowlands Drive, Ottawa, ON
   K2C 3N2. Tel. (613) 224-4144, fax (613) 224-4145
   Web site: www.cich.ca

Child Care Advocacy Association of Canada, 323 Chapel Street, Ottawa, ON K1N 7Z2. Tel. (613) 594-3196, fax (613) 594-9375

Family Service Canada, 600–220 Laurier Avenue West, Ottawa, ON K1P 5Z9. Tel. (613) 230-9960, fax (613) 230-5884

Other Web Sites of Interest

Canadian Association of Health, Physical Education, Recreation and Dance: www.activeliving.ca (cahperd)

The Canadian Health Network (Health Canada): www.canadian-health-network.ca

The Canadian Lung Association: www.web.netcando

National Institute of Environmental Health Sciences: www.niehs.nih.gov

Printed Matter

Alternative Health Care, The Canadian Directory (1997), by B.L. Harden and C.R. Harden (Noble Ages Publishing).

Child Care Policy in Canada: Putting the Pieces Together (1994), by M. Friendly (Addison-Wesley).

Complete Canadian Health Guide (1993), by J.V. Engel (Key Porter).

Health Promotion in Canada: Provincial, National & International Perspectives (1994), by Ann Pederson et al. (W.B. Saunders Canada).

National Statement on Quality Child Care (1991), by Canadian Child Care Federation (Ottawa).

► **B I B L I O G R A P H Y**

Aronson, S.S. (1991) *Health & Safety in Child Care*. Toronto: HarperCollins.

Beach, J., J. Bertrand, and G. Cleveland (1998) *Our Child Care Workforce—From Recognition to Remuneration: More Than a Labour of Love*. A Human Resource Study of Child Care in Canada. Ottawa: Human Resources Development Canada.

Brown, I., et al. (1998) *Quality of Life Profile*. Toronto: Centre for Health Promotion, University of Toronto.

Campaign 2000 (1998) *Child Poverty in Canada: Report Care 1998*. Toronto: Family Service Association of Canada.

Canadian Institute of Child Health (1994) *The Health of Canada's Children: A CICH Profile*, 2nd ed. Ottawa: Canadian Institute of Child Health.

Canadian Paediatric Society (1996) *Well Beings: A Guide to Promote the Physical Health, Safety and Emotional Well-Being of Children in Child Care Centres and Family Day Care Homes*. Toronto: Creative Premises.

Canadian Public Health Association (1996) *Caring about Health: Canadian Public Health Association Issue Paper on Federal/Provincial Territorial Arrangements for Health Policy*. Ottawa: Canadian Public Health Association.

Doherty, G. (1993) *Quality Child Care: Contextual Factors*. Prepared for the Canadian Child Care Federation (April). Unpublished.

Epp, J. (1986) *Achieving Health for All: A Framework for Health Promotion*. Ottawa: Supply and Services Canada.

Friendly, M. (1994) *Child Care Policy in Canada: Putting the Pieces Together*. Don Mills, ON: Addison-Wesley Publishers.

Gestwicki, C., and J. Bertrand (1999) *The Essentials of Early Education*, 1st Canadian ed. Toronto: ITP Nelson.

Gonzalez-Mena, J. (1997) *Multicultural Issues in Child Care*, 2nd ed. Toronto: Mayfield Publishing.

Guy, K. (1997) *Our Promise to Children*. Ottawa: Health Canada.

Hertzman, C. (1998) "The Case for Child Development as a Determinant of Health." *Canadian Journal of Public Health* 89, supplement 1:S14–S19.

Health and Welfare Canada (1992) *Brighter Futures: Canada's Action Plan for Children*. Ottawa: Supply and Services Canada.

——— (1990) *Status of Day Care in Canada 1990: A Review of the Major Findings of the National Day Care Study*. Ottawa: National Child Care Information, Centre Child Care Programs Division.

Jesuit Centre for Social Faith and Justice and South Riverdale Community Health Centre (1993) "Community Action for Health Issue." *The Moment* 6:3.

Kirkey, M. (1998) "One-on-One with Dr. Michael Rachlis: 1998 Review/1999 Forecast," *Hospital News* (12):11, 18.

Labonté, R. (1993) *Health Promotion: Theory and Practice Background Material #1.* Toronto: Centre for Health Promotion, University of Toronto.

Lalonde, M. (1974) *A New Perspective on the Health of Canadians: A Working Document.* Ottawa: Queen's Printer.

Mhatre, S.L., and D. Raisa (1992) "From Equal Access to Health Care to Equitable Access to Health: A Review of Canadian Provincial Health Commissions and Reports." *International Journal of Health Services* 22(4):645–68.

Morgan, P. (1993) "Illiteracy Can Have Major Impact on Patients' Understanding of Health Care Information." *Canadian Medical Association Journal* 148(7):1196–97.

National Forum on Health (1997) *Canada Health Action: Building on the Legacy, vol. I (Final Report).* Ottawa: Minister of Public Works and Government Services.

National Forum on Health (1997) *Canada Health Action: Building on the Legacy, vol. II (Synthesis Reports and Issue Papers).* Ottawa: Minister of Public Works and Government Services.

Network of the Federal/Provincial/Territorial Group on Nutrition & National Institute of Nutrition (1989) *Promoting Nutritional Health during the Preschool Years: Canadian Guidelines.*

Paul, A. (1994) "Patient Health to Pay Off: Reforms to Tie MDs' Wages to Value of Their Services." *Winnipeg Free Press*, 29 December, A1.

Pederson, A., et al. (1994) *Health Promotion in Canada: Provincial, National & International Perspectives.* Toronto: W.B. Saunders Canada.

Premier's Council on Health, Well-Being and Social Justice (1994) *Yours, Mine and Ours: Ontario's Children and Youth Phase One.* Toronto: Queen's Printer.

Rachlis, M., and C. Kushner (1992) *Second Opinion: What's Wrong with Canada's Health Care System.* Toronto: Collins Publishers.

Ross, D.P., et al. (1994) *The Canadian Fact Book on Poverty.* Ottawa: Canadian Council on Social Development.

Royal Commission on Aboriginal Peoples (1996) *National Forum on Health. vol. VII: The Need for an Aboriginal Health Institute in Canada.* Ottawa: Supply and Services Canada.

Shah, C.P. (1987) *An Introduction to Canadian Health and the Health Care System,* 2nd ed. Toronto: SN.

Stevens, T., and D. Fowler Graham, eds. (1993) *Canada's Health Promotion Survey 1990: Technical Report*. Ottawa: Minister of Supply and Services Canada.

Tyson, H. (1991) "1,001 Home Births: A Retrospective, Descriptive Study of 5 Years of Home Births in Toronto, Ontario." *Birth* (March):14–18.

Villeneuve, P., and H. Morrison (1994) *Health Consequences of Smoking in Canada: An Update, Chronic Diseases in Canada* 15(3): 102–4.

Walker, W. "Update Natural Health Product Rules, Report Urges," *Toronto Star*, 2 November 1998, p. A1.

Wilkins, R. (1988) *Special Study on the Socially and Economically Disadvantaged*. Ottawa: Supply and Services Canada.

World Health Organization (1984) *Health Promotion: A Discussion Document on the Concept and Principles*. Copenhagen: World Health Organization Regional Office for Europe.

World Health Organization, Health and Welfare Canada, and Canadian Public Health Association (1986) *Ottawa Charter for Health Promotion*. Ottawa.

Appendix 1.1

Getting Started in Your Community: A Checklist

Those communities that try to identify the needs of their children, and develop comprehensive plans to address those needs, are more likely to find effective solutions. But there is no one blueprint for successful community action. Each community has its own particular needs and its unique combination of resources.

Building on community-based success stories and the latest research and best practices can help lead the way, but in the end it is the needs of children in your community, your community's collective assets, and the possibilities for community-wide collaboration that will help define your community's particular goals and implementation strategies.

Here are a few questions to keep in mind:

❑ Who are the key people in the community concerned about the well-being of children, the community's social environment, and the local economy? For example, individuals who are:
- currently involved in caring for, educating, and providing services for children
- researchers and experts in child development and social policy
- leaders in local politics, business, labour, and the media
- young people, community activists, members of parent organizations, and volunteers

❑ What is the best forum for bringing these partners together? For example:
- a task force set up by the mayor's office, by municipal leaders, or by a planning association
- a coalition of community-based organizations that serve children, youth, and families
- a dedicated group of community members who have potential access to resources, research, and expertise
- a "child-friendly" community effort

❑ How can you use data effectively to guide your efforts? In other words, how do you measure how well your community's children are doing and assess the community assets at your disposal?
- Who in the community collects data on children—a district health council, school boards, a child care association, a university, municipal/regional government, etc.?
- Whom can you recruit to help pull this information together or to look at developing new indicators to help measure the well-being and competence of children in your community?
- What are some of the assets within your community, such as voluntary networks, service systems that are open to change and collaboration, equity of opportunities and outcomes for children, and financial and in-kind sources of support?
- How can your group develop an action plan that lays out steps to improve the outcomes for your community's children? Based on the assessment of both the key strengths and weakness in your community:
  - What do you want to achieve or, in other words, what problems do you want to address?

- How can you make the best use of the expertise that exists in your community?
- What are the most practical next steps? What are some of the issues that require more long-term planning?
- What indicators can you use that will show whether you achieved your objectives? For example, what is the percentage of low birth weight babies, and how many children are assessed to be ready to learn when they arrive in Grade 1?

❏ How can you build broad-based support for your action plan?

- What are the key messages you would like to convey to the community as a whole?
- What practical steps can you recommend to people who might be interested in getting involved in the community? For example, you might target individual members of neighbourhoods, labour, business, government, non-governmental organizations, charities, and religious congregations, and professional organizations.
- Who can help you develop and implement a public relations and media strategy?

Source: Adapted with permission from K.A. Guy, ed., *Our Promise to Children* (Ottawa: Health Canada, 1997), 132–33.

Unit 2

Occupational Health

Unit 2: Occupational Health

CONTENTS

Students in community colleges and universities are not a homogeneous group but instead reflect the communities in which they live. While many students are right out of high school, others are mature students returning to school after time spent in the work force. Some are parents. Some are in their first educational program since arriving in Canada. Many are juggling school and part-time jobs or other commitments. You too are entering the early childhood education program with experiences different from those of your classmates, and you have responsibilities beyond the classroom and placements in centres.

·Even at the best of times, school is stressful. It is a period of transition: establishing new friendships and study habits, trying to budget your time and money. There can be additional adjustments to make, such as moving away from home for the first time or to a new community. It's not surprising if you are experiencing stressors, suffering emotional ups and downs, feeling tired and at times discouraged, feeling pulled in different directions. Recognizing and managing stress in your life is essential now and on graduation, when you will be working in a child care program.

There is growing recognition that employees' overall health plays a significant role in job satisfaction, productivity, and turnover rates. Occupations that we tend to think of as stressful are those that are inherently dangerous, such as mining, operating heavy machinery, firefighting, and police work. Yet every occupation presents potential risks to its employees' physical and emotional health. Store clerks who repeatedly drag groceries over the scanner at the checkout counter can develop severe wrist pain as well as sore legs or varicose veins from standing. People who work at computer terminals all day may suffer from eyestrain, lower back pain, and carpal tunnel syndrome. Employees who perform repetitive tasks and work that permits them little control over their jobs experience a low level of autonomy, which leads to low job satisfaction.

Child care is *not* baby-sitting! Many still believe that working in child care is just an extension of being at home with children. In addition, the fact that child care is a predominantly female profession has accorded it low status historically, and many people believe that women naturally have the aptitude, knowledge, and skills needed to care for groups of children. In other words, the popular myth is that anyone can look after children. Many people also don't believe that child care (unlike education and health care) is an essential service to families. These attitudes contribute to the low status, low salaries, and the lack of respect accorded to caregivers. Beach et al. (1998,77) note from a variety of sources that salaries of centre-based caregivers with a college diploma or certificate working full time were less than 75 percent of those of the average full-time female worker with the same education. In addition, they reported a wide discrepancy in wage rates for centre-based staff, even within the same province or territory (79).

Fortunately, change is happening, however slowly. More people are recognizing what quality child care is. Other professions are identifying the important impact that child care can have on children's lives (e.g., preventing child abuse). The child care community and its professional associations tirelessly advocate at all levels of government for child care. Most parents recognize that child care is an essential service, and that their children's early experiences are critical to their overall development.

As in any other occupation, not everyone is suited to the work. Yes, children are amazing, energetic, curious, active learners. Yes, it can be exciting and rewarding to be involved in their lives and development. But contrary to the stereotype addressed earlier, caregivers must have developed the attitudes, knowledge, and skills necessary to be competent in their career. In addition, child care is both physical and emotional work. Always having to be "on" with children can be emotionally tiring. Combine this with the working dynamics of co-workers, the administrative organization, and management styles of supervisors and directors, and caregivers can experience job stress and, possibly, burnout.

Low salaries and limited opportunities for advancement are two factors that contribute to staff turnover. Neither is likely to change to caregivers' advantage in the near future. However, you can control other aspects of the work to increase your job satisfaction. In recent decades a holistic approach to health has often been translated into dimensions of wellness to facilitate self-awareness and enhance individual goal-setting. Although dimensions are listed separately in the accompanying table, there is recognition that all aspects of wellness are interrelated (Montgomery et al. 1997). Table 2.1 provides descriptions of eight commonly identified dimensions of wellness. See also Appendix 2.1, page 107.

TABLE 2.1   DIMENSIONS OF PERSONAL WELLNESS
Physical: awareness of and respect for body—nutrition, physical activity, relaxation, sleep, use of tobacco, health habits
Emotional: level of self-esteem, security, flexibility, ability to express feelings, recognition of strengths and weaknesses
Social: level of involvement with others, sense of belonging, membership, or affiliation
Intellectual: active mind, inquiring, curious, seeking new information and ideas
Occupational: clarity of direction, satisfaction with development of skills and potential, as well as autonomy, motivation to investigate options
Spiritual: ability to achieve a sense of renewal, see purpose in life, find things that nourish your soul
Environmental: level to which your external environment contributes to or detracts from your wellness, commitment to environmental cleanup
Financial: becoming financially literate, and learning to take control over money (once basic needs are met)

Goals can be short-term (usually accomplished within a year), long-term, or ongoing (e.g., lifelong inclusion of daily physical activity). Montgomery et al. (1997, 51–54) state that when you write goals you need to include:

▶ goal statements that are specific and measurable
▶ action steps that explain exactly how you will attain each goal
▶ target dates
▶ a statement about which resources you have to help you, as well as barriers that may block you and how you plan to overcome them

Appendix 2.1 (page 107) provides you with a sample of financial criteria. Completing such a checklist can help you decide on goals and an action plan.

This unit begins with an exploration of the physical dimension of child care work for caregivers and ECE students. The second section explores the social and emotional dimensions for caregivers and ECE students. Although the topics are organized in sections, they are all interrelated. To explore other dimensions (e.g., spiritual, environmental) more specifically, you may want to refer to wellness manuals such as those by Donatelle et al. (1998) or Montgomery et al. (1997). (See also Resource Materials, page 102.)

Promoting Your Physical Well-Being

▶ **OBJECTIVES**   To identify and evaluate a personally balanced lifestyle.
To identify physical risks to caregivers working in centres.
To discuss prevention strategies for physical risks.

What are your health concerns about working with children? When instructors ask new ECE students this question, many students worry about catching chickenpox, head lice, colds, and the flu. We know that when children are first enrolled in centres, they get sick more often; but as time passes, the rate of illness declines. This pattern applies to students as well. Adults benefit from a mature immune system; they are fully immunized, one hopes, and most have already experienced the common childhood diseases (e.g., chickenpox). Adults can also implement hygiene practices

that protect them and reduce the opportunities for illness to spread among children and adults. Even so, you may experience a few viral infections when you begin your centre placements.

It probably will take only a couple of days of work in a centre to experience first-hand how physically demanding work with children can be. It is physically strain-ing for caregivers to lift and carry infants and toddlers, move play equipment, sit on the floor, lean over child-sized tables, sinks, and toilets, and be constantly on the move in the playground to supervise children or take part in a physical activity. The positive side is that this constant and varied movement, when performed correctly, contributes to physical fitness.

Achieving a Balance in Your Lifestyle

As adults we make individual lifestyle choices that can have positive or negative effects on our health.

NUTRITION

One of our basic needs is food. However, emphasis placed on food and our health varies among individuals and throughout society. The bottom line—nutrition has a significant impact on our health. The principles of nutrition discussed in Unit 4 apply to children's and to your own nutritional status. As well, factors that shape eating habits are discussed; these can assist you in developing insight into why, what, and when you eat. Some people's nutritional habits fall far short of the recommended principles of nutrition. Others know what good nutrition includes and put these prin-ciples into practice every day. Of course there are times when nutrition is less of a priority—especially to someone experiencing a great deal of stress. There is concern, however, that this becomes a pattern of behaviour or a vicious circle, because our bodies have increased nutrient needs at times of emotional or physical stress.

Lynn, an ECE student, is studying frantically for term tests and is trying to stay awake by drinking lots of coffee. Not surprisingly, the coffee keeps her awake even when she wants to sleep. Lynn doesn't believe she has time for sit-down meals and instead eats doughnuts in the cafeteria. By week's end, Lynn is snap-ping at everyone and can't imagine how she'll ever survive her weekend job at the mall.

This example highlights the interplay between nutrition and physical, social, and emotional well-being. Lynn's nutritional habits have *raised* her stress level rather than lowered it. How can she use nutrition in her favour when she is stressed out during test week? Recognizing the problem, Lynn has made it a point to learn more about nutrition and how nutrients (especially B and C vitamins) nourish the nervous system. As test week approaches, Lynn eats a variety of foods high in these vitamins—whole-grain breads and cereals, milk and yogurt, dark-green leafy vegetables, broccoli, tomatoes, oranges, and bananas. During that week she brings in nutritious snacks like whole-grain crackers with cheese or hummus, and fruit that she can refuel on. She limits her coffee to a couple of cups during the morning. She was pleasantly surprised that by the end of the week she wasn't a bear! Let us hope that this experience has a positive impact on Lynn, that she makes some permanent changes to her eating patterns that help her in the long term.

Eating nutritiously reaps benefits daily and over time for all of us. Foods that are high in nutrients keep our minds and bodies in good working order, providing ongoing energy. Eating patterns that maximize the intake of wholesome foods while minimizing the intake of processing and additives contribute to the prevention of serious chronic diseases (e.g., a diet that is low in fat is thought to help prevent heart disease and some cancers). In addition to feeling good and preventing disease, we also provide healthy role-modelling for children. *Canada's Food Guide to Healthy Eating* (included in *Using the Food Guide*; see Health and Welfare Canada 1992, 3) is based on five principles, which can be adapted to ethno-cultural preferences:

1. Enjoy a *variety* of foods.
2. Emphasize cereals, breads, other grain products, vegetables, and fruit.
3. Choose lower-fat dairy products, leaner meats, and foods prepared with little or no fat.
4. Achieve and maintain a healthy body weight by enjoying regular physical activity and healthy eating.
5. Limit salt, alcohol, and caffeine. (See Appendix 4.2, page 294.)

The fourth principle affirms that Health Canada does not recommend dieting, which is recognized as counterproductive. Canadians are urged to reject the popular myth that healthy body size is narrowly defined. Realistically, body images are achieved and maintained through healthy eating, without dieting, and through incorporating regular physical activity into one's lifestyle.

How does your eating pattern rate? Try recording what you eat for the next few days or, even better, for a week. Although Figure 2.1 (page 65), "Create Your Own," was designed for school-agers to draw the foods they eat, it can be used as an easy way to compare what you eat with the recommendations in *Canada's Food Guide to Healthy Eating*.

 e.g.

▶ You are doing everything right and this review confirms and supports your healthy lifestyle.

▶ You have a low energy level and feel that your overall health (e.g., complexion, dullness of hair, frequency of colds, headaches) can be improved.

▶ If you are a woman, perhaps you have chronic premenstrual syndrome (PMS) and have heard that changes in diet, such as eliminating caffeine and alcohol, may help reduce the symptoms.

▶ You know that you overeat when you're bored or that you crave salty food when you study.

Any habit is hard to break or adjust, so don't expect change to happen overnight. The first step is to find out what influences your eating. As children, we develop positive and negative associations with food. Using examples, Table 4.1 illustrates what food can mean to someone. (See page 223.) Sometimes you eat food because you feel like it, whether it is nutritious or not! If we feel deprived of food we enjoy, we are more likely to abandon our progress in making changes. Here are a few other suggestions:

▶ If you are not currently a breakfast eater, try gradually to make changes. Eating from at least three of the four food groups has short- and long-term benefits.

▶ Increase the whole foods you eat. Choose whole-grain bread rather than white bread made with refined flour, and eat more vegetables and fruit.

▶ Eat vegetables and fruits containing phytochemicals, which are natural plant compounds that have disease-fighting properties when they work with vitamins, minerals, and other nutrients.

▶ Reduce the percentage of animal foods in your diet, and eat some fish and soy foods (e.g, tofu). More specifically, Lambert-Lagacé and Laflamme (1995) report that it is healthy to eat the "good" fats:
  ▷ foods rich in monosaturates (e.g., olive oil, almonds, avocado)
  ▷ foods rich in alpha-linolenic acid (e.g., linseed oil, soybeans, walnuts, dark-green leafy vegetables)
  ▷ foods rich in the other omega-3 fatty acids (e.g., fish and seafood)

▶ Reduce foods rich in hydrogenated fats, because foods rich in saturated fats (e.g., meat, poultry, dairy products, butter) compete with the essential fatty acids. At present most people eat too many of these fats. And limit foods rich in polyunsaturated fatty acids from the omega-6 family (e.g., sunflower, safflower, corn oils) because of their competitiveness with the omega-3 family.

▶ Gradually reduce the number of processed foods you buy, though some convenience foods may be too convenient to give up! Most, but not all, processed foods have a lot of fat, salt, sugar, and additives. Read labels to determine nutrition content.

▶ Bring your own food to school or work as often as possible, or at least part of the meal, or bring snacks to ensure some high-nutrient foods.

▶ Share ideas with your friends. Potluck lunches or two or three friends taking turns bringing lunch may be enjoyable and time-saving. This idea can promote openness to try new foods.

PHYSICAL ACTIVITY

Generally, physical activity includes any bodily movement caused by muscle contraction that results in using energy. The benefits of regular physical activity are well known to virtually everyone nowadays. It's common knowledge that physical activity at a moderate level for even 20 minutes three times a week contributes to a healthy heart, an increased metabolic rate that improves bodily functions, stronger bones, relief from stress, and a higher energy level. These benefits have a positive impact on one's sense of

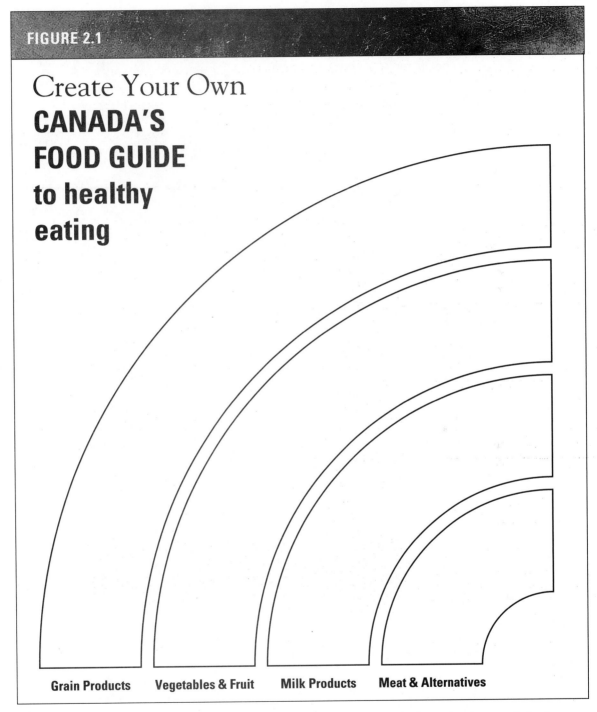

FIGURE 2.1

Create Your Own
**CANADA'S
FOOD GUIDE**
to healthy
eating

Grain Products   **Vegetables & Fruit**   **Milk Products**   **Meat & Alternatives**

Source: The Nova Scotia Department of Health is the original source for this publication and author permission has been obtained from the Nova Scotia Department of Health.

well-being, and they enhance one's physical and intellectual abilities.

The fitter you are, the better your body is able to deal with the everyday demands you put on it and to recover from any injury. The reasons why physical activity is healthy for us are listed in *Canada's Physical Activity Guide to Healthy Active Living* (Appendix 2.2). Refer to this guide for Health Canada's physical activity guidelines for all Canadians.

Some people don't give exercise a second thought because being active is just part

of their lifestyle (e.g., walk or ride a bicycle to work rather than drive, take the stairs rather than an escalator). Those of us who have not incorporated regular physical activity into our lives may find it easier to start by taking small steps rather than big leaps. A drastic change can be motivating at first but soon becomes discouraging if the work and effort don't bring quick results. It may be difficult to fit one more thing into an already crowded schedule, and exercise may seem to be expendable. Single parents of young children, for example, may not see how it is possible. Maybe riding a stationary bike while watching television with the children would be workable. Perhaps making a conscious effort to be more active while at work or school is a possibility. While supervising on the playground, caregivers can keep moving as much as possible; or they can go for a brisk walk during the coffee break. The four components of physical fitness universally recognized with reference to health are aerobic, endurance, flexibility, and strength. Aerobic (or cardiovascular) fitness is considered the most important component, and refers to how well your heart is able to pump oxygen-rich blood to your cells and carry waste out of your cells. The term aerobic means "with oxygen." In aerobic activity, the body performs low- to moderate-intensity tasks over an extended period of time. By working our heart muscle at 70 to 80 percent of its capacity for a minimum of 10 minutes (progressing to 30 minutes) four days a week, we increase and maintain our aerobic fitness level.

Individuals need to choose activities and times that suit their life situations. Busy people often try to fit aerobic activity into their workday, such as walking or climbing stairs at lunch, or getting off public transit a few kilometres from work or home and walking the rest of the way. A bonus is that we get outside and have a change of scenery, which is also good for stress management.

Flexibility refers to the ability of your joints to move through the full range of their motion. Proper stretching is the best way to increase flexibility. Good back

health, and the prevention of pulls and other muscle damage, are important benefits of flexibility (see Preventing Musculoskeletal Injuries, page 73).

Strength refers to the ability of one of your muscle groups to exert force in one
motion (e.g., lifting a toddler or moving a table). Endurance refers to the ability of
one of your muscle groups to perform muscular contractions of moderate force over
an extended period (e.g., lifting half of your maximum capacity a few times a minute
over five minutes). If you walk, ride a bike, or climb a hill, you are working on
muscular endurance. In the work environment, muscular endurance may translate
into putting all the cots away after nap time. Both strength and endurance are
increased through activity involving resistance training (usually with weights),
because your muscles get stronger when you condition them to lift more weight and
gain endurance when you increase repetitions. It is essential that you learn and practise the proper techniques to prevent injury.

An active lifestyle should include all four fitness components, but your goals and
the level of activity you want in your life will help to determine how much of each
component will be included. For example, someone who wants to improve her overall well-being but doesn't have the time or interest in focusing a lot of attention on
a program may place more emphasis on aerobic activities and some gentle stretching to improve flexibility. Regardless of the aerobic activity chosen, strength and
endurance should be relatively easy to incorporate.

Recognizing the short- and long-term benefits of moderate physical activity for
one's personal and professional lives is the first step toward fitness. Remember:

▶ Start your program gradually and choose activities you enjoy.
▶ Make sure you have the right equipment and clothing for the activity. If cost is
  a factor, choose an activity that has lower equipment costs.
▶ Learn and use the proper techniques to prevent injury and maximize fitness
  benefits.
▶ Stop if it hurts! Listen to your body. Pain means there is something your body
  is not ready for and you can injure yourself if you continue.

Provincial or local chapters of the Back Association of Canada, the Heart and
Stroke Foundation of Canada, and many other agencies and resources are available
to help you get started with suggestions for components of fitness.

Leisure and Rest

Balancing our need for meaningful work with our need for leisure contributes to
well-being. Leisure means different things to different people. For example, most
individuals have a *need for solitude* that can be fulfilled through a variety of activities such as completing puzzles, doing crafts or artwork, or meditating. Many people
use meditation to relax and manage stress. Although different techniques and
philosophies are advocated, in general meditation utilizes deep breathing, allowing
tension to leave the body. Most forms of meditation involve sitting quietly for 15
to 20 minutes, focusing on a particular word or symbol (a mantra), controlling

breathing, and becoming more in tune with the inner self. With meditation, as with other forms of coping with or managing stress, it is the individual who determines how effective it is as a tool. To satisfy our *need to relate to others*, we may like going to a movie with a friend, talking on the phone, entertaining at home, fishing with others, or going camping. Religious or political meetings may also fulfill this need. We might satisfy our *need to be a participant* through organized sports or physical activity, a gardening club, or an ethno-cultural group. Most individuals also *need to be a spectator* at times. They may satisfy that need by visiting amusement parks, watching parades, sitting on the porch and watching passersby, or browsing in a bookstore (Bolles 1980).

These are but a few examples, but they highlight the fact that for most of us there is an overlap between physical activity and relaxation, because going to the gym or taking a brisk walk may achieve both ends. In the discussion on stress later in this unit, the topic of leisure activities—whether physically active and social or quiet and solitary—appears again as a means to cope with stress. Being aware of what is relaxing for you and finding regular opportunities to unwind is part of every-day health promotion.

Our bodies need time to rest and sleep in order to revitalize and to provide time for the bodily functions and organs to slow down. The amount of sleep that adults need varies, but most of us need seven to eight hours a night. Illness, pregnancy, or other factors may increase the amount of sleep needed.

Stress factors such as financial or personal problems, exam-time worry, or a colicky baby can affect the amount or quality of our sleep. Stress coupled with sleep deprivation is very taxing on one's emotional and physical health. Individuals in situations like these need to be able to talk with someone (a friend or counsellor) to seek short- or long-term solutions.

Especially when we are younger, and often as students, socializing in the evenings may take precedence over getting enough sleep every night. When lack of sleep affects our health or work/school performance, we are faced with making some decisions and establishing priorities. And when we work with children, we must be especially alert to our surroundings from the standpoint of safety. As well, sleep deprivation often makes us irritable—not an appropriate frame of mind when working with children and co-workers. These decisions are sometimes difficult, especially for young adults who are training for a career, but responsibility does involve setting priorities.

Reducing Other Risk Factors

Health behaviour either promotes your health or undermines it. Here are important examples of health behaviour that contribute positively to our health:

▶ quitting smoking and avoiding passive (secondhand) smoking
▶ limiting your consumption of alcohol, and refraining from drinking alcohol during pregnancy and breast-feeding
▶ avoiding illegal drugs and being careful about medication use
▶ practising safer sex to prevent sexually transmitted diseases (STDs), including HIV infection and hepatitis B
▶ maintaining a regular schedule of physical and dental checkups, and monthly self-exams of breasts or testicles for early detection of breast or testicular cancer

In keeping with the health promotion philosophy discussed in Unit 1, the continuum of responsibility between individual and society depends very much on your circumstances.

Selecting health care professionals that best suit our health needs can play a significant role in health promotion. If you live in an area where there is more than one choice, choose the health professional or agency that

▶ answers your questions clearly and directly
▶ gives you access to your medical file, should you choose to see it
▶ is linguistically and culturally relevant to you

You may have additional criteria, and it is important that you feel like a partner in your health care. It's in your best interest to take an *active* role in decision-making and to agree to medical treatments. This is our individual responsibility. When in doubt, ask for a second or third opinion. Women in particular often feel uncomfortable with or even intimidated by physicians and do not ask them questions about their own health care. Even today, some physicians prescribe tranquillizers for women with complaints like premenstrual syndrome (PMS).

One of the best ways that people who smoke can improve their long-term health is by quitting, but that's not easy. It's especially difficult when other stress factors are present and beyond the smoker's control. Smoking may be relaxing or a stress reliever for that person in that situation. *Pursuing ways to quit smoking, though, is well worth the effort, and many communities have support systems that can help.* At a time when so many Canadians are quitting smoking, it is discouraging that teens and young women are the fastest-growing groups starting to smoke. Young people who have been smoking only a short time are strongly encouraged to quit before the addiction becomes stronger. What messages are caregivers and ECE students sending to children who see them smoking outside the centre on breaks, who smell the smoke on their clothes and hair, who see them smoking in the mall or on the street?

The issue of partner abuse is included to raise awareness and sensitize readers to the possibility that fellow students, future co-workers, children's parents, or even you yourself may be a victim. Violence against women can take many forms, including physical, sexual, emotional, social, and financial. You will need to expand your knowledge in this area, since we are only touching the surface of abuse.

 Lidia was a victim of spousal abuse. She felt powerless to escape. She believed that if she left her husband, he would find and possibly kill her. Her co-workers talked among themselves about how weak Lidia was for not leaving her husband. Yet it's too simple to say, "Just leave him!" Family violence is a very complicated situation. Lidia eventually found the support and legal assistance she needed at the local women's shelter, but not before years of violence had taken a great toll on her well-being.

A telephone survey of 12 300 Canadian women conducted by Statistics Canada in 1993 concluded:

► One-half of Canada's ten million women over age 18 have experienced one or more incidents of physical or sexual assault since 16 years of age.
► Almost one-third of women experience violence by their partner.
► More than one in 10 women who have experienced violence in marriage have at some point feared for their life (*Toronto Star* in McGillicuddy 1993, 6).

Women stay in abusive relationships for a number of reasons: fear, low self-esteem, a lack of economic and social supports, cultural taboos, religion, obligation, and oppression. When a women discloses abuse to you, listen and believe her. This is the first step for her, and the emotional support you provide may encourage her to take action, although the decisions should be her own. In the future, possibly with your support, she may seek options (e.g., shelters, legal advice, services sensitive to women's needs) and make a safety plan.

Familiarize yourself with your community's emergency shelters and the telephone hot line as well as any available long-term services. Partner abuse, date rape, and other forms of violence, particularly against women, are known to be prevalent in our society. With support, many women can escape the vicious circle of violent relationships. Stopping the violence is a complex task and requires a multifaceted societal response.

Infectious Diseases and You

When you start working in centres, you'll probably find that you get sick more often than usual. Although this is to be expected, there are things you can do to prevent being ill as frequently, including being immunized, implementing hygiene practices, and maintaining a well-balanced lifestyle.

Early childhood education training programs should require students to have up-to-date immunizations before they do their first placement in a centre. The training institution's health personnel collect and review students' immunization records and other related medical information. In addition to the vaccines we get as children, adults should receive a booster shot for diphtheria and tetanus every 10 years. Depending on the community, the public health agency may recommend that caregivers be tested for tuberculosis.

To reduce the spread of infectious disease in centres, caregivers are responsible for implementing hygiene practices. Steps taken to reduce the spread of germs among children will have a positive affect on caregivers' health. On a daily basis, caregivers must pay particular attention to how and when they wash their hands. Unit 3 outlines what you need to know, including the ins and outs of hand-washing and information on hygiene practices.

There will be times when caregivers who are ill should be excluded from work. (See Appendix 2.4, page 111.) Much of what we know about child-

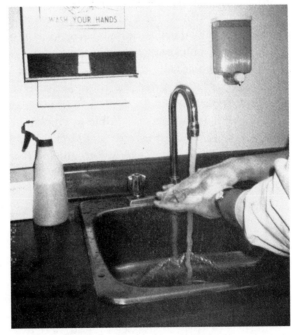

hood infections applies also to adults, who can get the same infections. The more common childhood illnesses are discussed in Unit 3, which includes a table that summarizes the management of children's illnesses in the centre. (See Childhood Infections: Just the Basics, page 174.)

A comment about hepatitis B, a virus that causes infection of the liver and is spread by direct contact with blood or bloody body fluid: hepatitis B has so rarely been reported in child care centres that routine screening of children or staff is not recommended (Canadian Paediatric Society 1996, 182, 690). Although the hepatitis B virus immunization (a series of three injections over six months) has been added to the routine childhood immunization schedule in almost all Canadian jurisdictions, vaccinations for caregivers are not routinely recommended on account of their line of work. Vaccinations may be beneficial on account of caregivers' own personal health behaviour (i.e., sexual practices), however. Universal precautions are always important when cleaning blood and bodily fluids. (See Universal Precautions, page 153.) There is no documented risk in allowing a caregiver who has recovered from hepatitis B to care for children. (Canadian Paediatric Society 1996, 691).

Pregnancies are not always planned. Working with children increases your exposure to infections. Female ECE students and caregivers may have peace of mind if they talk with their physician. Three infections are particularly important to pregnant women: chickenpox, rubella, and cytomegalovirus.

Chickenpox Fortunately, most people have chickenpox when they are children. Although chickenpox is usually mild in children, it can cause severe illness in adults. Students and caregivers who can't recall whether they had chickenpox as children may wish to ask their doctor to do an antibody test, which will tell them whether they have had the disease. Working in centres puts you at risk of caring for children with chickenpox. Susceptible adults exposed to chickenpox or shingles should receive varicella-zoster immune globulin (VZIG) within 72 hours of exposure. The chicken pox vaccine is available in Canada. For more information about it, contact your physician.

For women who are susceptible to chickenpox and become infected during the first half of pregnancy, the fetus is at high risk of malformation. As soon as a woman knows that she has been exposed to chickenpox or shingles, she must contact her physician or the public health agency. When an infant is born to a mother who developed chickenpox a few days before or after delivery, the baby will likely develop a severe case of chickenpox.

Rubella (German Measles) If your immunization schedule is up-to-date, you will know if you received your rubella vaccine. If not, ask your physician about the antibody test. If a pregnant woman is susceptible and has been exposed to rubella, she should talk to her physician immediately. Susceptible pregnant women who are infected with rubella during the first four months of pregnancy are at high risk of a miscarriage or, if the fetus goes to term, of delivering a baby with malformations.

Cytomegalovirus (CMV) A person who is infected with CMV may not have any symptoms or may develop ones that are similar to those of mononucleosis (i.e., swollen glands, fatigue, fever). Usually we aren't aware that we have been exposed to CMV, because our bodies produce antibodies to protect us. In fact, we may have had CMV as children. During pregnancy, women pass their CMV antibodies to the fetus. After birth, children excrete the virus in the urine and saliva for a year or two and intermittently throughout life. Because of the relatively close contact between caregivers and children, some susceptible caregivers will probably become infected with CMV. Caregivers' best protection is effective hand-washing, effective diapering and toileting routines, and cleaning/sanitizing surfaces that have been contaminated with body secretion (e.g., saliva, vomit, urine, stool).

The only real concern about CMV is when women who are susceptible to CMV become infected *during their pregnancy*. When this happens, a very small percentage of newborns have physical or developmental challenges (e.g., deafness, cerebral palsy, visual impairment). A vaccine or immune globulin for CMV is not available (Canadian Paediatric Society 1996).

Preventing Musculoskeletal Injuries

Markon and Le Beau's research in 54 Quebec child care centres (1994, 1–3, 12) concluded that the most common injury experienced by caregivers is back injury. The injuries were due to excessive lifting, pulling, pushing, or carrying, although the layout and design of the centre, its furniture, the number of people, and available floor space all play a role in the likelihood of injury. Fortunately, over half of the caregivers who were injured did not have to leave work as a result. Of the 50 caregivers studied, 33 percent were found to have experienced musculoskeletal disorders over the previous two years. More than 70 percent of these were strains and sprains—a muscle pulled when lifting a child awkwardly, for example, or an ankle sprained when tripping on a toy (Maxwell and Huot 1994, 29).

According to the Back Association of Canada, every year over 1.5 million Canadians see their family physicians about back pain. Backaches are second only to colds as a reason for staying home from work (Back Basics video, 1996). Not all back pain or injury is preventable, but certainly there are ways to reduce the risk of back injury, and also to manage back pain when it does occur:

► Maintain the three natural curves of your spine, to take undue pressure off your spine.

► *Change* posture, even slightly, every few minutes, because the disks, like the rest of our body, take in nutrients and get rid of waste products. When we remain in one position for too long, that process can't happen efficiently.

► Take part in regular physical activity, which helps increase our muscles' ability to support our back.

► Do stretching exercises to increase flexibility, decrease risk of injury, and correct posture.

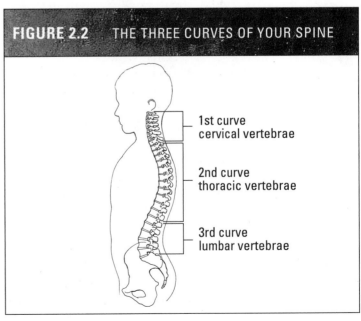

FIGURE 2.2   THE THREE CURVES OF YOUR SPINE

1st curve
cervical vertebrae

2nd curve
thoracic vertebrae

3rd curve
lumbar vertebrae

Source: Reprinted with permission from the Back Association of Canada, *Back Basics* (Toronto: Back Association of Canada, 1996).

▶ Use proper lifting techniques, as described below.

When back pain does occur, the Back Association of Canada recommends that individuals:

▶ consult with their family physician
▶ resume routines gradually but as soon as possible—it is now widely believed that bed rest for more than two or three days usually does more harm than good.
▶ pursue physiotherapy, chiropractic, acupuncture, massage, and yoga as more conservative therapy options. Surgery is not recommended as a therapeutic option in the vast majority of back problems.

In particular, improper lifting and carrying can result in back injuries, which may lead to long-term back problems, loss of wages, and even the need for a career change. Awareness of the potential problem and proper lifting techniques can help to prevent back problems. Whether you are standing, walking, sitting on a chair or floor, or lifting or carrying something, your goal is to maintain the natural curves of your spine.

Some readers may think that the following list of preventive steps applies only to people who lift boxes in a warehouse, not to caregivers who lift infants off the floor. Granted, lifting a baby off the floor in the same way as you might bend to touch your toes may not hurt your back the first time, but using this technique repeatedly almost guarantees eventual back injury. You may lean over a table or reach down to pick up a piece of paper and then find you can't straighten up. A baby may not look as heavy as a large box or suitcase, but a nine-month-old could weigh 8 kilograms (18 lbs.) or more. When we lift something by using our back (by bending over) rather than our legs, that 8 kilograms baby puts 82 kilograms (180 lbs.) of pressure on our back. To prevent injury, follow these steps (from Markon and Le Beau 1994, 131–48) when you are lifting something or someone from the floor:

▶ Keep your back straight. This maintains the curves of your spine.
▶ Stand in front of what you are going to lift and as close to it as possible.
▶ Keep your feet about hip-width apart, with one foot slightly behind the other for stability. This reduces the risk of falling, twisting the spine, or putting more weight on one side of the body.
▶ Bend your knees, but not so much that you are sitting on your heels, which makes getting back up much more difficult.
▶ Keep the arms as straight as possible, which prevents you from lifting with your arms and straining your shoulders and back. Obviously, when you lift a child you hold the child against your chest and your elbows are bent.
▶ Look ahead before straightening your knees, to avoid turning at the waist.

Learning how to lift properly and ensuring that you actually follow the steps each time helps to prevent back injuries. (See Appendix 2.3, page 110.)

Furnishings and Centre Layout

The centre's design and the actual layout of space, including the height of counters and storage shelves, contribute to our health status. The equipment and furnishings in child care centres are designed for children's (not adults') comfort and accessibility. Many activities happen on the floor. In addition, caregivers always put the children's safety before their own (Maxwell and Huot 1994). Of course this is necessary, but it may mean that unforeseen twists and turns are a reality. From a list of 24 factors that create stress for caregivers (Markon and Le Beau 1994, 18–20), five relate to the physical workspace: noise, tempera-

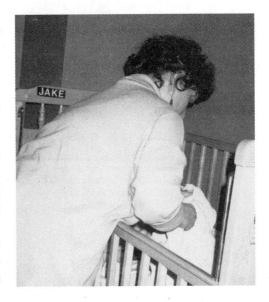

ture, lack of rest areas, inadequate furnishings, and lack of equipment. As students, you have little or no control over the physical aspects of the centres where you do placements. However, if you observe questionable or unsafe situations, you are obliged to report them to centre staff. Table 2.2 outlines some activities that caregivers are constantly involved in and provides suggestions for avoiding injury.

Research conducted in Quebec centres found that less than two-thirds of centres provided a separate staff room. Most centres did not provide an adult-sized table, chair, or sofa to be used in rooms with children or adult-sized seating outside (Markon and Le Beau 1994, 83). Caregivers, like other employees, need to get away from their work for breaks and to do administrative work. A staff room provides an area in which caregivers may relax and socialize.

The general layout of centres can impede the movement of caregivers and children.

- ▶ The layout does not provide easy access to all areas. While heights keep objects out of children's reach, caregivers often have to stretch to reach across or up high on shelves and in cupboards.
- ▶ The layout lacks storage space. Caregivers resort to piling boxes on the floor, which not only reduces walking space but forces caregivers to do more lifting.
- ▶ Rooms have limited space. In preschool centres, the same space is used for playing, eating, and napping. Therefore staff must lift and move equipment and furniture daily. The limited space increases the likelihood of tripping, falling, and running into one another (Markon and Le Beau 1994, 87–90).

TABLE 2.2	WORK SITE ANALYSIS OF THE CHILD CARE WORK ENVIRONMENT
PROBLEM	**RECOMMENDATIONS**
1. Incorrect lifting of children, toys, supplies, equipment, etc.	1. Education on proper lifting and carrying techniques 2. Promote task rotation where possible 3. Encourage independence in children whenever feasible
2. Inadequate work heights (e.g., child-size tables and chairs)	1. Create a chair that allows the staff to slide their legs under the table 2. Use sit/kneel chairs 3. Educate staff on using proper body mechanics 4. Provide the staff with adult-size chairs for occasional use
3. Difficulty lowering and lifting infants in and out of cribs	1. Modify crib sides to enable them to slide down or modify the legs of the cribs to accommodate the staff 2. Educate staff on using proper body mechanics 3. Have step stool available in sleep room
4. Frequent sitting on the floor with back unsupported	1. When possible, have staff sit up against a wall or furniture for back support 2. Perform stretching exercises 3. Educate staff on using proper body mechanics
5. Excessive reaching above shoulder height to obtain stored supplies	1. Redesign kitchen area, placing heaviest items at waist height, lightest above 2. Reorganize snacks and supplies to simplify snack preparation procedures 3. Utilize step stools when retrieving items that are above cupboard height
6. Frequent lifting of infants and toddlers on and off diaper changing tables	1. Educate staff on using proper body mechanics 2. Have toddlers use steps in order to decrease distance staff are lifting
7. Forceful motions combined with awkward posture required to open windows	1. Use step stool to allow for better leverage and reduce awkward posture 2. Have maintenance staff improve quality of window slide
8. Carrying garbage and diaper bags to dumpster	1. Provide staff with cart to transport garbage 2. Relocate garbage cart closer to work area 3. Reduce size and weight of loads 4. Educate staff on using proper body mechanics

Source: Adapted with permission from P. King et al. (1996), The Ergonomics of Child Care: Conducting Worksite Analyses. *Work: A Journal of Prevention, Assessment & Rehabilitation,* 6:25–32.

In the long term, ergonomic research will provide architects and child care licensing offices with vital information on designing centres that meet the physical needs of adults as well as children. Lack of funding and resources impedes needed improvements for adults in the child care environment. In the meantime, how can we improve workplace conditions? The most obvious answer is to purchase more adult-sized furniture and relatively inexpensive equipment to prevent musculoskeletal problems. For example, legless chairs are available that provide the caregiver with the necessary back support while sitting on the floor with the children.

A couch in a play area provides a comfortable spot for adults and children to sit and talk or read and for staff to bottle-feed infants. Perhaps a set of steps can be built that slide in and out under the diaper counter to give toddlers the opportunity to climb onto or down from the table rather than being lifted—an experience that most toddlers would prefer!

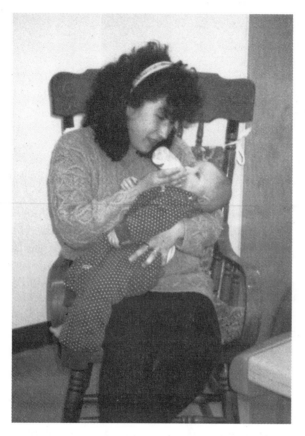

Caregivers should gather all the necessary diapering supplies before they bring the child to the change area. This eliminates the caregiver's having to keep one hand on the child while reaching and/or turning to get supplies during the change.

When replacing worn equipment such as cribs, look for ones that meet Canadian Standards Association (CSA) safety standards and that have rails that can be lowered to mattress level. Caregivers looking at their own workspace, talking about the issues, and referring to resources will

undoubtedly come up with many more ideas. Centre directors and employers need to assess how work is organized to avoid excessive demands on staff. Work tasks should also be evaluated on the basis of physical demands (Canadian Paediatric Society 1996, 657). Of course, the primary obstacle in implementing improvements is accessing funds.

Working with Art and Cleaning Products

Art supplies and cleaning products can be hazardous to caregivers and children. Caregivers must select play materials that are non-toxic and read labels for any special handling instructions. Pay particular attention to solvents, glues, dyes, and pottery products.

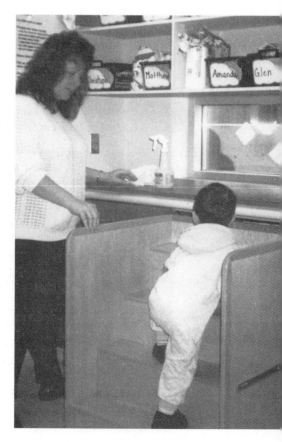

Painting is a desirable ongoing experience for children. Rather than buying ready-to-use paints, centres may purchase powder paint and then mix colours as needed. Caregivers need to exercise caution when handling the powder. If inhaled, the powder can harm the lungs' airways. To protect themselves, caregivers should mix paint in a well-ventilated area away from children (Canadian Paediatric Society 1996, 670). Caregivers with asthma may need to avoid mixing powdered paint or wear a filter over their nose and mouth.

In terms of cleaning products, many centres choose soap and water for cleaning surfaces and objects. Many use a dilute solution of bleach and water for sanitizing. Centres with automatic dishwashers will use the detergent recommended for the machine. All kinds of commercial products are on the market that we can use in our homes and in centres. Many companies advertise the product's sanitizing qualities and claim it makes things sparkling and fresh. For the most part, however, soap and water and good old elbow grease, which creates friction, remove most of the germs. Bleach kills any germs that may remain after cleaning. When one part bleach is diluted with 100 parts water, the bleach is strong enough to be effective yet dilute enough that it won't ruin clothes or make everything smell like bleach. And it is safe to use around children. An environmentally friendly alternative to bleach—one that falls within public health guidelines—will be welcomed when it arrives.

To protect themselves and others when using products, caregivers need to take precautions:

- ► Read and follow the product's instructions.
- ► Wear household rubber gloves to protect your hands from drying, if you prefer.
- ► Never mix two products (e.g., when ammonia and bleach are mixed, a poisonous gas is produced).
- ► Keep solutions in their original container and locked out of reach of children.
- ► Choose cleaners that are safer for our environment.

Workplace Hazardous Materials Information System (WHMIS)

The legislation for the Workplace Hazardous Materials Information System (WHMIS) applies to workplaces, which include centres. Employers are obligated to provide employees with information on the products they use at work. Certain "controlled" products have been defined as hazardous because they are compressed gas, flammable and combustible, oxidizing, poisonous, or infectious. These products must have labels that list their ingredients, their toxic effects, instructions on safe handling, and first-aid treatments. This legislation applies mainly to industries that use these types of products. For centres, the PHI may be consulted to verify whether any of the cleaning and sanitizing products are controlled products. Generally, centres buy their cleaning products at grocery stores, and products for sale there would not be controlled.

Read the label for directions and the first-aid treatment on the container (e.g., "If splashed in eyes, flush thoroughly with water. If swallowed, give water or milk.

TABLE 2.3	MAKING YOUR CENTRE'S CLEANING PRODUCTS
PRODUCTS	**SAFER ALTERNATIVES**
Carpet Stain Remover	• mix 60 mL (1/4 cup) Borax and 500 mL (2 cups) cold water
Drain Cleaner	• put 60 mL (1/4 cup) baking soda and 125 mL (1/2 cup) vinegar in the drain, put in the plug, wait, and rinse with water
Glass and Mirror Cleaner	• mix 1 part vinegar and 100 parts water in a spray bottle
Laundry Detergent	• mix 1.25 L (5 cups) soap flakes and 250 mL (1 cup) washing soda; use 60 mL (1/4 cup) per load
Oven Cleaner	• cover spills with table salt while the oven is still hot, and then scrape them off once the oven has cooled; or • warm oven and then turn it off; mix 60 mL (1/4 cup) ammonia and warm water in a glass bowl, leave it overnight in the oven, and then wipe clean
Toilet Cleaner	• use baking soda and a toilet brush

Call a physician"). The first-aid treatment also includes the name of the hazardous ingredient (e.g., "contains sodium hypochlorite"). This information will be very helpful to your poison control centre, whose number is listed in the front of your phone book, if someone ingests the product.

Role of Public Health Agencies in Health Promotion

Public health nurses (PHN) and public health inspectors (PHI) work within public health agencies. PHNs may be available for consultation on staff illnesses, immunizations, and other concerns. PHIs conduct environmental sanitation inspections of centres. At least annually, PHIs inspect the building—its lighting, ventilation, kitchen facilities, garbage disposal, and so on. They submit a report to the child care office (with a copy to the centre) that includes any concerns and recommendations for improvement. As well, they may consult with centre staff and answer questions about cleaning and sanitizing procedures and products. If the role of public health personnel in your community has been curtailed due to cutbacks, it is important for centre directors and staff to seek other consultants to perform this role. The maintenance of the physical environment with current information and changes is essential for children's and adults' health in the child care program.

Workplace Environmental Issues

Heating/air conditioning, ventilation, noise, and light levels all contribute to caregivers' and children's emotional and physical well-being. If it's too hot inside, we get drowsy and irritable, and are more prone to making mistakes. Inadequate lighting causes eyestrain and headaches. Centres should allow as much natural light into the building as possible.

A well-ventilated centre helps to remove indoor air contamination. Indoor air is tainted by hair sprays, perfumes, cleaning products, and dust; by odours from photocopiers and computer laser printers; by formaldehyde (e.g., unsealed plywood or particleboard, urea formaldehyde insulation, fabrics, glues, carpets); by germs from people's respiratory tracts; and by outdoor pollutants. These pollutants are particularly irritating to people with asthma, respiratory illnesses, and contact lenses. Staff should suspect the quality of the air in the centre when people are frequently experiencing symptoms such as headaches, fatigue, dizziness, and irritation in eyes, nose, or throat. Children and caregivers may be suffering from "building-related illness" (Clarke and Nikkel 1994, 7–8).

Ideally, there are windows in every room that staff open every day for some time, year-round. However, for centres located within larger buildings (e.g., in an office tower), the air is part of the building's ventilation system. Centres located in workplaces (e.g., in a manufacturing plant) *should* have a separate ventilation system to ensure that the children and staff are not breathing air from the plant. If staff or children frequently experience symptoms of illness, the ventilation system must be evaluated.

Finally, the noise level in centres can be an issue, considering the number of children and adults in the same place for extended periods. Although the noise level in centres is never in a range that could potentially damage someone's hearing, a constant noise level can make people feel tired and irritable. Couches, curtains, carpets, pillows, dress-up clothes, etc., all absorb sounds within the room. Caregivers can manage noise by

▶ alternating quiet and active programs
▶ guiding children to use their "indoor voice" indoors
▶ alternating caregivers who supervise the playground
▶ taking staff breaks in a separate room

In a broader environmental perspective, as citizens and professionals we have much to be concerned about with regard to our health and the health of our planet. North Americans are on a binge of consumption, at a rate that is clearly unsustainable for the planet. Many individuals have recognized the importance of taking action on all health promotion levels in order to reduce their own feelings of powerlessness and of course to make a difference. In particular for women, the increase in breast cancer rates is alarming and environmental risks must be considered. For example, among other causes, radiation, pesticides, and some plastics have been linked to breast cancer. Although radiation and pesticides have long been of concern as powerful carcinogens, there is growing concern (and controversy) about the ingredients (nonylphenols) in some plastic wraps used to cover food, added to make the wraps more flexible. Nonylphenols, known carcinogens, are not chemically bound and can leach out of the plastic fairly easily. Other ingredients in plastics (e.g., phthalates) are hormone disruptors. For more information on the environment, your health, and actions you can take to lessen your exposure to potentially hazardous products, refer to *Taking Action for a Healthy Future* (1997), a publication of the Women's Network on Health and the Environment. (See Resource Materials, page 102.)

Injury Reports

When caregivers are injured at the centre, they must complete an injury report. Sometimes they are tempted to avoid the extra paperwork, especially if they believe that the injury is minor. However, a report is important for a number of reasons:

▶ to maintain adequate workplace injury records for liability
▶ to document any injury that seems minor at first but becomes serious later (e.g., a cut that becomes infected)
▶ to prevent further injuries, potentially

When centre staff can assess the conditions that caused or contributed to an injury, they can implement preventive practices, review or provide training (e.g., in proper lifting), or modify the physical space to make it safer (e.g., by installing a handrail by the stairs or improving the lighting of the staff parking lot), which benefit everyone. Often centres use the same injury report for the children and caregivers. (See Appendix 5.2, page 391.)

Promoting Your Emotional and Social Well-Being

▶ **OBJECTIVES**   To discuss the major role that communication plays in caregivers' emotional and social well-being.

To identify the sources of stress and their impact on our well-being.

To understand the role and benefits of networking with community professionals and agencies.

Workplaces don't present only physical risks and benefits; there are emotional and social factors that can have positive and negative effects on employees' health. Although working with children and families is rewarding, no job is without elements that can create feelings of stress for employees. By recognizing potential stress factors, students take the first step in preventing or reducing the negative impact, resulting in richer professional and personal lives.

Creating a Supportive Child Care Environment

The single most important component of quality child care, in terms of promoting healthy child development, is the nature of the daily relationship and interactions between caregiver and child. The relationship is of course affected by the other quality factors. Although caregivers are the key component of quality, there is little recognition of the value of child care as an occupation. Those in the occupation are relatively poorly paid, and many have few traditional occupational benefits and lack adequate professional development opportunities (Beach et al. 1998, 13).

Caregivers who are content with their work conditions are much more likely to develop self-confidence and competence, and are less likely to be dissatisfied and resign. Lower turnover rates mean more consistent care for children. In Table 2.4, Bloom et al. (1991) identify 10 dimensions of the work climate that support professionalism. As you review the 10 dimensions, you will see the implied partnership between employee and employer.

A centre emphasizes personal and professional growth of the employees. The employer (e.g., director, board of directors, agency, college or university) provides support and access to professional development activities (e.g., conferences, workshops). However, caregivers need to be motivated to attend, learn, and incorporate their learning into their work with children.

ROLE OF DIRECTORS

How can centre directors promote staff health? Directors' philosophies and management styles play an integral role in supporting a healthy work environment. First, directors often set the tone in the program—if they are committed to employee health and ongoing training, their commitment will likely have a positive effect on caregivers. These directors will advocate for proactive employee health policies that are clearly outlined in centres' policy manuals. These policies may include

▶ an interview and selection process that assists in hiring individuals that fit their specific program
▶ job descriptions for all staff members
▶ an orientation program and job performance appraisals
▶ lines of communication and conflict resolution

TABLE 2.4	THE TEN DIMENSIONS OF ORGANIZATIONAL CLIMATE
DIMENSION	**DEFINITION**
Collegiality	the extent to which staff are friendly, supportive, and trust one another
Professional Growth	the degree of emphasis placed on personal and professional growth
Supervisor Support	the degree of facilitative leadership that provides encouragement, support, and clear expectations
Clarity	the extent to which policies, procedures, and responsibilities are clearly defined and communicated
Reward System	the degree of fairness and equity in the distribution of pay, fringe benefits, and opportunities for advancement
Decision-Making	the degree of autonomy given to the staff and the extent to which they are involved in centre-wide decisions
Goal Consensus	the degree to which staff agree on the goals and objectives of the centre
Task Orientation	the emphasis placed on good planning, efficiency, and getting the job done
Physical Setting	the extent to which the spatial arrangement of the centre helps or hinders staff in carrying out their responsibilities
Innovativeness	the extent to which the organization adapts to change and encourages staff to find creative ways to solve problems

Source: Adapted with permission from P.J. Bloom et al., *Blueprint for Action: Achieving Center-Based Change through Staff Development* (New Horizons, 1991), 178.

► an immunization schedule to ensure that all staff are up-to-date
► techniques for staff to implement that reduce the physical hazards of the work, such as proper lifting techniques, methods for safely handling potentially hazardous products, and methods for cleaning up spills of those products and bloody body fluids
► exclusion criteria for caregivers and pregnant women in relation to infectious diseases
► reporting of workplace injuries and compensation for illness or injury
► opportunities for professional development and in-service training
► role of substitutes, students, and volunteers in the centre

Regular job evaluations (at least annually) are acknowledged as a learning tool rather than a punitive device. A health-promoting director supports caregivers in goal-setting and in achieving those goals. She implements measures to decrease stress for staff whenever possible. She serves as an advocate for caregivers with the board of directors and the outside community.

Directors also have the following responsibilities for caregivers' health:

▶ conduct regular inspections of centres (see Appendix 5.1, page 380)
▶ ensure that caregiver–child ratios and group sizes are maintained throughout each day
▶ regularly review the work assignments to assess whether the work is too demanding and how tasks can be modified
▶ review and discuss work-related injuries and determine what preventive steps are required

Probably the director's most important role in promoting caregivers' emotional and social well-being is to establish clear lines of communication. Most of the dimensions in Table 2.4 are directly related to communication. Caregivers who receive effective administrative support, encouragement, and clear expectations tend to experience job satisfaction. Directors can also provide opportunities for caregivers to participate in decision-making and professional growth. The purpose of health promotion is to increase the amount of control that individuals and groups have over their lives. It makes sense that the more autonomy caregivers have at work, the more they feel in control. With the director's support, they feel free to express themselves on the job, especially when they view the director as an advocate. Directors help to solve problems when they arise, such as inadequate opportunities for regular breaks, or issues around communication with a parent. A director's role is also paramount in difficult issues such as suspected child abuse. Caregivers often need to relieve feelings of stress by talking frankly with the director without fear of repercussion. Effective directors expect professional confidentiality from caregivers and also model this behaviour.

ROLE OF CAREGIVERS

It goes without saying that working with children has many rewards. It's probably the main reason you chose to enroll in an early childhood education program. "If poor pay is the dark cloud hanging over the heads of child care staff, then the nature of the work and the opportunity to make a difference in the lives of children is the silver lining" (Canadian Day Care Advocacy Association and Canadian Child Day Care Federation 1992, 1). The *Caring for a Living Survey* (same survey) conducted in 1991 asked staff in child care centres about the positive aspects of their work. Eight in 10 people said it was the nature of the work, and 55 percent had positive feelings about working with children; also, there was a high satisfaction rate working with co-workers. The reason for the focus on negative stress factors is to ensure that you

consider all aspects of caregiving and have realistic expectations, which will help to prevent burnout.

Many caregivers prefer to work with a particular age group because their experience tells them that their aptitudes and interests fit best there; they usually find the stress factors manageable. Yet some caregivers may work with a particular age group because they have no choice. Others may have lacked prior experience or ECE training and assumed that they would fit well and didn't. Caregivers who don't have a "fit" with their work or the age group may find the nature of the work overwhelming. Working with infants is quite different from working with preschoolers, which is quite different from working with school-agers. During your centre placements, you will have opportunities to work with various age groups, gain realistic perceptions of working with children, and talk with caregivers about how they feel about their work and what they find rewarding and challenging (or stressful). You may have assumed, for example, that working with infants would not match your personality, but after your placement were pleasantly surprised that you preferred this age group and that you have decided to begin your career there.

One thing is certain about work stress in centres: caregivers who develop and practise effective communication skills have lower stress levels. We have discussed the director's role in creating a supportive child care environment—let us not overlook the caregivers' attitudes, knowledge, and behaviour. Much of caregivers' work involves communicating with children, co-workers, and parents. Caregivers who demonstrate collegiality with co-workers are likely to have it reciprocated.

Directors who are appreciated for their efforts find it easier to support staff. The opportunity for autonomy assumes that the caregiver has the ability and motivation to make responsible decisions. In other words, communication is not a one-way street! A checklist such as the one in Table 2.5 provides feedback on listening skills. However, communication skills are complex and require work, practice, and a willingness to learn. Cross-cultural communication, for example, assumes that you recognize that your usual way of communicating is only one way, not the best way.

TABLE 2.5 ARE YOU LISTENING?		
When you and I are talking together . . .	**Often**	**Seldom**
you make me feel as if this is the most important thing you could be doing right now and that your time is truly mine.		
your attention is divided. You interrupt our conversation by answering the phone or addressing the needs of others who come by your door.		
you begin shaking your head or saying "no" before I finish.		
you make references to other conversations; there is a history to communication.		
you fidget and squirm and look at the clock as though you cannot wait to get on to other, more important, projects and conversations.		
you begin asking questions before I finish my message.		
you look me in the eye and really focus your attention.*		
you ask questions that let me know you were not really listening.		
you finish my sentences for me as though nothing I have to say could be new to you.		
you express interest by asking thoughtful questions and by contributing your insights.		
you change the agenda by taking over and changing the content of the conversation.		
you follow up on what we discussed and keep me posted on what is happening.		
you are sensitive to the tone of what I have to say and respond respectfully.		

(table continues on next page)

*Making direct eye contact during conversation is considered disrespectful in some ethno-cultures. This practice alone doesn't indicate poor communication.

TABLE 2.5 ARE YOU LISTENING? (continued)		
When you and I are talking together . . .	**Often**	**Seldom**
you give me credit for ideas and projects that grow out of our communications.		
you try to speed things up and leap ahead with ideas or conclusions as though we are in a rush.		
you smile at me and make me feel comfortable and valued.		
you make jokes about things that are serious to me and thereby belittle my concerns.		
you get defensive and argue before I can fully explain my point.		
you seem to assume I have something worthwhile to say.		
you ask questions that demonstrate your efforts to understand what I have to say.		
whether or not you agree with me, you make me feel that my opinions and feelings are respected.		

Source: Reprinted with permission from Child Care Information Exchange, P.O. Box 2890, Redmond, WA 98073, 1-800-221-2864.

MEN WORKING IN CHILD CARE

Historically, the overwhelming majority of caregivers in early childhood education have been female. If you are a male student, you probably have accepted that you will be working mainly with female colleagues. Although the following three criteria apply to all caregivers, they are discussed specifically as they relate to men: accountability, reciprocal support, and establishing positive working relationships.

Accountability Male caregivers demonstrate professional behaviour such as open communication with parents and awareness of the need to be visible to another adult whenever possible when they are with any one child. In this way they find that they are not likely to be considered suspect. Male caregivers may find it stressful that parents (and sometimes female caregivers) place them under scrutiny. However, most men understand that this fear results from the fact that men commit the vast majority of sexual abuse. As each caregiver demonstrates his commitment and care for the children, these suspicions usually disappear.

Caregivers who take an active role in speaking with parents about the child's day help parents realize that caregivers are knowledgeable and care about their child. Parents can then get to know and trust the caregivers rather than simply view them as "male." Male caregivers who demonstrate professional behaviour avoid subtle and overt sexist remarks, jokes, and other such slights. One hopes that female caregivers also refrain from this type of behaviour so that working relationships are not tainted with sexist overtones.

Men find ways to nurture children without placing themselves under suspicion. Centres should not, however, attempt to avoid suspicious circumstances for male caregivers by creating separate job responsibilities for males and females.

 All caregivers are involved in diapering or toileting. A division of different responsibilities only serves to increase suspicion and centre animosity among caregivers.

Reciprocal Support Men who seek and provide support from other male caregivers reduce their feelings of isolation, which is one of the most significant stressors for males in child care (Bloom 1989, 47). Often a male caregiver is the only male staff member at the centre and he rarely, if ever, has the opportunity to talk with adult males at work other than with fathers at drop-off or pickup times. He will feel added stress from female caregivers or parents if he is stereotyped in particular roles.

▶ He may be expected to do all the heavy lifting or repairs, or to take a lead role in disciplining children. Obviously, the assumption of roles or abilities on the basis of gender is inappropriate.
▶ Male caregivers often have to deal with the stereotype that they are not as masculine as other men. The stereotype is based on the traditional view of women taking responsibility for caring for children.

This stereotype is stressful to male caregivers, so it is beneficial to them if they can informally or formally network with others. It may be challenging to find out where other male caregivers work (your local ECE college faculty may know), but when you do there are a number of ways to establish networks: a telephone buddy system, monthly meetings of a support group, or biannual sessions or workshops through the local ECE association. Opportunities to talk about issues that arise, and possible ways to handle them, can be helpful in managing stress and preventing problems. Male ECE students may be interested in pursuing some kind of support while in training, either informally, by talking with a male caregiver in placement, or by finding out if there is (or could be) a support system in which male caregivers serve as mentors to students and new graduates.

Establishing Positive Working Relationships Emphasizing effective communication with the other caregivers reduces or avoids the "them and me" attitude. One study

found that female caregivers and administrators hold the most rigidly stereotypical views about men's suitability for child care (Skeen et al. 1986).

 Some female caregivers believe that men receive special treatment because of gender, and are offered opportunities that female caregivers are not offered.

A key factor in reducing negative views was the experience of working with a male colleague in the child care setting (Skeen et al. 1986). Obviously, then, energy put into communication is worth the effort. Male caregivers feel less isolated when they have positive working relationships. Camaraderie is fostered when all staff are included in social events after work or in lunchroom discussions.

THE JUGGLE STRUGGLE: STRESS

In 1993 Statistics Canada surveyed a sample of Canadians aged 15 and over about how they felt about their personal time (Vanier Institute of the Family 1994). The three most popular responses were:

► At the end of the day, I feel that I have not accomplished what I had set out to do.
► I often feel under stress when I don't have enough time.
► When I need more time, I tend to cut back on my sleep.

Students and caregivers are no exception and have very busy lives—juggling a number of roles that contribute to a time crunch and ultimately *stress*.

Stress is a fact of life. Both positive and negative events in our lives create stress. Stress is defined as "the wear and tear on our bodies that is produced by the very process of living" (Elkind 1981, 142). Stress affects the mind and emotions as well as the physical self. In moderation, stress is positive: it motivates us to learn, to develop, to cope with life's frustrations. But the way that it is perceived and managed depends on the individual and the environment (e.g., family, work, school, socioeconomic class, community).

Coping refers to the ways that a person tries to decrease or eliminate a stress factor—a person's response to it. Stress management plays a major role in our wellness. If the individual is able to find ways to cope with stress, this has a positive impact on health. We all have had days when one thing after another goes wrong, usually minor things, and we feel "stressed out." We may stomp our feet, shout, slam a door, cry, or feel defeated. Eventually those feelings pass. But when stress is severe or long-term, the body and mind are weakened, making the person vulnerable to a number of physical and emotional conditions. This is especially true in individuals who have inadequate coping strategies or whose environment contains insurmountable barriers. These people may experience symptoms of stress overload, including headaches, insomnia, back or neck pain, repeated cold or canker sores, higher than usual susceptibility to illness, ulcers, addictions, anxiety, or depression.

Stress factors can result from a number of sources: our personal and professional lives, and societal pressures.

Personal Stress Factors   Stress factors can be short-term (e.g., an argument with a family member or friend, a minor injury, a busy week). Some stress factors are long-term (e.g., separation or divorce, financial difficulties, death of a loved one).

How we perceive and cope with personal stress depends on our temperament, tolerance level, and experience. Individuals' temperaments play a part in how we perceive the stress in our lives. People who prefer (innately) stability and predictability experience change as stressful.

 The idea of moving to another city and beginning a new job is quite exciting and positive for some people. Yet for others that change is perceived as anxiety-producing and negative.

We all have individual tolerance levels for stress. When our tolerance level is reached and surpassed, we can experience feelings of distress. Past experiences with stress and the types of coping mechanisms that we have developed either help or hinder our ability to manage stress. An individual whose childhood was fraught with insecurity is likely to react differently to stressful events as an adult than a person whose childhood was happy and secure.

Our personal lifestyles can either magnify to our feelings of stress or help us manage them. A balanced lifestyle contributes to our health; part of that lifestyle is helping our mind and body manage stress. Adequate sleep and leisure, physical activity, and healthy eating are effective body defences against stress. We can help our body by avoiding certain substances that can trigger stress responses, such as caffeine and nicotine.

Professional Stress Factors   Every profession and workplace has inherent stress factors; even people working from their homes experience stress. Identifying stress

factors and eliminating, or at least reducing, them fall into the domain of occupational health. Working with children and staff in a centre is not a calm and tranquil experience. Although the majority of caregivers express high job satisfaction while working with young children and making a difference in their lives, the following stress factors are commonly experienced by caregivers (Beach et al. 1998, 91–93):

► The increasing demands on, and expectations of, child care. The sector is trying to respond to the needs of parents while providing high-quality care. Parents are becoming increasingly aware of the importance of quality care and early experiences to their child's development, and are expecting more of caregivers.

► The need for more skills in guiding children with behaviour challenges, in culturally sensitive practice, and in inclusive care for children with special needs.

► The constant attention needed to ensure the safety and security of young children.

► Low compensation rates, which fail to reflect the responsibilities and skills involved in the work. This reality is, obviously, due to the lack of government commitment to public funding for early childhood education—families are expected to pay the lion's share of the cost of child care.

▶ The lack of benefits, typical in other workplaces, such as paid sick leave, extended health care, or long-term disability. These are not available to many in the early education field.
▶ The lack of resources needed to maintain a good environment.
▶ The isolation from other adults.
▶ The lack of opportunities for career advancement.

In addition, communication issues with co-workers, directors, and parents can be stressful.

Individuals may be managing their personal life very well but may experience feelings of stress at work. Without a resolution of, or at least a reduction in, the stress factors, their personal life is affected. There are ways to manage some workplace stress (e.g., limiting coffee, going for a walk at lunch), but often stress is the result of issues that need to be addressed by the organization (e.g., division of workloads, improving lines of communication, evaluation of ventilation, ergonomically correct furniture). Making changes involves identifying stress factors and, with the commitment of staff and management, working toward that change. Beach et al. (1998) report that caregivers in all settings expressed considerable interest in additional training, education, and professional development. Evidence suggests that caregivers do take advantage of training opportunities available to them. Increased skills increase the quality of care that children experience and improve caregivers' work environments and recognition.

Societal Pressures   The quality of child care across Canada and the issues of afford-ability, accessibility, and comprehensiveness for parents are national issues. Many families are affected by government's lack of commitment to child care, and care-givers in centres across Canada experience every day the effects of society's attitudes toward child care. Other societal pressures affect everyone, caregiver and non-care-giver alike:

▸ the expectation, especially for women, to have multiple roles and to perform them all well (e.g., to have two full-time jobs: one inside and one outside the home)
▸ issues of discrimination
▸ the fast-paced, ever-changing world, particularly its technology, which makes many of us feel that we are being left behind
▸ growing concern about violence in our communities and around the world
▸ serious concerns about other national and global issues such as the economy and the environment

Identifying sources of stress in our lives is the first step in managing them and avoiding stress overload. Some stress factors may be impossible to change. Fortunately, many can be addressed, with problem-solving and commitment. The Canadian Mental Health Association (1997, 17) suggests asking yourself three questions before deciding which coping skill to use in a situation:

1. Is this an appropriate thing to do in *this* situation? (e.g., chanting during a job interview may not be advisable)
2. Is this a *positive* way of coping? (e.g., excessive alcohol or even excessive exercise may not be positive)
3. Is this going to help in the long run? (e.g., a short-term solution may not be enough)

In our professional lives, possible approaches include improving relationships with co-workers, management, or parents; seeking further training in a specific area (e.g., child guidance; see *Meeting the Challenge* in Resources, page 104); and address-ing occupational hazards (e.g., noise levels in the centre, the risk of back injury). Specific problems or more general stress factors are more likely to change when we collaborate with others (i.e., practise teamwork).

▸ A centre institutes a family responsibility leave for its staff, allowing caregivers whose own children are ill to be at home with them. This significantly reduces their overall stress level as working parents.
▸ All caregivers who belong to their provincial child care association benefit from lower premiums for disability insurance.

Societal pressures are more difficult and complicated. Anxiety is often reduced through education—taking courses to enhance our understanding of issues or to build skills (e.g., computer, self-defence). Get involved in national, regional, or local organizations advocating for change in areas such as child care and the environment. Participating in and working for positive change, even if it seems daunting, is one of the best ways to gain a sense of control over the world around you.

The Heart and Stroke Foundation developed the G-E-T S-T-R-E-S-S F-I-T plan to help us to manage stress and enjoy healthier lives:

Give yourself a break. Go for a walk. Get a good night's sleep. Get away from it all.
Eat a healthy diet.
Talk it out.

Spend time with family and friends.
Take a course. For fun or for improvement.
Relax. With a good book, a great movie, or your favourite music.
Exercise. Walk. Jog. Swim. Dance. Go to the gym.
Set priorities.
Schedule your time.

Find alternative sources of satisfaction.
Increase your awareness of what causes you stress.
Take action! Address the person or situation that's causing your stress. And, if you're still not sure how to manage, talk to your health care professional or contact the Heart and Stroke Foundation for more information.

Source: Reprinted with permission from *How Fit Are You When It Comes to Managing Stress? Stress Test,* Heart and Stroke Foundation (1993).

Early Childhood Educational Experience: Setting the Stage

The process of becoming a professional begins the day you start your ECE training. You have chosen a career that requires a vast range of attitudes, knowledge, and skills. ECE students are on the road to lifelong learning that begins with recognizing their individual and social responsibility and taking ownership of their responsibilities. Here are some examples of the professional behaviour that you can take ownership of now:

► Promptness for classes and centre placements—a behaviour that is not only expected throughout your professional life but is also appreciated in your personal life.
► Good personal hygiene.

▶ Communication skills that demonstrate respect for others' opinions, such as listening respectfully in class when the instructor or a classmate is speaking (as a matter not of authority but of respect) and using body language that conveys interest and learning (while recognizing a range of ways of communicating that reflect ethno-cultural diversity). Communication is a lifelong learning process and is obviously a critical skill for professionals. It is important to become aware of how you, as a student, communicate, and to be open to learning new skills (see Table 2.5, pages 88–89).

Assessing the situation:
How would you proceed?
Scenario: As a student, you are frustrated by a clique of three students who sit together and regularly disrupt the class.

Placements in centres provide you with opportunities to observe and analyze, which help you to formulate your personal philosophy of education, which is in turn based on an integration of theory and practice. Placements also offer the advantage of starting your professional child care career with some experience working with caregivers already behind you. This experience helps you identify some of the attitudes, knowledge, and skills that either contribute to quality care or detract from it. Some examples of human qualities that are beneficial for early childhood educators include warmth, patience, high energy, openness to new ideas, flexibility, curiosity, and maturity. Caregivers who possess these qualities are positive role models for students and graduates. With every placement experience, you meet a variety of caregivers who have their own styles yet fulfill these criteria. However, some caregivers demonstrate physical and emotional exhaustion through behaviour like impatience and sarcasm with children, tension with others at work, and apathy toward their job. Unfortunately, these caregivers are modelling as much for students as are their positive co-workers.

Centre placements allow you to experience different management styles. The working environment is created by the caregivers' personal styles and the levels of education, how well they work together, the types of policies, and the style of the director. Some individuals like to work in an environment that is more laid-back; others like a structure with rules clearly laid out. Whatever the administrative style you prefer, remember the 10 dimensions of organizational climate from Bloom et al. (1991). As a student, you probably will not see the inner workings of the centre's organization (e.g., salaries and fringe benefits, how promotions are handled, how the centre implements change). Yet you can get a sense of how staff work together, the level and effectiveness of the supervision, and staff morale. Bloom et al. created a list of statements (see next page) to accompany the 10 dimensions of the organizational climate. As you work through the list, check off one of the three choices for each statement. You will see how healthy that centre's work climate is and whether you would like to work in that environment on graduation.

Among the most important training opportunities that placements offer you as a student are self-evaluation and, of course, an evaluation of your progress by experienced professionals. Ongoing feedback of your demonstrated skills assists you in identifying areas of strength and areas in which you need to make immediate or long-term changes. Students who view evaluation positively as a valuable learning tool can incorporate constructive criticism into their learning and make consistent progress in their skill levels. Self-evaluation and evaluation by others will be essential aspects of your career.

	Seldom	Sometimes	Almost always
Staff are friendly and trust one another.			
Morale is high. There is a good team spirit.			
Staff are encouraged to learn new skills and competencies.			
The centre provides guidance for professional advancement.			
Supervisors are knowledgeable and competent.			
Supervisors provide helpful feedback.			
Communication on policies and procedures is clear.			
Teachers help make decisions about things that directly affect them.			
People feel free to express their opinions.			
Staff share a common vision of what the centre should be like.			
The program is well planned and efficiently run.			
The work environment is attractive and well organized.			
There are sufficient supplies and equipment for staff to do their jobs.			
Staff are encouraged to be creative and innovative in their work.			

Source: Adapted with permission from P.J. Bloom et al., *Blueprint for Action: Achieving Center-Based Change through Staff Development* (New Horizons, 1991), 179.

Graduates: Starting the Job Search

Your first position in child care will probably leave a lasting impression on you. Starting in a centre where you are treated with respect by caregivers who remember what it's like to be the new kid on the block, and who provide you with guidance and support, helps to build your confidence and self-esteem. New graduates are influenced significantly by their first director. "It becomes apparent that the kind of assistance, support, opportunities and guidance that graduates receive contributes greatly to their ability to move forward" (Taylor 1993, 7). Therefore, during job interviews it's in your best interest to consider the qualities of the director—will they fit with yours?

Graduates often bring a breath of fresh air, new ideas, and enthusiasm into centres. Graduates who demonstrate an openness to learning from others—not an "I've learned everything I need to know" attitude—will start off on the right foot with their co-workers. A commitment to lifelong learning means that you recognize that your ECE training has set the stage for future learning rather than being the final curtain.

Revisiting the Health Promotion Action Plan

With reference to the Action Plan Blueprint for Health Promotion introduced in Unit 1, the following discussion illustrates this plan put into practice in terms of occupational health.

Individual Problem-Solving and Self-Reliance   With the awareness of health issues that affect caregivers, each caregiver is able to identify her or his own health concerns, and can be proactive in preventing or reducing the impact. You, for example, are making changes to include more whole foods and less fat in your diet, and are gradually becoming more physically active. You are also cutting down on your smoking and getting support during this difficult transition. You are beginning to notice that you have more energy in working with the children. You feel like a better role model. You are practising lifting and bending techniques that are back "smart." Your commitment to lifelong learning through reading and attending workshops, seminars, and conferences on health issues enhances your ability to make choices in your personal life and professionally. All education plays a role in your ability to advance in your career.

Collective Self-Help   Together, the centre's director and staff support each other, parents, and families. Staff meetings are based on the premise that you can learn from one another through sharing resources and acknowledging each caregiver's expertise, experiences, and contribution. Stress relief through knowledge that you can share concerns with a co-worker or director, and trust their professional confidentiality, contributes to a positive working environment. Conferring with professionals and agencies with expertise in occupational health, management, communication, and other areas also helps staff reduce stress and increase caregivers' knowledge and skills.

Community Action   Becoming involved in local organizations related to work with children and families (e.g., local breakfast clubs, joint health and safety committees) can enhance caregivers' understanding of issues and help to effect change. As the early childhood profession is enhanced, so too are caregivers' feelings of self-worth and status as professionals.

Societal Change   Advocacy at the provincial/territorial and federal levels can create change that affects occupational health on a broader level, such as a national child care plan, family responsibility leave, or positive, supportive changes in child care legislation.

> As they develop skills in the process of thinking about and addressing problems, advocates also develop increased pride in their work and growing confidence in their ability to communicate outside of the classroom.... Passive acceptance of disheartening conditions in schools or programs, which leads to cynicism and burnout, can be replaced with optimistic attempts to impact on situations whenever possible. (Fennimore 1989, 195–96)

Conclusion

A proactive way to achieve job satisfaction and avoid burnout is to be aware of how well you are implementing healthy physical, emotional, and social practices. It is also important to examine your workplace—are the centre's policies and practices contributing to staff well-being or to burnout? Appendix 2.5 (page 113) provides a checklist for this purpose. Can you identify practices that could be improved? Can you identify supports and barriers and possible solutions? Look back to the eight dimensions of wellness. Achieving balance in your life through setting achievable goals and action plans will contribute to your sense of control.

Where are we going in the future? Pence and Griffin (1991, 28) bring together research on career advancement in the field of child care. The career ladder integrates education with career advancement, one level building on the next along a continuum. Each level or step—based on training, job skills, and experience—broadens your role and responsibilities. With career advancement come increases in salary and job status.

Career advancement shouldn't mean that once you have worked with children for a certain period, the only place to advance to is the position of supervisor or centre director. Community colleges and some universities offer post-diploma training to ECE graduates. Caregivers may want to continue working with children and their families within a centre but have more specialized skills and knowledge, such as infant and toddler care, special needs, child assessment, program evaluation, or health promotion advocate. Here again, salaries must reflect the level of education and roles. Beach et al. (1998) reveal that increased career opportunities in child care depend in part on better bridges between levels of education and training and between different types of child care programs and related early childhood services. Recognizing that caregivers are the key component of quality child care, the steering committee from the Child Care Workforce—From Recognition to Remuneration, made 23 recommendations to all levels of government. Some of the commitments that underlie these recommendations include (Beach et al. 1998, 134–43):

► affordable, accessible quality care and acceptance of the value of a well-paid, competent, and stable workforce
► equitable wages, benefit levels, and working conditions
► an educated and competent workforce
► opportunities for career mobility

Government actions and inactions have always been of key importance in shaping the direction of development of the child care sector. Governments need to begin acting more progressively on behalf of children, families, and the child care workforce in Canada.

WHAT'S YOUR OPINION?
TO TAKE A BREAK OR NOT TO BREAK?

Annie, a very enthusiastic student in her centre placement, insisted that she didn't need breaks during the day. Although the staff in the room pointed out opportune times to leave the floor for 10 or 15 minutes, Annie said she was fine and didn't want to miss a minute of learning opportunity. The caregivers appreciated her eagerness but were concerned that this was not a physically, emotionally, or socially healthy pattern to get into. What is your opinion?

► **A S S E S S   Y O U R   L E A R N I N G**

Define terms or describe concepts used in this unit.

- balanced lifestyle
- workplace injuries
- public health agencies
- workplace environmental issues
- WHMIS
- supportive child care environment
- stress factors
- stress reduction
- professional conduct

Evaluate your options in each situation.

1. A colleague buys her lunch from the nearby fast-food restaurant almost every day. You can't resist having her pick up something for you too, even though you often feel full after eating the nourishing hot lunches with the children before you have your lunch break. The fries or burger taste great, but you feel sluggish all afternoon.

2. You and a co-worker rarely agree on program-related issues. As a result, your relationship deteriorates to the point where you speak as little as possible and the tension is felt by the other staff, children, and parents.

3. After 18 months of working with toddlers, you find that all of the lifting, bending, and reaching are taking their toll on your physical well-being. You are coming home exhausted every evening, collapsing in front of the television. You pulled a muscle last month, and you are starting to notice lower back pain.

4. You enjoy communicating with parents but are not confident trying to communicate with parents whose first language is other than English. You feel that you are being patronizing, speaking loudly and very slowly and making hand gestures.

5. To the best of your parents' and your own knowledge, you never had chickenpox as a child. You are now pregnant and are working in a centre where three children have chickenpox.

► **R E S O U R C E   M A T E R I A L S**

Organizations

The Back Association of Canada, 83 Cottingham Street, Toronto, ON M4V 1B9. (Producers of the video *Back Basics*, 1996.)

Canadian Association of Toy Libraries and Parent Resource Centres (TLRC Canada), 120 Holland Avenue, Suite 205, Ottawa, ON K1Y 0X6. Tel. (613) 728-3307 (or contact the resource centres in your region).

Canadian Centre for Occupational Health and Safety, 250 Main Street E., Hamilton, ON L8N 1H6. Tel. (905) 572-2981, fax (905) 572-2206, national toll-free for inquiries (800) 263-8466, national toll-free for ordering publications (800) 668-4284; Web sites: www.ccohs.ca (centre) and www.ccohs.ca\oshanswers\ (inquiries).

Canadian Child Care Federation, 120 Holland Avenue, Suite 301, Ottawa, ON K1Y 0X6. Tel. (613) 729-5289, fax (613) 729-3159.

Canadian Mental Health Association, 2160 Yonge Street, 3rd Floor, Toronto, ON M4S 2Z3. Tel. (416) 484-7750.

Child Care Advocacy Association of Canada, 323 Chapel Street, Ottawa, ON K1Y 7Z2. Tel. (613) 594-3196, fax (613) 594-9375.

Heart and Stroke Association of Canada, 222 Queen Street, Suite 1402, Ottawa, ON K1P 5V9. Tel. (613) 569-4361.

Women's Network on Health and the Environment, 517 College Street, Suite 233, Toronto, ON M6G 4A2. Tel. (416) 928-0880.

Printed Matter

Architectural Strategies to Avoid Noise Problems in Child Care Centres (1988), by L. Melançon et al. (National Child Care Information Centre, Health Canada).

Avoiding Burnout: Strategies for Managing Time, Space and People in Early Childhood Education (1982), by P. Jorde (Acropolis Books).

Blueprint for Action: Achieving Center-Based Change through Staff Development (1991), by P.J. Bloom et al. (New Horizons).

"The Caregiver's Physical Health" and "The Caregiver's Emotional Health," in *Well Beings: A Guide to Promote the Physical Health, Safety and Emotional Well-Being of Children in Child Care Centres and Family Day Care Homes* (1992), by the Canadian Paediatric Society (Creative Premises).

Cornerstone: Building on Your Best, Canadian ed. (1997), by Rhonda Montgomery et al. (Prentice Hall/Allyn and Bacon Canada).

For Your Back: Self-Help Manual (1992), by H.D. Saunders (the Saunders Group, Inc., 4250 Norex Drive, Chaska, MN 55318-3047. Tel. [612] 368-9214).

A Great Place to Work: Improving Conditions for Staff in Young Children's Programs (1988), by P.J. Bloom (National Association for the Education of Young Children).

Handbook for Canada's Physical Activity Guide to Healthy Active Living (1998), by Health Canada, Ottawa. (For copies contact Health Canada, national toll-free [888] 334-9769.)

Health and Safety at Work for Day-Care Educators (1994), by P. Markon and D. Le Beau (National Library of Quebec).

Health—The Basics (1998), by Rebecca Donatelle et al. (Prentice-Hall/Allyn and Bacon Canada).

Looking Good … Feeling Great! A Lifestyle Diary and *Teacher's Guide* (1991), by J. and R. Zacour, Gillette Canada, Ontario Ministry of Health, and Ontario Physical and Health Education Association. (For copies contact the Ontario Physical and Health Education Association, 1185 Eglinton Avenue E., Suite 501, Toronto, ON M3C 3C6. Tel. [416] 426-7120, fax [416] 426-7373.)

The Man's Guide to Good Health (1991), by A.B. Weisse (Yonkers: Consumer Report Books).

Meeting the Challenge: Effective Strategies for Challenging Behaviours in Early Childhood Environments (1999), by B. Kaiser and J.S. Rasminsky (Justice Canada, Health Canada, and Human Resources Development Canada). (For information or copies, contact Canadian Child Care Federation, 30 Rosemount Avenue, Suite 100, Ottawa, ON K1Y 1P4. Tel. 1-800-858-1412, fax [613] 729-3159; www.cfc-efc.ca/cccf.)

Our Bodies, Ourselves for the New Century (1998), by Boston Women's Health Book Collective (Simon & Schuster).

The New Ourselves, Growing Older: Women Aging with Knowledge and Power (A Book for Women Over Forty) (1994), by P.B. Doress-Worters and D.L. Siegal (Simon & Schuster).

Self-Help for Premenstrual Syndrome (1985), by M. Harrison (Random House).

Taking Action for a Healthy Future (1997), by the Women's Network on Health and the Environment (Women and Environment Education and Development Foundation).

Understanding and Managing Stress: Instruments to Assess Your Lifestyle (1989), by J.D. Adams (University Associates).

The Wellness Workbook (1988), by J.W. Travis and R. Sara (Ten Speed Press).

"Working with Children of Different Ages," in *Well Beings: A Guide to Promote the Physical Health, Safety and Emotional Well-Being of Children in Child Care Centres and Family Day Care Homes* (1992), by the Canadian Paediatric Society (Creative Premises, 744–52).

▶ B I B L I O G R A P H Y

"Are You Listening?" *Child Care Information Exchange*, Sept.–Oct. 1990, 62.

Aronson, S. (1991) *Health & Safety in Child Care*. New York: HarperCollins Publishers.

Beach, J., J. Bertrand and G. Cleveland (1998), *Our Child Care Workforce—From Recognition to Remuneration, More Than a Labour of Love* (A Human Resource Study of Child Care in Canada). Human Resources Development Canada, Ottawa.

Bloom, P.J. (1989) *Avoiding Burnout: Strategies for Managing Time, Space, and People in Early Childhood Education*. Illinois: Gryphon House.

——— (1988) *A Great Place to Work: Improving Conditions for Staff in Young Children's Programs*. Washington, DC: National Association for the Education of Young Children.

Bloom, P.J., et al. (1991) *Blueprint for Action: Achieving Center-Based Change through Staff Development*. Lake Forest, IL: New Horizons.

Bolles, R.N. (1981) *The Three Boxes of Life: and How to Get Out of Them*. Berkeley, CA: Ten Speed Press.

Boston Women's Health Book Collective (1992) *The New Our Bodies, Ourselves: A Book By and For Women*. Toronto: Simon & Schuster.

Brehm, B. (1998) *Stress Management: Increasing Your Stress Resistance*. Don Mills, ON: Longman Press (div. of Addison-Wesley).

Canadian Day Care Advocacy Association and Canadian Child Day Care Federation (1992) *Caring for a Living: Executive Summary*. Ottawa.

Canadian Mental Health Association and Heart and Stroke Foundation (1997) *Coping with Stress*. Toronto: CMHA.

Canadian Paediatric Society (1997) *Your Child's Best Shot*. Ottawa: Canadian Paediatric Society.

——— (1996) *Well Beings: A Guide to Promote the Physical Health, Safety and Emotional Well-Being of Children in Child Care Centres and Family Day Care Homes*. Toronto: Creative Premises.

Clarke, D., and D. Nikkel (1994) *Office Air: A Worker's Guide to Air Quality in Offices, Schools, and Hospitals*. Ottawa: Minister of National Health and Welfare.

Daneault, S., et al. (1992) "Air Quality during the Winter in Québec Day-Care Centers." *American Journal of Public Health* (March) 83(3):432–34.

Donatelle, R., et al. (1998) *Health: The Basics*, Canadian ed. Scarborough, ON: Prentice Hall/Allyn and Bacon Canada.

Elkind, D. (1981) *The Hurried Child*. Don Mills, ON: Addison-Wesley Publishers.

Fennimore, B.S. (1989) *Child Advocacy for Early Childhood Educators*. New York: Teachers College Press.

Health and Welfare Canada (1992) *Using the Food Guide*. Ottawa: Minister of Supply and Services.

Heart and Stroke Foundation (1993) *How Fit Are You When It Comes to Managing Stress? Stress Test*.

King, P., R. Gratz, G. Scheuer, and A. Claffey (1996) "The Ergonomics of Child Care: Connecting Worksite Analyses." *WORK: A Journal of Prevention, Assessment & Rehabilitation* 6:25–32.

Lambert-Lagacé, L., and M. Laflamme (1995) *Good Fat—Bad Fat*. Toronto: Stoddart Publishing.

Maxwell, A., and Huot (1994). "Health and Occupational Safety for Child Care Educators." *FOCUS*, January:29–34.

McGillicuddy, P. (1993) *Prevention Initiative: Violence against Women Partners—Module #1*. Toronto: George Brown Community College.

Markon, P., and D. Le Beau (1994) *Health and Safety at Work for Day-Care Educators*. National Library of Quebec.

Montgomery, R., et al. (1997) *Cornerstone: Building on Your Best*, Canadian ed., Scarborough, ON: Prentice Hall/Allyn and Bacon Canada.

Pence, A., and S. Griffin (1991) "A Window of Opportunity: Part I." *Interaction*, Winter:12–17.

——— (1991) "A Window of Opportunity: Part II." *Interaction*, Spring:24–29.

Public Health Nutrition Services, Nova Scotia Department of Health (1992) *Having Fun with Healthy Foods: A Daycare Menu Planning Manual*. Halifax: Province of Nova Scotia.

Saunders, H.D. (1994) *For Your Back: Self-Help Manual*. Chaska, MN: Saunders Group.

Skeen, M., et al. (1986) "Gender-Role Attitudes of Professional Female Educators toward Men in Early Childhood Education." *Psychological Reports* 59:723–30.

Skillen, L. (1989) "Assessing Occupational Hazards." *The Canadian Nurse*, June:25–28.

Taylor, A. (1993) "So They're Trained . . . What Now?" *Interaction*, Summer:7–9.

Truchon-Gagnon, C., and R. Hétu (1988) "Noise in Day-Care Centers for Children." *Noise Control Engineering Journal* (March–April) 30(2):57–64.

Vanier Institute of the Family (1994) *Profiling Canada's Families*. Ottawa: Vanier Institute of the Family.

Women's Network on Health and the Environment (1997) *Taking Action for a Healthy Future*. Toronto: Women and Environment Education and Development Foundation.

Appendix 2.1

The Financial Dimension

_____ I have written down my dreams and have a clear view of my priorities.

_____ I know my net worth (assets minus liabilities) and what my debt equity ratio is.

_____ I have calculated my monthly cash flow (in out).

_____ I recognize my spending patterns and am able to take control of them to work for me rather than against me. I know that I can work toward financial wellness if I live within my means.

_____ If I have one, I use a credit card for convenience only, and I pay the balance when the monthly statement comes in. I do not view the credit card as an effective method of long-term payment.

_____ I pay down my debts, giving priority to those with the highest interest rates (e.g., credit cards).

_____ I consistently use the budget process, allocating funds for specific items. I don't see borrowing as an option. Instead, I use a savings plan to eventually afford desired items or vacations.

_____ I know how to get what I need and want from my banking institution (e.g., best bank fees, the account type that suits my needs).

_____ If my situation allows it, I have an emergency fund and a regular savings plan in place, putting aside a reasonable amount as an ongoing routine.

_____ I am trying to save for my retirement every year (e.g., RRSP).

_____ I am taking advantage of all tax deductions to which I am entitled and am filing my own annual taxes.

_____ I use tax-return dollars to pay down debt, or to invest (e.g., RRSP) rather than spending them on consumer items or vacations.

_____ I have a good understanding of programs that are mandatory and optional with my employer (e.g., vacation, sick leave, extended health, life insurance, pension)

_____ I am financially literate, keep up-to-date in understanding basic financial information, and can communicate with investors in my best interest.

_____ I am working toward having control over money rather than having it control me.

Appendix 2.2

Canada's Physical Activity Guide

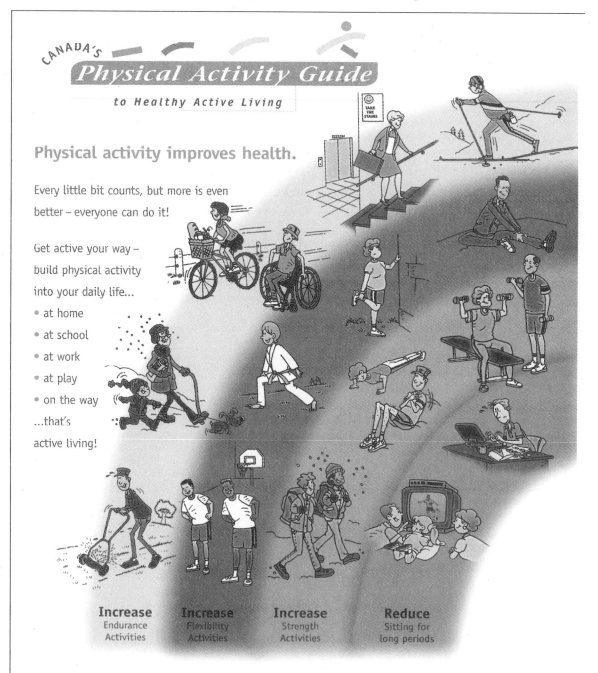

 Health Canada   Santé Canada

 CSEP SCPE Canadian Society for Exercise Physiology

Choose a variety of activities from these three groups:

Endurance

4-7 days a week
Continuous activities for your heart, lungs and circulatory system.

Flexibility

4-7 days a week
Gentle reaching, bending and stretching activities to keep your muscles relaxed and joints mobile.

Strength

2-4 days a week
Activities against resistance to strengthen muscles and bones and improve posture.

Starting slowly is very safe for most people. Not sure? Consult your health professional.

For a copy of the *Guide Handbook* and more information: **1-888-334-9769**, or **www.paguide.com**

Eating well is also important. Follow *Canada's Food Guide to Healthy Eating* to make wise food choices.

Get Active Your Way, Every Day—For Life!

Scientists say accumulate 60 minutes of physical activity every day to stay healthy or improve your health. As you progress to moderate activities you can cut down to 30 minutes, 4 days a week. Add-up your activities in periods of at least 10 minutes each. Start slowly... and build up.

Time needed depends on effort

Very Light Effort	Light Effort *60 minutes*	Moderate Effort *30-60 minutes*	Vigorous Effort *20-30 minutes*	Maximum Effort
• Strolling	• Light walking	• Brisk walking	• Aerobics	• Sprinting
• Dusting	• Volleyball	• Biking	• Jogging	• Racing
	• Easy gardening	• Raking leaves	• Hockey	
	• Stretching	• Swimming	• Basketball	
		• Dancing	• Fast swimming	
		• Water aerobics	• Fast dancing	

Range needed to stay healthy

You Can Do It – Getting started is easier than you think

Physical activity doesn't have to be very hard. Build physical activities into your daily routine.

- Walk whenever you can – get off the bus early, use the stairs instead of the elevator.
- Reduce inactivity for long periods, like watching TV.
- Get up from the couch and stretch and bend for a few minutes every hour.
- Play actively with your kids.
- Choose to walk, wheel or cycle for short trips.

- Start with a 10 minute walk – gradually increase the time.
- Find out about walking and cycling paths nearby and use them.
- Observe a physical activity class to see if you want to try it.
- Try one class to start – you don't have to make a long-term commitment.
- Do the activities you are doing now, more often.

Benefits of regular activity:

- better health
- improved fitness
- better posture and balance
- better self-esteem
- weight control
- stronger muscles and bones
- feeling more energetic
- relaxation and reduced stress
- continued independent living in later life

Health risks of inactivity:

- premature death
- heart disease
- obesity
- high blood pressure
- adult-onset diabetes
- osteoporosis
- stroke
- depression
- colon cancer

 ACTIVE LIVING

No changes permitted. Permission to photocopy this document in its entirety not required. Cat. No. H39-429/1998-1E ISBN 0-662-86627-7

 CANADA'S *Physical Activity Guide* to Healthy Active Living

Appendix 2.3

Back Care

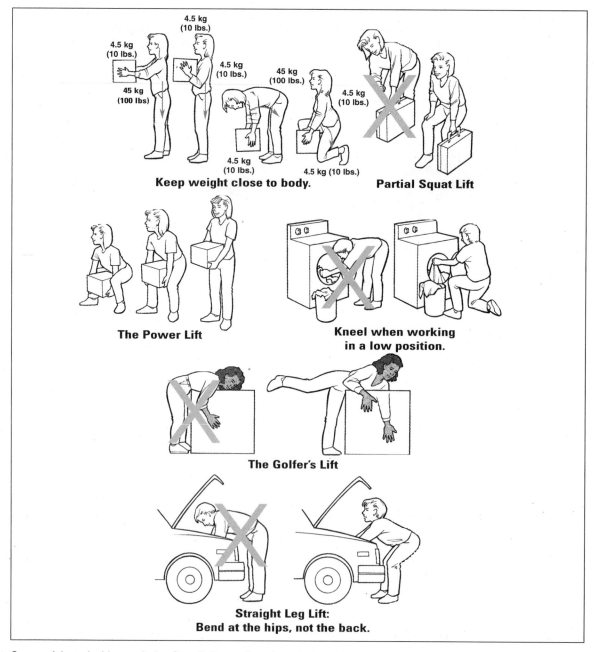

Source: Adapted with permission from H. Duane Saunders, *For Your Back: Self-Help Manual* (Chaska, MN: Saunders Group, 1994), 31–32. Tel. (612) 368-9214.

Appendix 2.4

Staff Exposed to Infectious Diseases

Infection	Management of Staff Who Have Been Exposed to Infection	Management of Staff Who Have Been Diagnosed with an Infection
Respiratory Infections		
Colds	Observe for illness. Ensure hand-washing.	Exclude if too ill to work. Ensure hand-washing.
Influenza (Flu)	Observe for illness. Caregivers with cardiac disease, respiratory disease, or diabetes should contact their physician about a vaccination.	Exclude if too ill to work. Ensure hand-washing.
Pinkeye (Conjunctivitis)	Observe for illness. Ensure hand-washing.	Exclude only if discharge is pus (thick, yellow) and until the antibiotic has been taken for 1 full day.
Tuberculosis	Contact LPHA.[1]	Contact LPHA.[1] Exclude until treated and non-infectious.
Whooping Cough (Pertussis)	Contact LPHA.[1] Observe for illness.	Contact LPHA.[1] Exclude until 5 days after start of antibiotics. If not treated, exclude for 2 weeks.
Gastrointestinal Infections		
Diarrhea	Observe for illness. Ensure hand-washing.	Exclude if too ill to work. Ensure hand-washing. Ensure person does not prepare or serve food.
Hepatitis A	Contact LPHA.[1] Obtain immune globulin. Contact physician if pregnant.	Exclude for 1 week after onset of jaundice.
Vomiting Illness	Observe for illness. Ensure hand-washing.	Exclude if too ill to work. Ensure hand-washing. Ensure person does not prepare or serve food.

[1]Local public health agency

Infections with Rash

Chickenpox (Varicella)	Contact LPHA.[1] Check if susceptible and in need of VZIG.[2] Contact physician if pregnant.	Contact LPHA.[1] Exclude until 5 days after onset of rash or until all blisters have crusted, whichever is shorter. May return sooner if illness is mild and able to return to work.
Fifth Disease (Parvovirus B19)	Contact physician if pregnant.	Contact physician. No exclusion required.
Measles	Contact LPHA.[1] Exclude if susceptible and unvaccinated until 2 weeks after onset of last case in the child care facility.	Contact LPHA[1] immediately. Exclude until at least 4 days after onset of rash.
Rash with Fever	Contact LPHA.[1]	Contact LPHA.[1] Exclude until diagnosis has been made by physician.
Rubella (German Measles)	Contact physician if pregnant.	Exclude until 7 days after onset of rash.
Shingles (Zoster)	Contact physician if susceptible, especially if pregnant.	Exclude until lesions have crusted only if lesions cannot be covered by clothing or a dressing.

Infections Spread by Contact with Blood

Hepatitis B	Contact LPHA.[1] HBIG[3] may be indicated for certain exposures to infected children, e.g., bites or contact with blood. Contact physician.	No exclusion required.

Other Infections

Boils	Ensure hand-washing.	No exclusion required. Ensure hand-washing.
Cytomegalovirus (CMV)	Ensure hand-washing. Contact physician if pregnant.	No exclusion required. Ensure hand-washing.
Infectious Mononucleosis	Ensure hand-washing.	Exclude if too ill to work.

[1]LPHA: Local public health agency
[2]VZIG: Varicella-Zoster Immune Globulin
[3]HBIG: Hepatitis B Immune Globulin

Source: Reprinted with permission from *Well Beings,* Canadian Paediatric Society (Ottawa: Canadian Paediatric Society, 1996), 696–97.

Appendix 2.5

Health Practices: You and Your Centre

The following checklist summarizes the aspects of occupational health discussed in this unit. How do you rate yourself and a centre where you've done a placement? You may find it enlightening to check again after you've been working in child care for a year.

DO YOU...	YES	NO	SOMETIMES
maintain healthy eating habits by			
• being aware of your eating pattern	❑	❑	❑
• lowering fat intake	❑	❑	❑
• drinking water every day	❑	❑	❑
• increasing fibre	❑	❑	❑
• decreasing processed foods	❑	❑	❑
balance work, rest, and exercise by			
• making time for regular physical activity	❑	❑	❑
• ensuring you get adequate sleep	❑	❑	❑
• finding ways for leisure daily	❑	❑	❑
• spending time with friends and family	❑	❑	❑
prevent the spread of illness by			
• keeping your immunization up-to-date	❑	❑	❑
• effectively washing your hands	❑	❑	❑
• implementing cleaning and sanitizing routines	❑	❑	❑
prevent workplace injuries by			
• using proper lifting techniques	❑	❑	❑
• identifying and reporting required adjustments to workspace, equipment, and furnishings	❑	❑	❑
• following product's safety recommendations	❑	❑	❑
• using environmentally friendly products	❑	❑	❑
• implementing the principles of WHMIS	❑	❑	❑
• reporting workplace injuries	❑	❑	❑
• keeping your first aid and CPR certificates up-to-date	❑	❑	❑
promote your social-and emotional well-being by			
• demonstrating respect for self and others through professional behaviour such as promptness and confidentiality	❑	❑	❑
• developing and practising effective communication skills	❑	❑	❑
• knowing and using designated lines of communication to share concerns	❑	❑	❑
• being actively involved in your self-evaluation and evaluation by others	❑	❑	❑

(continues on next page)

DO YOU...	YES	NO	SOMETIMES
• being flexible and open to learning new ideas	❏	❏	❏
• identifying your stress factors and developing coping mechanisms that eliminate or reduce them	❏	❏	❏
• seeking further professional development	❏	❏	❏
• being a member of a child care association	❏	❏	❏

lower other risk factors by

	YES	NO	SOMETIMES
• stopping a smoking habit	❏	❏	❏
• conducting monthly breast self-examinations or testicular self-examinations	❏	❏	❏
• limiting regular consumption of alcohol	❏	❏	❏
• practising safer sex	❏	❏	❏
• feeling good about your health care professional	❏	❏	❏
• keeping up-to-date on health issues	❏	❏	❏

evaluate balance in your life through awareness of wellness dimensions:

	YES	NO	SOMETIMES
• physical	❏	❏	❏
• emotional	❏	❏	❏
• social	❏	❏	❏
• intellectual	❏	❏	❏
• occupational	❏	❏	❏
• spiritual	❏	❏	❏
• environmental	❏	❏	❏
• financial	❏	❏	❏

Goal statement (specific and measurable)

action steps:　　1.

　　　　　　　　2.

　　　　　　　　3.

　　　　　　　　4.

Target date:

Resources available to help you:

Barriers and how to deal with them:

(continues on next page)

DOES YOUR CENTRE ...	YES	NO	SOMETIMES
support caregivers' healthy eating habits by			
• ensuring adequate break times	❏	❏	❏
• providing a relaxing place to eat and relax	❏	❏	❏
recognize the importance of staff balancing work, rest, and exercise by			
• maintaining adequate caregiver–child ratio	❏	❏	❏
• ensuring all staff take regular breaks each day	❏	❏	❏
• incorporating sufficient time in the daily schedule for program planning and documenting	❏	❏	❏
• curtailing overtime and discouraging staff from taking work home	❏	❏	❏
prevent the spread of illness by			
• keeping track of staff's immunization records	❏	❏	❏
• providing orientation and regular in-service training in			
• infection control strategy	❏	❏	❏
• food-handling and preparation	❏	❏	❏
• providing adequate supplies and posters for hand-washing, diapering, toileting	❏	❏	❏
• developing and posting the cleaning and sanitizing routines	❏	❏	❏
prevent workplace injuries by			
• providing orientation and regular in-service training in			
• proper lifting techniques	❏	❏	❏
• WHMIS and product safety	❏	❏	❏
• responding to inadequacies in workspaces, equipment, and furnishings	❏	❏	❏
• purchasing environmentally friendly products	❏	❏	❏
• providing workplace injury reports, ensuring they are completed, and responding to injuries	❏	❏	❏
• requiring evidence that staff's first aid and CPR certificates are up-to-date and arranging for staff to renew as a group	❏	❏	❏
promote staff's collegiality and emotional well-being by			
• providing job descriptions for each position and ensuring that all understand one another's role	❏	❏	❏
• outlining lines of communication	❏	❏	❏
• providing adequate supervision	❏	❏	❏
• conducting regular performance evaluations	❏	❏	❏
• organizing staff meetings and in-services on communication, conflict resolution, etc.	❏	❏	❏
• providing a comprehensive employee benefit package that includes family responsibility leave	❏	❏	❏
• providing time and possibly financial support for professional development	❏	❏	❏
• actively participating as a centre member in the regional or a national child care association	❏	❏	❏
• encouraging opportunities for staff to socialize	❏	❏	❏

(continues on next page)

DOES YOUR CENTRE . . .	YES	NO	SOMETIMES
lower other risk factors by			
• networking with community health resources	❏	❏	❏
• providing current health literature for staff (e.g., public health pamphlets)	❏	❏	❏

Goal statement (specific and measurable)

action steps: 1.

                  2.

                  3.

                  4.

Target date:

Resources available to help you:

Barriers and how to deal with them:

Unit 3

Illness Prevention and Management

Unit 3: Illness Prevention and Management

Young children get sick whether they are cared for at home or in a centre, but the rates of common illness are two to three times higher for children enrolled in centres (Canadian Paediatric Society 1996, 50–51). Wald et al. (1988, 542) studied groups of children over a three-year period. In the first year of the study, they found that children in centres with seven or more children had an average of 7.1 illnesses per year, compared with 4.7 per year for children in family day care. Over the next two years of the study, the difference in the rate of infections between the types of child care became smaller. Therefore, the longer that children are in a centre's care, the less often they are sick, and in fact they aren't sick much more often than children in family day care. This information is reassuring for parents who choose centre care.

Among the reasons for higher rates of childhood infections are these:

▶ The children enrolled in the centre are from different families, which increases the number of infections that could be spread. Each child may be exposed to germs or infections from his or her parents, siblings, friends, or even from strangers riding on the bus in the morning. So every day it is likely that children spread germs among themselves and staff.
▶ Preschool children are still learning good personal hygiene habits.
▶ Infants and young children are more susceptible to illness because their immune system is still developing.

In the past, most infants, toddlers, and preschoolers remained at home with their mothers. It was not until the children were in kindergarten or Grade 1 that they frequently experienced common childhood illnesses during the first few months of starting school, for the reasons outlined above. But by the time children are 5 or 6 years old, they are better able to fight infections. Their immune system has matured and they have almost completed their series of immunizations. Obviously every child must eventually become part of a group, so the concern lies in the age at which this occurs, and what can be done to reduce the number of infections that each child experiences as a result of that participation.

The opportunities for illnesses to spread are even higher among infants and toddlers than among preschoolers. Young children wear diapers, may be learning to use the toilet, require a great deal of hands-on care, crawl on the floor, put hands, toys, and objects in their mouths and then share these wet objects with others. They are only beginning to learn how to wash their hands. They are also quite affectionate with each other (e.g., kissing, hugging, touching). Although this physical contact can contribute to the spread of respiratory infections, the emotional and social benefits of physical affection far outweigh the risk of illness. Rather than discourage this social behaviour, caregivers implement hygiene practices that reduce the spread of germs among infants and toddlers (e.g., hand-washing, cleaning and sanitizing mouthing toys, diapering and toileting routines).

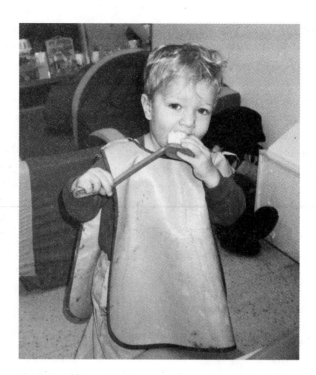

Centre staff's understanding of how infections are spread and their ability to implement health practices reduce the incidence of infections in children. The less often children are ill, the less often parents and staff need to manage illness. In other words, the discomfort and stress experienced by children, parents, and staff is reduced. Also, the fewer visits that children make to their physician, the less money government is obliged to spend on physicians' fees, laboratory tests, and prescriptions, which reduces health costs (Bell et al. 1989).

Most common childhood illnesses are minor and don't last more than a few days. The most typical childhood illnesses are the common cold, ear infections, other respiratory infections, and diarrhea. There are also several more serious communicable diseases that children and adults are susceptible to if they have not developed immunity either through immunizations or by having had the disease. (See Immunity, page 123; Immunization, page 132.)

Our Body's Natural Defence Mechanisms

 OBJECTIVE   To identify and describe our body's natural defence mechanisms.

Because germs are everywhere, we are fortunate that our body has a built-in defence system; otherwise we would have some kind of infection all the time. *Our skin is our*

body's first defence, and one of the most important defence mechanisms, against the germs that we contact every day. The oily substance excreted by glands in the walls of the hair follicles is acidic; it kills germs that would otherwise grow on our skin. Normal intact skin is impermeable to germs and to fluids like water and blood. Where the skin is non-intact (because of cuts, scrapes, sores, burns, for example), germs can enter. Some chemical agents such as pesticides can enter our body through the hair follicles.

Many germs enter our body through the nose. The nasal hair that you can see and the cilia that cover the mucous membrane in our nose and throat filter and collect air particles such as dust and germs. The mucus produced by the mucous membranes traps the particles, which are then swallowed and destroyed by gastric and acidic secretions in the stomach. We also expel mucus by coughing or sneezing, which rids our body of germs. As well, the mucous membranes in the gastrointestinal and urinary tracts can inactivate or destroy germs, which the bloodstream then clears out of our body. The urine's bacteriostatic action (destroys bacteria) keeps the urinary tract sterile. Tear secretions destroy bacteria in our eyes. Wax protects our ears.

You have probably heard the sayings "You'll catch a cold if you go outside with wet hair" and "If you sit in a draft, you'll get a cold." In fact, the only way to catch a cold is through exposure to a cold virus that infects our body. Therefore, neither saying is true. But both remind us to think about vulnerability to viruses and bacteria. In other words, every day we can provide our body with the nutrients and energy to fight off an infection or to get better. Our body needs these essential elements:

▶ nutritious food/a well-balanced diet
▶ adequate sleep
▶ adequate physical activity
▶ fresh air

And, of course, we need to live in a home that provides us with the basic needs of clean water, sewage disposal, and comfortable temperature, and we need warm clothes, coats, shoes, and boots in the winter. If we were always using our energy to keep warm in the winter, our body wouldn't have energy left for everything else we must do to keep healthy.

Immunity

Immunity provides us with protection from specific infections. Each time a germ enters your body, your immunity increases. When a specific germ multiplies in your body, it produces large numbers of its specific protein (antigen), which enters the bloodstream. The immune system responds by producing specific antibodies. Even when an infection is over, your body may continue to make antibodies for long periods, sometimes even for life.

But after many infections, the antibodies disappear from your body over time. Despite this disappearance, cells in your immune system remember the germ so that if it is contracted again, the immune system makes antibodies very rapidly. Most people who have had chickenpox have a lifelong immunity to it. It is rare to get it again, even after being exposed to a person who has it. The body has a harder time warding off the common cold, however. There are approximately 200 different viruses that cause the common cold.

> Being infected by a virus which causes a cold may not lead to immunity to that virus. In fact, infection by the same cold virus can occur many times over. The many different cold viruses, plus the failure of infections to produce immunity, explain why people get so many colds. (Canadian Paediatric Society 1996, 135)

We develop immunity to a disease in one of two ways:

▶ naturally or actively
▶ passively (see Immune Globulin, page 135)

For the first few months of life, infants are resistant to some diseases. This natural acquired immunity is passed on to babies from their mother before birth. Breast milk contains antibodies, which help to protect infants from some bowel, ear, and respiratory infections. However, this natural immunity is short-lived. The immune systems of infants and young children mature through actively acquired immunity. Children develop different antibodies in two ways: either by actually having an infection or through immunizations. (See Immunization, page 132.)

How Infections Spread

 OBJECTIVE   To explain how germs are spread.

Germs are everywhere. By examining how germs are spread, you can break the chain of transmission and ultimately reduce or stop the spread of germs that cause illness. The chain of transmission has four links:

▶ the germ
▶ the host (person who is ill)
▶ the vehicles of transmission
▶ the new host (next person who becomes ill)

The Germ

The term "germ" is used generically to include viruses, bacteria, parasites, and fungi. Though most germs can't be seen by the naked eye (they are microscopic), they are

FIGURE 3.1   THE LINKS IN THE CHAIN

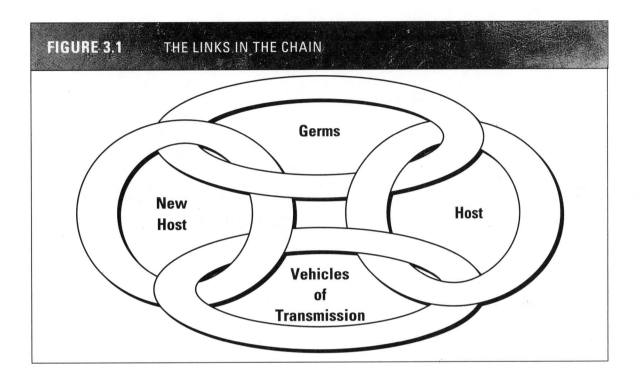

capable of causing infections that range in severity from minor to fatal. We all have germs that live in our body and play an important role in keeping us healthy. Women, for example, have small numbers of bacteria and a fungus known as *Candida* living in the intestinal tract and the vagina. Let's use this example to see how the germs normally found in the body can cause infections in the following two scenarios.

In the first scenario, women may experience vaginal yeast infections while they are taking an antibiotic for a bacterial infection. While the antibiotic is destroying the bacteria that have caused the infection, it may also destroy the bacteria normally found in the vagina. Consequently the fungus in the vagina multiplies, causing a yeast infection, because the natural balance of the vaginal bacteria and fungus has been altered by the antibiotic. *Candida* diaper rash can develop in young children in a similar way. An antibiotic given to an infant or toddler to treat a bacterial infection may also destroy bacteria normally found in the bowel, which then permits the fungus to multiply.

In the second scenario, you don't have to have diarrhea yourself to cause someone else to get diarrhea. We all have bacteria that live in our bowels and help to keep us healthy. But when those bacteria contaminate an environment and someone else comes in contact with them, he or she may develop diarrhea. Effective hand-washing is the key to preventing the stool from contaminating an environment.

Germs, surprisingly enough, can live outside our body for several hours or even weeks and can still cause infection. Rotavirus and hepatitis A can live for weeks on objects such as toys, and germs that cause respiratory infections can live for several hours. This longevity contributes to the spread of infection. Germs thrive and multiply in food, causing intestinal infections that can, in rare cases, be fatal. (See Through Food, page 128.)

Finally, children and adults who have an infection are often infectious (or contagious) for a period of time, which fluctuates depending on the type of germ. Children with the common cold may be infectious for a day or two before the cold symptoms start and may remain so for the next seven days. (See Appendix 3.1, page 209.)

TABLE 3.1   LIFE OF VIRUSES ON SURFACES

VIRUS	COUNTERTOPS/TOYS	CLOTH	SKIN
Respiratory Syncytial (common cause of bronchiolitis and pneumonia)	8 hrs.	1 to 2 hrs.	25 min.
Influenzae A and B	24 to 48 hrs.	8 to 12 hrs.	5 min.
Rotavirus (common cause of diarrhea)	8 days to wks.		
Cytomegalovirus (CMV)	8 hrs.		
Hepatitis A	2 wks.		

Source: Reprinted with permission from *Well Beings,* Canadian Paediatric Society (Ottawa: Canadian Paediatric Society, 1996), 53.

The Host

Health and medical professionals use the term "host" to describe the person with the infection. Think of the ill person as the host of a dinner party. The ill person's body provides the germs with the nourishment and warmth that they need to thrive. Germs may be spread to others during the three stages of an infection: before we know we are ill, while we are ill, and in some cases even after we have recovered. A "carrier" is a host who does not actually have symptoms of an infection but has the germ living dormant in his or her body. Carriers can spread germs (e.g., hepatitis B) to others, and sometimes the germs may reactivate and cause an infection (e.g., shingles) in the carrier.

The Vehicles of Transmission

Hosts have germs in their body secretions (such as stool, saliva, blood) that can be transmitted (or spread) in a number of ways. The germs contaminate our environment and are spread directly from person to person through the air or by direct contact (e.g., touching, kissing, biting), or indirectly on vehicles (e.g., toys, hands, food, objects).

Through Direct or Indirect Contact

Infections are spread directly and indirectly from one host to another. The direct spread of infection takes place when we breathe in the germs that cause infections such as colds, chickenpox, and flu. Another way we come into contact with germs that cause skin infections is by touching the host's infected skin (e.g., impetigo, cold sores, scabies, the fluid in the blisters of chickenpox, the rash of shingles) or by coming into direct contact with head lice.

Germs are spread indirectly on contaminated vehicles. Vehicles can be anything around us that germs can contaminate. *The vehicles in centres that we need to pay particular attention to are hands, food and food-related objects, facial tissue, diapers, potties, mouthing toys, hairbrushes, toothbrushes, and blow toys/pipes/straws used in water tables.* The germs on these vehicles can easily and frequently find their way into our body.

Caregivers of toddlers and young preschoolers are often concerned about children biting. From the standpoint of infection control, the risk of children transmitting hepatitis B or human immunodeficiency virus (HIV) through biting is very slight. In fact there has not been a single reported case of HIV transmitted in any centre. However, there has been at least one case of hepatitis B in an American centre. It is very unusual for a child's bite to actually break (cut) the victim's skin and cause bleeding. Saliva has not been shown to spread HIV (Canadian Paediatric Society 1996, 55–56, 182–85; Aronson 1991b, 143).

If a bite mark does bleed, caregivers should wash the wound with soap and water, rinse, dry, and apply a bandage. Then the victim should be seen by a physician as soon as possible to have the wound cleaned and treated, possibly with medication. Even normal, healthy mouths are full of germs, and these germs could pass through an opening in the skin and cause an infection. In terms of the victim's potential exposure to blood-borne infections, the physician and public health staff will advise whether treatment is required. The medical officer of health (MOH) may determine that the child or adult be given hepatitis B immune globulin (HBIG).

As an aside, biting is a guidance issue for caregivers. Consideration may need to be given to children who are known to be biting and to the pain they inflict on others in the centre. Biting is usually a short-term behaviour. Parents and caregivers will need to discuss a consistent way to manage the biting.

Through the Air Young children frequently experience colds and eye, nose, and throat infections. It is easy to understand why. The germs, both viruses and bacteria, that cause minor or serious infections are in the host's saliva and nasal secretions. The germs are spread by droplets of secretions that move through the air when we cough or sneeze. We can breathe in the droplets or they can land in our eyes, nose, or mouth. Or the droplets, saliva, or nasal discharge land on an object or our hands and the germs find their way into our mouth.

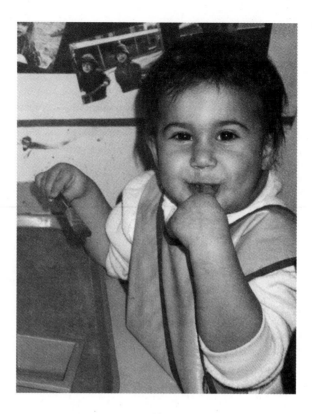

Through Contact with Stool   Diarrhea can be caused by bacteria, parasites, or viruses found in the host's stool. As we have discussed, we have bacteria in our bowels that help to keep us healthy. However, if those bacteria contaminate our environment, they can cause an intestinal infection in someone else. Whenever stool contaminates our hands, food, water, cooking surfaces, toys, taps on sinks, and other objects, the germs spread *very easily* among us. Germs enter our mouth from our hands and from toys or through food or water. This means of transmission is also known as the fecal/oral route.

Through Food   Food is an ideal medium for germs to grow on and multiply. Typically, food is contaminated in either of two ways: germs may be in or on the food before we buy it or we can contaminate food when we handle or prepare it. Regardless of the way germs get into food, the way we prepare, cook, serve, and store food determines whether the germs multiply or are destroyed.

Although most food will have some germs in it, you don't get sick every time you eat because your body's defence mechanisms can destroy many germs. Only when germs multiply in numbers before you eat the food can they cause mild, serious, or, rarely, fatal infections. The severity of the infection depends on the type of germ and/or the number of germs that have entered the body. Breaking the chain of food transmission involves several safe food-handling practices: hand-washing, purchasing, storing, preparing, cooking, and serving. (See Food Safety Practices, page 275.)

Through Contact with Blood and Bloody Body Fluids   Two serious infections, hepatitis B and human immunodeficiency virus (HIV), are blood-borne diseases and in most cases spread to others through direct contact with blood or semen. These viruses are spread three ways:

▶ by sexual intercourse
▶ by sharing needles used for illegal intravenous drug use
▶ by an infected woman to her fetus and, in the case of HIV, during breast-feeding

The HIV virus creates enormous anxiety in schools, centres, and hospitals, but routine screening of patients, students, employees, or children in centres, schools, and hospitals is *not* permitted under human rights legislation. Nor is it recommended or necessary under the guiding principle of universal precautions in infection control. Following possible exposure to the HIV virus, there is a "window period" during which your body either will or will not develop antibodies to HIV, which will then be detected in the blood. This period varies from a few weeks to about six months. When someone is concerned that she or he may have been exposed to HIV and is tested during this period, the result could be negative. Testing after this window period confirms whether she or he is HIV-negative or HIV-positive. If these later tests are positive, the initial test was false-negative. False-negative tests are one of the important reasons why routine screening for HIV is not conducted. The HIV blood test tests individuals only for a moment in time.

It is important to understand that someone's HIV status is confidential medical information and that it is against human rights legislation either to insist on HIV testing or to demand that someone disclose her or his HIV status to centre staff or to anyone else. If parents disclose their child's HIV-positive status to one caregiver, that caregiver must maintain confidentiality by not telling her or his co-workers, director, or other parents. This information can be shared only by the parents. Many people who are HIV-positive fear discrimination, rejection, and isolation after disclosing their HIV status, so they keep it a secret. Through education and public awareness, sensitivity, and respect, perhaps the social climate will change and we will embrace and support people living with HIV/AIDS.

Neither HIV nor hepatitis B is spread by casual contact. The work that is done in centres is defined as casual, and the risk of transmitting HIV and hepatitis B within centres must be put into perspective. Working in centres with children and co-workers does not put caregivers at risk of HIV transmission. We must focus instead on our *personal* lives to reduce our risks. Caregivers, like the general population, put themselves at risk if they participate in unprotected sexual intercourse or share needles and syringes. Child care providers and parents who participated in a three-hour information session on blood-borne diseases demonstrated a positive shift in their understanding of the diseases and policy decisions made around children and adults living with HIV/AIDS or hepatitis B (Renaud et al. 1997). Not only were these caregivers prepared to care for children who were infected with HIV, but they understood that centre policies must not discriminate against children or staff living with

HIV or hepatitis B. To learn more about HIV and hepatitis B transmission and about reducing your risk, contact your college/university resource or health centre, the public health agency, physicians, or the AIDS committee in your province or territory. (See *HIV/AIDS and Child Care* in Resources, page 203.)

The New Host

The term "new host" refers to the next person who gets the infection after the germs enter the body, whether through the mouth, eyes, nose, an open cut, or a rash or sore on the skin, or by way of the genito-urinary or gastrointestinal tract. The type of germ usually determines which part of the body develops the infection. This explains why we develop different infections such as colds, strep throat, ear or chest infections, impetigo, urinary-tract (bladder) infections, or diarrhea.

The incubation period begins when the germ first enters the new host's body. Then the germ multiplies in number. The body's natural defences try to destroy the germs, and if they are successful we don't get sick. But if they are unsuccessful we experience symptoms within hours, days, or weeks, depending on the germ and how much time it needs to multiply before it causes infection. By the time you feel that cold coming on, however, you have already been spreading the cold virus among others. This is relatively common for infections, including chickenpox, which makes controlling the spread of infection very difficult. Therefore, *the control of infections is an ongoing job; you don't do it just when you know someone is ill.*

TABLE 3.2 SUMMARIZING THE LINKS OF THE CHAIN	
The Germ	<ul><li>viruses</li><li>bacteria</li><li>parasites</li><li>fungi</li></ul>
The Host	person who is ill (germs found in saliva, stool, and blood, on skin or hair, etc.)
The Vehicles of Transmission	<ul><li>directly from person to person (e.g., through air, by touching, kissing, biting)</li><li>indirectly from person to person (e.g., on hands, toys, food, objects)</li></ul>
The New Host	new person who is ill

Breaking the Chain: Developing an Infection Control Strategy

▶ **OBJECTIVES** To explain the role that each of the seven areas of policies and procedures plays in infection control.

To describe the principles and recommended practices for immunization.

To state the rationale for effective hand-washing as the most important health practice in reducing the spread of infections.

To describe the when, what, and how of hand-washing for caregivers and children.

To explain the rationale behind the steps in diaper-changing and toileting routines.

To understand why certain items must be cleaned and sanitized before and/or after use, or on a daily or regular schedule.

To understand the goal of universal precautions and how to put them into practice.

Our initial defence against germs is understanding that although germs are everywhere, we neither want to, nor are we able to, produce a sterile environment (as in an operating room). Child care environments are designed to be friendly, nurturing, interesting, and child-centred. Although children do become ill, our underlying assumption is that most people are healthy most of the time. Thus, we carefully choose where to focus our energy to prevent or reduce environmental contamination and the spread of germs. Maintaining our own health and that of the children in our care prevents the germs normally found in our bodies from causing infection, and in many cases helps us resist germs from other sources. Thus, a centre's infection control strategy demonstrates the staff's understanding of the chain of transmission by developing and implementing specific policies and procedures. To break the chain of transmission, centres' policy manuals will include infection control policies and procedures on the following:

▶ immunization
▶ hygiene practices
▶ cleaning and sanitizing routines
▶ daily observation of children
▶ documentation of health observations and sharing observations with parents and physicians
▶ exclusion criteria
▶ effective communication with parents

FIGURE 3.2 BREAKING THE CHAIN

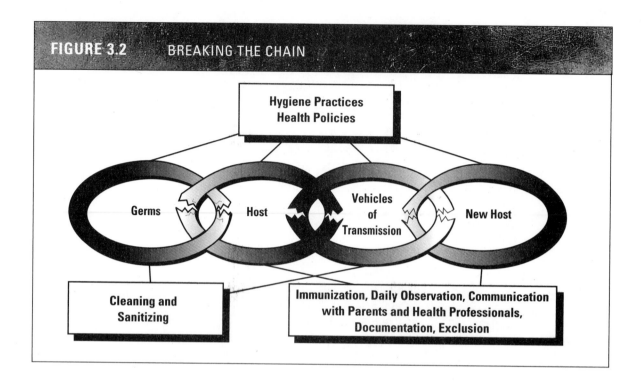

Immunization

Before vaccines were developed, epidemics occurred in which thousands of people died or, in the case of polio, were left physically challenged. Currently, there are nine serious infections—communicable diseases—that can be prevented through routine immunization. "In 1993, 95% of all children 2 years of age had completed immunization for measles, 85% had completed polio and 83% had completed pertussis" (Canadian Institute of Child Health 1994, 52). In Canada, the occurrence of many of these infections is so rare that when an outbreak does occur, it makes the news. For example, in the early 1990s there was an outbreak of measles in Quebec schools. An estimated 10 000 children contracted measles either because they had never been vaccinated or because the vaccine had failed to immunize, combined with the fact that measles spreads easily. The failure rate for the measles vaccine is 5 to 10 percent.

Immunization is one of the most important ways of promoting the health of children. Vaccines, however, have not eliminated these viruses. Without immunizations, children are susceptible to these infections. Canadian children are fortunate that routine vaccination costs are covered by medicare, but this is not the case for millions of other children around the world. Even American children are not guaranteed routine immunizations; children from financially disadvantaged families who aren't covered by private health insurance may not be immunized.

Some parents in Canada, however, choose not to immunize their children for personal reasons. And we live in a country that welcomes people from around the world. Consequently, many immigrant children may not have been vaccinated and could be carrying the virus for polio or diphtheria, which would put unimmunized persons at risk. To ensure the health of Canadian children and those arriving in Canada, public health agencies must work toward 100-percent immunization.

Your body responds to a vaccination by forming antibodies against specific diseases. The vaccination almost always results in lifelong immunity. In other words, the antibodies remain in your body ready to destroy the virus every time it enters, whether you know you were exposed to it or not.

For measles, mumps, and rubella, we require two doses of each vaccine. For the other diseases, we need a series of vaccinations to achieve immunity. For lifelong immunity against tetanus and diphtheria, adults require booster shots every 10 years. An exception is pertussis (whooping cough), whose vaccine protection wears off over time. As a result, previously immunized children and adults can develop pertussis, though the infection would not be as severe. Vaccinations against pertussis are not given to people over age 7 because the risk of severe complications from pertussis is low in older children and adults. Moreover, adverse reactions from the vaccine, such as fever and pain, are common.

A series of three doses of vaccine for hepatitis B is recommended for children around the ages of infancy or between 9 and 13. This protects them before they might become sexually active or use illegal intravenous drugs.

The chickenpox vaccine has been used in Japan for at least 20 years. The chickenpox vaccine is available in Canada and some parents are vaccinating their children. However, due to current cost restraints and the fact that the vaccine must be kept frozen during shipment and during storage in health clinics and doctors' offices, the universal immunization of children for chicken pox does not appear imminent.

The polio vaccine is available in two forms: oral and injection. Other vaccines can be given as individual injections. Fortunately, they are commonly given in a combined solution, so children are given just one shot. Imagine how popular the doctor or nurse would be otherwise!

IMMUNIZATION RECORDS

Considering the importance of immunization, you may be surprised to learn that child care regulations on immunization at enrollment vary across Canada. But even in regions where immunization is not mandatory in the child care regulations, many centres require children to be immunized on enrollment and document it in their policy manual.

Although most parents agree that immunizing their children is important, many children's immunization schedules are not kept up-to-date. Depending on where they live, individual physicians and/or a local public health clinic are responsible for immunizing children. As a result, there is often no systematic way of notifying parents of an upcoming appointment.

The physician or public health nurse usually gives parents an immunization record card for each child. The card is updated whenever the child is vaccinated. At the time of enrollment, parents provide the director with a copy of their child's record. Directors compare the information on these cards with the standard

TABLE 3.3	ROUTINE IMMUNIZATION SCHEDULE FOR INFANTS AND CHILDREN					
AGE AT VACCINATION	**DTaP[1]**	**INACTIVATED POLIO VACCINE**	**Hib[2]**	**MMR**	**Td[3]**	**Hep B[4] (3 doses)**
Birth						
2 months	X	X	X			Infancy
4 months	X	X	X			
6 months	X	(X)[5]	X			
12 months				X		or
18 months	X	X	X	(X)[6]		
4–6 years	X	X		(X)[5]		
14–16 years						preadolescence (9–13 years)

DTaP   Diphtheria, tetanus, pertussis (acellular) vaccine
Hib   *Haemophilus influenzae* type b conjugate vaccine
MMR   Measles, mumps, and rubella vaccine
Td   Tetanus and diphtheria toxoid, "adult type"
Hep B   Hepatitis B vaccine

Notes

1. DTaP (diphtheria, tetanus, acellular or component pertussis) vaccine is the preferred vaccine for all doses in the vaccination series, including completion of the series in children who have received ≥ 1 dose of DPT (whole cell) vaccine.
2. Hib schedule shown is for PRP-T or HbOC vaccine. If PRP-OMP, give at 2, 4, and 12 months of age.
3. Td (tetanus and diphtheria toxoid), a combined adsorbed "adult type" preparation for use in persons > 7 years of age, contains less diphtheria toxoid than preparations given to younger children and is less likely to cause reactions in older persons.
4. Hepatitis B vaccine can be routinely given to infants or preadolescents, depending on the provincial/territorial policy; three doses at 0, 1, and 6-month intervals are preferred. The second dose should be administered at least 1 month after the first dose, and the third dose should be administered at least 4 months after the first dose and at least 2 months after the second dose.
5. This dose is not needed routinely, but can be included for convenience.
6. A second dose of MMR is recommended, at least 1 month after the first dose given. For convenience, options include giving it with the next scheduled vaccination at 18 months of age or with school entry (4–6 years) vaccinations (depending on the provincial/territorial policy) or at any intervening age that is practicable.

Source: *Routine Immunization Schedule for Infants and Children—Routine Canadian Immunization Guide,* 5th ed., Health Canada (1998). Reproduced with the permission of the Minister of Public Works and Government Services Canada, 1999.

immunization schedule. If any discrepancy is found, the director asks the parents to discuss it with their physician and/or the director contacts the public health agency. (See Children's Medical Examination at Enrollment, page 156.)

Children's immunizations may not be up-to-date for the following reasons:

▶ families' hectic schedules
▶ children of different ages in a family needing immunizations at different times
▶ the family's lack of a regular physician

For most parents, a simple reminder that their child is due for an immunization prompts them to make an appointment with the doctor or clinic. Centres play an important role in ensuring that children are immunized at enrollment and by regularly reviewing these records to ensure that children don't miss a booster shot.

Some parents have decided not to immunize their children for religious or moral reasons. Children cannot be denied access to centres if they are not immunized. In these cases, directors should have the parents provide a letter from the child's physician. If a child or caregiver develops a communicable disease, the public health agency then excludes all unimmunized children and staff from the centre for a certain period. This eliminates further contact with the infected child and attempts to protect the unimmunized individuals. (See Appendix 3.1, page 209.)

If a child develops a serious disease, all susceptible children must be identified quickly and the illness managed properly. Consequently, the director and the public health staff must have immediate access to the current immunization record for every child and staff in the centre.

ADVERSE REACTIONS

Before children are immunized, the physician or public health nurse discusses the vaccines' possible adverse reactions and contra-indications with the parents. A day or two after a vaccination, children commonly experience mild side effects, ranging from redness, slight swelling, and tenderness at the injection site to a low-grade fever and irritability. Directors may suggest that parents arrange to have the vaccination appointment on a Friday. This way children can spend the weekend getting the extra care they might need at home.

Children rarely experience serious allergic reactions following a vaccination. If one does occur, the child's physician and public health officials will determine whether the child receives further vaccinations.

IMMUNE GLOBULIN

Passively acquired immunity results when a susceptible individual is exposed to a certain disease and then given the immune globulin for it. Immune globulins are injections of antibodies that temporarily protect the individual from the disease or at least reduce the symptoms. In the case of chickenpox, within 72 hours of exposure susceptible caregivers are given the varicella-zoster immune globulin (VZIG). Immune globulins are available for only a few diseases.

Hygiene Practices

You may initially feel overwhelmed by the number of health practices that you are expected to perform in a centre. You may wonder, for example, why so many steps are involved in changing a diaper. Over time, effective hand-washing and diapering routines become second nature. And you will see that the time spent learning these steps reduces the number of ill children and caregivers. Infection control is an essential component of centres' disease prevention strategies.

Let's begin by examining the vital role hand-washing plays in reducing the spread of infections in centres. *This practice is important for everyone in the centre: children, caregivers, and parents.* The physical care of infants and toddlers poses challenges for infection control for caregivers. Without stringent adherence to diapering and toileting routines, outbreaks of diarrhea are inevitable.

HAND-WASHING

The most common and efficient way for germs to enter our body is through our mouth. Take a moment to think of everything that our hands touch each day: the number is staggering. Combine that with the number of times we put our hands or objects (e.g., pencils, toys, eating utensils) into our mouth.

Hand-washing is the most important health practice that caregivers and children must implement to reduce the spread of infections. From the moment we wash our hands, we begin to collect germs all over again. Yet we can't spend the day with our hands in running water and soap. But if we pay particular attention to *when* and *how* we wash our hands, we accomplish the most significant practice in infection control.

When Do We Wash Our Hands?   Certain activities expose our hands to large numbers of germs. To prevent contamination, it is important that we wash our hands immediately *after* completing the following activities. Washing our hands is important

► after using the toilet or helping children at the toilet
► after changing a diaper
► after caring for ill children
► after cleaning up spills of blood and body fluids
► after wiping a child's nose (if possible)
► after cleaning or sanitizing routines, even if you wore disposable or rubber gloves
► after handling animals

While we care for children and carry out tasks in the centre, we collect germs on our hands. By washing off germs *before* we begin particular activities, we greatly reduce the opportunity to spread germs to others. Washing our hands is important

► before preparing, serving, or eating food
► before feeding infants and children
► before giving a medication
► before playing in the water table
► before carrying out first aid

What We Use for Effective Hand-Washing The five important components in the hand-washing routine are running water, soap, friction, drying the hands, and turning off the taps.

Running water is essential to rinse the germs off the hands and down the drain. A comfortable water temperature allows you to keep your hands in the running water for 10 seconds. Take disposable alcohol-based hand wipes with you on field trips when you don't have access to running water.

Using running water may raise concerns over water conservation and our environment, but washing in a full sink or basin of water is *not* the solution. You defeat the purpose of hand-washing by rinsing off the soap and germs in a pool of water. This practice recontaminates your hands with all the germs that are now in that pool of water. To conserve water, don't turn on the tap full blast.

All you need is plain, mild hand soap for hand-washing, regardless of the activity you have just completed. Soaps with germ-killing ingredients are expensive and unnecessary and may kill "friendly" protective bacteria as well. Soaps with an alcohol base dry the skin. It is actually the *friction* that is created by rubbing hands and soap together that removes the germs from our skin.

Liquid hand soap is recommended for two reasons: the soap pump is convenient and it's easier for children to use than a slippery bar of soap, which often falls on the floor. Also, germs, dirt, paint, and sand collect on the soap bar and in the soapy water at the bottom of the soap dish.

Caregivers wash their hands frequently, which may dry and chap their skin. Using mild soap and hand lotion helps to prevent this. And, as discussed earlier, germs can enter our body through non-intact skin. As you'll see in step two of the hand-washing routine, you wet your hands before adding the soap. This reduces soap's drying effect on your skin.

Many centres refill rather than replace empty soap pumps and hand lotion containers. Before you refill them, however, clean out the containers with soap and water and rinse them with water to remove the remnants and any germs that may have travelled down the pump during use. If the insides of the containers are not properly cleaned, these germs will contaminate the fresh liquid that is added.

Occasionally, caregivers' and children's fingernails need to be cleaned. Nailbrushes should not be used, for two reasons. First, the brushing action can cause very small cuts on the cuticles and under the nails, which can trap germs. Second, a communal nailbrush accumulates and transmits germs from everyone who has used it. Instead, use a disposable manicure stick to clean under fingernails (Canadian Paediatric Society 1996, 69).

Drying our hands and turning off the taps are the final steps in hand-washing. These steps can either remove further germs or recontaminate our hands before we leave the sink.

Towels can be either cloth or paper. Centres base their decision on cost, access to laundry facilities, storage space, and the number of staff and children. Rolling towel dispensers and electric hand dryers are not used in centres. We've all used rolling cloth towel dispensers that wouldn't let us pull out clean towel or had run out of towelling, and we've all seen someone use a section of towel that someone else has used already. Electric hand dryers are not used for two reasons: they can break down and they take a long time to dry hands thoroughly. It is not practical to expect groups of children and staff to wait in line to dry their hands.

Since we turn on taps with dirty hands, we don't want to wash and dry our hands and then turn off the taps with our clean hands. Some centres' sinks may have elbow taps, foot pedals, or sensors, which eliminate the need to use hands to turn the water on and off.

The scrubbing and rinsing during hand-washing remove most of the germs. The drying action may remove even more. But reusing a wet or dry cloth towel increases the likelihood of recontaminating our hands with the germs that were left on the towel from the previous use. *Single-use* towels, however, whether cloth or paper, ensure that we dry our hands with a fresh towel each time. Then the towel can be used to turn off the taps before it is put into the laundry or the garbage.

Some centres may choose to use individual cloth towels, each one clearly marked with the child's or caregiver's name, hung to dry without touching, and changed at least daily. Individual cloth towels have disadvantages, however. They should not be used to turn off the water, because the taps then contaminate the towels used throughout the day. As well, it is likely that the same towel will be used by more than one person during the day.

How We and Children Wash Our Hands *How, when,* and *what we use* to wash our hands help to ensure effective hand-washing. The eight steps in the handwashing routine ensure that as many germs as possible are removed. Remember, you are not trying to sterilize your hands, which is impossible, but rather to remove as many germs as you can.

Here are the eight essential steps (Canadian Paediatric Society 1996, 957) in an effective hand-washing technique:

1. Use warm *running* water.
2. Wet your hands and add soap.
3. Rub your hands vigorously for 5 to 10 seconds.
4. Wash all surfaces, including the backs of hands and between fingers.
5. Rinse your hands well under *running* water for 5 to 10 seconds.
6. Dry your hands well with a towel. Turn off the taps with a single-use towel.
7. Dispose of the cloth or paper towel.
8. Apply hand lotion as needed.

Just as it is important for us to wash our hands, it is equally important for *all* children to wash their hands. Effective hand-washing is one of the health habits we need to develop for a lifetime. Learning this habit begins in infancy. (See Hand-Washing for Infants and Toddlers, page 140.)

For preschool and school-age children, the caregiver's role evolves from one of physically washing their hands to one of encouraging, supervising, and modelling effective hand-washing. In school-age programs, children often need to be reminded to wash their hands, since their attention turns easily to more exciting activities. Basically, children should wash their hands before and after the same activities that were listed for caregivers. But children must be encouraged to focus especially on washing their hands after they use the toilet and before they eat or handle food. (See Hand-Washing and Germs, page 515.)

Monitoring Hand-Washing We have all been in public washrooms that didn't have soap or towels, have seen the tail end of the rolling towel lying on the floor, or have

experienced electric hand dryers that don't blow hot air! The next time you are in a public washroom, compare the number of people who wash their hands thoroughly to the number who simply run one hand under the water or don't wash at all. How would you feel about sharing a box of popcorn at the theatre, being served at a restaurant, or having as a co-worker someone whose hand-washing was so perfunctory?

Though we know the importance of the eight hand-washing steps, we may tend to skip steps or cut down on the time we spend at the sink because we are in a hurry. A poster close to the sink will act as a reminder to caregivers and parents. Regular monitoring of caregivers' hand-washing compliance is very important in order to maintain a high level of hygiene. *Remember, this simple, inexpensive, low-tech routine is the most important health practice in the centre's infection-control strategy.*

Hygiene Practices for Infants and Toddlers

The rate of gastrointestinal infection is highest for infants and toddlers. The responsibility for infection control rests squarely on the caregivers' shoulders. This section highlights the hygiene practices that should be in place to reduce the opportunity for infection.

Hand-Washing for Infants and Toddlers   Have you ever wondered why babies would need to have their hands washed during the day? Watch them to see what their hands touch as they explore and you will know the answer to this question! And remember, germs can be almost anywhere. Washing their hands is important

- ▶ after they have a diaper change or use the toilet/potty
- ▶ before they eat or are bottle-fed
- ▶ after they play outside or with materials such as sand or paint

To wash an infant's hands, use a warm, wet, soapy single-use towel, rinse with a second, wet towel, and dry with a third. When toddlers are able to stand at a sink, with careful supervision and help they will follow the same steps for hand-washing as the older children and caregivers.

Caring for Children in Diapers   Before we discuss the steps involved in changing a diaper, we will examine other hygiene practices related to diapers. Either cloth or disposable diapers are used in centres. To prevent stool from contaminating the environment, diapers must

- ▶ absorb the urine and stool
- ▶ fit snugly around the thighs and waist to contain the urine and stool
- ▶ have a waterproof cover
- ▶ be covered with clothing

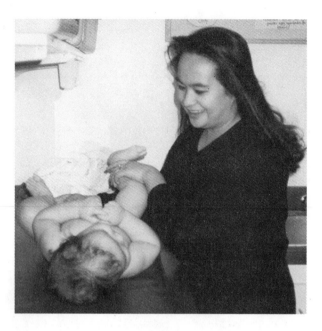

Researchers continue to compare the amount of fecal contamination in centres from disposable diapers to that from cloth diapers. Generally, disposable diapers are more absorbent and leak less than cloth diapers. However, the Canadian Paediatric Society and many public health officials do not recommend one type of diaper over another in centres. Centres and parents can choose the type of diaper that best meets their needs, based on financial considerations, environmental issues, access to a commercial diaper service, and laundry facilities.

If cloth diapers are chosen, care must be taken to ensure that the diaper covers ("pants") are laundered properly to ensure that urine and stool are removed. Many centres use a fresh diaper cover at each diaper change. The use of diaper covers that are pulled up and down the legs is discouraged. Problems arise if the leg elastics have stool on them, since as the pants are pulled off stool contaminates the child's legs. Instead, diaper covers that fasten at the waist permit the caregiver to remove the cover and diaper in one step, reducing the risk of contaminating the centre's environment. Obviously if stool has leaked out of the diaper onto the legs, it will be washed off with soap and water during the change.

Studies have shown that the amount of fecal contamination is significantly reduced when children wear clothes over their cloth *or* disposable diapers. Clothing is an additional barrier between the diaper, its contents, and the room (Van et al. 1991). Permitting children to wear just a T-shirt and diaper, or to eat in just a diaper and bib, to make cleanup easier is *not* acceptable practice for infection control. Babies soon figure out how to open a diaper, and will learn even more quickly when there aren't any clothes to slow them down. Sitting beside another child provides another opportunity to gain easy access into another's diaper if that other child is wearing no outer clothing.

Second in importance only to hand-washing, a strict diapering routine is essential in infant and toddler programs to control the incidence of gastrointestinal infection. Regardless of the type of diaper used, the caregiver's actions are crucial in determining the level of fecal contamination. Children learn to use the toilet at different ages; for many this occurs after age 2. Preschool centres may have children in diapers and, if so, the diapering routine applies to preschool staff and parents.

The diaper change surface, the surrounding area, and diapering supplies should always be considered contaminated. The area should never be used for anything else, including putting a baby bottle down on the counter even for a minute.

Posting a diapering routine by the changing area acts as a reminder for caregivers and parents. However, regular monitoring of the caregiver's diapering technique helps to ensure that the routine is properly implemented all the time.

Effective diapering involves the following steps:

1. Assemble all the necessary supplies.
2. Place the child on the changing surface and remove the soiled diaper. Fold the soiled surface inward and set it aside. If safety pins have been used to fasten the diaper, close them and put them out of the child's reach. Never put the pins in your mouth.
3. Clean and dry the child's skin.
4. When necessary, use a facial tissue to apply ointments or creams.
5. Put a fresh diaper on the child.
6. *Wash the child's hands.* Return the child to a supervised area.
7. Formed stool can be flushed down the toilet. Do not rinse the diaper.
8. Dispose of the cloth or disposable diaper and, if used, the disposable paper covering.
9. Spray the sanitizing solution onto the entire surface of the changing surface. Leave for 30 seconds.
10. Put away all diapering supplies.
11. *Wash your hands.*
12. Dry the changing surface with a single-use towel. Dispose of the cloth or paper towel.
13. *Wash your hands thoroughly.*
14. Record skin condition and bowel movements, as necessary.

Source: Courtesy of the Canadian Paediatric Society. From *Well Beings* (Ottawa: Canadian Paediatric Society, 1996), 958.

You may be thinking, "I've changed a lot of diapers and it didn't take me 14 steps—or 10 minutes to change a single diaper," and "There must be a ton of diapers to change during a day's work in an infant centre!" However, if you were to write down everything you did during a diaper change, you may be surprised at just how many steps you did take. Furthermore, parents and others who change one child's diapers at home do not need to follow the same stringent guidelines, because one

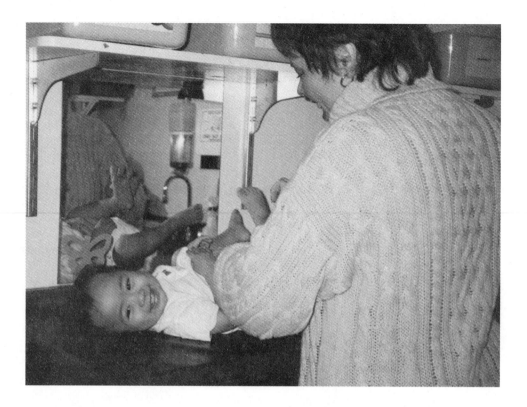

baby at home is quite different from 8 or 12 infants and toddlers in a group setting. At home, every family member gets used to each other's germs. Older siblings are past the developmental stage at which they put everything in their mouth, and their own personal hygiene habits are improving.

Caregivers' compliance depends on their understanding of the importance of and the rationale for the routine. The list below provides the rationale for a number of steps from the diapering routine.

Step 1: It is not necessary to wash your hands before starting. We assume that caregivers have been washing their hands whenever necessary during the day. As well, the diapering area and supplies are always considered to be contaminated. So it doesn't make sense to wash your hands and then contaminate them immediately after taking off the soiled diaper or picking up a tube of ointment. After you take off the diaper and wash the child's skin, your hands are covered with germs.

Step 4: Using a facial tissue to scoop ointment out of the jar or to squeeze it from a tube onto the tissue has two purposes. First, the tissue provides a barrier between your hands and the ointment, which keeps the ointment (whether in a jar or at the end of a tube) from being contaminated by your hands. Second, the tissue is then used to spread the ointment onto the skin. This keeps the germs that are already on your hands off the child's washed skin. If you need more ointment, use a new tissue to get more from the jar or tube. This rule applies regardless of whether each child has her or his own jar of diaper cream or a communal container is used. From what you've read so far, you should be able to come up with the rationale for this last requirement.

The routine use of diaper creams and ointments on children's healthy skin is discouraged. Changing diapers frequently and cleaning the skin at each change prevents urine, stool, or ammonia from contacting the skin long enough to cause irritation. These preparations are also difficult to wash off thoroughly with every change, so urine and stool can be trapped under the cream and irritate the skin. When you use these products, apply them sparingly. Do not use baby powders or talc because the infant's airways can be damaged by inhaling powder in the air when the container is shaken.

Step 6: Before children arrive at the diaper table, they may have already had their hands in their diaper. During diaper changes, children will likely touch the wet or soiled diapers, the changing surface, and the caregiver's hands. If children don't have their hands washed after the diaper change, they will immediately begin contaminating the environment with their hands.

Step 7: To reduce the amount of stool going to landfills or to commercial diaper services, use toilet paper to pick up formed stool or roll it off the diaper into the toilet. At home, parents who use cloth diapers often soak soiled diapers in the toilet, but caregivers *must not* do this in centres. The number of times the diaper is then handled increases by at least three times, and it is difficult not to splash and drip the water in the diaper over the toilet and onto the floor. The amount of fecal contamination would be phenomenal.

Step 8: During a diaper change, stool or urine can end up on the changing surface. Diapering surfaces need to be smooth, durable, and easy to clean, which allows caregivers to wipe up any visible urine or stool with toilet paper and then sanitize the surface. Cleaning first with soap and water is not necessary except in cases where a large quantity of stool or urine is left on the diapering surface. Some centres use disposable change-table paper (the kind used in doctors' offices), which provides a barrier between the baby and the surface. Yet when urine or watery stool touches the paper, the liquid leaks through, which defeats the paper's purpose. Remember, even if the paper is still dry following a diaper change, the paper must be discarded and the surface sanitized. This fact, along with the cost and the extra garbage created by the paper, are three reasons why change paper is not recommended.

Step 11: Caregivers must wash their hands to prevent them from recontaminating the surface while they are drying off the sanitizing solution and remaining germs. But by drying the surface and then discarding the towel, they have now recontaminated their hands and need to wash their hands again (Step 13).

The routine use of disposable gloves is *not* recommended for changing diapers, even with stool. Gloves provide little protection beyond the natural protection of your skin. The toilet paper or facial tissue used to wipe stool off the skin and the disposable or cloth towel to wash and dry the child's skin provide the barrier between the stool and your hands. If stool gets on your hands, germs can't get into your body through your skin. If you are concerned about a cut or scrape, use a bandage and replace it when it is soiled or wet. If you have dermatitis and you must change diapers, use disposable gloves as a temporary means to keep stool off your open skin. Sometimes diapers are filled with loose or watery stools, which may have covered the child front and back or run down the legs. Some caregivers find these diapers to be particularly difficult to stomach, and using disposable gloves makes them feel more comfortable.

Diaper changes provide ideal opportunities in your busy day for one-to-one interaction with the child. Wearing gloves puts plastic between your skin and the child's skin, which can't be comfortable for the child. And are we inadvertently sending children the message that bowel movements are somehow not a natural function of their body and that they are "dirty"?

The only time that disposable gloves are recommended is when blood is visible in the child's stool. Choosing disposable plastic gloves over latex gloves affords the centre the same kind of protection without the increased cost. In addition, reducing exposure to latex (e.g., gloves and balloons) is a safer alternative for staff and children who are allergic to latex. Regardless of the reasons for wearing gloves, you *must* wash your hands after removing the gloves. If you don't wash your hands well after every diaper change, you contaminate objects, food, and the environment, and the germs can then enter children's and caregivers' body through the mouth.

Toileting Routine   The toileting routine is made up of the following 15 steps:

1. If the child wears a diaper, remove it. If the diaper is soiled, clean and dry the child's skin. Dispose of the cloth or disposable diaper.
2. Place the child on the toilet or potty. Stay with the child for a specific period of time. Five minutes is usually long enough.
3. Wipe the child.
4. Flush the toilet or let the child flush it. If a potty was used, empty its contents into the toilet and flush.
5. If necessary, diaper the child and help the child get dressed.
6. *Assist the child in hand-washing.* Return the child to a supervised area.
7. Rinse out the potty and flush the water down the toilet. If there is any remaining stool in the potty, wear household rubber gloves and remove all the stool with toilet paper. Rinse the potty and flush the water.

8. If wearing rubber gloves, remove them. Spray the sanitizing solution onto the potty and the diaper-changing surface (if used). Leave for 30 seconds.
9. Put away all diapering supplies.
10. *Wash your hands.*
11. Dry the potty with a single-use towel. Dispose of the cloth or paper towel.
12. Dry the diaper-changing surface with a *different* towel. Dispose of the cloth or paper towel.
13. Return the potty to the storage area.
14. *Wash your hands thoroughly.*
15. Record the child's use of the potty, any bowel movements, and any skin condition, as necessary.

Source: Courtesy of the Canadian Paediatric Society. From *Well Beings* (Ottawa: Canadian Paediatric Society, 1996), 959.

For many of the same reasons that apply to the diapering routine, caregivers need to take extra steps when cleaning a potty to prevent environmental contamination:

▶ Utility sinks should be available for staff to use for cleaning, including potties. The utility sink must be cleaned and sanitized after every use. Hand-washing sinks should not be used to rinse or clean potties.

▶ You may prefer to wear rubber gloves while you remove stool stuck to the potty. However, wearing gloves does not eliminate the need to wash your hands. After all, you are not the only person to wear those gloves. Your hands had germs on them before you put on the gloves and so did the hands of the person who used the gloves before you. Therefore these germs may have gotten inside the gloves and may end up on the next person's hands. In addition, you get more germs on your hands when you put on and take off the gloves.

▶ Before taking off the gloves, rinse them with water and hang them to dry. You do not have to sanitize the rubber gloves. *Wash your hands* after you remove the gloves. These gloves may also be used for cleaning washrooms and larger amounts of stool, urine, and vomit. Labelling the rubber gloves prevents their being used for any other purpose, such as washing dishes or cleaning and sanitizing mouthing toys.

Cleaning and Sanitizing

You know that germs are everywhere. You know that germs can live on surfaces for hours, days, even weeks. You've read about the vehicles of transmission and the important role they play in spreading infections. The rationale for the cleaning and sanitizing routines in centres is to have staff focus on objects and surfaces that pose the greatest risk to children and staff.

It can be overwhelming to think about all the objects and surfaces that children and staff come into contact with every day, as well as everything and everyone who has come into contact with germs that are spread through the air from coughing, sneezing, and talking! "Where do I start?" "How often do I clean this and that?" "What do I clean with?" "How do I know that I am cleaning this object properly?" These are just some of the questions that are answered in this section.

One of the infection control practices carried out by staff to break the chain of transmission is regular cleaning and sanitizing of objects, surfaces, and areas within centres. To implement this, caregivers need to:

▶ identify what needs to be cleaned and/or sanitized
▶ use effective cleaning and sanitizing products and techniques
▶ understand how to protect themselves from potentially hazardous substances

What Needs to Be Cleaned and/or Sanitized?

By establishing priorities, you can identify the items to be cleaned and/or sanitized and how frequently. With the publication of *Well Beings*, much of the organizational work has been done for centre staff. Rather than repeating those recommendations, let's explore the rationale behind two of them:

Toys Toys that have been in infants' and toddlers' mouth are obvious vehicles of germ transmission. Many toys for infants are designed to be safe for them to put in the mouth (e.g., plastic stacking rings on a cone, squeak toys, rattles). These toys are often referred to as mouthing toys. Of course young children can put almost anything into their mouth (e.g., corners of books, puzzle pieces, plastic fruit and vegetables). For clarity, we will refer to any toy that children have chewed or sucked on as a mouthing toy. After one child has finished playing with a mouthing toy, it should be picked up by staff before a second child chews on it.

Toys that are mouthed should be cleaned and sanitized daily. Cleaning washes off organic materials, such as the children's saliva and any stool, that may have been on a child's hands and trasferred to the toys. As an added precaution, sanitizing removes germs that may remain after cleaning, before the toys are air-dried and returned to the children. Plastic books can be cleaned and sanitized by hand; cloth ones can be put in the laundry.

The potential for spreading germs via toys used by preschoolers or school-agers is much lower than via mouthing toys, for three main reasons. Older children are not constantly putting their toys and hands into their mouth; they aren't touching, hugging, and kissing each other as frequently as babies and toddlers do; and their personal hygiene is improving. For these reasons, these toys can be cleaned weekly and when they are obviously soiled, but sanitizing is not necessary.

Water Tables Although the water table is an important medium for learning, a pool of water can be easily contaminated and spread germs among the children using it. Germs enter the water from the children's hands and from everything they put in the water, such as toys, soap, and food colouring. Additional germs enter the water from blow toys and straws, as well as air-borne germs that land in the water from laughing, talking, and coughing. Adding bleach or other sanitizing solutions is not

necessary—saliva, soap, and sand in the water will reduce the bleach solution's effectiveness.

The Canadian Paediatric Society (1996, 99–100) recommends the following hygiene practices for communal water tables:

► Fill the table with fresh water each morning.
► Empty the table at the end of every day, sanitize, and leave to air-dry overnight.
► Sanitize and air-dry the water toys.
► Clean and sanitize blow toys and pipes and straws after use. These toys, like mouthing toys, should not be shared among children.
► Encourage children and caregivers to wash their hands before playing in the table.

► Discourage children who are not feeling well (e.g., cold, diarrhea), or who have a skin infection, from using the table.

► Close the table when the centre has an outbreak of diarrhea.

Knowing how much infants and toddlers love to explore, knowing their willingness to share toys, their affectionate nature, and their vulnerability to infections, it makes sense that infants and toddlers not use communal water tables. Instead, each child should have his or her own basin of water. The basins can be placed on the floor or on a table in a way that encourages social play. Individual basins permit children to use toys that can go between their own basin of water and their mouth and to splash and drool in the water and even drink it. In this way, the children do not share toys or come into direct contact with the contents of one another's basins. *Children must never be left alone* with the basins of water, even for a second. Children have drowned in as little as 4 cm (1½ ins.) of water.

Cleaning and Sanitizing Products and Techniques

The purpose of *cleaning* is to remove dirt (organic material) and germs from objects and surfaces. But, as in hand-washing, the cleaning solution must be combined with the scrubbing action to create the friction needed to remove dirt and germs. This is followed by *rinsing* with water and *air-drying*.

The purpose of *sanitizing* an object or surface is to ensure that as many germs as possible are eliminated. In most cases, objects and surfaces are cleaned and rinsed, then sanitized, and left to air-dry.

Household cleaning products and detergents that are safer for the environment are also effective cleaning products in centres. Cloth towels can be used for all cleaning and can be laundered after each use. When cleaning up blood and large amounts of stool, urine, and vomit, paper towelling is preferred because it can be safely discarded.

Household bleach is recommended for a number of reasons: it is highly effective, inexpensive, easy to use, readily available, and safe to use around children. When bleach is not used, centres usually consult their public health inspector before choosing sanitizing products. Other products are effective and centre directors consider each product's cost, and its safety around children and staff, as well as its environmental friendliness.

Using bleach may raise a few questions about chlorine in the environment, ruined clothes, and the smell of bleach in the air. You need add only a small amount of bleach to water to sanitize. The recommended dilution is 1 part bleach in 100 parts water—for example, 2.5 mL (1/2 tsp.) of bleach in 250 mL (1 cup) of water. When this proportion is used, the bleach solution is so dilute that problems with bleach odour and ruined clothing are eliminated. But the solution is still strong enough to be effective.

Remember the following points when you use bleach:

▶ Objects and surfaces are usually cleaned first to remove visible organic material (e.g., dirt, food, saliva), because organic materials reduce the effectiveness of the bleach solution.

▶ The bleach solution is mixed fresh each morning for spray bottles used for diaper-change surfaces. When the bleach solution is mixed in open containers and sinks, it should be prepared just before use. Otherwise, the bleach solution evaporates throughout the day and anything that falls into the pail could reduce its effectiveness. From a safety perspective, containers of water should never be left within reach of children.

▶ The bleach solution remains on the object or surface for 30 seconds to allow time for it to work.

▶ To protect your hands from the dryness that comes with using cleaning or sanitizing solution, you may wish to wear rubber gloves. Remember, take off your rings, watches, and bracelets to protect them from bleach.

Four Steps for Cleaning and Sanitizing   Having effective cleaning and sanitizing products, cloths, and rubber gloves—and being organized—takes some of the work out of cleaning.

Caregivers follow these four steps:

1. Fill one container (or sink) with soap (detergent) and water to scrub toys or objects and to wash surfaces.
2. Fill a second container with water to rinse what has been washed. (Soap needs to be rinsed off to ensure that sanitizing is effective.)
3. Fill a third container with the bleach solution. Bleach and water should be measured accurately. (To save time, the water level can be marked on the inside of plastic containers, then only the corresponding amount of bleach needs to be measured.)
4. The objects or surfaces are left to air-dry. The diaper-change surface is the one exception. After the solution has been on the surface for 30 seconds, caregivers dry it off with a fresh towel.

Some objects, such as books and puzzles in infant and toddler programs, need to be sanitized only. Obviously, these and other objects are not placed in a container of bleach and water. Instead, they are wiped with a cloth rinsed and wrung out in the bleach solution.

The dishwasher can be a time-saving device for cleaning and sanitizing smaller plastic toys. Make sure the toys can withstand the water temperature and the detergent.

Implementing the Routines throughout the Day

The number of times that caregivers wash their hands and the time spent on the routines discussed in this unit depend on the following factors: the size of the centre, the number of children and staff, the ages of the children, and whether meals and snacks are prepared in the centre or provided by parents.

Some centres, because of their location (e.g., workplace, office buildings, colleges, universities) have cleaning services that maintain bathrooms, floors, carpets, etc. In these centres, staff have more time for the remaining routines. However, it is important that staff monitor the external cleaning services to ensure that the quality is satisfactory, that the cleaning is done with the recommended frequency, and that the products used are safe around children.

A day in any centre is busy, and fitting in all the routines takes some finesse. But the importance of implementing routines to break the chain of transmission means that there can't be shortcuts. We must ensure that the time spent on implementing routines is valid, because the work reduces the frequency of infection.

A written schedule for all routines is essential to ensure that they are implemented consistently. Centres may design a schedule based on the frequency of the routines (e.g., daily, twice a week, weekly) or by room. The schedule breaks down what can seem like an overwhelming task into more manageable routines. It includes instructions on how each item is to be cleaned and/or sanitized so that caregivers aren't left questioning the effectiveness of their work.

When there is an outbreak of an infection, a review of these written schedules can provide insight into the effectiveness of the cleaning and sanitizing routines and whether the schedule should be revised on a short- or long-term basis.

 During an outbreak of diarrhea, it is advisable to close the water table. At the same time, staff's hand-washing, diapering routines, and food-safety practices need to be evaluated.

PROTECTING YOURSELF FROM POTENTIALLY HAZARDOUS SUBSTANCES

In this unit, we gain an understanding of the potential risks and steps to reduce caregivers' exposure to hazardous products related to infection control. These include the concept of universal precautions, the safe use of cleaning and sanitizing products, and the appropriate use of gloves.

Universal Precautions When patients are admitted to a hospital, they are not routinely tested for any number of diseases. This practice would be expensive and time-consuming. In addition, such tests may not provide the hospital's infectious disease experts with reliable information. You have already read that a person can spread germs to others before she/he develops symptoms and that some of us carry infections even though we are not ill.

Universal precautions is the fundamental principle in protecting staff from the potential risks in the workplace. Hospital staff assume that everyone has the potential to expose them to germs, so safe medical and nursing procedures are developed specifically for the task or medical technique being implemented. Universal precautions in turn protect patients from the hospital staff.

You may be wondering how anything in a hospital has any relevance to centres. Caregivers aren't changing bandages with blood, giving needles, routinely being exposed to blood, or caring for seriously ill patients. The fundamental principle on which hospitals build their infection control strategy is the same one as for centres. To reduce the spread of germs and to protect themselves from unnecessary exposure to potentially harmful organisms, caregivers must implement universal precautions in their daily work with children. *All of the procedures covered in this unit are based on universal precautions and, when implemented, protect not only the caregivers but also the children.*

Cleaning and Sanitizing Products and Gloves   Cleaning products used in centres should be safe to use around children and staff and preferably be friendly to the environment. This does not eliminate the need for the products to be stored out of reach of children. The majority of products used in centres are household products purchased in grocery stores. It is advisable to read all product labels for safe handling directions and any first-aid information. (See Workplace Hazardous Materials Information System, page 79.)

Just as water and soap can dry our skin, cleaning and sanitizing products can be abrasive. Using rubber gloves while dishwashing and during cleaning and sanitizing routines helps protect our hands. There may be times when disposable rather than rubber gloves should be used.

Disposable gloves are used when caregivers are at risk of exposure to blood or bloody body fluids. Once the gloves have been used, they can be disposed of carefully. Carefully remove one disposable glove at a time. While you are slowly peeling off a glove (starting at the wrist), turn the glove inside out. This method protects you from the germs on the gloves and it also protects the immediate area.

Disposable gloves are just one way of providing a barrier between your hands and the blood. Facial tissue used to stop a nosebleed provides a barrier between your hand and the child's nose. Cotton balls or sterile gauze in first-aid kits, when used appropriately to clean cuts and scrapes, can be effective barriers between your hands and the source of the blood. It is not necessary for staff to keep disposable gloves in their pockets in case a child is injured or gets a nosebleed. Our skin's natural ability to protect us from germs—along with effective hand-washing—is our best protection.

The routine use of disposable gloves for diaper changing is not recommended. The routine use of gloves is an unnecessary expense; it also needlessly adds plastic to our landfill sites. (See Caring for Children in Diapers, page 141.)

Regardless of which type of glove is used, there are two points to keep in mind:

▶ "Gloves can provide a protective barrier against germs that cause infection, but they offer little protection beyond that achieved by good handwashing" (Canadian Paediatric Society 1996, 104).

▶ *Caregivers must wash their hands after they remove the gloves.*

Assessing the situation:
Would you simply comply with the centre's practice? If not, how would you proceed in this situation?
Scenario: You are in your first centre placement. You are feeling nervous and, understandably, unsure of yourself. During your first few days at the centre, you

observe that all the caregivers wear disposable gloves whenever a child has stool in the diaper. When one of the caregivers runs through the diapering routine with you, she makes it clear that you are expected to wear gloves.

Children's Health Care

▶ **OBJECTIVES**   To describe the why, how, and what of daily health observations.
To identify the signs and symptoms of illness and describe how to proceed with concerns.
To explain the principle of exclusion and consider the issues surrounding exclusion from the child care program.
To describe how to respond to the most common childhood infections.
To describe the safe administration of medication to children.

This section focuses on the appropriate role that caregivers play in caring for children who are ill. In addition to implementing an infection control strategy, the caregivers' role includes

- ▶ working in partnership with parents
- ▶ identifying possible signs and symptoms
- ▶ implementing the centre's policy for ill children, including:
  - ▷ documenting observations in children's files and reports
  - ▷ sharing relevant health information with parents
  - ▷ communicating with health professionals
  - ▷ implementing the physician's recommendations
- ▶ helping children feel better, including:
  - ▷ excluding children
  - ▷ TLC (tender loving care)
  - ▷ administering medication, if necessary

Caregivers observe children throughout their daily activities. With experience, caregivers gain the expertise to differentiate between behaviour that is developmentally appropriate for children, behaviour that should be watched more closely, and behaviour that is cause for concern. If a caregiver is concerned about a child's behaviour or state of health, action is required on the part of caregivers and parents.

Caregivers' ability to articulate health concerns about children is an essential skill. As with any skill, experience and motivation on the part of the individual to continue learning assists caregivers in fine-tuning their writing skills for documentation. The methods used for documenting health observations vary among centres. Regardless of the method, the key to effective documentation is that it is objective, systematic, and concise. Caregivers are trained professionals communicating with other caregivers, with parents, and with health or social service professionals in the community.

The quality of the relationships that staff have with parents in managing illness is paramount, since parents are the decision-makers regarding their child's health. Establishing effective relationships with parents begins at the time of enrollment, not the first time caregivers have concerns about their child. Because children will get sick and be unable to attend the centre, the enrollment interview is the time for the director and parents to discuss the following issues: sharing information, centre policies on health observations, childhood illnesses, communicating with their physician, criteria for excluding children from the centre, and administering medication.

If the centre's health policies and practices are realistic, logical, practical, and based on current health information, parents will likely understand their purpose and work cooperatively with staff. If, however, policies and practices seem unrealistic or unrelated to current health information, parents may be less willing to cooperate.

- ▶ Centres that take children's temperatures at the hint of a warm forehead and then use only the temperature's value to exclude children and send them to the doctor.
- ▶ Centres that exclude children with colds when the nasal discharge is yellow or green in colour.

Neither example requires children to be excluded, nor do situations like these contribute to parents' viewing the centre and caregivers positively. Partnerships with parents in managing children's illnesses mean that centre staff

- ▶ ensure that exclusion policies and practices are parent-positive—respectful, realistic, non-punitive
- ▶ demonstrate empathy for the parents' situation, balancing this with the needs of the ill child, other children in the group, and staff
- ▶ are supportive with regard to health information and resources, but do *not* diagnose illness. Instead, caregivers document signs and symptoms that the parent can communicate to the physician.

Children's Medical Examination at Enrollment

Most centres in Canada require parents to have their children examined by a physician within a certain time period after starting in the centre. These examinations result in a number of health promotion benefits:

- ▶ They provide the parents, physician, and caregivers with an overview of the child's current health status, which can be used as a measure in the future.
- ▶ They ensure that the child's immunizations are up-to-date.

▶ They advise doctors that one of their patients is starting in group care, which gives doctors the opportunity to talk with parents about the frequency of childhood illnesses.

▶ They include caregivers as participants in the care plan for children with specific health care needs by encouraging the physician and parents to share relevant information with the staff.

Daily Observation of Children

As caregivers get to know the infants and toddlers in their care, they become increasingly aware of behavioural changes and other signs and symptoms that may indicate possible infections. Preschool and school-age children are generally better able to tell caregivers if they aren't feeling well and answer questions that the caregiver asks for clarification. This assists caregivers in determining whether the parents should pick up their child or whether the child is able to participate in the activities and can remain in the centre. There are times when children are excluded because of a specific infection.

When it comes to observing children for possible signs of illness, caregivers must first acknowledge the importance of daily health observations to identify ill children. Decisions regarding the care of children are based on the caregivers' observations, subsequent conversations with the parents, and physicians' diagnoses.

DAILY BASELINE HEALTH OBSERVATIONS

Centres that recognize the importance of baseline (starting point) health observations schedule enough staff at the start of the day to conduct them. Caregivers conduct baseline health observations of each child when he or she is dropped off so that caregivers can talk with the child and the parent. Staff encourage parents to take a few minutes at drop-off to ensure that parent, child, and caregiver have enough time to talk about

▶ how their child felt overnight and this morning
▶ whether he or she ate breakfast
▶ how well she or he slept
▶ whether they have any concerns about their child (e.g., "She had a sore tummy when she went to bed but seems to be feeling better this morning")

These conversations with parents, and the caregiver's familiarity with the children, establish a daily baseline to identify behavioural changes in a particular child for the rest of the day. *The most reliable indicator of possible infection in children is a change in behaviour.*

During the morning, there are times when the child just doesn't seem to be herself: she wants to lie around, turns down her snack, wants to be held a lot.

Caregivers watch her more closely, taking into account the time of day and whether there are other sick children. The director calls the parent to let him know that his daughter is feeling under the weather. Jointly they decide whether she can remain in the centre for the rest of the day or whether other steps should be taken.

Physical and Behavioural Signs and Symptoms Using a checklist that systematically evaluates children's signs of illness assists caregivers in checking children. With practice, using a checklist quickly becomes second nature. Start at the child's head and move down to the toes and in just a few moments caregivers have completed a baseline health observation.

Observing children calls on your senses of sight, hearing, touch, and smell. Caregivers should look for the following physical signs:

✔ Face: sad, tired, angry, upset, flushed
✔ Eyes: eyelids are puffy, whites of the eyes are red or yellow; eyes themselves are watery and clear or show thick (pus) discharge; sores or styes present; child rubs eyes
✔ Ears: child rubs or pulls at ears; drainage seen in the outer ear
✔ Nose: runny; red or chafed from wiping or rubbing; child sneezes
✔ Mouth: bleeding; swollen gums; cold sores
✔ Neck: swelling along the jawline
✔ Breathing and/or voice: wheezing, congestion, coughing; child sounds stuffed up (nasal) or hoarse
✔ Skin: rashes or patches of irritated skin; cuts, scrapes or abrasions, bruises, bumps; skin has a yellow colour; child scratches the skin. How does the skin feel to your touch?

It is not only unnecessary but inappropriate for caregivers to physically examine children by using a flashlight to look into children's mouth and throat, or by examining the skin for rashes or marks (e.g., bruises) on parts of the body that are covered by clothing. Even if a child complains of a sore throat, you are not responsible for examining the throat to determine whether the tissue is red or swollen or for concluding that he or she should be seen by a physician. Medical examinations are just that—medical—and can be intrusive to patients. Keep in mind that you are not expected or trained to be a doctor or nurse.

During the day, caregivers will naturally see the bodies of infants and children while changing diapers, helping them on the toilet, or helping them change into swimsuits. These occasions provide opportunities to note the presence of skin rashes, bruises, and so on.

In most situations where a child is injured or complains of itchiness or pain, it is appropriate for the caregiver to look at the child's skin and proceed accordingly. An exception is with preschoolers and school-agers, when the genitals or buttocks are involved. In such cases, the child's physician or parents examine the child. However, in

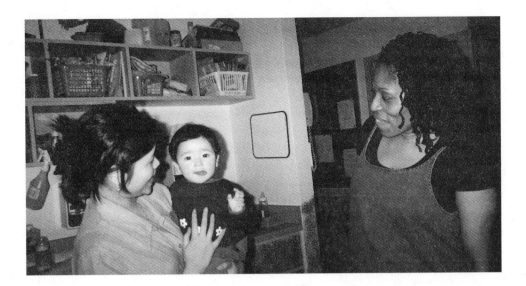

cases where sexual abuse is suspected, caregivers should follow their child abuse protocol.

The baseline health observation includes assessing children's hygiene, emotional health, and growth and developmental milestones. Early childhood courses in child development thoroughly cover the observation and documentation of children's milestone achievements. (See Chart 7.1, page 458.) Concerns about the emotional, physical, or sexual abuse of children and issues of neglect are examined in Unit 6.

The terms "personal hygiene" and "cleanliness" are often used interchangeably. However, personal hygiene is a broader term. It includes hand-washing, toileting practices, and dental care along with the cleanliness of one's skin, hair, and clothing. In hygiene, as in many other things, there is a range of what each person finds to be an acceptable level. The food we eat (e.g., spices), the way foods are prepared (e.g., fried), the laundry products we use (e.g., scented or unscented), and whether we smoke, as well as perfumes, colognes, shampoo/conditioners, deodorants, pets, incense, and so on all contribute to our individual scent and the aroma in our homes. You may be aware of children's individual scents (e.g., a child's T-shirts smell of fabric softener). Some scents may be different from your own and you may find particular scents unpleasant. In other cases, the scents may just be unfamiliar. Yet just because the scent is different doesn't mean the child is unclean. As in any other situation, caregivers' sensitivity to children and parents and respect for personal preferences are important to children's emotional well-being. Caregivers model appropriate comments and behaviour to children. There may be times when children have a distinctive odour because their skin, hair, or clothing is dirty from infrequent bathing or soiled clothes. Again, caregivers use their discretion in determining whether this is a common or infrequent occurrence. If it happens frequently, the child may be neglected.

If a caregiver observes more significant behavioural changes, the child should be seen by a physician as soon as possible. Parents or caregivers must seek medical attention for the child if the child shows any of the following *behavioural changes:*

- ▶ lethargy (or lacks energy)
- ▶ much sleepier than usual
- ▶ not alert
- ▶ uninterested in their environment (other children, toys, activities)
- ▶ unusually cranky, fussy, or irritable
- ▶ inconsolable
- ▶ refusal to eat or drink

Parents or caregivers must seek medical attention for the child if the child shows any of the following *physical symptoms:*

- ▶ change in breathing (rapid, shallow, or shortness of breath)
- ▶ pain or difficulty swallowing
- ▶ stiff neck
- ▶ rash with a fever
- ▶ rash with a change in behaviour

Fevers A fever is just one of a number of signs of illness, like a runny nose, sore throat, cough, diarrhea, or vomiting. *Fever is not dangerous. In fact, it is one of our body's defence mechanisms that helps us fight infection.* But when a child feels warm, many adults reach for the thermometer, give the child medication, and call the physician. Children can be seriously ill and not have a fever. Fever is unreliable as a sign in determining how sick a child is or whether to call the parents to pick up their child.

Parents' concern about fever is linked to a common belief that a child with a fever is sicker than a child without a fever. But this is not necessarily the case. Infants generally show less fever with a serious illness than older children (American Public Health Association and American Academy of Pediatrics 1992). Children can have a very serious illness (e.g., meningitis) and have a normal or below-normal body temperature. A mild viral infection can cause a fever as high as 40°C (104°F). It is important to remember that most infections accompanied by a fever in children are minor (e.g., upper respiratory infections). These are often caused by a virus and the child usually gets better without medical treatment (Ipp 1990; Tulk and Ipp 1992).

Another reason why parents become concerned when their child has a fever is the possibility of a febrile seizure. About 3 to 5 percent of children with a fever have one febrile seizure in their childhood. Febrile seizures are not harmful to children (Canadian Paediatric Society 1996, 132; Freeman 1992; Tulk and Ipp 1992). However, witnessing a seizure can be traumatic for parents, caregivers, and other children because of the thrashing movements, drooling, difficulty breathing, and other involuntary behaviour by the child. Febrile seizures occur when the body's temperature rises rapidly and are often the first sign that the child has a fever at all (Canadian Paediatric Society 1996, 132). There is no treatment or preventive care for children with a history of febrile seizures (Freeman 1992). But if centre staff know that a child may have febrile seizures, that knowledge itself can alleviate some of the anxiety if one does occur.

A fever is not caused by teething. There are a number of factors that cause our body temperature to rise:

▶ overdressing
▶ strenuous exercise/play
▶ time of day (our normal temperature varies during the day, being highest in late afternoon)
▶ a vaccination
▶ an infection

By definition, a fever is a rise in body temperature, to 38.5°C (101.3°F) or higher as a rectal temperature, or 38°C (100.4°F) or higher as an oral temperature. Axillary (armpit) temperatures are not reliable and are discouraged (Canadian Paediatric Society 1996, 131).

Centre staff often feel that they are in a Catch-22 situation—they observe a change in a child's behaviour and know that he or she is not feeling well. But when they call the parents, the parents want to know the child's temperature. And if the child does not have a fever, the parents may be reluctant or refuse to leave work. This situation causes the greatest concern. It could be dangerous to assume that because a child does not have a fever, he or she is not ill enough to be seen by a physician.

Observing a child's behaviour is much more important than taking a child's temperature. The child's behaviour helps you tell how sick the child is (Canadian Paediatric Society 1996). "In general terms, *how sick the child appears* is more important in establishing the severity of underlying illness . . . than the height of fever" (Tulk and Ipp 1992, 26).

As caregivers become familiar with each child, they can identify behaviour changes. When children feel warm to the touch, you can first rule out the other possible reasons for the fever. If you think a child is ill and that is why she or he feels warm, observe the child closely for changes in behaviour. If she or he feels warm but is playing and smiling, there is little to worry about. But if the child's behaviour changes, you must be concerned and take appropriate steps. A child with any of the following symptoms (Canadian Paediatric Society 1996, 132–33) must be seen by a physician as soon as possible, *regardless of whether the child has a fever or feels warm to the touch:*

▶ unusual sleepiness, drowsiness
▶ lack of interest in toys, books, other children
▶ irritability, fussiness
▶ persistent crying, weak cry, inconsolable
▶ difficult or rapid breathing
▶ rash with a fever
▶ poor skin colour
▶ excessive drooling
▶ diminished appetite

Suggestions for managing children's fevers:

1. Share with parents information on fever and the importance of responding to children's behaviour. Encourage parents to discuss the issue of fever with their child's physician, or invite a physician or public health nurse to speak to the centre staff and parents (Canadian Paediatric Society 1996; Freeman 1992; May and Bauchner 1992).

2. Post the list of signs and symptoms of illness that the centre staff will observe for in children at drop-off and throughout the day. Discuss this issue with each parent at the time of enrollment.

3. Taking children's temperature in centres is not recommended (Canadian Paediatric Society 1996, 809). Parents should understand this policy and the rationale for it. If the centre does take children's temperatures, the steps should be outlined in the centre's policy manual. Guidelines will ensure that taking temperatures is done safely and correctly.

4. It is not recommended that acetaminophen (e.g., Tylenol, Tempra) be given to children for the treatment of fevers. Although this medication does lower the temperature, its main purpose is to relieve aches and pains due to illness (Canadian Paediatric Society 1996; Freeman 1992; Ipp 1990; Kluger 1992). Children should never be given acetylsalicylic acid (e.g., Aspirin) for fevers without consulting the child's physician. Children who ingest this medication when they have the flu or chickenpox may develop Reye's syndrome. Although this disease is rare, it is often fatal.

5. Exclusion policy (Canadian Paediatric Society 1996, 134):
   ▷ Children with a fever or who feel warm to the touch can continue to attend the centre if they feel well enough to participate in the program.
   ▷ Infants under six months who feel warm to the touch, look flushed, or have a fever should be seen by a physician as soon as possible. This should be done regardless of whether the infant shows behavioural changes.
   ▷ Notify parents immediately if their child has a febrile seizure. The child should be seen promptly by a physician to determine whether the seizure is part of a more serious infection, such as meningitis.

HEALTH OBSERVATION THROUGHOUT THE DAY

The health observations made when the children begin their day provide caregivers and parents with a baseline with which to compare children throughout the remainder of the day. This baseline is of particular importance when caregivers note a specific sign or symptom and monitor its progress. In other words, they watch to see if the sign or symptom gets worse, is resolving itself, or remains the same. Documenting health observations also assists caregivers and parents to identify patterns in types of illnesses. Caregivers who observe the following early signs of allergies in children can assist parents and physician in the diagnosis: recurring colds and ear infections, nosebleeds, headaches, stomachaches, dark circles under the eyes, irritability. (See Allergies, page 192.)

Documenting Health Observations

Caregivers and parents of infants and toddlers in child care keep daily written records for each child. Form 3.1 (page 165) provides a section for parents to share relevant health information with their child's caregivers. Caregivers complete the remainder of the form during the day. Parents are interested in reading this information at pick-up time. "Anecdotal" notes elaborate on children's activities and their overall well-being. "Health Notes" is an ideal space for the caregivers to record their daily health observations (e.g., "Beginning to sound stuffed up" or "He didn't seem to be himself after his nap this afternoon").

Fewer caregivers are working with more children in preschool and school-age programs than in infant and toddler programs. Staff may not make daily entries in each child's file because children are older and because of time constraints. If nothing unusual happens, it may be unproductive for caregivers to write reports for the sake of it or for parents to read what they already know.

DOCUMENTING IN CHILDREN'S FILES

Caregivers' careful and accurate documentation of each child's health provides parents and, ultimately, health professionals with valuable medical information in making diagnoses. For example, a caregiver would not phone a parent and simply say, "Max is not feeling well and you need to pick him up right away." Rather, caregivers formulate their thoughts about their health observations before they write in a child's file or phone the parents. Their experience and training equips them with the skills needed to ask themselves the same questions that the parents will ask of them. The answers to these questions guide caregivers in determining what to do for the child:

▶ How has the child's behaviour changed, to lead you to believe that the child may be ill?
▶ What are the signs and symptoms that the child is experiencing? Describe the symptoms as clearly as possible.

In the case of a tummyache:
▷ Where is the pain in the abdomen, and does the pain move? (Depending on child's age, the child may be able to use a finger to point to where the pain is.)
▷ What kind of pain is it (sharp, throbbing, comes and goes, etc.)? (The answer will depend on the child's verbal ability.)
▷ Is the child feeling nauseated or has he vomited or had diarrhea?
▷ What has the child eaten that day? Does she have allergies?

▶ When were the signs and symptoms first noticed, and how long have they lasted?
▶ Have the signs and symptoms changed? If so, how? Are they getting worse? Have they stayed constant or are they coming and going (intermittent)?

▶ How is the child's appetite? Is the child experiencing difficulty urinating or having a bowel movement?

▶ Has the child started eating a new food, taken a medication, been immunized in the past two weeks, or been recently injured?

▶ Does the child have any long-term medical condition?

▶ Has the child had similar symptoms before?

▶ What have you done for the child so far? For example, have you continued to watch the child, administered a medication, or isolated the child from the other children?

▶ What time was the parent called? What was said by both parties, and what is to be done next?

▶ Did you call the child's physician or an ambulance?

If one child is ill, caregivers take into account what has happened in the centre over the past few days to consider factors that might be relevant to this child:

▶ Are any other children ill in the centre? What are their signs and symptoms? What was the diagnosis (if seen by a physician)?

▶ What activities have the children been involved in over the past couple of days? Have they been on a field trip?

Co-workers or parents often say that their child always seems to be sick with something. Rather than searching through daily entries to find the ones that concern illness, centres may find it useful to maintain a flow sheet that lists each child's illnesses or symptoms. It takes only a couple of moments to complete and it could be conveniently kept in the front of each child's file. Form 3.2 (page 167) enables caregivers and parents to review the frequency and types of illness that the child experiences or to refer back to a specific entry within the body of the child's file. Directors may even wish to include a copy of the immunization schedule.

Centre's Health Record

The frequency of illnesses is of concern to caregivers and parents. So in addition to maintaining the flow sheet for each child, staff are encouraged to keep an ongoing health record that includes the suspected and diagnosed illnesses of all the children in the centre on one form. (See Form 3.3, page 170.) Staff should include the following information in each notation:

▶ date

▶ child's first and last name

▶ brief description of the symptoms

▶ physician's diagnosis (if the child was seen)

▶ whether the child was excluded and, if so, for how many days

FORM 3.1 INFANT AND TODDLER DAILY CARE RECORD

Name of child: _____ Date: _____

Arrival time: _____ Departure time: _____

Part I: Parents:
Please complete all the following questions to help us meet the needs of your child today.
Please talk to the staff about any special or confidential information we should be aware of.

Your child slept from _____ to _____ . Did your child sleep well last night? Yes ☐ No ☐

If no, specify reasons (e.g., teething, illness, over-tiredness, etc.):

_____

_____

When did your child last eat or drink? Time: _____

Type and amount of food or formula: _____

Have there been any changes or disruptions in your child's routine at home?

_____

What kind of mood is your child in today?

_____

Do you have any special comments or instructions for the staff today?

_____

_____

LIST ANY MEDICATION (PRESCRIPTION OR OVER-THE-COUNTER) YOUR CHILD RECEIVED IN THE LAST 24 HOURS AND THE REASON FOR GIVING MEDICATION. (**PLEASE REMEMBER TO COMPLETE THE *PARENTAL CONSENT AND MEDICATION REPORT SHEET*.**)

_____

Part II (to be completed by the caregiver):

Morning snack	Afternoon snack
Lunch	Bottles (times and amounts)

Naps: _____

Bowel movements and toileting: _____

(form continues on next page)

FORM 3.1   INFANT AND TODDLER DAILY CARE RECORD (continued)

Anecdotal (to be completed by the caregiver):

_____

_____

_____

_____

_____

_____

_____

_____

_____

_____

_____

_____

_____

_____

_____

Health Notes (to be completed by the caregiver):

_____

_____

_____

_____

_____

_____

Caregiver's signature: _____

Source: Courtesy of the Canadian Paediatric Society. From _Well Beings_ (Ottawa: Canadian Paediatric Society, 1996), 865–66. Adapted from the Infant Care Centre, University of Winnipeg.

FORM 3.2   CHILDREN'S ILLNESS FLOW SHEET

Child's name: _____   Date of birth: _____

Date of enrollment: _____   Physician's name: _____

IMMUNIZATION SCHEDULE

Age	Immunization Against					Date Given
2 months	Diphtheria	Pertussis	Tetanus	Poliomyelitis	Haemophilus influenzae b[1]	
4 months	Diphtheria	Pertussis	Tetanus	Poliomyelitis	Haemophilus influenzae b	
6 months	Diphtheria	Pertussis	Tetanus	Poliomyelitis[2]	Haemophilus influenzae b	
12 months					Measles Mumps Rubella	
18 months	Diphtheria	Pertussis	Tetanus	Poliomyelitis	Haemophilus influenzae b	Measles Mumps Rubella[3]	
4–6 years	Diphtheria	Pertussis	Tetanus	Poliomyelitis		Measles Mumps Rubella[3]	
14–16 years	Diphtheria		Tetanus			

[1] The series may vary with the type of vaccine given.
[2] This dose is not needed routinely, but can be included for convenience.
[3] A second dose of MMR is recommended, at least 1 month after the first dose. For convenience, options include giving it at the next scheduled vaccination or at any intervening age that is practical.

SYMPTOMS/ILLNESSES

Date	Illness	Signs & Symptoms	Treatment	Excluded

At the very minimum, use initials on the daily attendance form to indicate trends in absenteeism. For example, use "D" for diarrhea, "R" for respiratory illnesses, and "O" for other health reasons (Ying et al. 1998, 312).

Reviewing this form provides caregivers with valuable information:

► the frequency of specific illnesses
► identifying which children are ill more often
► patterns in illnesses, which staff may begin to see because similarities begin to emerge in terms of the time of year, the age group of the children, and any one group of children experiencing more illnesses than other groups

Patterns in illnesses can help staff identify factors that might contribute to the spread of illness and what they can do to reduce that spread, such as improving the children's and caregivers' hygiene, cleaning and sanitizing routines, and food preparation practices.

Sharing Health Information with Physicians

Centre staff network with a variety of professionals in their community and share information verbally and in written reports. Because of the frequency of young children's illnesses, caregivers may communicate indirectly with physicians on a regular basis through the child's parents. To protect confidentiality, caregivers do not communicate directly with physicians. Before they do so, parents must give the caregivers permission to speak with their doctor and let the doctor know that a caregiver may call.

Caregivers' health observations are essential to assist physicians or other health professionals in caring for children. As professionals, caregivers are encouraged to document their health observations on a report form, which the parents take to their child's physician. (See Form 3.4, page 171.) For the staff, this form is a direct line of communication with the physician. In addition, parents benefit from this documentation because it saves them from having to remember all of the details conveyed verbally by the caregiver.

Obviously, effective communication results when all parties share accurate information. After the visit to the doctor's office, caregivers rely on the parents to share the relevant medical information with them. The Canadian Paediatric Society recommends that physicians share relevant medical information directly with the staff. To arrange this, centre staff provide the parents with a report form that they ask the physician to complete. Parents return the completed form to the staff when their child returns to the centre. This form provides staff with pertinent care information and provides the physician with the centre's exclusion criteria. Many centre directors experience situations in which the doctor's recommendations are not consistent with those of their centre. This inconsistency often results in unnecessary conflicts between staff, parents, and doctor. (See Form 3.5, page 176.)

Work experience familiarizes caregivers with the more common childhood illnesses. Caregivers may feel they know quite a bit about illness, especially if they are parents themselves. Once they have seen a few children with chickenpox or head lice, they are able to identify pox marks or lice eggs. Parents in the program, particularly those with infants or toddlers, often view individual caregivers as consultants on a range of topics, including their child's health. Of course caregivers want to be helpful and can answer some health questions for parents. However, giving out medical information is overstepping their professional boundaries. Diagnosing illnesses and medical consultation are the roles of health professionals, not caregivers.

Excluding Children from Centres

If you ask caregivers to list the issues that they find to be the most challenging, ill children will probably be among the top three, perhaps even the first. If you are not a parent, you may have a hard time putting yourself into a parent's position. As discussed earlier, parents are in work or school situations and face a vast range of reactions and expectations from employers or teachers. Imagine yourself sitting in a board meeting, working on an assembly line, or writing an exam, and you are called away to take a phone call. Your child's caregiver tells you that your daughter is ill and you must pick her up as soon as possible to see the doctor. Not only are you going to be worried about your child but you are also faced with rescheduling your workday or class work, making a doctor's appointment, and returning to the centre. As a student, are you able to concentrate on your exam when you know that your daughter may be ill?

Most employers do not provide family responsibility leave for their employees. This benefit entitles parents with paid leave to attend to a child who is ill or other family emergencies. Currently, most parents either use their personal sick-leave benefits, if eligible, or leave work without pay. Others may risk losing their job if they leave work. Few parents have jobs that afford them the flexibility to work from home during a child's illness. Families often do not live in the same community as their extended family, who may have been able to relieve the parents in a crisis. Travelling between work and the centre and then to the doctor's office may not be convenient, especially on public transportation in the middle of a Canadian winter! On the other hand, for many of the same reasons, parents may feel pressured to bring their children to the centre in the morning, even if the child is not feeling well.

Child care programs are not considered to be an essential service by the general population or by the various levels of government. Labour laws do not require *all* employers to provide their employees with benefits that acknowledge the reality of working parents. Children do get sick and must be excluded from centres, and do need to see doctors during the day, and other family emergencies do occur that take employees away from their work.

Caregivers and parents are responsible for establishing a clear understanding of the centre's exclusion criteria at the time of enrollment. Unnecessary exclusion of children is unacceptable. With the exception of certain infections, *the primary reason for excluding children is that the child does not feel well enough to participate in the centre's activities* (see page 184). Staff–child ratios in centres are such that it is seldom

FORM 3.3	CENTRE'S HEALTH RECORD

Date:	Child's name:
Symptoms:	
Physician's diagnosis:	Exclusion:

Date:	Child's name:
Symptoms:	
Physician's diagnosis:	Exclusion:

Date:	Child's name:
Symptoms:	
Physician's diagnosis:	Exclusion:

Date:	Child's name:
Symptoms:	
Physician's diagnosis:	Exclusion:

Date:	Child's name:
Symptoms:	
Physician's diagnosis:	Exclusion:

FORM 3.4   CAREGIVER'S REPORT ON ILLNESS

Name of child: _____   Date: _____

Onset (time): _____   How long it has lasted? _____
Please specify symptom(s) (e.g., vomiting, diarrhea, pain, rash, sore throat, cough, runny nose, sore/stiff neck, trouble breathing, etc.):

_____

_____

_____

If taken: Temperature: _____   Circle: Oral / Rectal / Axillary   Time: _____
Any problems eating or drinking?

_____

Any problems with urinating or bowel movements?

_____

OTHER INFORMATION

List any new foods, animals, insects, medication, etc., the child was exposed to:

_____

_____

Please specify if this child has been in contact with other ill children:

_____

_____

What has been done for the child?

_____

_____

Comments:

_____

_____

Caregiver's signature: _____

Name of child care facility: _____

Telephone: _____

Source: Courtesy of the Canadian Paediatric Society. From *Well Beings* (Ottawa: Canadian Paediatric Society, 1996), 853.

possible to give a great deal of individual care to a sick child and still have enough staff to meet the needs of the other children. Also, where would you rather be when you are sick—in a centre with a group of energetic children and adults or at home with someone to bring you food and beverages and to care for your needs in quiet surroundings? Obviously, most children would prefer to be at home when they are ill.

Directors evaluate each situation individually. A director will think twice before she calls a parent to pick up her child when she knows that the parent works in a factory and has been warned about taking time off. However, a director is expected to give equal consideration before calling a parent who has a flexible work schedule. Who are the child care staff concerned about in managing illness?

▶ The ill child. Caregivers and the director want to ensure that the child is comfortable while in their care.
▶ Other children and staff. Caregivers may be concerned that the child's illness is contagious. Another concern may be the extent of one-to-one care that the ill child needs, and how this affects the quality of supervision available to other children.
▶ The ill child's parents. Caregivers and the director consider the effects of the child's illness on the family.

The centre's exclusion policy states that children are excluded when

1. an illness prevents the child from participating in routine activities
2. a child requires more individual care than the staff are able to provide without compromising the needs of the other children
3. a child risks infecting other children or caregivers as defined in the exclusion guidelines

Two children (Erik and Anastasia) in the preschool room have bad colds with runny noses and coughs and are irritable and lethargic. According to the third point, excluding children with colds is not recommended. (See also Appendix 3.1, page 209.) However, both children's behaviour is affected, so the director needs to consider the first two points of the exclusion policy. She must decide if she will

▷ call both sets of parents to come immediately to pick up their children, *or*

▷ call the parents and discuss what is in the best interests of each child. Erik's parents will be able to leave work in an hour and drop him off with his grandfather. Anastasia's mother is a single parent who recently moved to the city to attend university. She is in the middle of exam week. She is already stressed and has no one to help care for her daughter. The director and mother discuss the issue and decide that Anastasia will rest in the director's office for the afternoon. If she is still feeling unwell tomorrow, the director will arrange for a volunteer to come to the centre and care for her.

Each medical officer of health (MOH) in Canada is responsible for the health of children in centres within his or her geographic area. One of the responsibilities of the MOH is to establish the exclusion criteria for centres. These should be communicated to the physicians as well. There are usually several MOHs working in one province or territory. Because they work independently of one another, centres in different regions may be provided with different exclusion criteria. In some cases, neither centres nor physicians have received written criteria. So it is not surprising that there can be inconsistent expectations among everyone. In *Well Beings*, the Canadian Paediatric Society recommends exclusion criteria that centres, MOHs, and physicians are encouraged to implement. (See Appendix 3.1, page 209.)

Centres are required to have space available to temporarily isolate ill children. The director's office is often used, or a cot is set up in a quiet, separate part of the play or nap area that allows caregivers to supervise the resting child. The decision to keep the child in the centre until the end of the day is made by the director and caregivers. They base the decision on issues such as these:

► what the caregivers think is wrong with the child
► the time of day
► whether they feel they can care for the child

ALTERNATIVE CARE ARRANGEMENTS

There are times when children must be excluded from the centre. For some families this is a minor glitch in their schedule. For others it creates chaos. Centres require every family to have backup, or alternate, care available (e.g., relative, neighbour, friend) in the event that a child is ill. For parents who have neither job flexibility, nor relatives or friends available as backup, alternate care arrangements can be makeshift, unreliable, or inconsistent. This latter situation often puts directors in an awkward position: they know the ill child's home situation but must balance the needs of the other children and staff. In some instances the director may decide to keep the mildly ill child at the centre. In other cases, the director may have to exclude the child and the parents must deal with this decision.

CENTRES AND HEALTH SERVICES FOR ILL CHILDREN

The pressure experienced by parents trying to continue to work or go to school while managing the care of ill children has led to the establishment of centres and health care services specifically for ill children. These services can range from a centre that cares only for ill children to private nursing or trained caregivers who go into the child's home. The parents pay the cost of these services. In addition, the parents continue to pay the centre for the days that the child is excluded.

These services are relatively few, and they raise questions about the best interests of the ill child. No one disagrees that an ill child at home with a loving parent is best. And at best, these health services are feasible only for parents who can afford them. Parents who can't miss work, can't afford private care, and don't have access to alternate adults may be forced to leave a child at home alone—which may raise questions about neglect.

Caring for ill children is a political issue that has not been dealt with in any substantial way. Where does this situation leave children and families?

Childhood Infections: Just the Basics

Fortunately, most common childhood infections are short-lived and minor. Children become ill regardless of the disease prevention practices implemented in centres, but these practices do reduce the spread of infection. There are far more childhood infections than we have included in this textbook. Our focus is on health promotion in children, not on cures. As caregivers, your role is not to diagnose but to recognize potential signs of infection and refer children to health professionals. Caregivers can refer to a number of books and resources describing childhood infections once a physician has made a diagnosis. *Well Beings* is the resource manual of preference for Canadian centres and it includes fact sheets for parents on a variety of infections. Therefore, we have included only the common childhood infections. Understanding the basics and how to manage them addresses the needs of the ill child, parents, other children, and staff. Refer to Appendix 3.1 (page 209) for additional information about managing illness.

THE COMMON COLD

Children in centres can get as many as 8 or 10 colds a year. It may seem that at any one time at least one child has a runny nose or cough. Cold viruses, approximately 200 of them, are spread easily through the air and on contaminated hands and objects. That's why preventing colds is nearly impossible. Another reason is that we spread the cold virus a day or two before we feel a cold coming on. Typically, colds last five to seven days. Symptoms include coughing, sneezing, runny nose, fever, fatigue, and lack of appetite. A child's runny nose may produce a clear discharge at first and then a yellow or green one.

Q. Should children with colds be excluded from the centre?
A. No, not from the point of view of infection control. Can you imagine the havoc that would be created both in the centre and for the families if every child and caregiver with a cold were excluded? Instead, caregivers can

▶ wash their hands and the child's hands carefully
▶ model and encourage children to cover their mouth when they cough and sneeze
▶ discard used tissues after use and never use the same tissue to wipe more than one child's nose, tempting as reuse might be when you are out in the playground in the winter
▶ ensure that mouthing toys in infant and toddler areas are removed once a child has used them and that all these used toys are cleaned and sanitized daily
▶ observe those with colds to ensure that children are feeling well enough to take part in activities
▶ reassure parents that if their child feels well enough to be at the centre he or she is well enough to play outside, even in the winter (fresh air is good for the child)

FORM 3.5	PHYSICIAN'S REPORT ON ILLNESS

Name of child: _____   Date: _____

PART I

Diagnosis: _____

Medication(s) (give name, dosage and how many times a day it is to be taken)
Prescription(s): _____

Over-the-counter: _____

Note: If possible, please prescribe medications to be taken at times when the parents can administer them.

Recommendations for Parents and Caregivers

(Parents are encouraged to discuss any of your recommendations or restrictions of activities with the child care staff to determine if the child's specific needs can be accommodated.)

General: _____

_____

Diet: _____

_____

Level of activity: _____

_____

Date the child can return to child care (see Part II):

_____

Physician's signature: _____   Telephone: _____

PART II: Exclusion Criteria for Child Care Facilities

Physicians please note that reporting requirements to public health may vary between jurisdictions.

Disease	Exclusion	Report
Respiratory Tract Infections		
Colds with Fever/ Common Cold/*Otitis media*	*Do not* exclude unless too ill to take part in the activities.	No
Conjunctivitis	Exclude only if discharge is pus and then until the antibiotic has been taken for one full day.	No
Pneumonia	Exclude until evaluated by physician.	No
Strep Throat	Exclude until 24 hours after treatment begun.	No

(form continues on next page)

FORM 3.5 PHYSICIAN'S REPORT ON ILLNESS (continued)

Disease	Exclusion	Report
GastroIntestinal Infections		
Campylobacter/Giardia/ Rotavirus/*Salmonella*	Exclude until diarrhea is gone.	Yes
Diarrhea	Exclude until diarrhea is gone or physician determines child is not infectious.	Yes: *any* case of bloody or diagnosed bacterial diarrhea
Escherichia coli/Shigella	Exclude until diarrhea is gone and cultures are negative.	Yes
Food Poisoning	No exclusion required.	Yes
Hepatitis A	Exclude for 1 week after onset of jaundice. Immune globulin may be indicated for children, staff, and family members to control epidemic.	Yes
Norwalk Virus	Exclude until diarrhea and/or vomiting are gone.	Yes
Skin and Scalp Infections		
Head Lice	Exclude until treated. Removal of all nits may be necessary to cure some cases.	No
Herpes Simplex	Exclude for severe illness. Exclusion not indicated for recurrent cold sores.	No
Impetigo	Exclude until antibiotic treatment has started.	No
Scabies	Exclude until treated. Treatment of contacts may be necessary to control outbreak.	No
Other Infections		
Chickenpox	Exclude until 5th day after onset of rash or until all the blisters have crusted, whichever is shorter; may return sooner if illness is mild and able to take part in activities.	Yes
Cytomegalovirus	No exclusion required.	No
Hepatitis B	No exclusion required unless open sores are present. Hepatitis B vaccine and/or Hepatitis B immune globulin may be indicated under special circumstances.	Yes. Immediately report any bites that cause bleeding.
Measles	Exclude all cases until at least 4 days after onset of rash. Exclude the child who lacks proof of immunization until vaccinated or until 2 weeks after last case in the child care facility.	Yes. Immediately. Speed is essential in limiting outbreaks of measles.
Meningitis	Exposed children and adults may need antibiotics or vaccine.	Yes. Immediately.
Mumps	Exclude for 9 days; may return sooner if the illness is mild and able to take part in the activities. Ensure all children are vaccinated.	Yes
Pertussis	Exclude until 5 days after start of antibiotics or 3 weeks if no treatment given. Contacts may need antibiotics or vaccine.	Yes
Rubella	Exclude for 7 days after onset of rash. All adults should be vaccinated or have blood test to prove immunity. There is risk of severe damage to fetus if a pregnant woman gets rubella during the first trimester.	Yes
Shingles	Do not exclude if lesions can be covered; if uncovered, exclude until all blisters have crusted.	Yes

Source: Courtesy of the Canadian Paediatric Society. From *Well Beings* (Ottawa: Canadian Paediatric Society, 1996), 874–75.

EAR INFECTIONS

The eustachian tube that runs between the middle ear and the back of the nose is shorter and straighter in young children than in adults. The tube creates a path for fluid behind the middle ear to drain to the back of the throat. The straightness of the tube also permits fluid in the back of the throat and nose to travel into the ear. Ear infections often occur at the same time as colds, which seems logical, since coughing, sneezing, and blowing the nose can force mucus from the nose or throat into the eustachian tube and into the middle ear. The tube may become swollen, which prevents fluid from the middle ear from draining. In such cases, the trapped bacteria may cause infection. The Canadian Paediatric Society (1996, 139) esti-mates that "almost all children will have had one or more of these infections before 3 years of age." Children with language can tell you whether they have an earache; for infants you'll observe a change in behaviour—they often become cranky or unhappy. Parents and caregivers often comment that they see infants pulling or rubbing their ears, but this can be coincidental and shouldn't be relied on as a sign of infection. Physicians can confirm ear infection by looking into the child's ear. When children have ear infections, they are prescribed antibiotics and they should feel better in a couple of days.

Q. Should children with ear infections be excluded from the centre?
A. No. The infection is in the child's middle ear. The bacteria will not spread to other children or caregivers. If the child is prescribed antibiotics, he or she should be kept at home for 24 hours. During that period, the antibiotic will have begun to work and the child to feel better, and the parents can watch for any side effects or allergic reaction.

GASTROINTESTINAL INFECTIONS: DIARRHEA

Diarrhea is the most common symptom of gastrointestinal infection. Basically, diarrhea is a change in the consistency and/or frequency of an individual's bowel movements. The stool may be very loose or even watery. And—depending on the virus, bacteria, or parasite causing the infection—the stool may contain blood or mucus, and be foul-smelling, or mushy in consistency. In addition to the diarrhea, children may have abdominal cramps, fever, nausea, vomiting, or a loss of appetite. Others may just have a couple of loose stools and be fine otherwise.

Caregivers play an important role in preventing other children or staff from getting the infection. Diarrhea spreads easily among children and if other children do come down with it, the hygienic practices in that centre must be called into question. Effective hand-washing, strict diapering and toileting routines, and food safety every day, not just when someone is ill, are essential in reducing the spread of intestinal infection.

As caregivers become familiar with the infants and toddlers, they are able to notice any change in a particular child's bowel movements. Caregivers follow steps when caring for children with diarrhea:

▶ Tell the other caregivers that the child has had one episode of diarrhea. All the caregivers should be extra vigilant when hand-washing and diapering to ensure that stool does not contaminate the environment. The child can remain in the centre as long as the child feels well enough to participate and the stool is contained in the diaper (or the older child is able to get to the toilet in time). Parents appreciate being called so that they are aware of this situation.

▶ After the second episode of diarrhea, call the parents to pick up the child. If the child is less than six months old and/or has additional symptoms (such as a fever, loss of appetite, vomiting, blood or mucus in the stool), signs of dehydration (i.e., less than four wet diapers in 24 hours, no tears, dry skin, mouth, and tongue, sunken eyes, grayish skin, or a sunken soft spot on the head), or changes in behaviour, he or she must be seen by a physician as soon as possible (Canadian Paediatric Society 1996, 147).

▶ While waiting for the parents to arrive, prevent the child from becoming dehydrated. Children, especially infants and toddlers, can become dehydrated quickly because they lose more of their body fluids in diarrhea and vomit than they are able to drink. Pediatricians recommend that centres with infants and toddlers have oral rehydration solution (ORS) available for these situations. ORS is available in liquid or powder (e.g., Lytren, Gastrolyte, Pedialyte) and is used to replenish the child's fluid and electrolytes. Offer the child ORS every hour and after every loose bowel movement, either by bottle or in a cup. For infants on expressed breast milk, continue to bottle feed them on demand or at least every two hours. For formula-fed children and toddlers, stop their formula or food and beverages. The physician will advise the parents on the child's diet and fluid replacement (Canadian Paediatric Society 1994, 19–20). Do not offer the child sugary drinks such as fruit juice, pop, sweetened tea, or broth. These fluids do not contain the proper combination of water, salts, and sugar, and may in fact make the child's diarrhea worse (Canadian Pediatric Society 1996, 897).

▶ Notify the public health agency if two or more children have diarrhea within 48 hours of each other. These situations are called "outbreaks" and steps have to be taken to control the gastrointestinal infection, including determining the cause.

Q. Should children with two or more episodes of diarrhea be excluded from the centre?
A. Yes, children must stay home until the diarrhea stops and they have a normal bowel movement. If the diarrhea is caused by bacteria, the child will be prescribed antibiotics. Some children may return earlier if their physician determines that the germ is no longer in the stool (Canadian Paediatric Society 1996, 147–48). Refer to Appendix 3.1 (page 209) for the exclusion criteria that relate to the various types of gastrointestinal infections.

PINKEYE

Pinkeye (or conjunctivitis) is another childhood infection that is easily spread among children. The causes are viruses, commonly, and bacteria, occasionally. These infect the covering of the eyeball. However, children who have allergies or have been exposed to pollutants may develop pinkeye. Watch for the following symptoms in one or both eyes:

▶ The whites of the eye are pink or red.
▶ The child rubs the eye because it is itchy.
▶ The eye may be tearing a lot.
▶ There is a clear or pus (thick or yellow) discharge from the eye; the parents may tell you that the eyelid is stuck shut after sleeping.

Pinkeye is a good example of an infection caused by germs spread by indirect contact. A child with pinkeye touches or rubs her eyes; the eye discharge contaminates her fingers. During her activities, she touches other children's hands or objects, which in turn become contaminated. Now those children who have the eye discharge on their fingers and who touch their own eyes will get pinkeye. Sharing towels among children is another way that pinkeye is spread. The cycle continues until it is broken.

Q. Should children with pinkeye be excluded from the centre?
A. Maybe, depending on the cause of the pinkeye. The child's physician needs to see the child to diagnose the infection and determine the cause. When there is pus discharge, the child is usually prescribed an antibiotic (eyedrops or ointments) to treat the bacteria. If this is the case, children should be excluded until they have taken the medication for 24 hours. Otherwise, the child can return to the centre. Regardless of the cause, caregivers must pay particular attention to hygiene practices to reduce the spread to other children and staff.

▶ Effective hand-washing is critical, for both staff and the child, after wiping or touching the infected eye.

▶ Never share towels, facial tissues, and so on, among children regardless of whether someone has pinkeye.

CHICKENPOX

Chickenpox—a word that parents dread, though most of them want all the children in their family to get the illness at the same time and have done with it. For adults who did not have chickenpox as children, it's usually a much more serious infection.

Chickenpox is common in children because the varicella-zoster virus spreads easily through the air and by touching the liquid in the pox. When red bumps appear, children may have had a mild fever for a couple of days. Spots appear over two or three days. Gradually the bumps turn into liquid-filled blisters (or pox), which crust over. Some children may be covered in pox; others may have just a few. For many children, the infection is mild and the primary complaint is the itchiness of the pox. It takes 10 to 21 days to tell whether a susceptible person exposed to chickenpox is going to get it. Never give the child acetylsalicylic acid (e.g., Aspirin) to treat a fever or aches and pains from chickenpox.

Having chickenpox once provides most people with lifelong immunity to it, although some people get chickenpox twice. The virus can remain inactive in our bodies for life, but it can become reactivated and cause shingles. Children or adults with shingles can spread the virus to those susceptible to chickenpox. Shingles is a painful rash of itchy blisters, which often develop around the trunk of the body.

Q. Should someone with chickenpox or shingles be excluded from the centre?
A. Yes. It is recommended that children be excluded for five days after the rash (red bumps) appears or until all the pox have crusted over, whichever is shorter (Canadian Paediatric Society 1996, 164). Experts on infectious disease and experts on child care continue to struggle with the question of excluding children with chickenpox. Chickenpox is most infectious a couple of days before the rash appears. This means that while the virus is spreading, no one knows and everyone in the centre is exposed. Once the pox appear, what will excluding the child accomplish? Furthermore, the current exclusion recommendation leaves room for interpretation by centre staff. Unfortunately, this leads to inconsistencies among centres and even caregivers within a centre. Caregivers are advised to assess each child individually. What is in the best interests of this child? If the child feels well enough to take part in activities, or if you have enough staff available to provide more individualized care, the child can remain in the centre.

HEAD LICE

Having head lice does not reflect a lack of parenting ability or cleanliness, despite the old wives' tale to the contrary. Yet some adults and children still make derogatory comments about people with lice, which can be very hurtful. Children who have head lice may already feel embarrassed, fearful, or ashamed, and caregivers need to be sensitive to these feelings. Know the facts and effective ways to treat head lice, listen to parents' concerns, dispel stereotypes, and you can manage an outbreak.

Head lice are tiny, greyish insects that live on human hair. Usually they lay their eggs (or nits) on hair behind the ears, on the crown, or the back of the head. Nits look like dandruff but stick to the hair so that you can't pick or wash them off. You may first suspect head lice when you see a child scratching or complaining that his or her head is itchy. Check for nits on the hair, close to the scalp. The hatched lice shy away from light, so it is unlikely that you will actually see the lice. Although you may be scratching your head just thinking about lice, they actually don't hurt, spread disease, or jump between people. Head lice spread quickly when children have their heads together or share items such as combs, brushes, hats and scarves, headphones, and play clothes. Staff can reduce the opportunities for head lice to spread by

▶ providing space for each child to store his or her outerwear and a change of clothes without coming into contact with the next child's clothes (e.g., in a cubby/locker, or in bins/baskets, or on hooks)

▶ stuffing hats and scarves down coat sleeves, especially when coats are hung on hooks

▶ having parents provide a comb and/or brush for their child's personal use, to be kept in the child's space

▶ laundering dress-up clothes weekly. In the event of an outbreak of head lice, the clothes and accessories should be laundered and put away until the outbreak is over. The hats and wigs that can't be washed must be sealed in a plastic bag for 10 days. Dramatic play is an important element of child care programs, and wigs, hats, scarves, and dress-up clothes should be available for children despite the chance of head lice.

Basically, head lice are a nuisance that creates work for the centre's staff and parents at home. If you find one child or caregiver with head lice, you must check everyone. Then caregivers must notify all parents, especially those whose children have the lice. Head lice are easily treated with special shampoos and conditioners containing medication, a pediculicide (e.g., NIX). These products kill lice and nits and prevent reinfestation (if nits are not destroyed, they hatch in seven days). Parents can purchase NIX or check with their physician or pharmacist about different brands. Parents need to check every person in the household for nits but treat only those who have them. A cautionary note: Some brands of shampoo contain an ingredient called lindane. This chemical is toxic and can be absorbed through the scalp, leading to poisoning (Burroughs Wellcome n.d.).

Q. Should someone with head lice be excluded from the centre?
A. Yes. However, children or caregivers with head lice can return to the centre once they have been treated. Whether the centre has one child or 10 children with head lice, the centre must be cleaned the same way, including vacuuming, washing, sending children's clothes home for laundering, washing stuffed toys/puppets, and so on. Refer to the list provided in *Well Beings* or the public health agency for advice on dealing with head lice. Some public health authorities do not recommend extensive

environmental cleaning in family homes. However, because of the number of children and the amount of head-to-head social contact that occurs while children are playing, it is recommended that centres perform these tasks.

In the past, public health nurses were called into centres and schools to do "nit-picking" on every child. Nowadays, directors simply consult with their public health nurse and receive up-to-date information on prevention and treatment, perhaps in a number of languages. However, if a centre has recurring outbreaks of head lice or a particular child's parents are not responding to the centre's requests to use the treatment, the public health department should become directly involved.

Antibiotic-Resistant Bacteria

The discovery of penicillin was a medical breakthrough. Since then, more and more antibiotics have been developed for the treatment of bacterial infections. As a result, lives have been saved and the quality of lives improved. Ironically, pharmaceutical firms today are faced with the immediate challenge of discovering new, more potent antibiotics to be used to treat infections caused by bacteria resistant to previously effective antibiotics.

Levy (1998, 49) explains how antibiotics play a role in bacteria resistance:

When an antibiotic attacks a group of bacteria, cells that are highly susceptible to the medicine will die. But cells that have some resistance from the start, or that acquire it later (through mutation or gene exchange), may survive, especially if too little drug is given to overwhelm the cells that are present. Those cells, facing reduced competition from susceptible bacteria, will then go on to proliferate. When confronted with an antibiotic, the most resistant cells in the group will inevitably outcompete all others.

As you read earlier in this unit, bacteria live in our body and work to keep us healthy by fighting invading bacteria. When we take antibiotics, some of the beneficial bacteria are killed, which gives the diseasing-causing bacteria the opportunity to multiply and cause an infection. And there is the potential for the normal bacteria to become resistant to antibiotics too. Such resistance would, if conditions are right, enable the bacteria to multiply, creating an infection that would be difficult to treat because of the resistance.

Of course any person who has a bacterial infection should be treated with antibiotics. But the soaring overuse of antibiotics for non-bacterial infections (i.e., those caused by viruses) must stop. Treating a cold with antibiotics does not work—period. "Researchers at the Centers for Disease Control and Prevention have estimated that some 50 million of the 150 million outpatient prescriptions for antibiotics every year [in the U.S.] are unneeded" (Levy 1998, 50). Consider that in every developed country one-third of all antibiotics are probably prescribed unnecessarily, and that there are fewer controls on such prescriptions in developing countries, and that the use of antibiotics is widespread in livestock breeding and agriculture. Clearly the effect on antibiotic-resistant bacteria is staggering and is ringing alarm bells worldwide.

You may be asking yourself how this information relates to your work in child care centres. There is a direct correlation. We know

▶ that young children in groups are exposed to more illnesses
▶ that the additional needs of ill children in attendance make it difficult for care-givers to provide quality care for all children in the group
▶ that the exclusion of children may prevent others from getting sick

This last point is where caregivers should recognize the significant role they can play in decreasing the unnecessary use of antibiotics. These infections are common among young children; also, they are easily spread, and antibiotics are often used as a treatment for some upper-respiratory infections (URIs).

Well Beings' table on the management of illness (1996, 194–201) lays out clearly the recommended exclusion criteria and conditions for a child's return to a centre. (See Appendix 3.1, page 209.) As you can see, few respiratory illnesses require that a child be excluded in order to prevent the spread to other children. The most common reason for a child's exclusion is that she or he is too ill to participate in the centre's activities. Yet Skull et al. (1999) found the following practices in the Toronto centres that participated in their study:

Condition	Usually or always advise MD referral to parent		Usually or always exclude from child care for ...	
	Directors answering yes (%)	Correct	Directors answering yes (%)	Correct
Ear pain	30 (83%)	Yes	23 (64%)	No
Green/yellow runny nose	28 (78%)	No	20 (56%)	No
Cough with phlegm	23 (64%)	No	16 (44%)	No
Unusual behaviour	9 (25%)	Yes	15 (42%)	No
Sore throat	20 (56%)	Yes	11 (31%)	No
Clear runny nose	7 (19%)	No	7 (19%)	No
Dry cough	15 (42%)	No	5 (14%)	No

Source: Reprinted with permission from Dr. Susan Skull, Department of Pediatrics, Hospital for Sick Children, Toronto.

How do these exclusion practices impact on antibiotic use? If centres require parents to take their child to the doctor because of green nasal discharge (a common symptom of the common cold) and exclude their child from the centre, one may assume that staff will request that the child be on antibiotics before he or she can return. That is what Skull et al. (1999) found in their study. (The following extract is reprinted with permission of Dr. Susan Skull, Department of Pediatrics, Hospital for Sick Children, Toronto.)

> Appropriately, antibiotics were most often believed necessary for streptococcal sore throat (97%), ear infection (94%) and sinus infection (83%). However, antibiotics were also believed necessary by some for bronchitis (83%), cough (39%), non-streptococcal sore throat (33%), colds (19%) and "flu" (17%). Staff believed antibiotics were required in a child with non-specific URI to prevent bacterial infection (13/34, 38%), to prevent spread of infection (9/34, 26%) and to hasten recovery (7/34, 21%). Holding these beliefs was significantly more likely to result in a request for children to commence antibiotic therapy before returning to day care.

There are other practices—in addition to having caregivers understand the principles behind exclusion—that staff can implement in the centre to reduce infections:

▶ proper-hand washing. Ying et al. (1998, 310) found that 15 percent of the centres they studied did not meet the recommendations in *Well Beings*.

▶ proper diaper changing routine. Ying et al. (1998, 310) found that 2 percent of centres did not have a specific diapering policy/routine to follow and 8 percent had inadequate routines.

▶ proper food-handling practices. These include including washing off bacterial and possible antibiotic residue from fruits and vegetables.

▶ the observation of children's behaviour as a key indicator of illness. Skull et al. (1999) found that only 25 percent of the staff referred children to their doctor for this reliable sign of illness.

▶ practising the principles of universal precautions. Ying et al. (1998, 310) found that 62 percent of supervisors/directors were either unaware of the term "universal precautions" or lacked an accurate understanding of the term.

▶ the purchase and use of cleaning and hand-washing products that are *not* advertised to be antibacterial.

> … standard soaps and detergents (without added antibacterials) decrease the numbers of potentially troublesome bacteria perfectly well. Similarly, quickly evaporating chemicals—such as the old standbys of chlorine bleach, alcohol, ammonia, and hydrogen peroxide—can be applied beneficially. They remove potentially disease causing bacteria … but they do not leave long-lasting residues that will continue to kill benign bacteria and increase the growth of resistant strains long after target pathogens have been removed. (Levy 1998, 48)

We need to all understand when antibiotics are necessary and when they are not. When prescribed an antibiotic, follow the instructions and take the entire prescription. Do not stop taking a prescription once you start feeling better and then save the medication for later use, either by yourself or by someone else.

Administering Medication

Fortunately, most healthy children need medication rarely or not at all. And most of the common childhood infections are caused by viruses (e.g., colds, other upper-respiratory infections, diarrhea) that are not cured by antibiotics. Strep throat, ear infections, and sometimes pinkeye are caused by bacteria that are treated with antibiotics. Occasionally, caregivers administer medication to children in centres. Caregivers have a legal and professional responsibility to be familiar with their child care regulations on administering medication. You must know which medications caregivers are permitted to give, what type of parental consent is required, and how medications are stored, administered, and documented. Centres' medication policy should be accompanied by a list of procedures that all caregivers follow.

As an ECE student, you cannot administer medication to children when you are in centre placements; that remains a staff responsibility. After graduation you will eventually be assigned this role, however, so you need to be familiar with the fundamental principles of, and rationale for a medication policy.

PRESCRIPTION AND OVER-THE-COUNTER MEDICATIONS

What is the difference between prescription and over-the-counter (OTC) medication? We are all familiar with physicians prescribing medication when we have a short-term illness (e.g., urinary tract infection, yeast infection, strep throat, ear infection). Anyone with a particular medical condition, such as asthma, diabetes, cystic fibrosis, or a seizure disorder, is prescribed medication that is taken at specific times each day. On the other hand, over-the-counter medication is purchased off a shelf in a pharmacy. These medications include cough and cold remedies, painkillers, teething medication (e.g., Orajel), Ovol for flatulence in infants, and medicated creams and ointments.

Child care regulations require that all medication administered in centres be prescribed or, for OTC medication, recommended in writing by physicians. Some provincial/territorial child care regulations may include sunscreens, insect repellents, and diaper creams in their definition of medication and require that the child's physician recommend their use in writing. However, this is the exception rather than the rule across Canada. Why do OTC drugs require the physician's recommendation in writing before they are administered in child care centres? OTC medications are medications nonetheless and should not be treated casually. Whenever you take more than one medication at the same time, you put yourself at risk of side effects, because the ingredients from the different medications may interact. As well, drug interactions may influence the effectiveness of the medications.

Vitamins, including chewable ones, are medications. Eating well-balanced, nutritious food provides children with their daily requirement of essential nutrients. Physicians discourage the routine use of vitamins; they are prescribed only when a child has a vitamin or mineral deficiency. Prescribed vitamins can be given at home by parents. Caregivers do not have to administer the vitamins during the day.

Naturopathic and homeopathic medicine have been practised for centuries in many cultures and are gaining popularity in Canada. Herbal medicines, nutrition, vitamins, ointments, acupuncture, and hydra- and physical therapies are used to treat various maladies. Herbal medicines consist of different combinations of herbs and plants that are available over the counter or prescribed by naturopaths. As with any medication, they must be taken with care and knowledge. According to child care regulations' definition, medications must be prescribed by physicians or dentists— classifications that do not currently include naturopathic doctors. Consequently, parents who have herbal medicines for their children must give them to the children at home. Centre staff, currently, can't give these medications to the child at the centre.

Over-the-Counter Medications: Effective?

Many pediatricians do not recommend using OTC remedies for children (Canadian Paediatric Society 1996). Colds have to run their course. Children benefit from extra fluids, rest, and care, but not from many of the OTC medications. Smith and Feldman (1993, 2262) published a critical review of clinical studies on OTC cold medications. "Over-the-counter cold medications form a common part of every-day medical therapy," they wrote. "The data on their effectiveness are limited and weak, especially for children." Taylor et al. (1993, 801) studied the effectiveness of treating children's nighttime coughing with one medication containing codeine, another containing dextromethorphan, and a placebo: "The results of our study demonstrate that by 3 days after a visit to a paediatrician because of cough symptoms, the cough will be significantly reduced regardless of specific therapy." Hutton et al. (1991) reached a similar conclusion.

When a child is up all night coughing, parents often feel less helpless by giving cough syrup. But besides the ineffectiveness of such medication, other issues should be considered. In 1990, the fourth most common call made by parents to the Poison Information Centre at the Hospital for Sick Children concerned children ingesting cough and cold medications. The medications are colourful and tasty, and the liquid preparations do not come with child-resistant caps (which are *not* child-proof anyway). Children can experience mild to serious side effects from OTC cold medications (Correspondence 1984; Pender and Parks 1991; Smith and Feldman 1993).

We also wonder whether children who are given an OTC medication for every sniffle, cough, ache, or pain could potentially develop a lifelong reliance on medication. These medications treat symptoms, not the cause of the illness. We should focus instead on preventive strategies and, when we are ill with a viral infection, let the illness run its course.

Acetaminophen (e.g., Tylenol, Tempra) is an analgesic (or painkiller) and may be recommended by physicians for treating children's aches and pains from a cold and cough. Centres with infants and toddlers still commonly give acetaminophen whenever the child's temperature rises to certain degree. In these centres, parents are asked to sign a medication consent form, which is kept in the child's file and referred to each time the child's temperature is elevated. It is unlikely that each child's physician has provided the parents and caregivers with such a written recommendation. This practice shows how grey the interpretation of a specific child care regulation can be. (See Fevers, page 160.)

Ensuring the Safe Administration of Medication

Whether the medication is prescribed or recommended by the child's physician, the steps in its administration are identical to eliminate the chance of medication error. Following are the general principles and rationale for the administration of medication in centres:

▶ Obtain the parents' written consent to administer any medication. A medication consent form must be completed for *each* medication, both prescribed and physician-recommended. Consent forms should include at least the following information:
  ▷ name of the child and date
  ▷ name of the medication
  ▷ reason why it is needed (e.g., strep throat)
  ▷ amount to be given (dosage)
  ▷ time(s) it is to be given during the day
  ▷ time and date of the last dose in the centre. This is helpful to ensure that children don't continue to get medication longer than recommended by the doctor. This is particularly relevant to OTC medication, since the bottle holds more medication than required for two or three days (e.g., liquid cough syrup).
  ▷ parent's signature
▶ Before starting the medication at the centre, ask parents whether the child has taken it at home for the past 24 hours. This period allows parents to watch for side effects or signs of allergic reaction to the medication, for the child to get used to the way it tastes or feels (e.g., eye ointment), and for the medication to begin its work. Parents may have a helpful hint or two to share.
▶ Keep all medication in a locked container out of reach of children. Liquid medications usually require refrigeration, which won't harm capsules, tablets, or creams either. All can be kept in a locked container in the fridge. Sunscreens, insect repellents, and diaper creams do not have to be kept locked, but must be out of reach of children. Diaper creams are kept in the change area.
▶ Know who is responsible for giving the medication during the day. Centres usually assign this responsibility either to one caregiver who gives all the medications or to a number of caregivers who give medication to specific chil-

dren. Any confusion over this responsibility can lead to a child either getting a double dose or missing the medication altogether.

▶ Compare the information on the medication label with the information the parent filled in on the consent form. Discrepancies must be verified and corrected.

▶ *All medication, both prescription and OTC, must be in the original containers.* It is not acceptable, for example, for a parent to pour cough syrup into a glass jar and label it with masking tape. Prescription labels must include
  ▷ child's name (not a sibling's)
  ▷ name of the medication
  ▷ the dose (amount)
  ▷ the number of times it is given each day
  ▷ route (oral, nasal, rectal, eye, ear, injection)
  Sometimes pharmacists place stickers on the container with additional information: "Shake well," "Take with meals," "May cause a photosensitive reaction."

▶ Follow the steps provided in the centre's medication policy for preparing, giving, and recording medication. Know the procedure for reporting and responding to medication errors.

▶ When children have medication allergies, post the children's names and pictures and the names of the drugs at the place where medication is stored and prepared.

▶ For children who are prescribed adrenalin injections (e.g., Anakit, EpiPen) or inhalers (e.g., Bronkaid Misto-Meter) to treat allergic reactions, always have the medication in the same general area as the child. You have just read that all medication must be kept in a locked container. Adrenalin is an exception. Although it should be out of reach of children—perhaps in the first-aid kit in the play area—caregivers must be able to access and administer this medication on a moment's notice. If a child has a severe allergy to insect stings or other allergens found outside, you must take medication to the playground, on walks, and so on. For children with severe food allergies, take it outside only if the child might eat something there (e.g., picnic lunch or snack, on a field trip). All caregivers must know how to administer adrenalin. It is an emergency when a child needs adrenalin, so caregivers don't have time to look for the caregiver responsible for giving medication. Ask the pharmacist for the manufacturer's poster that shows how to give the injection. Caregivers may also be required by the child care regulations to receive training on injections from a health professional or the parents. In any case, auto-injectors are simple to use. (See Allergies, page 192.)

▶ Remember the following tips when you give medication to a child:
  ▷ Be honest with the child (e.g., if you don't know how the medication tastes, admit it).
  ▷ Especially for young children, the child who receives the medication should know and be comfortable with the caregiver administering it.
  ▷ Explain to the child what you are going to do and how he or she can cooperate.

▷ Never call medicine "candy." Medicines are potentially hazardous products and children must learn how to take medications safely.
▷ Give the child the medication away from the other children.

Preventing Medication Errors

Medication errors—such as giving medication to a child who wasn't prescribed a drug, mixing up medications among children, giving an incorrect dosage, or putting ear drops in the wrong ear—can occur for a number of reasons. The consequences of such errors range from minor to very serious. However, you can go through your child care career without making any medication errors.

Medication errors result when one or more of the "five rights" has not been verified:

► right child
► right medication
► right dose (amount)
► right time
► right route (oral, nasal, rectal, eye, ear, injection)

Safeguards:

► Always use a measuring spoon, dropper, or cup that is designed for medication.

- ► Check the sheet you use to record the administration of medication to ensure that no one has already given the drug to the child.
- ► Read the prescription label three times:

    1. when you take the medication out of the storage space
    2. before you pour the medication from the bottle
    3. after you pour it and are putting the bottle back in storage

    During the three checks, compare the prescription label to the parents' medication consent form. Verify that all of the "five rights" are correct.

- ► If a child tells you that someone else has already given him or her the drug, or that he or she is no longer taking the parents' medication, double-check with the other caregivers. Another caregiver could have given the drug and not recorded it, or the drug may have been stopped and the parent forgotten to tell you.
- ► Immediately record that you gave the medication on the parents' medication consent form.
- ► Document and report *every* medication error as soon as you are aware of it.

Assessing the situation:
How do we help school-agers understand that expectations differ for them between the school and the child care program? And how do caregivers in school-age programs advocate for change in child care regulations to bring these programs into line with the school, to create the "seamless day"?
Scenario: During school hours, school-agers with asthma or life-threatening allergies are encouraged to be responsible for their own Ventolin puffer or adrenalin kit and to carry it with them. However, while they are in the school-age program, caregivers are responsible for these medications.

Parents should be encouraged to tell caregivers when their children are taking medication at home, even when staff don't need to give the drug during the day. Caregivers may notice that the child is experiencing side effects such as dizziness or fatigue and can notify the parents, who can then talk with their physician.

Allergies and Asthma

► **OBJECTIVE**   To understand the importance of working with parents in the daily management of asthma and allergies.

Perhaps you have allergies or asthma. Lots of us do. In fact, experts estimate that about 10 to 15 percent, possibly even 20 percent, of children have asthma (Asthma Society of Canada 1993, 7). It is estimated that one in 10 people have been tested for allergies and are receiving treatment. However, one in four people believe they have allergies but haven't been tested. One in 100 people have severe allergies.

The number of children and adults with allergies and asthma is increasing. Environmental pollutants and sick-building syndrome are playing a significant role in this increase. We can assume that every centre has at least one child with allergies or asthma. As such, caregivers must be aware of these health conditions, and know how to avoid factors that trigger reactions and how to handle reactions when they occur. Depending on their age, children with allergies or asthma may wish to talk with other children about the illness, about how they feel when they get sick, about what they do to make themselves feel better, or about their hospital experiences. These opportunities are wonderful and natural times for children to learn about health.

Allergies

Basically, allergies are the result of our body's hypersensitivity to a substance(s). These substances are not usually harmful to most people (e.g., pollen, peanuts, feathers, animal fur); but for those with allergies, they can cause mild to severe allergic reactions.

Fortunately, most allergies are not life-threatening. The substances that cause allergies, called allergens, enter our body through breathing, eating, touching, or being stung or bitten. Once the allergen is in the body, our immune system responds by producing antibodies that attack it. These antibodies remain in our body to protect us the next time we are exposed to that allergen, providing immunity. But for people with allergies, repeated exposure to an allergen results in their immune system's becoming overly sensitive to that particular allergen. An allergic reaction results when the person is exposed to the allergen and the body produces chemicals such as histamines, which cause various physical symptoms (or reactions) such as sneezing, runny nose, vomiting, tightness in the chest, or hives. Table 3.4 lists allergens that are responsible for allergic reactions.

Allergic reactions can cause feelings of fear, discomfort, or anxiety in children and their parents. The goal should be to maintain as normal a lifestyle as possible. It is important to balance supporting a child's awareness of his or her allergens with knowing what to do if the child is exposed and avoiding overwhelming fear and excessive limits on the child's activities.

Most of the symptoms listed in Table 3.4 are from four of the body systems: upper and lower respiratory tract, skin, eyes, and gastrointestinal tract. The more body systems that are affected by an allergen, the more severe the allergic reaction. Severe allergic reactions are most commonly caused by peanuts and nuts, eggs, shellfish, bee and wasp stings, penicillin, and aspirin. In a severe allergy to bee sting, for example, the first sting results in a significant reaction. Any subsequent sting, however, could be fatal. When children are diagnosed with severe allergies, the physician prescribes adrenalin (e.g., Anakit, EpiPen, Bronkaid Misto-Meter) to be administered in the event of severe allergic reaction. In these instances, parents are required to provide the centre with an adrenalin kit.

The most severe allergic reaction is called anaphylactic shock, which affects the entire body. *This reaction happens quickly*. Within seconds the child's eyes, lips, and

TABLE 3.4   COMMON ALLERGIC SUBSTANCES AND REACTIONS

COMMON ALLERGIC SUBSTANCES	TYPICAL REACTIONS
Environmental dust, mould, pollen, grass, trees*	itchy eyes and nose, nasal discharge, blocked nasal passages, sinus headache, sneezing, wheezing, coughing, shortness of breath
Animals and Bird fur, feathers	itchy eyes and nose, nasal discharge, etc.
Insects stings from bees and wasps	wheezing, hives, swelling of upper airway with difficulty breathing, and in extreme cases swelling of face and anaphylactic shock
Foods eggs, peanuts, nuts, shellfish, milk, and wheat (the latter two are common causes of infant allergies)	vomiting, diarrhea, bloody stools, plus symptoms as for insect venom (such as hives, pallor, weakness, difficulty breathing, and collapse)
Medications and Chemicals medical (e.g., antibiotics) and non-medical (e.g., fabric softener)◊	any of the above reactions

* Poison ivy and poison oak cause allergic reactions in the majority of us when we touch these plants.
◊ Latex in balloons, gloves, condoms, and dental dams can cause reactions in some people.

Source: Reprinted with permission from Canadian Paediatric Society, *Well Beings* (Ottawa: Canadian Paediatric Society, 1996), 252.

face begin to swell, he or she may get a headache, hives may appear all over the body, the throat may swell and cut off the breathing, and he or she may vomit and have diarrhea. Finally the child becomes unconscious. All of this can happen in less than 10 minutes. *Caregivers must identify these symptoms immediately, administer the child's adrenalin, and call an ambulance. To save the child's life, further emergency medical care is needed.* Even if you aren't sure about the child's allergic symptoms, always give adrenalin to the child and call an ambulance. Parents should be encouraged to obtain a medical alert bracelet for any child who has been diagnosed with severe allergies. The bracelet must be worn at all times.

There is no cure for allergies. We must try to prevent the reactions by eliminating exposure to allergens whenever possible (e.g., peanuts, shellfish, animals) or at least limiting exposure to allergens (e.g., smoke, dust, pollen). The only treatment for allergies is to alleviate or reduce the effect of the symptoms (e.g., runny noses, itchy red eyes, nasal and sinus congestion) with medications such as antihistamines and decongestants. During hay fever season, children with hay fever may be more comfortable playing outside in the afternoon, because most plants pollinate in the morning.

Preventing Allergic Reactions

First, effective communication is essential between caregivers and parents to prevent allergic reactions. At the time of enrollment, parents must be asked for the following information about their children's allergies: the names of the allergen(s) and the specific symptoms, steps to prevent exposure to the allergen, what actions the caregivers should take when a child has symptoms, and what medication the physician has prescribed or recommended. Caregivers and parents can then develop an allergy care plan that meets the child's needs.

The centre's policy and preventive practices on allergies should include

► a medical form completed by the child's physician outlining the management of the allergies, what caregivers need to be aware of, and any instructions on handling emergency situations

► the sharing of allergy information with all staff members:
  ▷ A list of children with their allergies should be posted in the kitchen and eating areas. Adding photos of each child to the list ensures that children are not exposed to known allergens, especially when volunteers, students, and substitute caregivers enter the program.
  ▷ Add the pertinent allergy information to the emergency information cards kept in the first-aid kits.
  ▷ Caregivers may also find it useful to attach an allergy list to the top of the first aid kit used outdoors (i.e., on the playground, field trips, walks) that focuses on children who are allergic to substances found outside, such as bees, wasps, animal hair, and feathers. Caregivers can quickly refer to this list to prevent or respond to allergic reactions. Caregivers can also refer to the list before they leave, to make sure they take the adrenalin kits outside for those children who have been prescribed one. *The adrenalin kit must be in the same general area as the child.* Caregivers do not have time to go back to the centre and then return to the playground to give the injection. Remember, anaphylactic shock happens very quickly and caregivers cannot lose vital seconds to respond. (See Ensuring the Safe Administration of Medication, page 188.)

► an awareness of how food is purchased, prepared, and served. The cooks or caregivers responsible for snacks and meals must know which children have food allergies, read all the ingredients on labels, and so on. Use extreme caution for children with allergies to peanuts and peanut products. Caregivers must take parents' concerns very seriously, since for some children even the smell of peanuts or trace amounts of grated nuts in a cookie can cause anaphylactic shock.

► the posting of menus for parents to make substitutions for foods or food ingredients to which their child is allergic. When the centre provides substitute foods, try to offer foods that look similar to those the other children are having. This can help to normalize eating experiences for children with food allergies.

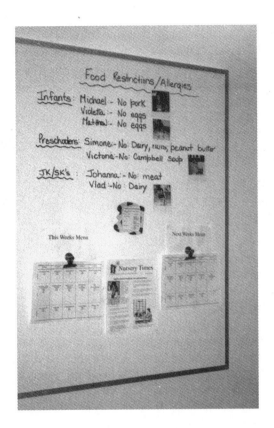

▶ the documenting of all allergic reactions in the child's file. The child's parents must be contacted.

Eighty percent of allergies develop before the age of 5. To ensure children's safety, centres need to

▶ require all parents to give their children prescribed or OTC medication for 24 hours before caregivers administer it in the centre. This allows parents to determine whether their child has any side effects or allergic symptoms.
▶ outline how new foods are introduced to promote early awareness of allergies. This is particularly important for infants. (See The Process of Introducing Semi-Solid Foods, page 254.)
▶ as a general practice, try to use unscented laundry and cleaning products and encourage staff not to wear perfumes and colognes, which many people are sensitive to.

Asthma

When someone has asthma, the mucous membrane that lines the lungs' airways is chronically inflamed, which narrows the airways (or bronchial tubes). The membranes produce more mucus, which is stickier than normal, resulting in less space in the airways for air to pass through. The cause of the tissue's chronic inflammation is not known.

Asthma varies in severity and is diagnosed when children have recurring episodes of wheezing, coughing, or shortness of breath. Wheezing has been considered the classic asthma symptom. Some people with asthma have a chronic dry cough rather than a wheeze, so their asthma may go undiagnosed because the wheezing can't be heard over the coughing. "The most common reason for a preschooler to be admitted to hospital for a respiratory condition is asthma. In fact, the rate of admission for asthma among preschoolers has increased by almost 25% over the last decade" (Canadian Institute of Child Health 1994, 41). The Asthma Society of Canada reports that deaths from asthma are increasing—approximately 10 Canadians die each week due to asthma. A startling 80 percent of these deaths could have been prevented through appropriate education.

About 50 percent of cases of children's asthma are mild; these children may exhibit symptoms only two or three times a year. Often these symptoms are triggered by colds. The child is prescribed medication for the duration of the symptoms. The medication is stopped after recovery. Other children with moderately severe asthma have episodes (or attacks) every four to six weeks and may even be hospitalized several times a year. These children take medication every day. Only about 5 percent of children have asthma severe enough that they experience symptoms almost daily, take several medications, and may find it difficult to exercise (Canny and Levison 1993, 12–13). Severe asthma episodes can be life-threatening and even fatal, because the airway completely closes and no air can get to the lungs.

The mucous membranes are more sensitive to allergens (e.g., dust mites, pollen, mould, grass, trees, and weed pollens), substances (e.g., air pollution, perfume, cologne, paint fumes, chemicals, tobacco smoke), cold weather, strenuous exercise (episodes in this connection are referred to as exercise-induced asthma [EIA]), upper-respiratory infection, colds, emotional upset, sudden changes in the atmosphere or weather, and food additives and preservatives. Any of these may irritate the mucous membranes and trigger an asthma episode. Viral infections are the most common asthma trigger in infants (Frieri 1998, 17). The child has to work hard at breathing because the muscles around the airway tighten, and the lining swells further and produces more sticky mucus. The child may cough frequently, wheeze, breathe at a faster rate, and complain that the chest feels tight, and may have behaviour changes (e.g., tiredness, restlessness, irritability).

Identifying and managing the triggers of the child's asthma episodes is the first line of prevention. Caregivers can work with the children's parents to identify triggers, to remove or at least reduce exposure to allergens, and to administer prescribed medications. The three most common allergens for children are dust mites' feces, pollen, and cat dander. For some children, even being around another child who has a cat at home and comes to the centre or school with cat hair on his or her clothes can irritate the airways. Dust mites thrive in warm, humid places, live off human skin scales, and can be found on pillows and mattresses, carpets, cloth-covered furniture, and soft toys. Caregivers can reduce the number of dust mites in centres by regularly dusting, vacuuming, and laundering cloth toys. Many allergens and irritants are found outdoors (e.g., pollens, fumes, tobacco smoke) and in public places and are more difficult to reduce or alleviate. Germs can grow in the water of humidifiers, which then spread them through the air. If humidifiers are used, particularly in the dry winter months, daily maintenance must be performed.

Children with asthma are often prescribed medications. Two of the more frequently prescribed are Ventolin and Beclovent, which are administered by aerosol inhaler (or puffer), Diskhaler, Rotahaler, Turbuhaler, or nebulizer. Younger children often use an AeroChamber because they are not developmentally able to exhale all the air, and then pump the puffer and breathe in one puff of the medication in one breath. Most individuals are prescribed two or three puffs. At one end of the chamber is the hole where the mouthpiece of the puffer is inserted; the face mask is on the other end. The mask is placed over the child's mouth and nose, one puff of the medication is pumped into the chamber, and the child breathes in the medication over at least six breaths. Before the second puff, the child needs to wait one minute to allow the medication to travel through the air passages. This wait between puffs applies to all ages and all types of inhaler.

The nebulizer is not as often used anymore. It runs on electricity and pumps a fine mist through tubing and into a face mask. It usually takes about 15 minutes, and a caregiver would have to supervise the child during that time.

Commonly, Ventolin is taken not regularly but either during an episode or to prevent one—for example, 10 to 30 minutes before participating in a strenuous activity. This medication is a bronchodilator, which quickly helps to relax the bronchial spasms/twitching of the bronchial walls so that the child can breathe more easily. It is referred to as a "reliever." Beclovent is an anti-inflammatory medication (a "preventer") that is taken one to four times daily, depending on the severity of the asthma. This medication treats the chronic inflammation of the mucous membranes. With less swelling, the person with asthma breathes easier and may be less likely to be irritated by triggers. Some children are prescribed both medications to be taken regularly every day. They take Ventolin first to relax the airways and create more space so that the Beclovent can travel farther into the lungs. After the Beclovent, children must have a drink or rinse their mouth to remove residue from the mucous membranes in the mouth and throat in order to reduce the possibility of developing chronic thrush.

TABLE 3.5   SIGNS OF MANAGED AND POORLY MANAGED ASTHMA

MANAGED ASTHMA	POORLY MANAGED ASTHMA[1]
Sleep is not disturbed by cough, wheeze, or shortness of breath.	The number of symptoms increases: wheezing, coughing, and shortness of breath, along with a decreased capacity to exercise and/or go about your daily activities.
You don't have symptoms when you wake up.	The use of inhaled bronchodilators increases (i.e., you're not getting relief from the usual amount of medication).
Symptoms during the day are immediately and completely reversed with a bronchodilator inhaler.	The peak expiratory flow rates decreases.[2]
A bronchodilator inhaler is not needed more than twice a day on most days.	Sputum production increases or sputum changes colour (e.g., yellow, green, brown).
Symptoms do not interfere with day-to-day activities, including physical activity.	Nighttime or early-morning awakenings require use of the bronchodilator.

[1]If you experience any of the following warning signs, your asthma is out of control and you should adjust your medication and/or contact your doctor.

[2]A peak-flow meter is a hand-held device that you blow into to get a reading of how rapidly you can blow out. The meter measures "peak flow rate," or forced exhalation. The meter helps individuals manage their asthma and helps in the detection of worsening airway obstruction and asthma. Not everyone needs to use a peak-flow meter.

Source: Reprinted with permission from The Lung Association, *The Asthma Handbook* (1994), 6, 2.

The centre's policy and practices for the care of children with asthma should include

▶ providing parents with a medical form for the child's physician to complete, which outlines the management of the asthma, what caregivers must be aware of, and any instructions on medication and emergency situations. Have parents provide you with a copy of the child's asthma action plan.

▶ sharing this medical information with the child's caregivers

▶ observing the child during strenuous play and in cold weather. If the child starts wheezing or coughing or is short of breath, stop the activity. If the weather is cold or damp, bring the child inside. Have the child sit down to use the bronchodilator (e.g., Ventolin). Regular exercise is just as important for children with asthma as it is for other children; however, it is important to discuss the child's specific needs for exercise or being outside in the winter.

▶ documenting in the child's file all asthmatic episodes and contacting the child's parents. If an episode doesn't subside after two consecutive treatments of the bronchodilator medicine, the child should be seen by a physician as soon as possible.

Revisiting the Health Promotion Action Plan

Recall the Action Blueprint for Health Promotion introduced in Unit 1. The following example illustrates this plan in practice in terms of preventing and managing childhood illnesses.

Individual Problem-Solving and Self-Reliance Each day, caregivers have the opportunity to positively influence individual children's health by implementing the centre's infection control strategy. Granted, children get sick, and even if they are ill for only a few days the whole family's schedule can be disrupted. Health policies and practices should be supportive, empathetic, and respectful of parents' situations, and they should take into account the centre's responsibility for the health of the other children. We often forget that centres are also employers and, as such, the centre's board can demonstrate a commitment to employees' families by providing family responsibility leave for staff and permitting staff to bank overtime hours.

Collective Self-Help Centre directors can benefit from developing a pool of substitute caregivers and/or volunteers who can be called on when

▶ a child is mildly ill but stays at the centre and needs extra attention

▶ a caregiver is absent due to illness

▶ a centre needs extra adults (volunteers or paid), who come in for a few hours each day to cover busier times (e.g., meals, staff break times)

▶ a field trip is planned or an activity needs additional supervisors

Ideally, volunteers and substitutes are in the centre often enough that the children and the adults get to know one another. When they are approached by centre staff, these trusted adults may be interested in providing care for the mildly ill child in the family's home or in their own home when the need arises. For parents who don't have access to alternative (or backup) care, this service could be extremely valuable. In communities where there are a cluster of centres in close proximity, directors could work collaboratively to support families and their staff.

Community Action   Centre staff have identified the need for a community service that provides care for mildly ill children. Either on an individual basis or with a collective of centres, caregivers could advocate to a local agency to develop such a service (e.g., Victorian Order of Nurses [VON]). In communities with only one or two main employers, most, if not all, of the parents who use the centre(s) work for the same company. The centre's board could meet with the company's management to discuss establishing family responsibility leave for their employees. Perhaps the local public health agency would work cooperatively with the centre and the company.

Societal Change   As a member of your provincial/territorial and/or national child care association (e.g., Saskatchewan Child Care Association, Canadian Child Care Federation), caregivers collectively lobby the government to legislate employers to provide family responsibility leave. Individual caregivers can exercise their democratic right (and responsibility) to vote for political candidates who are committed to child care and the family.

Conclusion

One of the primary goals of high-quality child care programs is to maintain or improve the health status of children, which contributes to their growth and development and participation in the centres' program and activities. Indicators of a quality child care program include adequate caregiver–child ratios, small group sizes, staff trained in early childhood education, the provision of orientation and regular in-service training, and low staff turnover rates. These need to be in place to control infectious diseases.

The consistent implementation of an infection control strategy is one of the best ways to prevent infections or at least reduce their spread in centres. Such a strategy includes effective hand-washing as a priority for both caregivers and children to break the chain of transmission. It is inevitable, however, that children experience some childhood illness. In cooperation with parents, caregivers address the needs of the ill child yet consider the best interests of the other children and staff.

WHAT'S YOUR OPINION?
TO COLLABORATE OR NOT TO COLLABORATE?

The school-age program is located inside the elementary school. One part-time caregiver works in the afternoon and after school. Two full-time caregivers work in the centre, preparing activities and planning the curriculum in the morning, and working with children from the half-time kindergarten class in the afternoon. Classroom teachers often expect the caregivers to care for any mildly ill child who is also enrolled in the school-age program rather than call the parents or keep the child in the classroom until the end of class. At times, the caregivers manage to accommodate an older ill child in the afternoon. As a result, the teachers expect the caregivers to be responsible for ill children and to notify parents when the child becomes ill in the classroom. Caregivers feel resentment toward these teachers.

The teachers and caregivers need to work cooperatively and collaboratively. Debate both sides of the issue from the perspective of the teachers and the caregivers. How can this issue be resolved in a way that is in the best interests of the children? Design a policy and procedures for the management of ill school-agers that can be used by teachers and caregivers. Don't overlook the parents.

► A S S E S S   Y O U R   L E A R N I N G

Define terms or describe concepts used in this unit.

- immunity
- germs
- host
- vehicles of transmission
- new host
- immunization
- hygiene practices
- hand-washing
- cleaning and sanitizing routines
- potentially hazardous substances
- universal precautions
- health observations
- signs and symptoms
- exclusion
- alternative care
- prescription medication
- over-the-counter medication
- "five rights" for administering medication
- allergies
- allergic substances
- adrenalin kit
- anaphylactic shock
- asthma
- triggers of asthma episodes

Evaluate your options in each situation.

1. In the centre where you have recently started working, the routine hand-washing practice before lunch is to dunk the infants' and toddlers' hands into a communal basin of water and dry them with individual paper towels.

2. You have a close working relationship with a parent who discloses to you that her child is HIV-positive. You are the only person in the centre she has told and she has asked you not to tell anyone else, including the director.

3. One of the daily sanitizing routines in the centre is to add a capful of bleach to the water table each morning. This practice saves water and time because staff empty the water only once a week.

4. One of the two-year-olds is listless and unhappy today. He is unable to participate in the program and needs to be held and comforted. When the director calls his mother, she asks that you take his temperature. You do so, and because the child does not have a fever, the mother refuses to pick him up early.

5. A preschooler has a number of food allergies, so she is often offered other foods at lunch and snack. She feels centred out and says she wants only what the other children eat. Meanwhile, some of the other children feel that she is getting special treatment and want to eat the same food she eats.

▶ R E S O U R C E   M A T E R I A L S

Organizations

Allergy Asthma Information Association, 30 Bridgeland Avenue, Suite 424, Toronto, ON M6A 1Z4. Tel. (416) 783-8944, fax (416) 783-7538 (or contact provincial office).

Asthma Society of Canada, 130 Bridgeland Avenue, Suite 425, Toronto, ON M6A 1Z4. Tel. (416) 787-4050, fax (416) 787-5807. (or contact regional office). InfoAsthma 1-800-787-3880. Web site: www.asthma-society.com; E-mail: asthma@myna.com.

Canadian Institute of Child Health, 885 Meadowlands Drive, Suite 512, Ottawa, ON K2C 3N2. Tel. (613) 224-4144, fax (613) 224-4145. Web site: www.cich.ca; E-mail cich@igs.net.

Canadian Lung Association, 508–1900 City Park Drive, Gloucester, ON K1J 1A3. Tel. (613) 747-6776, fax (613) 747-7430. Web site: www.lung.ca; E-mail: info@lung.ca. 1-888-566-LUNG (connects to caller's own regional Lung Association) or contact regional offices. (The CLA provides educational sessions on asthma for parents.)

Canadian Paediatric Society, 100–2204 Walkley Road, Ottawa, ON K1G 4G8. Tel. (613) 526-9397, fax (613) 526-3332. Web site: www.cps.ca.

The Hospital for Sick Children, Centre for Health Information and Promotion, 555 University Avenue, Toronto, ON M5G 1X8. Tel. (416) 813-5819.

Printed Matter

The Asthma Handbook (1994), by the Lung Association, Ontario Provincial Office, 573 King Street E., Suite 20, Toronto, ON M5A 4L3. Tel. (416) 864-9911, fax (416) 864-9916 or contact your local Lung Association for more information. Web site: www.on.lung.ca.

"Child Care and the Pediatrician" (1989), by S.S. Aronson, in *Pediatrics in Review* 10:277–86.

Childhood Asthma (1993), by G.J. Canny and H. Levison (Burlington: Boehhringer Ingelheim [Canada])

Healthy Habits for Healthy Happy Kids (1990), by the Canadian Institute of Child Health, 885 Meadowlands Drive, Suite 512, Ottawa, ON K2C 3N2. Tel. (613) 224-4144, fax (613) 224-4145. (Concerns handwashing and infection control.)

HIV/AIDS and Child Care: Fact Book and Facilitator's Guide (1995), by B. Kaiser and J.S. Rasminsky (Ottawa: Canadian Child Care Federation and Health Canada). For copies, contact Canadian Council Care Federation, 30 Rosemount Avenue, Suite 100, Ottawa, ON K1Y 1P4. Tel. 1-800-858-1412, fax (613) 729-3159.

Immunize Your Kids: Boost Their Chances for Health (1998), by the Canadian Immunization Awareness Program, c/o the Canadian Public Health Association, 400–1565 Carting Avenue, Ottawa, ON K1Z 8R1. Tel. (613) 725-3769, fax (613) 725-9826. Web site: www.nald.ca/ciap.htm; E-mail: ciap@cpha.ca.

Management of Asthma at School (1993), by the Asthma Society of Canada (Burlington: Boehhringer Ingelheim [Canada])

Managing Childhood Asthma: A Parent's Guide. Medcom Inc. (video) and *Conquering Asthma* (1994), by M.T. Newhouse and P.J. Barnes (Empowering Press). Distributed by Medical Audio Visual Communications Inc., P.O. Box 84548, 2336 Bloor Street W., Toronto, ON M6S 1T0. National toll-free: (800) 602-1160. (Most appropriate for parents of children 4 and up.)

Managing Children's Asthma (1993), by the American Lung Association. A 23-minute video and a 40-page booklet are available from the Asthma Society of Canada, 130 Bridgeland Avenue, Suite 425, Toronto, ON M6A 1Z4. Tel. (416) 787-4050.

What to Do When Your Child Is Vomiting and Has Diarrhea (1996), by the Canadian Paediatric Society. (For contact information, see under Organizations, page 202.)

Sesame Street—A Is for Asthma (1998) by the Children's Television Workshop. The video and caregiver's guide is a Childhood Asthma Awareness Project. To order, contact the Children's Television Workshop, Health and Safety Outreach, P.O. Box 55742, Indianapolis, IN 46205–0742.

▶ **B I B L I O G R A P H Y**

Abley, M. (1994) "A Life-and-Death Situation." *Toronto Star*, 29 Aug., C3–C4.

American Public Health Association and American Academy of Pediatrics (1992) *Caring for Our Children: Health and Safety Guidelines*. Washington, DC: American Public Health Association and American Academy of Pediatrics.

Aronson, S.S. (1991a) "Ask Dr. Sue." *Exchange*, Sept./Oct.:23–25.

——— (1991b) *Health & Safety in Child Care*. New York: HarperCollins.

——— (1989) "Ask Dr. Sue." *Exchange*, Apr.:33.

——— (1987) "AIDS and Child Care Programs." *Exchange*, Nov.:35–39.

——— (1987) "Care of Ill Children in Child Care Programs." *Exchange*, July:34–38.

——— (1986) "Exclusion Criteria for Ill Children in Child Care." *Exchange*, May:13–16.

——— (1983) "How to Reduce Allergic Problems." *Exchange*, Sept.:29–30.

Asthma Society of Canada (1993) *Management of Asthma at School*. Burlington, ON: Boehringer Ingelheim (Canada).

——— (n.d.) *Asthma Facts*. Toronto: Asthma Society of Canada (pamphlet).

——— (n.d.) *Info Asthma*. Toronto: Asthma Society of Canada (pamphlet).

Baumgarten, M., et al. (1986) "The Immunization Status and Source of Immunization of Two-Year-Old Children in Montreal." *Canadian Journal of Public Health* 77:24–27.

Bell, D.M., et al. (1989) "Illness Associated with Child Day Care: A Study of Incidence and Cost." *American Journal of Public Health* 79:479–84.

Black, R.E., et al. (1981) "Handwashing to Prevent Diarrhea in Day-Care Centers." *American Journal of Epidemiology* 113(4):445–51.

Black, S.M. (1999) "HIV/AIDS in Early Childhood Centres: The Ethical Dilemma of Confidentiality versus Disclosure." *Young Children* March: 39–45.

Burroughs Wellcome Inc. (n.d.) *Head Lice Education Program*. Montreal: Burroughs Wellcome.

Canadian Institute of Child Health (1994) *The Health of Canada's Children: A CICH Profile*, 2nd ed. Ottawa: Canadian Institute of Child Health.

Canadian Paediatric Society (1997) *Your Child's Best Shot—A Parent's Giude to Vaccination.* Ottawa: Canadian Paediatric Society.

———— (1996) *Well Beings: A Guide to Promote the Physical Health, Safety and Emotional Well-Being of Children in Child Care Centres and Family Day Care Homes.* Toronto: Creative Premises.

———— (1994) *Little Well Beings: A Handbook on Health in Family Day Care.* Toronto: Creative Premises.

———— (1986) "Reye's Syndrome: All Parents and Teenagers Be Informed." *CPS Statement* ID:86–95.

Canny, G.J., and H. Levison (1993) *Childhood Asthma: A Handbook for Parents.* Burlington, ON: Boehringer Ingelheim (Canada).

Centers for Disease Control (1984) "Public Health Considerations of Infectious Diseases in Child Day Care Centers." *Journal of Pediatrics* 105(5):683–700.

Chang, A., et al. (1988) "Management of Illness and Temporary Disability in Children Enrolled in Day-Care Centres." *American Journal of Disease Control* 142:651–55.

Cohen, D.H., et al. (1988) *Observing and Recording the Behavior of Young Children*, 3rd ed. New York: Teachers College Press.

Correspondence (1984) *British Medical Journal* 288:1688.

Crouch, J.E., and J.R. McClintic (1976) *Human Anatomy and Physiology*, 2nd ed. Toronto: John Wiley & Sons.

Division of Infectious Diseases (1997) *Your Child and Antibiotics: Unnecessary Antibiotics Can Be Harmful.* Hospital for Sick Children (pamphlet)

Epstein, N. (1993) "Living with Allergies." *Lung Line*, Spring/Summer:8–9.

Evrard, H.M. (1998) "Coaching the Coaches—Managing Exercise-Induced Asthma at School." *Asthma Magazine*, November/December:5–7.

Freeman, J.M. (1992) "The Best Medicine for Febrile Seizures." *New England Journal of Medicine* 327:1161–63.

Friendly, M. (1994) *Child Care Policy in Canada.* Don Mills, ON: Addison-Wesley Publishing.

Frieri, M. (1998) "Managing Asthma in Infants (and Young Children)." *Asthma Magazine*, September/October:15–17.

Giebink, G.S. (1993) "Care of the Ill Child in Day-Care Settings." *Pediatrics* 91:229–33.

Gold, R. (1994) "Routine Childhood Hepatitis B Vaccination." *Canadian Journal of Paediatrics* 1(5):11.

Gyorkos, T.W., et al. (1994) "Practice Survey of Immunization in Canada." *Canadian Journal of Public Health* (July–Aug.); 85 (Supplement 1):31–36.

Health Canada (1998) *Canadian Immunization Guide*, 5th ed. Ottawa: Public Works and Government Services Canada.

Hendeles, L. (1993) "Efficacy and Safety of Antihistamines and Expectorants in Nonprescription Cough and Cold Preparations." *Pharmacotherapy* 13(2):154–58.

Hutton, N., et al. (1991) "Effectiveness of an Antihistamine–Decongestant Combination for Young Children with the Common Cold: A Randomized, Controlled Clinical Trial." *Journal of Pediatrics* 118(1):125–30.

Ipp, M. (1990) "Evaluation of Fever in a Child Aged Three Months to 24 Months." *Canadian Family Physician* 36:1563–66.

Jacob, S.W., and C.A. Francone (1974) *Structure and Function in Man*, 3rd ed. Toronto: W.B. Saunders Co.

Jordan, A.E. (1986) "The Unresolved Child Care Dilemma: Care for the Acutely Ill Child." *Reviews of Infectious Diseases* 8(4):626–30.

Klich, B. (1994) "Be Healthy Back at School." *Toronto Star*, 21 Aug., F1.

Kluger, M.J. (1992) "Fever Revisited." *Pediatrics* 90:846–50.

Kubiak, M., et al. (1993) "Comparison of Stool Containment in Cloth and Single-Use Diapers Using a Simulated Infant Feces." *Pediatrics* 91(3):632–36.

Landis, S.E., et al. (1988) "Day-Care Center Exclusion of Sick Children: Comparison of Opinions of Day-Care Staff, Working Mothers, and Pediatricians." *Pediatrics* 81(5):662–67.

Larson, E. (1985) "Handwashing and Skin: Physiologic and Bacteriologic Aspects." *Infection Control* 6(1):14–23.

Levy, S.B. (1998) "The Challenge of Antibiotic Resistance." *Scientific American* March:46–53.

Lovell, S. (1990) "Cough and Cold Preparations." *On Continuing Practice* 17(4):2–9.

Lung Association, The (1994) *The Asthma Handbook*. Toronto.

MacDonald, K.L., et al. (1990) "Evaluation of a Sick Child Day Care Program: Lack of Detected Increased Risk of Subsequent Infections." *Pediatric Infectious Disease Journal* 9(1):15–20.

May, A., and H. Bauchner (1992) "Fever Phobia: The Pediatrician's Contribution." *Pediatrics* 90:851–54.

National Advisory Committee on Immunization (1998) *Canadian Immunization Guide*, 5th ed. Ottawa: Public Works and Government Services Canada.

Nyquist, A.C., et al. (1998) "Antibiotic Prescribing for Children with Colds, Upper Respiratory Tract Infections, and Bronchitis." *JAMA* 279(11):875–77.

Oremland, E.K. (1990) "Childhood Illness and Day Care." *Psychosocial Issues in Day Care*, S.S. Chehrazi, ed. Washington, DC: American Psychiatric Press.

Pender, E.S., and B.R. Parks (1991) "Toxicity with Dextromethorphan-Containing Preparations: A Literature Review and Report of Two Additional Cases." *Pediatric Emergency Care* 7(3):163–65.

Platiel, R. (1995) "Food-Allergy Sufferers Live 15 Minutes from Death." *Winnipeg Free Press*, 3 Jan., C10.

Renaud, A., et al. (1997) "Knowledge and Attitude Assessment of Quebec Daycare Workers and Parents Regarding HIV/AIDS and Hepatitis B." *Canadian Journal of Public Health* January–February:23–27.

Rustia, J., and L. Barr (1986) "Feasibility of Screening Young Children in Day Care Centers: A Preliminary Investigation." *Public Health Reports* 101(2):191–200.

Sawyer, S., et al. (1985) "A Look at Toddlers' Immunization." *Canadian Public Health Journal* 76:259–61.

Shapiro, E.D., et al. (1986) "Policies for the Exclusion of Ill Children from Group Day Care: An Unresolved Dilemma." *Reviews of Infectious Diseases* 8(4):622–25.

Shirley, L.R., and S.A. Ross (1989) "Risk of Transmission of Human Immunodeficiency Virus by Bite of an Infected Toddler." *Journal of Pediatrics* 114(3):425–27.

Skull, S., et al. (1999) "Management of Upper Respiratory Infection in Day Care" (unpublished). To contact Dr. Sue Skull, tel. (416) 813-5288 or E-mail: susan.skull @utoronto.ca.

Smith, M.B.H., and W. Feldman (1993) "Over-the-Counter Cold Medications: A Critical Review of Clinical Trials Between 1950 and 1991." *JAMA* 269(17):2258–63.

Taylor, J.A., et al. (1993) "Efficacy of Cough Suppressants in Children." *Journal of Pediatrics* 122(5, Pt. 1):799–802.

Tulk, S., and M. Ipp (1992) "Assessment and Management of Childhood Fever and Other Common Pediatric Problems." *Contemporary Pediatrics* Mar./Apr.:26–30.

Van, R., et al. (1991) "The Effect of Diaper Type and Overclothing on Fecal Contamination in Day-Care Centers." *JAMA* 265(14):1840–44.

Wald, E.R., et al. (1991) "Frequency and Severity of Infections in Day Care: Three-Year Follow-Up" *Journal of Paediatrics* 118:509–14.

———— (1988) "Frequency and Severity of Infections in Day Care." *Journal of Pediatrics* 112:540–46.

Wong, D.L., et al. (1992) "Diapering Choices: A Critical Review of the Issues." *Pediatric Nursing* 18(1):41–54.

Ying, J., et al. (1998) "Needs Assessment of Child Care Centres in the Former City of Toronto." *Canadian Journal of Public Health* September–October:308–14.

Zigler, E., and S. Muenchow (1986) "Infectious Diseases in Day Care: Parallels between Psychologically and Physically Healthy Care." *Reviews of Infectious Diseases* 8(4):514–20.

Appendix 3.1

Management of Illness

Please note that requirements for reporting to the public health agencies may vary across Canada. If in doubt, these agencies can provide helpful information.

DISEASE	TRANSMISSION	SYMPTOMS AND SIGNS	INFECTIOUS PERIOD	EXCLUSION	REPORT
Respiratory Infections					
Common Cold	Spread person to person via droplets; indirect spread via contaminated hands, objects, surfaces. Almost always viral.	Runny nose, sore throat, cough, decreased appetite.	1 day before to 7 days after onset.	Do **not** exclude unless too ill to take part in the activities.	No
Cold with Fever	Same as above.	Same as above, plus fever, headache, muscle aches.	1 day before to 7 days after onset.	Do **not** exclude unless too ill to take part in the activities.	No
Ear Infection (*Otitis media*)	Complication of cold.	Earache or irritability, fever and cold symptoms.	Not infectious.	Do **not** exclude unless too ill to take part in the activities.	No
Pinkeye (**Conjunctivitis**)	Spread person to person by contact with secretions from eye.	Redness, itching, pain, discharge from eye.	For duration of illness or until 24 hours after treatment started.	Exclude only if discharge is pus (yellow, thick) and then until the antibiotic has been taken for 1 full day.	No

(appendix continues on next page)

DISEASE	TRANSMISSION	SYMPTOMS AND SIGNS	INFECTIOUS PERIOD	EXCLUSION	REPORT
Pneumonia	Spread person to person via droplets; indirect spread via contaminated hands, objects, surfaces. Usually viral.	Fever, cough, rapid or noisy breathing, wheezing, grunting, pale or blue colour.	Varies with cause.	Exclude until evaluated by physician.	No
Strep Throat	Spread person to person.	Fever, sore throat.	Until 24 hours after treatment begun.	Exclude until 24 hours after treatment begun.	Only if an outbreak occurs, i.e., more than 2 cases in a month
Gastrointestinal Infections					
Campylobacter	Germ excreted in stool. Poultry, beef, unpasteurized milk or other food may be source of infection.	Fever, diarrhea, blood in stool, cramps.	For duration of diarrhea.	Exclude until diarrhea is gone.	Yes
Diarrhea	Germ excreted in stool. Spread directly from person to person; indirectly by hands of staff and children, objects, surfaces, food, or water contaminated with germs (young children frequently put fingers and objects in mouth).	Increase in frequency of stools and/or change to unformed, loose, or watery stool. Fever, loss of appetite, nausea, vomiting, abdominal pain; mucus or blood in stool may also occur. Diarrhea may be dangerous in infants and young children because the loss of fluid may cause dehydration.	For duration of diarrhea.	Exclude until diarrhea is gone or physician determines child is not infectious. Notify parents at once if any of the following are present: 2 or more episodes of diarrhea or diarrhea with a fever over 39°C (102°F); repeated diarrhea; vomiting; dehydration; blood or mucus in stool.	Yes. Report outbreaks of 2 or more cases of diarrhea occuring within 48 hours and also any case of bloody or diagnosed bacterial diarrhea.
Escherichia coli (E. coli)	Germ excreted in stool. Poultry, beef, unpasteurized milk or other food may be source of infection.	Fever, diarrhea, blood in stool, cramps.	For duration of diarrhea.	Exclude until diarrhea is gone and the cultures are negative.	Yes

(appendix continues on next page)

DISEASE	TRANSMISSION	SYMPTOMS AND SIGNS	INFECTIOUS PERIOD	EXCLUSION	REPORT
Food Poisoning	Acquired from contaminated food.	Nausea, vomiting, cramps, diarrhea.	Not infectious.	No exclusion required.	Yes
Giardia	Germ in stool. Spread person to person. Common in child care.	Most children have no symptoms. May have loss of appetite, vomiting, cramps, diarrhea, mushy stool, excessive gas.	Until cured.	Exclude until diarrhea is gone.	Yes, if 2 or more cases occur within a month
Hepatitis A	Virus in stool. Spread person to person; may also be spread in contaminated food or water.	Most children have no illness. May have fever, loss of appetite, nausea, vomiting, jaundice (yellow colour in skin and eyes).	2 weeks before to 1 week after onset of jaundice.	Exclude for 1 week after onset of jaundice. Immune globulin may be indicated for children, staff, and family members to control epidemic.	Yes
Norwalk Virus	Spread person to person and via air.	Vomiting and prostration for 1 to 2 days.	Duration of illness.	Exclude until diarrhea and/or vomiting are gone.	Yes
Rotavirus	Germ in stool. Spread person to person. Most common cause of diarrhea in child care.	Fever and vomiting precede watery diarrhea. Dehydration may occur rapidly in infants.	For duration of diarrhea.	Exclude until diarrhea is gone.	Yes
Salmonella	Acquired mainly from food, especially eggs and egg products, beef, poultry, unpasteurized milk.	Diarrhea, fever, blood in stool.	While having diarrhea.	Exclude until diarrhea is gone.	Yes
Shigella	Germ in stool. Spread person to person.	Diarrhea, fever, blood and/or mucus in stool, cramps.	For duration of diarrhea. Highly infectious.	Exclude until diarrhea is gone and the cultures are negative.	Yes

(appendix continues on next page)

DISEASE	TRANSMISSION	SYMPTOMS AND SIGNS	INFECTIOUS PERIOD	EXCLUSION	REPORT
Skin and Scalp Infections					
Head Lice	Spread person to person. Requires close direct contact. Infested hats, clothes may also be involved in spread.	Most children have no symptoms. Some will have itching of scalp. Nits (eggs) are seen attached to hairs near scalp.	Until treated.	Exclude until treated. Removal of all nits may be necessary to cure some cases.	No
Herpes Simplex	Spread person to person. Virus in saliva and infected sores.	Many infections occur without any symptoms. May cause high fever, many painful ulcers in mouth. May recur as cold sores.	For one week during first infection; 5 days during recurrent cold sores.	Exclude for severe illness. Exclusion not indicated for recurrent cold sores.	No
Impetigo	Person to person by direct contact.	Pustules or crusted rash on face or exposed parts of body (arms and/or legs).	From onset of rash until 1 day after start of treatment with antibiotics.	Exclude until antibiotic treatment has been taken for 1 full day.	No
Scabies	Spread person to person. Requires close direct contact.	Very itchy rash. In infants under 2 years, rash may occur anywhere on body. In older children, rash usually appears on fingers, elbows, armpits, abdomen.	Until treated.	Exclude until treated. Treatment of contacts may be necessary to control outbreak.	No. Public health agencies available to help if the problem persists.
Other Infections					
Chickenpox (Varicella-Zoster)	Spread person to person and via air. Very infectious.	Rash with small blisters on top, which become crusted, along with fever, itching.	2 days before to 5 days after onset of rash.	If illness is severe, exlude until 5th day after onset of rash or until all the blisters have crusted, whichever is shorter. If mild and child is able to take part in activities, no exclusion is required.	Yes

(appendix continues on next page)

DISEASE	TRANSMISSION	SYMPTOMS AND SIGNS	INFECTIOUS PERIOD	EXCLUSION	REPORT
Cytomegalovirus (CMV)	Spread person to person. Virus in urine and saliva.	Usually causes no illness. Can infect fetus during pregnancy.	Whenever virus present in urine or saliva.	No exclusion required.	No
Hepatitis B	Virus present only in blood and certain body fluids (semen, cervical secretions). Virus is not in stool. Spread by contact with blood or by sexual intercourse.	Illness uncommon in children. Illness in adults is more severe and more prolonged than hepatitis A. May cause severe liver disease or liver cancer.	From weeks before onset to months or years after recovery from illness. May be infectious for life.	No exclusion required unless open sores are present. Hepatitis B vaccine and/or hepatitis B immune globulin may be indicated under special circumstances.	Yes. Immediately report any bites that cause bleeding.
Measles	Virus in respiratory secretions. Spread person to person. Very infectious.	Fever, cough, runny nose, inflamed eyes for 1 to 3 days before onset of rash. Rash is large red spots that often join together; starts on face and spreads rapidly over body. Illness lasts 5 to 10 days.	2 days before onset of fever and cough (3 to 5 days before onset of rash) until 4 days after onset of rash.	Exclude all cases until at least 4 days after onset of rash. Exclude all children who lack proof of immunization until vaccinated or until 2 weeks after last case in the child care facility.	Yes. Speed is essential in limiting outbreaks of measles: notify health department at once.
Meningitis	Spread person to person, requiring close direct contact.	Fever, marked fussiness and/or sleepiness, vomiting, stiff neck, coma, seizures. Very severe infection. Seek emergency care immediately.	Until treated with antibiotics (if caused by bacteria).	Exposed children and staff may need antibiotics or vaccine.	Yes. Immediately.
Mumps	Virus in respiratory secretions. Spread person to person.	Enlargement of salivary glands causing swelling of cheeks and face. May have fever, headache, abdominal pain. Many children have no illness.	7 days before to 9 days after swelling. Most infectious 2 days before onset of swelling.	Control difficult because many children have no symptoms. Exclude for 9 days, less if the illness is mild and child is able to take part in the activities. Ensure all children are vaccinated.	Yes

(appendix continues on next page)

DISEASE	TRANSMISSION	SYMPTOMS AND SIGNS	INFECTIOUS PERIOD	EXCLUSION	REPORT
Rubella (German Measles)	Virus in respiratory secretions. Spread person to person.	Many children infected but have no illness. May have mild fever, sore throat, swollen glands in neck but no rash. Rash consists of small red spots that start on scalp and face and spread rapidly over entire body.	Few days before until 7 days after onset of rash.	Exclude for 7 days after onset of rash. All staff should be vaccinated or have blood test to prove immunity. There is risk of severe damage to fetus if a pregnant woman gets rubella during the first trimester.	Yes
Whooping Cough (Pertussis)	Bacteria in respiratory secretions. Spread person to person. Very infectious.	Begins as cold with profuse runny nose and cough. Cough gets progressively worse and occurs in paroxysms, or spasms. Face red or purple during coughing spells and child may vomit. Fever uncommon.	From onset of runny nose until 3 weeks after onset of paroxysms or whooping.	Exclude until 5 days after start of antibiotics or 3 weeks if no treatment given. Contacts may need antibiotics or vaccine.	Yes

Source: Courtesy of the Canadian Paediatric Society. From *Well Beings* (Ottawa: Canadian Paediatric Society, 1992), 973–76.

Unit 4

Nutrition

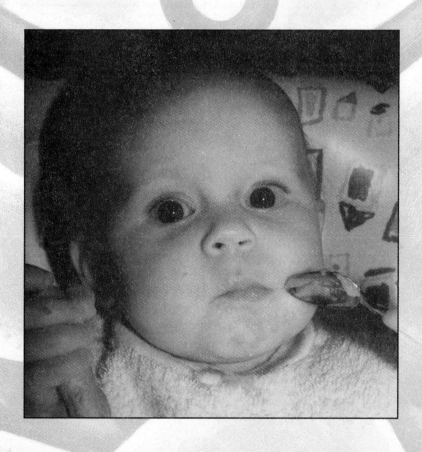

Unit 4: Nutrition

Nutrition is the science of food and how it is used by the body. Discussion on nutrition includes these facts:

▶ Food has different meanings for each individual.
▶ Eating patterns are shaped by interrelated factors in our lives.

Nutritious food is essential for all dimensions of our health. This key factor is the cornerstone in developing and evolving nutrition programs for young children. Caregivers' motivation plays an essential role in promoting children's well-being. It is important to balance children's rights to have control over what and how much food they consume with adults' responsibility to provide

▶ enough food
▶ a variety of wholesome foods
▶ an eating environment that promotes healthy eating

Factors That Shape Eating Habits

▶ **OBJECTIVES**   To list and discuss six factors that shape our eating habits.
To be aware of food insecurity in Canada.

For most people, food usually means more than just relieving hunger and providing nourishment. The meaning that food carries can be positive and healthy and be associated with celebrations, including special foods, holidays, social time with family and friends, and religious or ethno-cultural events. Other meanings may be negative and not conducive to health or well-being; these may result in eating for the wrong reasons. (See Emotional, page 222.)

Think about how you view food generally, how you feel before, during, and after eating, and the food choices you make. Awareness of our emotions, attitudes, and behaviour around food and eating is essential before we can foster healthy eating habits in children. If we perpetuate myths or model poor eating habits—such as a focus on dieting—we influence children negatively and may unwittingly foster in them lifelong eating problems.

Six Factors That Affect Eating Habits

Six factors must be considered when we look at nutrition: physical, emotional, social, cultural, body image, and economics. The interaction of these factors and others results in complex dynamics that caregivers need to be aware of to promote healthy attitudes toward nutrition and eating.

Physical

The first factor that comes to mind is our physical need for food. Nutrients in food provide the building blocks for cell and tissue growth, provide the regulators for many of the body's functions, and provide fuel for energy. Each nutrient can have a specific role or multiple roles in the body. The way nutrients interact with other factors in the body is very complex. Nutrition affects a child's thinking and learning capacities, for example. A child who is weak from poor nutrition will have little energy to learn or socialize (Guy 1997, 51). Canadian nutritional guidelines have been established for the intake of nutrients (vitamins, minerals, proteins, fat, carbohydrates) for children and adults. The guidelines take into account that variations exist in the requirements for nutrients among individuals. Growth rates and body types vary, because we all differ in our genetic makeup, even from our siblings. The human body's need for energy varies with age, body size, growth patterns, gender, level of physical activity, and basal metabolic rate (the rate at which your body uses energy for essential bodily functions).

Physical Activity   We know that physical activity goes hand in hand with nutrition as part of a healthy lifestyle. Individuals who maintain a moderate level of daily activity help their bodies work more efficiently, often by increasing their basal metabolic rate and bone density. Children enjoy physical activity just for the fun of it, but it supports their physical fitness and positive self-image.

Approximately one hour a day of physical activity is healthy for most young children. Child care legislation requires a *minimum* amount of time each day for outdoor play. However, this requirement doesn't ensure that children are physically active during that time; the specified time is just a minimum. Caregivers should ensure that children are outside for longer periods or more than once during the day. Are the children running, jumping, hopping, climbing, swinging, riding tricycles, moving to music, or playing ball and active games? Or are they standing around or spending the majority of time at more sedentary activities—playing in the sandbox

or at the water table, playing marbles, or taking part in dramatic play? Although they don't have to be moving all the time, caregivers should be aware of how much each type of activity is occurring. Since activity patterns are established early in life, caregivers should encourage each child to be physically active. What kind of behaviour are we modelling as caregivers? Are we standing around, passively supervising, or talking with staff? This behaviour may discourage children's enjoyment of physical activity. On the other hand, our active involvement encourages children and increases our own fitness levels.

Sensory Experiences Eating is a truly sensory experience. When you watch young children eat, they see, smell, taste, and touch the food. They hear the crispy, crunchy, and squishy sounds that food makes. From infancy, we begin to develop taste preferences. Several studies have shown that newborn babies innately prefer sweet tastes. This preference, however, may be altered early on by introducing other tastes (Lawless 1985). Older infants and young children often prefer a saltier taste. Children's love of dill pickles and salty broth sometimes surprises adults. There is interest in, but no conclusions yet on, some of the genetic links between taste preferences. Young children also react to texture, generally preferring soft, fluffy foods (e.g., pudding) and crisp vegetables. Meats are not favoured generally, because they are difficult to chew with primary teeth.

Families' ethno-cultural food habits are powerful, especially for children's developing tastes. A study was conducted in a Mexican community to see how the people developed a taste for chili peppers. This food is a daily staple in their community and the gradual respectful introduction of chili peppers from infancy resulted in a preference for this taste by preschool age. Lambert-Lagacé (1993) suggests that, using this approach, broccoli should be easy!

Emotional

The emotional component of nutrition is related to individual likes and dislikes. It may simply be a matter of taste differentiation, or a desire for or aversion to food associated with either a positive or negative experience. For example, a child who is forced to eat yams may develop an aversion to yams. Table 4.1 shows ways that children can develop positive or negative associations with food. As you read the list, consider which food meanings may have a positive or negative effect on children's emotions.

Children enter child care programs with their repertoire of familiar foods based mostly on what their families served and the emotional and social status that these foods hold. Children quickly pick up messages that may make them more or less responsive to a new food.

If the 2-year-old's parent has told her to eat all her vegetables before she can have dessert, it is no mystery that she will give the dessert a higher status than the vegetables, reinforcing her preference for dessert.

Social and Cultural

The social and cultural aspects of eating have significant influence in our lives and are linked with physical and emotional forces; food often has deep personal meaning. It would be rare not to see food playing a significant role in any social gathering. Some foods are more likely to be served in certain social situations—such as hot dogs at ball games and popcorn at movies. Many food traditions in social gatherings are related to particular ethno-cultural or religious holidays, such as cabbage rolls as one of the 12 meatless dishes prepared on Ukrainians' Christmas Eve, Chinese cake on Chinese New Year, special breads on Passover or Easter, and turkey on Thanksgiving.

Eating with other people tends to be viewed as a more enjoyable experience than eating alone. Do you, or someone you know who lives alone, eat in front of the television for company? Eating together can promote positive values, like awareness of your needs and desires as well as those of others, sharing, learning respectful rhythms of talking and listening, and celebrating as a community. (See Creating a Positive Eating Environment, page 247.)

Young children who eat with positive adult companionship eat better than those who have no or negative adult intervention (Stanek et al. 1990). The way foods are viewed by others in our midst affects the status of the food. If parents and caregivers treat all nutritious foods with equal respect, children are more likely to try a variety of them. If certain foods are given lower status, children are liable to share that view.

TABLE 4.1	WHAT FOOD CAN MEAN
POSITIVE AND NEGATIVE ASSOCIATIONS WITH FOOD	
Security	When an infant cries, someone feeds and cuddles her, which contributes to a sense of security.
Insecurity	When a family is unable to provide enough food on a regular basis, the child's sense of predictability may be jeopardized.
Pacifier	A child is always given food whenever he cries, regardless of whether he is hungry. He views food as a pacifier rather than a means of nourishment.
Learning	A young child learns about her world by experiencing food through the five senses.
Punishment	Parents withdraw food, often dessert, because of inappropriate behaviour, or may send the child to bed hungry.
Reward	Children are offered food, usually sweets, as a reward for success or "good" behaviour.
Individuality	A child uses food as a way to express her individuality (i.e., her food likes and dislikes).
Love	The child learns to give and eat food to show love (e.g., chocolates on Valentine's Day or a mother saying, "Don't you like mommy's dinner?" which equates rejection of the food with rejection of her).
Comforter	Food is used to relieve boredom or loneliness, to handle anxiety or disappointment (e.g., following rejection by a friend, a child is comforted with cookies or candy). He is learning to use food as a coping mechanism.
Fear	An unpleasant experience with food (e.g., choking) causes a child to fear eating that food in the future.
Approval	A child tries to win the approval and acceptance of her peers by eating and refusing what they eat and refuse (e.g., a school-age child refuses foods from home that she had accepted readily until her friends commented negatively on it) or by "cleaning off the plate" for daddy.
Weapon	A child with little control over her environment uses food for revenge or to get attention (e.g., by refusing to eat, demanding food, throwing food).

Traditional ethno-cultural preferences for food are usually strongest in families who have recently come to Canada. When ethnicity is an important aspect of family life, parents often continue to prepare traditional foods and perhaps combine them with contemporary foods of North America. We often associate North American foods with the highly processed, high-fat, and refined-sugar foods that are

not as nutrient-rich as many of the more traditional, ethno-cultural foods. *Canada's Food Guide to Healthy Eating* encourages Canadians to reduce their intake of highly processed, refined foods. We need to return to eating more traditional foods if these are less refined and higher in nutrients (particularly vegetables, fruits, breads, cereals). "In virtually every developing country in the world, diet-related chronic diseases are becoming the new health problem as populations, typically first in the cities, abandon traditionally healthy diets in favour of 'affluent' foods" (World Health Organization 1991, 301). Caregivers should try to be aware of and reinforce ethno-cultural food preferences.

We are bombarded daily with information and pressure from media—newspapers, magazines, radio, television, movies, videotapes, video games. Television has the most dramatic influence on young children, as evidenced by the amount of television that children watch. Statistics Canada (cited in Canadian Paediatric Society 1996, 540) estimates that children aged 2 to 11 watch an average of 20 hours per week. Young children are unable developmentally to discriminate between the commercials and the television show, which makes them vulnerable to advertisements for non-nutritious foods. Also, children notice that many shows depict "cool" children and adolescents regularly eating low-nutrient snack foods such as chips and cookies or complaining as they eat vegetables. Furthermore, the significant amount of sedentary TV time that children *could* be spending in physically challenging activities does not contribute to optimal health. Watching television is also associated with snacking on high-fat and high-sugar foods.

Parents, caregivers, and other adults in the child's life can have a significant influence on her or his acceptance of a variety of foods. The more a child experiences different foods, the more likely he or she is to develop a taste for them. Children who have had less exposure to new foods are more likely to be picky eaters and unwilling to try new foods, which creates a vicious circle (Pelchat and Pliner 1986).

BODY IMAGE

Maintaining weight within a normal range is conducive to health. However, the range that has been considered normal, particularly for women (though it is becoming more of an issue for men), has been narrowly defined by the fashion industry and the media. Society has focused too much on body weight. The ideal body image is often portrayed as the unattainable "perfect" body (usually associated with thinness). Children, especially girls, from a very young age can become obsessed with their weight if they are surrounded by these dangerous messages. "Little girls as young as three, four, and five are expressing a wish to diet" (Sheinin 1990, 1). A survey of 7-year-old girls and boys found that they consistently ranked depictions of obese children the lowest in attractiveness (Feldman et al., cited in Sheinin 1990). Women receive pervasive messages from the fashion, media, and diet industries that they are never good enough, and that they must deprive themselves to continually fight the natural size of their body.

> Weight prejudice has only developed in affluent cultures—in societies that enjoy a widespread availability of adequate nutrition—thus thinness, being more difficult to attain, has become a new symbol of wealth and status. (Rice 1988, 3)

The "fear of fat" attitude that pervades our society results in social prejudice and discrimination against individuals whose weight exceeds that which is deemed acceptable. This can damage their self-esteem and result in extreme dieting to prevent or correct obesity. According to the National Eating Disorder Information Centre (Sheinin 1990, 1):

▶ almost 90 percent of women in Canada have some degree of body dissatisfaction

▶ over 80 percent have dieted by age 18
▶ 40 percent of 9-year-old girls have already dieted

Children gain some fat prior to puberty as part of the normal growth process. This gain often coincides with an increased concern with body image, and the cycle of dieting may begin. Paradoxically, the number of preschool and school-age children who are overweight is increasing (Evers 1995, 5–7). Many of these children are eating *less* than the recommended amount of food and calories and are showing low muscle mass. This evidence suggests that lack of physical activity is playing a role in their weight gain. The tendency in our society to *diet* will add to the problem rather than help, because lowering food intake tends to slow our metabolism rather than make it run more efficiently.

Dieting doesn't work—for adults or children—so messages that convey a narrow definition of acceptable body image lead to lower self-esteem. Poor self-esteem can't improve health in any way (Pitman and Kaufman 1994, 5).

Canada's Food Guide to Healthy Eating acknowledges Canadians' preoccupation with weight and body image by shifting the previous focus on weight control to vitality—a concept that integrates eating well, being active, and feeling good about oneself: "One of the first steps in adopting the positive principles of Vitality is to help consumers view their own weight and the weight of others more realistically" (Health and Welfare Canada 1992b).

This issue is important in child care because caregivers, like everyone else, are profoundly influenced by media messages. Remember the great impact you have on children and how they look up to you. It is important to be sensitive to the subtle messages (e.g., you are constantly on a diet) and the overt ones (e.g., you comment to a child that she is chubby or skinny) that you send to children.

ECONOMICS

In Canada, an exciting range of foods is available in many urban communities. However, this is not the case in all Canadian communities. Even when a vast range of foods are available, they may not be used due to cost or perhaps because many people are unsure of how to prepare them.

Family incomes and parents' awareness of nutrition directly influence the quality of the family's dietary intake. That is, higher levels of family incomes and parents who are knowledgeable about cooking contribute to better dietary intake. Better-off parents can afford and prepare a wider variety of wholesome foods. Families with lower incomes not only have less money in their food budget but also may lack adequate transportation, which limits their access to bulk purchases, sales, or lower-priced but more nutritious foods. Small neighbourhood convenience stores, for example, may not carry a variety of fresh fruits and vegetables or may charge higher prices.

Parents may choose to spend part of their food budget eating in restaurants. Eating out shapes eating habits because restaurant menus limit food choices and determine how foods are prepared. Even so, many families with young children eat

in fast-food places that serve mainly high-fat and fried food. Children's choices are influenced by marketing of children's "meal deals," comprising a hamburger, fries, pop, and toy.

Food Distribution Food is one of the three basic needs of every human being. However, in Canada and around the world, people do not have equal access to food, which leads us to some of the social issues that affect food distribution. When we think about health, one of the most basic human rights is having enough food to eat. The world's food system is complex in some ways and simple in others. Many of us assume that inadequate food production causes many people, especially in developing counties, to go hungry. This is not the case. In some developing countries, much food is exported to meet commitments to pay the national debt. Consequently, the people of these countries go hungry not only because of their inability to pay for food but also because inadequate quantities of food stay in the country. Hunger is a matter of food distribution, economics, and politics (White 1990).

"Since the word *hunger* evokes images which make it difficult for some people to seriously consider hunger as a problem in Canada, it has been proposed that the term *food insecurity* be substituted" (McIntyre 1994, 34). Let's look at Canada's food system to illustrate this point of view. Many areas in Canada have access to an array of foods throughout the year due to national and regional food production, high-tech food processing and storage, international trade, and transportation. The overproduction of food in North America and Europe has actually led to major storage problems and incredible wastage (Kneen 1987, 4). Plentiful harvests, however, don't make the food

producers (farmers) rich. Instead, farmers are at the mercy of the retailers—the huge food corporations that buy their produce. The rise of transnational food corporations and the high cost of farming are two of the main reasons why so many farms have gone bankrupt. For those of us who do not go hungry, convenient and cheap food may seem to be in our best interest. But when we look at the overall picture, we see that these are not the priorities that will improve the human condition. Looking at the sheer quantity of food in grocery stores, it is hard to comprehend that so many Canadians go hungry because of food insecurity due to poverty.

Food banks are "Band-Aid" solutions to the poverty and food insecurity experienced by families in Canada. Food banks have become an institution in Canada for many families whose breadwinners work at low-paying jobs or depend on social assistance and who can't manage the cost of food on top of rent, utilities, clothing, and transportation. Many children are hungry day in and day out, which affects their short- and long-term physical, emotional, and social well-being. In a country as rich as Canada, that so many children and families go hungry is atrocious. Poverty is a complex social issue that must be addressed by all levels of government and communities across Canada.

Nuts and Bolts of Nutrition

 **OBJECTIVES**   To list the seven categories of nutrients and describe main functions.
To understand the five guiding principles behind *Canada's Food Guide to Healthy Eating.*
To explain the important aspects of *Canada's Food Guide to Healthy Eating* as it relates to children.

Understanding the basics of nutrition enables us to understand the important role that eating healthy food plays in promoting health.

Role of Nutrients

Nutrients are substances that are found in food. They are divided into seven categories.

TABLE 4.2 FUNCTIONS OF NUTRIENTS	
CATEGORIES OF NUTRIENTS	**FUNCTIONS**
• carbohydrates • proteins • fats	• provide calories (or energy) needed for work and physical activity • support bodily functions; for example, proteins are needed for cell growth and repair
• vitamins • minerals • fibre • water	• are essential for helping the body regulate its functions; for example, water-soluble vitamin C helps the body absorb iron (a mineral) as it is transported through the body by water

Appendix 4.1 (page 291) expands on the description of nutrients, what foods they are found in, and their functions. Remember the following points about nutrients:

▶ All nutrients needed by the body are found in food. There is no such thing as the perfect food. Eating a varied diet usually provides our body with all the vitamins and minerals we need. Supplements such as folic acid for pregnant women or vitamin D for breast-fed babies are routinely recommended by health care practitioners. However, parents who give their children daily vitamin and/or mineral supplements "for their health" should evaluate the short- and long-term safety of this practice. Keep in mind that these supplements are not a substitute for food. "Real food is complex and offers many substances including antioxidants and phytochemicals in desirable proportions" (Deverell 1998, E5).

▶ Many nutrients work best when combined with one or more other nutrients.

e.g. Our body absorbs iron better in the presence of vitamin C, and calcium needs both phosphorus and vitamin D to build bones and teeth.

▶ Many foods are not simply a carbohydrate, protein, or fat but are a combination of two or three nutrients.

e.g. The yolk of an egg is high in fat, but the white is high in protein. Most cheeses and meats are a combination of protein and fat. The energy from whole-grain bread comes mostly from carbohydrates with a little from protein and fat.

▶ We all need the same nutrients, but how much we need of each nutrient varies with age, size, activity level, and other factors.

e.g. Children need more calcium because of bone and tooth formation. A very physically active teenager needs more food energy than a less active one.

▶ The quality of nutrients is affected by how food is grown, harvested, stored, and prepared.

e.g. Broccoli provides more of the B vitamins, especially folate, and vitamin C when it is raw than when it is boiled until soft, because most of the B and C vitamins are lost in the water—they are water-soluble.

▶ Rinsing fresh fruit and vegetables under running water with a mild soap removes soil and pesticide residue. Although peeling produce (e.g., apples, cucumbers) results in a loss of fibre, vitamins and minerals, peeling may be advisable if there is concern about pesticide use. Other ways to avoid vitamin and mineral loss are to
  ▷ cut, tear, or chop produce just before use to reduce the loss of vitamin C
  ▷ microwave, pressure cook or steam, or stir-fry vegetables just until tender
  ▷ avoid boiling vegetables
  ▷ save cooking water for soups or stews
▶ Eating too much or too little of any nutrient can contribute to or cause disease. Reduce the amount of fat, sugar, and salt you eat by using less or none at all in cooking and at the table. The taste for salt is learned. Herbs and spices provide interesting alternatives.

e.g. A high-fat diet can contribute to heart disease and some forms of cancer. A low-iron diet can cause iron deficiency (anemia).

The Foundation for Healthy Eating: *Canada's Food Guide to Healthy Eating*

Health Canada's *Food Guide to Healthy Eating* is based on five principles of healthy eating for everyone over 4 years of age. The guide emphasizes a variety of higher-fibre, lower-fat foods, and an active lifestyle. (See page 62; Appendix 4.2, page 294.) The four food groups have a range of recommended daily servings to accommodate individual nutritional needs, even as these vary with age and level of activity:

Food Group	Servings per Day
Grain products	5 to 12
Vegetables and fruit	5 to 10
Milk products	children 4 to 9 years: 2 to 3

youth 10 to 16 years: 3 to 4
adults: 2 to 4
pregnant and breast-feeding women: 3 to 4

Meat and alternatives   2 to 3

e.g.

A young woman who is moderately active may eat five or six servings of grain products (e.g., 30 g [1/2 cup] of cereal, two slices of whole-grain bread, 120 g [2 cups] of noodles in a particular day), which is adequate for her needs. If she increases her daily physical activity or becomes pregnant, her daily need for grain products will increase to seven or eight servings.

Table 4.3 lists the key nutrients in each food group and highlights the importance of eating a variety of foods to obtain the daily recommended nutrients.

Canada's Food Guide to Healthy Eating includes a final category, Other Foods, that reflects the philosophy that all foods can be part of a healthy eating pattern. It includes products such as butter, jams, potato chips, and ketchup. Coffee and alcohol are included for adults. Most of these foods contribute few nutrients (except perhaps energy through calories), are usually high in fat, salt and/or sugar, and fit into none of the four broad food categories. However, many of us find these foods to be tasty and enjoyable. They are a part of most people's diet but, like all foods, should be taken in moderation. If individuals eat these other foods to the extent that they are not getting the nutrients they need, their poor eating habits will have adverse short- and long-term effects. In child care programs, nutrition policies and practices that minimize the use of "other foods" can contribute to children's interest in more nutritious foods.

Research on diet and disease has shown that most Canadians have a lower-fibre and higher-fat diet than is optimal for health and for lowering risk factors for chronic illnesses such as heart disease, some cancers, and obesity. Canadians are urged to increase their intake of foods composed of complex carbohydrates (i.e., breads, cereals, vegetables, fruit) to replace the energy derived from the fat in meat and milk products. In response to this research, *Canada's Food Guide to Healthy Eating* puts great emphasis on eating grain products, vegetables, and fruit. For anyone ready to improve his or her eating habits, these two strategies are good places to start. Remember that too much fibre can be a problem for growing children, whose small stomachs must be able to contain enough calories for growth. Serving raw vegetables with a dip made with a dairy product, for example, is a good way both to promote fibre and to provide enough food energy.

Currently, most Canadians get almost 40 percent of their daily calories (or energy) from fat. Fat is important for body functions such as the provision of essential fatty acids and the carrying of fat-soluble vitamins through the body. However, it is not advisable to take more than 30 percent of our total calorie intake from fat. And only 10 of this 30 percent should be saturated fat (i.e., fats found in meat, milk, and butter and in some plant-based fats such as palm and coconut oils).

TABLE 4.3		KEY NUTRIENTS IN *CANADA'S FOOD GUIDE TO HEALTHY EATING*				
GRAIN PRODUCTS	+	**VEGETABLES & FRUIT**	+	**MILK PRODUCTS**	+	**MEAT & ALTERNATIVES**	=	*THE FOOD GUIDE*

GRAIN PRODUCTS	+	VEGETABLES & FRUIT	+	MILK PRODUCTS	+	MEAT & ALTERNATIVES	=	THE FOOD GUIDE
protein				protein		protein		protein
				fat		fat		fat
carbohydrate		carbohydrate						carbohydrate
fibre		fibre						fibre
thiamin		thiamin				thiamin		thiamin
riboflavin				riboflavin		riboflavin		riboflavin
niacin						niacin		niacin
folacin		folacin				folacin		folacin
				vitamin B_{12}		vitamin B_{12}		vitamin B_{12}
		vitamin C						vitamin C
		vitamin A		vitamin A				vitamin A
				vitamin D				vitamin D
				calcium				calcium
iron		iron				iron		iron
zinc				zinc		zinc		zinc
magnesium		magnesium		magnesium		magnesium		magnesium

Note: Each food group is essential. That's because it provides its own set of nutrients.

Source: Reproduced with permission of the Minister of Public Works and Government Services Canada, 1999. *Using the Food Guide,* Health Canada.

Relating *Canada's Food Guide to Healthy Eating* to Children

During the first two years of life, children undergo a period of rapid growth and development. At no other time in your life does your body need a diet as high in fat—approximately 50 percent of the total daily calories—to provide you with adequate energy and fatty acids. This is the primary reason why children under 2 are not included in Canada's food guidelines. A second reason is that the gradual introduction of solid foods over the first two years does not relate to *Canada's Food Guide to Healthy Eating*. What about children over 2 years old? Health Canada (1995) has shown us how to adapt the *Food Guide* to meet preschoolers' nutritional needs. These recommendations are integrated into this unit.

Because of the important role that dietary fat plays in children's growth and development, we'll look now at the recommendations on fat intake for children:

► Children are individuals and between the age of 2 and adolescence their developmental needs differ greatly in terms of growth patterns and energy needs.

► In the preschool years, growth rate slows, activity levels are generally high, and appetite varies greatly, resulting in erratic food intake. Energy-dense foods enable preschoolers to meet energy and nutrient needs. Despite an erratic food intake, there is evidence that young children can self-regulate food intake over a 24-hour period. Small, frequent feedings, with a variety of food choices, are important for meeting nutritional requirements during this phase.

► In young school-agers, growth is more constant. Their growth patterns and energy needs continue to vary among individuals. Fluctuations in appetite are common, and fatigue, excitement, and vigorous activity can all interfere with daily food intake.

Conclusions

► Providing enough energy and nutrients to ensure adequate growth and development remains the most important consideration in children's nutrition. Small, frequent feedings play a significant role in providing energy in children's diets.

► During childhood years, nutritious food choices should not be eliminated or restricted because of fat content. During early adolescence an energy intake adequate to sustain growth should be emphasized with a gradual lowering of fat intake. Once linear growth has stopped, fat intake as currently recommended [for adults] is appropriate.

► Food patterns that emphasize variety and complex carbohydrates, and include lower-fat choices, are appropriate and desirable for children.

► Physical activity and healthy eating are important lifestyle habits for children.

Recommendations

► From the age of 2 until the end of linear growth, there should be a transition from the high-fat diet of infancy to a diet that includes no more than 30 percent of energy as fat and no more than 10 percent of energy as saturated fat.

► During this transition, energy intake should be sufficient to achieve normal growth and development. Food patterns should emphasize variety and complex carbohydrates, and include lower-fat foods. Physical activity should be stressed. There is no evidence to show that restricting fat intake in children reduces illness in later life or provides benefits during childhood.

Source: Adapted from *Nutrition Recommendations Update ... Dietary Fat and Children*, Health Canada, 1996. Reproduced with permission of the Minister of Supply and Services, 1996.

Milk Products In the second year of life, infants make a transition from breast milk or formula to cow's milk. Between 12 and 24 months, children should drink homogenized milk. These children need whole-milk fat for brain development. Toddlers are not yet eating the variety and quantity of food to provide them with the daily dietary requirement for fat, so milk products remain the primary source of fat.

Some parents and even some doctors start the 1-year-old on lower-fat milk (skim, 1%, 2%) if they believe the baby is too chubby—though there is little or no correlation between body fat in infancy and later childhood. This example illustrates society's fear of fat. In fact, if the 1- to 2-year-old drinks lower-fat milk, he or she may be hungry and tend to eat more food. Whole milk not only provides babies with essential fats but contributes to their sense of fullness.

Partly skimmed milk (1% and 2%) is not recommended and skim milk is inappropriate in the first two years (Canadian Paediatric Society 1998, 4). By this age, most children are eating a number of foods that are higher in fat, which reduces the need for milk to supply essential fatty acids. By the time children are school-age, they can be offered 1% or skim milk. Although they still need the calcium and other nutrients that milk provides, they don't need the same percentage of dietary fat and are usually eating adult-sized servings.

What Is a Child-Sized Serving? To determine developmentally appropriate serving sizes, look at the recommendations in *Canada's Food Guide to Healthy Eating* and cut the quantity by approximately

- ▶ 2/3 to 3/4 for toddlers
- ▶ 1/4 to 1/2 for preschoolers
- ▶ 1/4 or nil for school-agers

See also Table 4.4. But remember that every child is an individual. His or her appetite can vary greatly with age, gender, activity level, and other factors.

MULTICULTURAL FOODS AND *CANADA'S FOOD GUIDE TO HEALTHY EATING*

Often caregivers caring for children from various ethno-cultural backgrounds are unfamiliar with the foods that they commonly eat at home. They may wonder whether the foods fit into the four food groups. *Canada's Food Guide to Healthy Eating* is designed to be flexible enough to include most foods. Table 4.5 shows an assortment of foods that are commonly used in a variety of cultures. Obviously, many foods are eaten by almost all cultures, where available. Often the style of cooking and the spices used differ between cultures. Chicken, for example, may be fried, baked, boiled, roasted, or cooked with different spices, batters, and sauces, depending on preferences and availability of ingredients. A Mexican chicken dish that is prepared with chocolate tastes quite different from chicken Kiev, chicken parmesan, or stir-fried chicken with vegetables. Refer to Table 4.5 and identify the foods commonly associated with particular ethno-cultural backgrounds.

Kidney and pinto beans are common in Latin American dishes; tofu is often used in Chinese dishes; roti, chapati, and naan are breads used by many Southeast Asians; and wild berries are commonly used by non-urban Native Canadians.

TABLE 4.4 EXAMPLES OF SERVING SIZES FOR PRESCHOOLERS

FOOD GROUP	ONE CHILD-SIZED SERVING
Grain Products	
bread	1/2 to 1 slice
cold cereal	15 to 30 g
hot cereal	75 to 175 mL (1/3 to 3/4 cup)
bagel, pita, or bun	1/4 to 1/2
muffin	1/2 to 1
pasta or rice	50 to 125 mL (1/4 to 1/2 cup)
soda crackers	4 to 8
Vegetables and Fruit	
fresh vegetable or fruit	1/2 to 1 piece (medium size)
frozen or canned vegetables or fruit	50 to 125 mL (1/4 to 1/2 cup)
salad	125 to 250 mL (1/2 to 1 cup)
juice	50 to 125 mL (1/4 to 1/2 cup)
Milk Products	
milk	500 mL (2 cups) per day
cheese	25 to 50 grams
yogurt	75 to 175 grams (1/3 to 3/4 cup)
Meat and Alternatives	
meat, fish, or poultry	25 to 50 grams
egg	1
beans	50 to 125 mL (1/4 to 1/2 cup)
tofu	50 to 100 grams (1/4 to 1/3 cup)
peanut butter	15 to 30 mL (1 to 2 tbsp.)

Source: Reproduced with permission of the Minister of Public Works and Government Services Canada, 1999. *Canada's Food Guide to Healthy Eating,* Health Canada.

VEGETARIANISM

Vegetarianism means different things to different people. Generally, it means choosing a plant-based way of eating. It is hard to determine how many people in Canada are currently vegetarian, but at least reducing the percentage of animal foods we eat seems to be a practice growing in popularity. Some people become vegetarians because they don't like the taste of meat. Others may have a difficult time digesting meat. Many, however,

TABLE 4.5	VARIETY OF FOODS
FOOD GROUPS	**FOOD IDEAS**
grain products	pita, bagels, bannock, roti, tortilla, chapati, naan, baguette, pretzel, challah, pasta, couscous, bulgar (e.g., in tabouli salad), buckwheat, millet, quinoa, basmati rice, rice cakes, dumpling wrappers, cassava bread, taro root
vegetables and fruit	okra, guava, mango, papaya, star fruit, breadfruit, soursop, plantain, coconut, wild berries such as huckleberries and thimbleberries, Asian pear, cassava (a root vegetable), ackee, lychees, bok choy, mushrooms, dandelion and beet greens, water chestnuts, fern root, vegetable marrow, mustard greens, bamboo shoots, soybean sprouts, summer squash, longam, cactus fruit, chayote
milk products or calcium-rich foods	goat milk, evaporated milk, feta cheese, tofu made with calcium, yogurt, fish or animal bones used in soups and stews, almonds
meat and alternatives[1]	moose, venison, beaver, wild game, chickpeas or garbonzo beans (e.g., in falafel, hummus), soybean (e.g., in soymilk, tofu), peas and rice, black-eyed peas, legumes (e.g., kidney beans, peas, navy beans, lentils, peanuts), organ meats such as kidney, heart, and liver, chorizo (a hot sausage), squid, shellfish, cockles, mussels

[1]Some cultural beliefs and religions restrict eating some meats or advocate vegetarianism. For example, Hindus and Sikhs can eat goat, fish, and pork but not beef. Muslims can eat goat, beef, and chicken but not pork. All meat must be prepared according to Muslim dietary law. Many cultures use meat sparingly, as a complement to the meal rather than the main focus. This may at times be due to the higher cost of meat, but it is becoming apparent that less rather than more meat is an effective way to reduce fat in the diet.

have based their decision on reasons of personal health, ethics and animal rights, the environment, concerns about world hunger, the cost of meat, and religion (Melina et al. 1994, 5–8). Some people are not vegetarian but have decided to eliminate some meat, such as red meat, from their diet. Their reason may be to lower cholesterol or fat intake, or to help themselves in the transition to vegetarianism. Soybean, a staple for vegetarians and available in many forms (e.g., tofu, flour, milk) is now recognized as a nutritional powerhouse and is recommended for everyone (Driedger 1997, 55).

Vegetarians are classified according to the foods that they include in their diet:

▸ Lacto-ovo vegetarians, who comprise the vast majority of vegetarians in Canada, do not eat animal flesh but do eat animal products such as milk and eggs.
▸ Lacto vegetarians eat milk and milk products but not eggs.
▸ Ovo vegetarians eat eggs but not milk.
▸ Vegans eat only foods of plant origin.
▸ Macrobiotic vegetarians base their diet on a system of 10 regimes that become more food-restrictive as they move from one to the next. At one end they can

eat small amounts of fish and dairy products with plant-based foods and at the other end they eat *only* brown rice and water.

People who are vegetarian have to be conscious of what this means nutritionally. They need to ensure that they are getting adequate amounts of complete protein and minerals (e.g., iron, zinc) and vitamins (e.g., B12) found in meat. The building blocks of protein are amino acids; we get eight essential amino acids from foods. Animal flesh and its products include all of these simultaneously, whereas most plant foods have fewer. Simply eating a lot of vegetables, grains, and fruits without complete protein is not healthy eating. Learning how to complement protein is easy. Ideally, the complementary proteins are eaten together or within a few hours of each other to ensure that they form a complete protein. Some critics of vegetarianism believe that growing children cannot get the nutrients they need, such as calcium, without eating meat. This concern is unfounded, particularly for lacto-ovo vegetarians, who consume milk products. It is important to remember that any family, vegetarian or not, can have adequate or poor nutrition. Following are examples, from Melina et al. (1994, 56), of complementary proteins, along with the country or region known for them:

Combining grains and legumes:

▷ bread and split pea soup (Canada)
▷ crackers and lentil soup (Middle East)
▷ rice and tofu (Orient)
▷ cornmeal tortillas and vegetarian chili (Mexico)
▷ chapatis and dahl (India)
▷ pita bread and falafel (Middle East)
▷ pita bread and hummus (Greece)
▷ sticky bun with black bean sauce (China)

Combining grains and nuts:

▷ granola or muesli with nuts (Switzerland)
▷ pasta with pine nuts (Italy)
▷ rice with cashew-vegetable stir-fry (China)

It is more challenging for vegans to get all the nutrients they need, but if they understand and practise good nutrition principles they will ensure that their nutrient needs are met. In vegan families, it is important that pregnant women's and children's increased need for protein, fat, calcium, iron, B12, and other nutrients be considered. For vegan infants who are not breast-fed, commercially prepared soy-based infant formula is recommended during the first two years to provide adequate nutrients and energy for growth and development (Canadian Paediatric Society et al. 1998, 40).

Macrobiotic diets, which are very restrictive, are of particular concern for children. Milks made from grains, beans, and seeds, for example, are inadequate for infants and children. "Severe nutritional deficiencies and growth retardation have been reported on numerous occasions in macrobiotic children" (Melina et al. 1994, 3).

Caregivers who have concerns about a child's nutritional intake, regardless of the type of diet, should talk with the parents. If you still have questions or need clarification, you may wish to consult with a dietitian-nutritionist.

Nutrition Labels and Food Processing

▶ **OBJECTIVES**   To identify the type of information found on food labels and describe how this information helps consumers to evaluate its nutritive value. To be aware of what food additives are, and what they do, and to recommend caution about some additives.

With few exceptions, the more processed the food, the more additives are used. A number of processes are included in the general definition of food processing, including curing meat (e.g., bacon, ham), increasing the length of time for storage/shelf life (e.g., canned fruit, vegetables), or combining a number of ingredients to make a food (e.g., hot dogs, bread).

Everything we eat seems to be potentially hazardous, so how do we reduce risk? Over the years, many early childhood education students, caregivers, and centre cooks have voiced frustration over the information printed on food labels. However, food labels can increase our understanding of healthy eating, enabling us to make more informed decisions about choosing foods that are nutritious. As a matter of fact, 71 percent of Canadians surveyed by the National Institute of Nutrition in 1997 reported using product labels as a source of nutrition information (Mongeau 1998, 2).

Nutrition Labels

We can learn a lot about foods by reading labels. Although almost all packaged foods in Canada must list their ingredients, the listing of nutrition information is optional. Many manufacturers have chosen to participate in Canada's voluntary nutrition labelling program, which began in 1988. Due to consumer interest in this information, a nutrition information panel is under consideration. It is likely that nutrition labels on products will become more widespread in the future.

Ingredients are listed in reverse order by weight. That is, the first ingredient listed is present in the largest amount, the last ingredients in the smallest. For individuals with food allergies (e.g., to peanuts, milk solids, soya, wheat, dehydrated eggs), this list is essential, since it names ingredients to be avoided. It is also useful for people on special diets (e.g., gluten-free).

One problem with labelling regulations is that variations of the same ingredient can be listed separately. Consider the list of ingredients on a box of cereal. The label may list corn syrup, icing sugar, brown sugar, honey, dextrose, and lactose. All of these are sugars. If the manufacturer had added the weight of all the sugars and printed that total under a single name, "sugar" would appear as the first ingredient. By listing them all separately, however, the manufacturer has sugars appear at various points down the label. Unless consumers read the label carefully, they may assume that this cereal is low in sugar.

The optional nutritional information is usually highlighted on a side panel with reference to a specific serving size (e.g., 4 crackers, 30 g [1.06 oz.] cereal, 100 g [3.5 oz.] frozen fish fillet). Values for energy (in calories) and weight (in grams) of protein, fat, and carbohydrates are given. Sometimes more specific information is given, such as the carbohydrate breakdown into sugars, starches, and dietary fibre, or the total fat breakdown into fatty acids and cholesterol. Percentages of recommended daily intake of particular vitamins and minerals are sometimes listed.

An expiry date or "best before" date or a code is stamped on the label or somewhere on the package (e.g., the bottom or top of the cereal box) to indicate when the contents may spoil or lose nutrients or taste. A date must appear on all foods that spoil within 90 days, except for meats, which show the date the food was packaged. Actual calendar dates are useful to both the consumer and the store manager.

ADVERTISING AND THE FOOD GAME

Every day, it seems, you hear about a new or improved product that is either lite, no-fat, or reduced fat, or has no sugar, fat, or salt! Be aware of nutrition claims highlighted on labels.

Popular claims and what they mean:

▷ *Low* is always associated with a very small amount.
▷ *Less* is used to compare one product with another. For example, a box of crackers claiming to contain "50% less salt" will have half the salt of the food to which it's compared. It doesn't necessarily mean the product is *low* in salt. Half the salt can still be a lot of salt.
▷ *Light* or *Lite* is a popular claim. When it appears on a label, consumers should look further to find out which feature of the product is "light." This claim is often used to describe a food reduced in fat and energy, but not always. Sometimes it describes the taste or texture of a food or even a lighter colour!
▷ *Low in Saturated Fat* or *Cholesterol Free* may lead consumers to think the product is low in fat. It's not necessarily so. Vegetable oils contain no cholesterol, and may be low in saturated fat, but are very high in total fat (Health and Welfare Canada 1992b, Number 10).

High-powered advertising campaigns shape our food choices, often when no real difference exists between two food products other than the packaging. Some advertisers direct our attention to the product's logo, the spokesperson's photo, or the picture on the package. Advertising influences our purchasing decisions between brands of the same product (e.g., three brands of Caesar salad dressing) or between a brand-name product and its generic competitor (White 1990, 6).

Food Additives

Since 1964, Health Canada's Health Protection Branch has required rigorous testing on food additives before they are approved. Currently about 2800 food additives are approved for use in Canada (Driedger 1997, 59). Some food additives work as preservatives. Others are used simply to make the food look appealing (e.g., with colouring).

The good news is that research shows that most additives do not pose a threat to your short- or long-term health. However, some additives may be of concern when used regularly for long periods. (See Appendix 4.3, page 296.) In these cases, we must consider the concept of synergy. Synergism is defined in the *New Lexicon Webster's Dictionary* as "the combined action of two or more which have a greater total effect than the sum of their individual parts." We are exposed to hundreds of chemicals daily, most of them necessary and harmless. However, when we have a choice of ingesting some chemicals that may not be in our best interests, why not choose the healthier alternative?

Food quality suffers when additives and processes are used to ensure cosmetic attractiveness and a long shelf life. The less real (natural) food there is in a product, the less corporations need to rely on natural growing (farmers' livelihoods) and weather conditions (White 1990, 6). Misleading claims frustrate consumers—a fact recognized by lobby groups that advocate for change in labelling laws (Health and Welfare Canada 1992b, Number 10).

Pollution Probe (1994) defines food additives as any chemical, whether natural or synthetic, that is deliberately used in the growth, processing, storage, or distribution of food. Food additives are grouped into two categories:

- ► Food-processing additives include
  - ▷ colours, which make food look more appealing
  - ▷ preservatives, which keep food from going bad
  - ▷ flavours and flavour enhancers, which make food taste better
  - ▷ sweeteners, which make food taste sweeter (e.g., aspartame)
  - ▷ texture agents, which give food a pleasing texture
  - ▷ processing agents, which make processing easier (Pollution Probe 1994, 24)
- ► Unintentional additives are those that are intentionally used in the cycle of food production but "unintentionally" remain in or on food when we eat it (e.g., chemicals from food packaging, pesticide residue, and hormones or antibiotics from animal products) (Pollution Probe 1994, 97).

Many children favour meats that are highly processed, such as hot dogs, ham, bacon, bologna, salami, and other luncheon meats. Children often like processed meats because they are easy to chew and have a salty taste. If children eat these meats regularly, they often choose processed meats over other meat and alternatives. Children's consumption of these meats raises concerns because they are highly processed, usually high in saturated fat and salt, and contain nitrates and nitrites.

Nitrates and Nitrites

Nitrates and nitrites are additives used to preserve meat. They prevent the growth of bacteria that cause a type of serious food poisoning called botulism (see Food Safety Practices, page 275), and they preserve the red colour in meats and enhance flavour.

When we eat nitrates, our body first converts them to nitrites. Then the body converts nitrites to nitrosomines, which are thought to cause cancer. "Nitrosomines have been described as 'the most potent cancer-causing agent known to science'" (Trum Hunter, cited in Pollution Probe, 1994, 50). You may wonder why nitrates and nitrites are added to foods in Canada if they are known carcinogens. The most plausible reason is that they have preservative qualities. Since botulism is so serious, there is legitimate public concern about the potential for outbreaks of botulism in the absence of adequate food preservation. Nitrates can be found in vegetables that have been exposed to nitrogen fertilizer: due to leaching, nitrates can get into the ground water. There is less concern about the vegetable sources because of the presence in the foods of vitamin C, which prevents the formation of nitrosomines in our bodies.

According to Pollution Probe (1994, 51), nitrate-free and nitrite-free brands of processed meats are available, so their wide use is not necessary. Eating a hot dog or salami sandwich now and then is not as great a concern as the regular consumption of highly processed meats. Many people eat processed meats daily because they are convenient, inexpensive, and tasty. When children are offered them both at home and in the centre, they develop a way of eating that is likely to perpetuate the regular consumption of these meats for a lifetime. Even if the processed meat is nitrate- or nitrite-free, the large amounts of saturated fat and salt makes it inadvisable as a regular food choice.

You can introduce other types of protein—without nitrates and nitrites—that children enjoy. Perhaps in addition to the obvious other meat and fish options, you could try more vegetarian dishes that combine foods to provide complete protein. There are also soy products, such as TVP (textured vegetable protein), which resemble meat and provide complete protein. TVP is easy to use in pasta or rice sauces, chili, lasagna, and so on, and is an inexpensive way to get protein without saturated fat. (See Vegetarianism, page 235.)

Aspartame

Aspartame is being added to many foods, beverages, and snack products. This sweetener is manufactured from an amino acid and so is easily digested by your body. Many adults regularly consume products with aspartame—gelatin desserts, puddings, beverages, gum. Some parents encourage their children to eat these products because they are concerned about children eating too much sugar.

Although the long-term health effects on children who consume high quantities of aspartame are not yet known, the amount of aspartame that children consume should be limited. Research has shown that sugar is not the evil we once thought it was. It does not cause hyperactivity. And concern about high-sugar foods replacing more nutritious foods can apply also to foods containing aspartame. If children are filling up on high-sugar, low-nutrient foods, they should be encouraged to eat fewer sweet foods rather than substitute with sweet foods containing aspartame. Although aspartame doesn't contribute to tooth decay, regular toothbrushing and flossing should be fostered in children.

In child care programs, staff should provide foods that are as natural as possible and have been processed as little as possible. Aspartame does not comply with this recommendation.

PESTICIDES

Pesticides are commonly used in farming, except in organic farming, to kill organisms (or pests) on vegetables, fruits, and grains during the growing season. Pesticides are an example of *unintentional* additives, because some chemicals remain *in* or *on* the food after harvest. As a general rule, all of us should try to minimize our exposure to pesticides, due to short- and long-term concerns about health. Agriculture Canada approves all pesticides before use and has banned some that are still used in other countries (e.g., DDT). Relative to most countries, Canada uses fewer pesticides in agriculture. However, imported produce may have higher concentrations of pesticides, including those that are banned in Canada.

There are particular concerns about the potential effects of pesticides on children, because their developing bodies may be more readily affected by toxins. Children also tend to eat a lot of fruit and drink a lot of fruit juice. What can we do to reduce the amount of pesticides we eat? Pollution Probe (1994, 112) suggests that you wash produce in a mild solution of dish soap with water or a diluted mixture of water and vinegar. Although you will lose some fibre and vitamins by peeling fruits and vegetables, you will reduce your exposure to pesticides. Buying organic produce and lobbying policymakers to reduce both the commercial and residential use of pesticides, are two ways to promote everyone's health.

Being Informed Consumers

Nutrition labels help us select foods for healthy eating. If you are not in the habit of reading product labels, you will probably be overwhelmed by a list of unpronounceable and obscure ingredients. You will also find that it is a time-consuming process, especially if you are comparing your favourite brand with its competitors.

No one expects you to remember the names of all the ingredients, what they are and do, and which should be avoided or at least limited in consumption. Lists such as the one in Appendix 4.3 are useful tools to take shopping. By reading the labels of the products used in the home or centre, you will soon compile a list of acceptable and unacceptable products for the shopping list. This will drastically reduce the time that is needed to shop. (See page 296.)

Whether you are at home or at the centre, when you are trying to reduce the amount of fat, sugar, salt, and suspicious additives, here are a few tips for reading labels to evaluate products for healthy eating:

Fat:
▶ Use equal serving sizes when comparing two products for fat content.
▶ Choose milk, yogurt, or cottage cheese with 2 percent fat rather than whole milk for children over 2 years of age. For school-age children and adults the fat content can be reduced to 1 percent or skim.
▶ Choose cheeses with 15 percent milk fat (m.f.) or less.
▶ Select meats that are lower in fat (e.g., poultry, fish), and when selecting red meats choose leaner cuts (e.g., lean ground beef).
▶ Look for canned fish packed in water or vegetable broth.

Sugar:
Note that ingredients ending in "ose" are types of sugar—glucose, maltose, lactose, dextrose, fructose. You may be familiar with the obvious types of sugar, such as granulated and icing sugar, brown sugar, honey, corn syrup, and molasses.

Salt:
"Sodium" is the key word to alert you to the presence of salt. If the word "salt" does not appear on the list of ingredients, don't assume that there is no salt in the product. There may be a number of sodium additives, such as monosodium glutamate, sodium bicarbonate, sodium metabisulphite, disodium guanylate.

Healthy Eating Habits

 **OBJECTIVES** To state the practices that create a positive eating environment and encourage children to try new foods.
To describe appropriate principles and practices in infant feeding.
To consider the unique aspects of toddler growth and development that affect their nutrition and eating habits.
To identify developmental issues for preschoolers and school-agers that affect their eating behaviour.
To consider reasons why there may be concerns about children under- or overeating.

TABLE 4.6	DEVELOPMENTAL CHARACTERISTICS RELATED TO EATING	
AGE	**PHYSICAL**	**SOCIAL / PERSONAL**
Birth to 4 months	• turns mouth toward nipple that brushes cheek • sucks and swallows	• recognizes the breast or bottle as the source of food by about 10 weeks • excited by sight of food (e.g., breast, bottle)
4 to 6 months	• sucking strength increases • chewing motion begins • uses tongue to move food in mouth • begins to finger-feed	• excited by sight of food
6 to 9 months	• holds a bottle • drinks from a cup held by adult • rotary chewing begins • tongue has increased movement and allows for more manipulation of food	• begins to show likes and dislikes for foods
9 to 12 months	• tries to use spoon • chews up and down • finger-feeds with a refined grasp	• conscious of what others do and imitates their examples
12 to 18 months	• grasps and releases food with fingers • holds spoon, but use is awkward • turns spoon in mouth • uses cup, but release poor	• wants food others are eating • loves performing
18 to 24 months	• appetite decreases • likes eating with hands • likes experimenting with textures	• ritual becomes important (e.g., has to have milk in red cup) • displays food preferences • distracts easily
2 to 3 years	• holds glass in hand • places spoon straight into mouth • spills a lot • chews more foods, but choking still a hazard	• has definite likes and dislikes • insists on doing it "myself" • ritualistic • dawdles • has food jags (e.g., refuses to eat anything but peanut butter sandwiches) • demands foods in certain shapes or whole foods • likes to help in kitchen

(table continues on next page)

TABLE 4.6	DEVELOPMENTAL CHARACTERISTICS RELATED TO EATING (continued)	
AGE	**PHYSICAL**	**SOCIAL / PERSONAL**
3 to 4 years	• holds handle on cup • pours from small pitcher • uses fork • chews most food	• improved appetite and interest in food • favourite foods requested • likes shapes, colours, ABCs • able to choose between two alternate foods • influenced by TV commercials • likes to copy food preparer
4 to 5 years	• uses knife and fork • good use of cup • good self-feeder	• rather talk than eat • food jags continue • motivated to eat by incentives • likes to help • interested in nature of food and where it comes from • peer influence increasing
5 to 6 years	• feeds self	• conforming • less suspicious of mixtures but still prefers plain foods • social influence outside home increasing • food important part of special occasions
6 to 8 years	• refined small motor skills and eye–hand coordination (e.g., able to use some simple kitchen equipment such as can opener, toaster) • slow growth • high energy level	• shares and takes turns • table manners improving • eager to please • significant peer pressure (e.g., less willing to try new foods) • can follow steps for simple recipes almost independently • good sense of humour (e.g., creating funny names for recipes) • can delay gratification for a short time
8 to 11 years	• more coordinated (can usually use most kitchen equipment, e.g., knives, microwaves; may need supervision with stove) • physical competence important for self-concept status with peers • responsible for most self-care	• setting standards for own behaviour • often conforms to rules set by peers (e.g., high-status foods, trading lunch foods) • enjoys choosing and preparing foods, connecting nutrition with everyday life

(table continues on next page)

TABLE 4.6	DEVELOPMENTAL CHARACTERISTICS RELATED TO EATING (continued)	
AGE	**PHYSICAL**	**SOCIAL / PERSONAL**
11 to 13 years	• dramatic physical changes associated with onset of puberty, approximately a year earlier for girls than boys • increased nutritional needs (e.g., calcium, iron)	• may be moody with hormone changes • looking for self-identity, may resist adults' nutritional advice • may restrict food intake due to body image pressures, especially but not only girls

Source: Adapted with permission from *Promoting Nutritional Health during the Preschool Years: Canadian Guidelines,* Network of the Federal/Provincial/Territorial Group on Nutrition and National Institute of Nutrition (1989), 23.

Satter (1990, 14) defines the division of responsibility in feeding: "Parents are responsible for what is presented to eat and the manner in which it is presented. Children are responsible for how much and even whether they eat." This philosophy is based on respect for children and a desire to give them control over what they eat, so that they can respond to their own bodily needs and learn to eat for the right reasons. When this independence is taken away, they can soon learn to eat for the wrong reasons. An obvious example is when we insist that children finish a plate of food after they have already told us they are full. It is no wonder that children then become anxious about mealtime, and may become overweight because they are eating more food than they need to, or may have low weight gain because they assert themselves and refuse to eat. These mealtime situations can affect children's relationships with parents and caregivers when tensions and frustrations run high.

Children's growth and development play a key role in determining their readiness for food as well as their interests in food and socializing. By accommodating children's development, caregivers ensure that individual nutritional needs are met and that eating environments are designed to promote positive eating habits.

Creating a Positive Eating Environment

As important as the foods offered to children is their eating environment, which either promotes or hinders healthy eating and meets or inhibits social and emotional needs. Nutritious foods are of no value to children if they don't eat them. On the other hand, we know that any form of force-feeding or pressuring children does not work, especially for the long term. A positive environment is a much better option, regardless of the age group. When meals or snack times become negative experiences, with unhappy children and/or caregivers, work through the following checklist and identify which criteria have not been met.

Encourage children to try new foods. Here are a few suggestions:

▶ Present one new food at a time.

▶ Introduce the food when children are most hungry (e.g., at the beginning of a meal as an appetizer). You may be surprised at how excited preschoolers get when they hear you mention the word "appetizer," and how much they enjoy eating raw vegetables and dip, or celery in a glass of tomato juice.

▶ Serve the new foods with ones that the children are already familiar with.

▶ Offer small amounts.

▶ Talk about the colour, texture, taste, shape, and smell of the food.

▶ Encourage the children to help you prepare the new food.

▶ Encourage but don't insist that children taste the new food. If they reject it or say "I don't like it," accept their comments and offer it again in a week or two. The more often they see the new food, the more familiar it becomes, and the more willing they will be to accept it.

▶ Ask children what they didn't like about the new food. Maybe you need only change the way the food is prepared. If this food is familiar to families in the centre, ask the parents for ideas about preparing it for or with the children.

TABLE 4.7 POSITIVE EATING ENVIRONMENT: CHECKLIST	YES	NO
The atmosphere is relaxed. For example, if children are expected to come in from outdoor play and immediately wash hands to eat, their difficulty in relaxing at the meal is not surprising. Caregivers need to think about sequence and transition needs for children.		
Distractions are at a minimum, and children are encouraged to focus on what they eat. Balance this with a warm social environment where children can talk calmly while sitting.		
Children's rights are respected (i.e., not forced to eat foods they don't like or teased for not being skilled with spoons or forks).		
Individual food likes and dislikes are acknowledged, promoting the child's self-esteem.		
Children are guided (by adult modelling) to observe certain behaviour while eating, developing a sense of self-respect and respect for others. Caregivers eat meals with children and model positive eating attitudes and behaviour.		
Children are encouraged to develop their five senses in enjoying a variety of foods.		
Children are *not* forced to conform to rigid rules or expected to have perfect table manners. For example: Positively reinforcing children's use of "please" and "thank you" is far more effective than demanding that every time a child wants or receives something at the table she must use these words (e.g., repeatedly asking children, "What's the magic word?"—which is not only patronizing but misleading, since we don't always get what we want). (If only life were that simple!)		
Food, beverages, and desserts are not used as bribes or punishments. Depriving children of food is not an acceptable practice. When unacceptable behaviour does not relate to eating (e.g., arguments over toys at playtime), there is *never* any association made with food as a punishment or as a reward if he or she stops (e.g., "If you keep fighting, you won't have snack," or "If you stop doing that, you can have dessert").		
Children are provided with developmentally appropriate opportunities to be involved in serving themselves. Children can start with giving themselves small servings and can have more if they would like, giving them control over the amount of food on their plate. Toddlers, preschoolers, and school-agers serve themselves as often as possible. • Snacks are set out where two or three children can serve themselves at a table. • Milk is served in small pitchers so children can pour their own. • Family-style serving dishes are used at the table.		
There are well-maintained chairs, tables, plates, and utensils suited to the children's size and development.		

(table continues on next page)

TABLE 4.7 POSITIVE EATING ENVIRONMENT: CHECKLIST (continued)	YES	NO
The table is made as attractive as possible (e.g., by laminating place mats that children make). Children are involved whenever possible in setting the table.		
Foods served for celebrations and holidays are nutritious and fun.		
Children are encouraged to share food experiences from their own ethno-cultural or regional backgrounds and are introduced to foods from around the world as a part of the regular menu.		
Parents are encouraged to: • comment/ask nutritional questions about the centre's and their child's nutrition • contribute nutritional foods/snacks for special occasions and are invited to participate • provide favourite ethno-cultural recipes		

▶ Remember that if children see caregivers enjoying or at least trying the new food, they may be encouraged to try it too. However, you aren't expected to force yourself to eat something you dislike. Besides, if you have it in your mouth but your body language says "It's disgusting" and your comments are negative, the children will understand your true feelings.

Infant Nutrition

At no other time in our lives will there be as dramatic a rate in our growth and development as during the prenatal period and infancy. Infants double their birth weight by five months of age and triple it within the year. In the same year, they will be 1 1/2 times as long as they were at birth (e.g., 20 ins. [50.8 cm] at birth and 30 ins. [76.2 cm] at 12 months). Infants' brains continue to grow and they quickly develop motor skills. As well, infants move from being able only to suck and swallow to finger-feeding in 12 months. (See Table 4.6, page 244; Chart 7.1, page 458.) During the first year of life, one of infants' fundamental needs is to have their nutritional requirements met by their parents and caregivers. Without all the essential nutrients, growth, development, learning, and play will be negatively affected. Parents and caregivers must communicate effectively—meaning daily written and verbal communication—so that consistency of care between home and centre can be provided.

Breast Milk and Infant Formula

The best nutritional choice for infants is breast milk, for a number of reasons:

▶ Human milk is perfectly suited to infants.

▶ It contains the ideal quantities and quality of the three energy-producing nutrients (carbohydrate, fat, protein).

▶ The large amount of lactose (sugar) helps in the development of the central nervous system.

▶ It contains the right balance of most essential vitamins and minerals. Breast milk does not contain vitamin D, and the physician may prescribe a vitamin D supplement while infants are exclusively breast-fed.

▶ The protein in breast milk is easily digested in comparison to proteins from other foods. Protein is the most difficult nutrient for us to digest. Cow's milk, peanuts, and eggs are some of the most highly allergenic foods because they are high in protein.

▶ The essential fatty acids promote brain development.

▶ Breast milk contains antibodies that provide infants with immunity against some infections during the breast-feeding period.

▶ Breast-fed infants are less likely to develop allergies. Infants may react to certain foods that their mother has recently eaten (e.g., after she eats broccoli, the infant experiences flatulence).

Many mothers who breast-feed need support from caregivers in making the transition from home to work. A mother may want to continue with nursing after her infant is enrolled in the centre. Those few women whose workplace is located close to the centre may be able to come to the centre during the day to nurse their infant. Other mothers may bring in bottles of expressed breast milk and may breast-feed the infant at the beginning and end of the day at the centre. However, most mothers nurse at home and provide formula for the child during the day in the centre. There are also mothers who wean their infants before returning to work, so the child has infant formula exclusively. There should be a comfortable chair or rocker for the mother and child in the centre and a relatively private place if she chooses.

Infants who are offered expressed breast milk or formula at the centre will usually have been introduced to a bottle at home first. Infants who are used to receiving their nourishment from the breast may have a difficult time with this transition or they may accept the bottle readily.

We know that HIV can be spread from a pregnant woman who is HIV-positive to her unborn child through her breast milk after the baby is born. When her HIV status is known, her physician will advise her not to breast-feed. We also know that individuals can be HIV-positive and not know they are, so there may be HIV-positive mothers who are breast-feeding their babies.

Centres are *already* required to have *all* baby bottles labelled with the children's full name. *Caregivers must ensure that the baby receives only his or her bottle.* If a baby is fed a bottle of breast milk that is not his or her own, caregivers must call the local public health agency. Public health staff will then determine whether the baby has been exposed to HIV and how to proceed. The centre director should also be instructed about notifying the baby's parents. Expressed breast milk does not present risks when it comes in contact with someone's skin (e.g., spit-up, or during a test of the milk's temperature on the top of your hand). Discouraging mothers from providing expressed breast milk for their infants in centres is *not* an acceptable response to the issue of HIV. High-quality centres already implement the practices that prevent the spread of HIV in children.

For babies who are not breast-fed, commercial formula is essential for the first 9 to 12 months of life. Most formulas are made of either modified cow's milk or soy protein and include the infant's needs for water, fatty acids, carbohydrate (lactose), protein, and vitamins and minerals. Iron-fortified formulas are recommended for the first 9 to 12 months. The importance of preventing rather than treating iron-deficiency anemia is emphasized because anemia is a risk factor for possible irreversible developmental delays (Canadian Paediatric Society et al. 1998, 39). Commercial formulas are designed to be as similar to breast milk as possible. For more information on infant nutrition, refer to *Nutrition for Healthy Term Infants* (1998). (See Resource Materials, page 284.)

Bottle Feeding   Bottle-feeding time is an ideal time for caregivers to hold and cuddle infants. Bottle feeding is not a time to be rushed. The practice of bottle propping is absolutely unacceptable because of the risk of choking and dental caries (tooth decay). Feeding is one of the important daily care routines; it helps infants to develop safe, secure, and trusting relationships with their caregivers. Infants who can sit without support and especially toddlers may prefer to sit and drink their bottle independently. Caregivers should discourage toddlers from walking around with a bottle in their mouth. Obviously, the child must never be left unsupervised.

In many infant programs, parents bring in one bottle for each feeding during the day. Each bottle is filled with approximately the amount of formula or expressed breast milk that the infant drinks in one feeding. There could be four bottles, each with 90 mL (3 ozs.) of formula. After the child has drunk from the bottle, do not give him or her leftovers at the next feeding. Formula and breast milk are perfect media for the growth of germs, and during the sucking motion germs enter the bottle. Therefore, leftovers must be discarded. (See Food Safety Practices, page 275.)

Some centres are in the practice of having caregivers prepare the formula for each infant every day. The parents provide cans of their infant's specific brand. However, considering the amount of care and interaction that infants and toddlers need from their caregivers and that the caregiver–child ratio is already 1:3 or 1:4, caregivers' time should be spent more productively. Since parents already make formula for their infants to drink at home, it is not unrealistic to expect them to bring bottled formula needed at the centre. As well, the logistics of clearly identifying all the individual bottles and nipples, sterilizing water, containers, measuring equipment, the bottles (unlined) and nipples, and ensuring sterility of the formula are an unnecessary burden on the caregivers.

First Foods

Early introduction of semisolid foods is not good practice in promoting optimal nutrition. Before 4 months of age, children's bodies are not ready for food. Breast milk or formula provides all the essential nutrients. Between 4 and 6 months of age, most infants are ready to try chewing and swallowing some semisolid foods (Canadian Paediatric Society et al. 1998,5).

If a young infant is fed semisolid food, most of it will be found undigested in the stool. Infants' digestive and renal systems are too immature to cope with anything other than breast milk or formula. Infants don't produce enough saliva or digestive enzymes, and their immature kidneys cannot filter much protein. These infants are also more vulnerable to developing food allergies. Semisolid foods are less of an allergy risk to infants once they've reached the age of 6 months and their immune system has begun to mature.

Parents may believe that their infants need to eat solid foods as early as 2 or 3 months of age because the child seems more hungry or is waking up more often during the night. Many parents interpret this to mean that the breast milk or formula isn't filling up the child. In fact, infants simply go through growth spurts and need extra nutrients; all they need is extra breast milk or formula for a week or two to get through the spurt. Lambert-Lagacé notes that it is a myth that very young babies sleep better at night when they are fed infant cereal. In reality, "prolonged sleep reflects the baby's total neurological development and has very little to do with the food she eats, colic being one exception" (1992, 84). Understandably, parents want the best for their baby and are concerned about why she or he seems hungry. Relatives and friends may also have assumed that adding solid foods early was good practice and may be encouraging (or pressuring) parents to do the same. They may suggest, for example, adding infant cereal to the formula in the bottle.

Ideally, parents consult their infant's physician to determine on an individual basis when to introduce semisolid foods. This decision will be based somewhat on increased nutrient needs and the infant's having at least doubled his or her birth weight, although motor abilities and interest in other family members' foods also influence the decision. In turn, the parents and caregivers work together in the feeding process.

The introduction of semisolid foods should be a slow process. This respects the infants' nutritional and emotional needs, so that eating food is a positive experience for self-esteem rather than a process that infants can fail at or experience negative feelings about because it happened too early. Infants should have as much control as possible in the feeding process. Watch for the following signs of infants' readiness to start with semisolids:

► better able to sit up
► can move their head back to indicate fullness or uninterest
► can move their head forward to indicate hunger or interest
► can hold a spoon, although it will be months before they use it effectively
► have shown interest in putting food on their hands and some food has eventually reached their mouth

Developmentally, infants need sensory experiences, including food experiences, to begin to understand their world. Some babies need and enjoy this type of sensory

exploration more than others. Don't be surprised if some parents are concerned about seeing their infants with their hands in the food—perhaps feeling that caregivers are encouraging their infants to play with their food. Once again, effective communication between parents and caregivers is important in negotiating compromise.

One obvious difference in feeding practices has to do with fundamental values in cultures.

 Your program's goal is to encourage infant and toddler independence. You encourage the infant to use a spoon while you have a second spoon to feed him. However, the parents' philosophy emphasizes the importance of interdependence—connection with the family is a priority; the feeling of being connected is much more important than self-sufficiency. Feeding with interdependence in mind means that the adult feeds the infant, perhaps into the preschool years, as part of this value. This is not an issue of right or wrong but of two different views. With discussion, a compromise will be reached. (See Table 1.2, page 43.)

THE PROCESS OF INTRODUCING SEMISOLID FOODS

Even though infants are now ready for semisolid foods, they are not ready to have the food replace the nutrients in the breast milk or formula. Until the age of around 9 months, the infant should be offered the formula or breast milk first and then semisolid food. After 9 months, the child can eat the semisolids first and then finish the meal with a bottle. By this time they are eating a variety of foods and in enough quantity to ensure they are getting the essential nutrients.

Parents should introduce each food at home several times before it is offered in the centre. Parents know their child best and will recognize any allergic reaction to the new food. Parents should wait three to five days before trying the next new food to observe any reaction the child may have, such as undigested food in the stool, gas, rashes, breathing difficulties, or any other sign that the child may be sensitive or allergic to the food. Parents often introduce cereals first, followed by vegetables, fruit, and meat and alternatives.

Cereals Infant cereals are usually introduced first. Rice cereals are least likely to cause allergies; they can be followed by other single-grain cereals and then mixed-grain cereals. The commercially prepared infant cereals, often called pabulum, are best suited to infants because they are a good source of iron and in a form that is easily absorbed. Their other nutrients, including protein, carbohydrates, and fats, are easily digested. Infants have an increased need for iron around 6 months. The introduction of cereals takes three weeks to a month if these foods are introduced gradually.

Vegetables and Fruit There are two schools of thought on the introduction of vegetables and fruit. Some experts believe that there is no difference between the two and that they can be alternated. Other experts suggest starting with vegetables because many are easily digested and because if fruit is introduced first, some infants may be less likely to accept the less sweet taste of most vegetables. Fruit would follow three or four weeks after the vegetables. Regardless of which perspective parents choose, here are some points to keep in mind:

▶ Carrots, squash, sweet potatoes, asparagus, green peas, cauliflower, and broccoli need to be cooked and puréed.
▶ Ripe fresh fruits like bananas, mangoes, and papayas can be mashed. Apples, pears, peaches, and plums need to be peeled, cooked, and puréed.
▶ Limited intake of fruit juice is acceptable, but the consumption of a lot can contribute to inadequate intake of other nutrients and energy, poor weight gain, and possibly diarrhea (Canadian Paediatric Society et al. 1998, 26).
▶ Real fruit juice should be diluted with equal parts water and given from a spoon or cup only. Centres can support this practice by having a policy which states that juice will be served in cups only, and that bottles of juice brought from home will be transferred to a cup. By the time a child is ready for juice, he or she is developmentally ready to drink from a cup. Juice in bottles encourages children to drink far more juice than the daily requirement of fruit and contributes to dental caries (tooth decay). (See Dental Health Education, page 511.)

Meat and Alternatives Meats and alternatives are high in protein, a number of minerals, and some fat. Meats are usually introduced about three months after cereals. These additional months give the infant's digestive system even more time to mature, which makes it better able to digest proteins.

When feeding infants, here are a few points to remember:

▶ All foods need to be of a puréed texture when they are introduced, and become less puréed and more choppy as the infant is better able to chew and may have some teeth. Some infants go from semiliquid cereals and puréed baby foods to finger

Lambert-Lagacé has suggested a pattern to follow in introducing these foods:

►   Start with white meat such as chicken, turkey, or fish.
►   Continue with beef, veal, liver, or lamb.
►   Introduce mashed tofu, the silken type.
►   Avoid processed meats such as ham and bacon because of high sodium and nitrite content.
►   Choose fish that have less PCB residue such as small farmed fish or ocean fish— sole, flounder, grouper, haddock, halibut, monkfish, salmon, or tuna.
►   Introduce one new meat (or alternate) every three to four days.
►   Offer homemade or commercial baby food.
►   At first, serve only 5 mL (1 tsp.) alone, not mixed with vegetables.
►   Offer this food group at the noon meal.
►   Never add salt or seasonings.
►   Gradually increase to a maximum of 90 mL (6 tbsp.) daily by the end of the first year.

Source: *Feeding Your Baby in the Nineties: From Conception to Age Two.* Copyright © 1992 by Louise Lambert-Legacé. Reprinted by permission of Stoddart Publishing Co. Limited.

foods and table foods in just a few months (Canadian Paediatric Society et al. 1998, 29).

►   It is *never* acceptable to pressure a child into eating.
►   Foods that are helpful for teething infants include dry toast, and soft pieces of fruit or vegetables (e.g., a ring of green pepper). Most store-bought teething biscuits contain sugar and are not recommended.

Table 4.8 provides you with approximate serving sizes for infant foods and is meant to be only a guide. As infants develop a repertoire of foods and can chew more effectively, fewer table foods need to be restricted from them, except foods that are a concern for choking.

Assessing the situation:
Identify the issues of concern for the caregivers and suggest a way to proceed.

Scenario: The parents of an 8-month-old girl haven't yet introduced semisolid foods, not even infant cereal. Marie's source of nutrition is her mother's breast milk. Marie is interested in what the other children are eating. She is hungry half an hour after you feed her a bottle of expressed breast milk. However, when you mention this to her mother, she assures you that she will be starting Marie on infant cereal soon. That was three weeks ago and Marie's mother hasn't followed through.

AGE	DRY CEREAL	VEGETABLE	FRUITS	MEAT
4 to 6 months	up to 120 mL (8 tbsp.) daily*			
7 months	120 mL (8 tbsp.)	60 mL (4 tbsp.)		
8 months	120 mL (8 tbsp.)	75 mL (5 tbsp.)	90 mL (6 tbsp.)	
9 months	120 mL (8 tbsp.)	90 mL (6 tbsp.)	105 mL (7 tbsp.)	45 mL (3 tbsp.)
10 months	135 mL (9 tbsp.)	120 mL (8 tbsp.)	120 mL (8 tbsp.)	45 mL (3 tbsp.)
11 months	135 mL (9 tbsp.)	135 mL (9 tbsp.)	135 mL (9 tbsp.)	60 mL (4 tbsp.)
12 months	150 mL (10 tbsp.)	150 mL (10 tbsp.)	150 mL (10 tbsp.)	60 mL (4 tbsp.) or 1 egg may be given

TABLE 4.8   APPROXIMATE SERVING SIZES: 4 TO 12 MONTHS OF AGE

*Many 5- to 6-month-old infants may eat vegetables and fruit too.

Toddler Nutrition

Toddlers are at a stage where they are developing a sense of autonomy (a sense of independence) and balancing that need with the need to feel connected with their parents, families, and peers. As a result, parents and caregivers have the challenging role of respecting the toddlers' need for autonomy but setting limits to promote trust and security. (See Table 4.6, page 244; Chart 7.1, page 458.)

Toddlers' growth slows to a rate of only-half to one-third of what it was in the first 12 months, but exploration speeds up! Except during growth spurts, toddlers won't be as hungry now as in the past and they may eat less overall. Their appetite can be inconsistent. Many toddlers can override any desire to eat when they are over-excited, over-tired, or angry with their parents or caregivers. Some parents and caregivers are concerned about this natural change in eating habits and pressure toddlers to eat. This is not appropriate practice at any age, but is a big mistake with toddlers, who will assert their independence. When an adult and a toddler get into power struggles, nobody wins!

Poor eating habits now can pave the way for eating problems that last a lifetime. Toddlers can become anxious about mealtimes, or refuse to eat, or have temper tantrums because of frustration. Parents and caregivers need to remember that most young children will eat when they are hungry and when they are offered a variety of nourishing foods. It is a toddler's job to assert his or her independence and it is the trusted adult's job to confirm his or her security by providing firm but reasonable limits.

Some things to keep in mind when toddlers are eating:

► Remember the division of responsibility: *caregivers have indirect control of feeding* (i.e., selecting and presenting nutritious foods, setting routine times for snacks and meals, creating a pleasant atmosphere, maintaining developmentally appropriate standards of behaviour at the table, helping the children attend to their eating) and *children have direct control of eating* (i.e., deciding what and how much they eat). Some enjoy or need adult assistance with feeding.

► Many have a hard time sitting long enough to eat a whole meal if it is holding them back from doing other things.

► Toddlers typically dawdle over food. Rather than focus on the dawdling and the inconvenience this brings to the flow of the program, it is more effective to give reasonable but firm limits, such as "You have 10 more minutes for lunch" and, after the allotted time, calmly remove the child's plate without commenting on how much the child ate.

► Practical hints:
  ▷ Use child-sized unbreakable plates, bowls, and utensils.
  ▷ Toddlers often eat very small serving sizes (sometimes one-quarter of an adult's serving size). Avoid dishing out large amounts of food; they may seem overwhelming to a toddler. This may turn the child off his or her food.
  ▷ Provide finger foods, so that toddlers are not always expected to use utensils, which is an emerging skill and not always an easy one to master.
  ▷ Thin soup enough to drink or have it thick enough to eat with a spoon.
  ▷ Cut foods into bite-sized pieces.
  ▷ Avoid serving very chewy foods.
  ▷ Children need to sit down to eat.
  ▷ Take special care to avoid foods that may cause choking. (See Reducing the Risk of Choking, page 274.)

► Toddlers are often afraid to try new things (neophobic) and so tend to be afraid of new foods. The more familiar toddlers are with foods, the more they like them. Coaxing toddlers to try new foods tends to make them more resistant to the idea. Instead, if they see a new food offered with no outside pressure *several* times, eventually they try it and the food becomes less and less an aversion. Expect toddlers to refuse a new food and avoid thinking, "Oh, they didn't like it so we won't make it again!"

► Toddlers learn to like most foods that they originally rejected. However, in the process they may do things like spit out the food if its texture, flavour, temperature, or other aspect is unusual to them. This is a learning process that should not be discouraged, because it usually leads to more openness toward food. If their behaviour (e.g., spitting out) is not tolerated, toddlers are less likely to risk trying new foods again. You may argue that permitting this behaviour wastes food or encourages poor table manners. Throwing away a piece of vegetable a few times is worth the long-term benefit when the children decide that they like that vegetable after all. In terms of manners, if you expect toddlers to demonstrate proper etiquette, you will be disappointed! Table manners are learned over time, and they should not be a priority for toddlers at mealtime.

▶ Toddlers have food jags, which means that they refuse all but one or two favourite foods for a period. This too is part of normal development and should be handled casually. Continue to offer a variety of foods at meals and snack times, and most children eventually start accepting other foods again.

▶ The Canadian Paediatric Society et al. (1998, 33) recommends small, frequent, nutritious, and energy-dense feedings of a variety of foods from the different food groups to meet the nutrient and energy needs during the second year.

Preschool Nutrition

During the preschool years, children gain only about 2.5 to 2.75 kg (5 to 6 lbs) per year. However, between the ages of 2 and 5, children's head and body shapes change dramatically—a 5-year-old no longer looks like a baby. Most preschoolers come through the toddler stage feeling that they have some power and autonomy, and most have an awareness that others have rights too. Preschoolers take increasing initiative as they become better at everything they do. With more language, they learn to express themselves in pro-social ways and to work things out with other people. Food jags, dawdling, fear of new foods, and other toddler nutrition issues tend to diminish and are fairly uncommon by 4 years of age, especially if the adults had not given these issues undue attention when they were toddlers. Children in this age group tend to be interested in their body and keen on learning about how foods affect their body, where foods come from, cooking, and advertising. (See Table 4.6, page 244; Chart 7.1, page 458; Nutrition Education, page 504.)

Some things to keep in mind when preschoolers are eating:

▶ Children are individuals, and their appetites and interest in food fluctuate.

▶ Establish clear expectations for mealtime behaviour. Preschoolers are capable of understanding what is and isn't appropriate behaviour, as well as logical consequences (e.g., Carlos spills milk on the floor and understands that he will help you clean it up, or Emily throws the second piece of her sandwich on the floor and understands from your earlier comments that now she is finished eating and needs to leave the table).

▶ They have a genuine interest in learning about others, so this is an opportune time to begin to learn about other cultures, foods, and ways of cooking.

▶ When introducing a new food, do not apply pressure on a child to try it.

School-Age Nutrition

This stage in a child's life brings many developmental changes, but in terms of actual physical change most children do not go through dramatic growth until early adolescence. School-agers vary in height and body shape and are aware of these differences. Concerns about dieting and the fear of fat may heighten in later school-age years, particularly in girls but also with boys. Children make the transition from a primary focus on their families to increasing influence from peers and other outside influences (e.g., media). Concerns about sedentary lifestyles can be an issue at any age, but there seem to be obvious differences in energy level during the school-age years.

 Most school-age children who are involved in sports and games with friends have a high energy level. Others who spend large periods of time at activities such as watching television or playing video games will likely be lethargic and lack motivation to be active.

The power of peers is evident in how children react to food among themselves, but these reactions are influenced also by their preschool experiences with foods. Children who are already open to trying new foods may continue in this positive way by increasing their repertoire. Children who have not been introduced to a variety of foods may be more judgmental about peers' food choices that are different from their own.

e.g. A vegetarian child who brings a tofu burger for lunch may be asked to share it by one child who is open to new foods, but teased by another child for eating something different.

School-agers need to understand the reasons for what they are doing. They are concerned with mastery and accomplishment as part of their self-esteem. For this reason, preparing food is popular with this age group. If a centre can provide opportunities for learning to make breakfasts, the children may also be able to do so at home. Through learning processes such as this, we promote their need to experience success that is recognized by self and others. School-age nutrition education can include the relationships between food production and consumption, recycling/composting, food wastage and packaging, and the environment. (See Table 4.6, page 244; Chart 7.1, page 458; Cooking with Children, page 506.)

Older school-agers may find it stigmatizing to be separated from other children (some of their friends) while eating lunch at the school just because they participate in the centre's lunch program. Children who bring lunches may do a lot of trading of foods among themselves, which may not be a problem unless some children bring in high-status, low-nutrient foods for snacks or desserts and encourage other children to bring candy or chips to trade.

Concern about Amounts of Food Eaten

Every child and adult fluctuates in the amount of food he or she eats, for any number of reasons—growth spurts, illness, fatigue, hot weather, time of day, or food preferences. Caregivers first determine whether the child's eating pattern is one that their program can easily accommodate or whether it is a legitimate reason for concern. To determine this, caregivers examine two issues:

▶ their personal perceptions and preconceived definitions of how much a child of that age should eat and at what times of day
▶ the child's body build—in other words, whether she or he is growing within the normal range of growth and development

Let's look at three reasons why children may be eating a lot of food, temporarily. If the child is growing within the normal range, there isn't cause for alarm, for the following reasons:

1. Perhaps the child is going through a growth spurt.

During a growth spurt the child's body requires extra nutrients and calories (or energy) for a limited time (a few weeks or a month or two). Interestingly, growth spurts often occur in the spring and may also follow a period of illness (e.g., in a child with asthma who had a difficult time during the winter). Understanding growth and development and getting to know children assists caregivers in expecting growth spurts.

2. Perhaps the child enjoys eating more at a particular time of day.

e.g. One child, like a lot of adults, is a slow starter in the morning and isn't ready to eat much of a breakfast before leaving home. By mid-morning she is ready to eat more than one serving of the snack. Another child is too busy playing to leave the activity to eat morning snack, but by lunch time he is ravenous. Remember, *Canada's Food Guide to Healthy Eating* suggests that we avoid looking at food intake on a meal-by-meal basis and instead look at overall intake in a 24-hour period. Centres that have incorporated some flexibility into the nutrition program can accommodate children's body rhythms. At the same time, we recognize that eating regularly during the day helps children maintain their energy level.

3. Perhaps the child does not have access to a lot of food at home.

e.g. The family's budget does not stretch far enough to buy a consistent amount of food throughout the month. As a result, the child comes to the centre hungry many days, or even every day. Centre programs need to have enough food available to provide extras and second helpings for hungry children. Caregivers' concern for the child and family does not end on Friday afternoon but extends to weekends and their access to enough nutritious food. Some centres work with food banks to supplement the food supply for families that live with food insecurity.

Therefore, daily observation of children and communication with parents play an important role in meeting their nutritional needs and in determining the child's eating habits at home. In a fourth example, the child's parent tells you that he eats a large breakfast at home, which explains why he usually does not eat a mid-morning snack or a full lunch. Although most children's high-energy hours mean that they are more interested in food in the morning or at lunch, every child's body rhythm and metabolism is unique.

Centres with children who have recently arrived in Canada should ensure that the menus reflect the types of food eaten at home. The nutrition program should include some foods that are familiar to every child in the program. You can achieve this by asking parents for their favourite recipes. This is one way that children learn about one another's ethno-culture. When you offer children familiar foods, they feel secure and relaxed and enjoy eating. New children in the centre, often shy and reserved around snack and mealtimes, need caregivers' extra support.

e.g. A 3-year-old boy, who was new not only to the centre but also to Canada, would eat nothing all day. The parents and caregivers were concerned about his well-being. The mother explained to the caregiver that her son did not like to eat around people he did not know. So she brought food from home and an adult whom the child was becoming attached to sat with him at lunch time with a partition between them and the rest of the group. He was more relaxed under these circumstances and enjoyed the one-to-one interaction and the familiar food. After a week of this arrangement, they moved into the room with the rest of the group but sat at a table on the other side of the room with the trusted adult. The child could observe the other children, who by now were more familiar to him. When he was offered the food prepared at the centre, he decided to try some. After this week of transition, the child felt much more relaxed, and by the third week he had joined his peers. He was soon eating well and his family no longer had to provide food from home.

CONCERN ABOUT BODY WEIGHT

We all have to be conscious of our society's notion of "ideal" body image and the role that we may play in perpetuating these stereotypes. Nevertheless, some children and adults are either below or above the average range of body mass by age, gender, and height. And physical or emotional concerns may be associated with being over- or underweight.

For children who are eating large amounts of food, the best time to determine whether an imbalance exists between food energy and the body's demand for energy is when the child is gaining so much weight as to become obese. If, however, the child is losing weight and is not growing in height, there may be concern about being underweight.

Caregivers' daily observations of children's eating patterns assist in identifying the contributing factors. When a child is overeating, he or she

▶ eats more than the recommended daily servings of any of the four food groups but in particular the milk products and meat and alternatives
▶ chooses foods that are high in fat and/or sugar (i.e., foods outside of the four groups) over nutritious foods
▶ does not participate in physical activity
▶ eats because of emotions—for example, boredom

When a child is undereating, he or she

▶ eats less than the recommended daily servings of any of the four food groups, especially from milk products and meat and alternatives, resulting in an insufficient fat intake
▶ chooses not to eat enough food for fear that he or she is overweight
▶ has a level of physical activity high enough that he or she uses more food energy than is obtained through eating
▶ is not active, but if he or she were his or her appetite would increase
▶ does not eat because of emotions—for example, stress or sadness

If the caregivers determine that there is reason to be concerned, the next step is to meet with the child's parents. Obviously, consistency between home and centre is beneficial. Some parents may not share the caregivers' concern for the child; others may need nutritional education and information to enable them to support their child. Parents should be encouraged to consult with the child's physician, and perhaps the child and the parents would benefit from consulting with a dietitian-nutritionist. To ensure that the physician's and/or dietitian-nutritionist's recommendations are carried out consistently between home and the centre, daily communication between parents and caregivers is essential.

Caregivers and parents can address the following reasons why children might be overeating:

▶ poor eating habits (e.g., consistently choosing high-fat foods)
▶ insufficient physical activity for the amount of food eaten
▶ eating for the wrong reasons, such as emotional reasons (see Emotional, page 222)
▶ adults in their lives who model overeating
▶ stress at home, child care, or school that may contribute to poor eating habits
▶ a physiological or psychological reason for weight gain (a physician would need to diagnose such a medical or emotional condition)

Caregivers and parents can address the following reasons why children might be undereating:

▶ poor eating habits (e.g., drinking too much milk or juice, leaving no room for food)
▶ fatigue
▶ limited variety of foods they will eat
▶ stress at home, child care, or school that may contribute to poor eating patterns
▶ adults in their lives who model excessive dieting or negative stereotypes around larger body types
▶ security felt only with family and the foods served at home
▶ a physiological or psychological reason for the weight loss (a physician would need to diagnose such a medical or emotional condition—for example, anorexia)

The most important point to remember in approaching overeating and children is that *dieting is not an option*. Dieting (restricting food) produces a vicious circle of unhealthy eating patterns. It is dangerous enough when adults begin this dieting cycle, but much worse when children begin to diet. Considering children's great needs for growth, dieting robs them of their potential by

▶ not providing their body with the daily nutrient requirements
▶ contributing to a lowered basal metabolic rate (when the body is not getting the energy it needs, it slows to function on fewer calories than it needs)
▶ making them feel deprived and centred out if the other children are not subject to dietary restrictions

Self-esteem is of great importance to children and adults, and dieting does not contribute to self-esteem, especially when over 95 percent of individuals who diet and lose weight eventually regain the weight. In a word, dieting is inappropriate! Rather than consider weight loss, it is more effective to focus on decreasing the child's rate of weight gain. We help children to develop a positive and balanced outlook around healthy eating and physical activity through increased awareness of foods and nutrition, by focusing on enjoyable daily physical activity, and by modelling healthy behaviour such as being active in the playground.

Providing Foods and Menu Planning

▶ **OBJECTIVES** To outline ways in which foods can be provided in a centre.
To explain rotation menus and list the steps in writing menus.

Food is provided in child care programs in a number of ways. The most common arrangements are

- ▶ preparing food in the centre
- ▶ having the food prepared somewhere else and brought to the centre (e.g., by a caterer, restaurant, or community kitchen). Often centres choose this option when they do not have complete kitchens.
- ▶ requiring the families to bring food for their children
- ▶ combining two of the above (e.g., an infant and toddler centre provides the snacks and the parents supply their child's lunch and formula/breast milk, *or* a preschool centre prepares the snacks, and meals are catered)
- ▶ having agency nutrition programs, often sponsored by government or foundations, conduct breakfast or lunch programs

Understanding the basics of menu planning helps you not only as a student but after you graduate. The menu is basically the culmination of the centre's nutrition program put into practice.

Providing Food in the Centre

Centres that prepare food on the premises usually offer one or two snacks and lunch and/or supper, depending on the hours of operation and their child care regulations. As part of the conditions for a centre's licence, public health inspectors usually review the food preparation, equipment, and storage and serving facilities annually.

Financial constraints or limited kitchen facilities are often the reason why parents bring in some or all of the food. Centres need a refrigerator to store food and a stove, a hot plate, or a microwave oven to warm food. In some cases, the centre provides milk and juice.

Regardless of how the food is provided in the centre, caregivers are responsible for ensuring that children have access to adequate nutrition each day. This job is simpler when food is prepared in the centre or is catered, since staff develop the menus and establish the list of acceptable foods and beverages to be served to the children based on the centre's nutrition policy. And, of course, enough food is available to provide children with second helpings.

You may think that when parents bring food for children, caregivers can relax and focus on other aspects of the program. However, since the caregivers are responsible for ensuring adequate nutrition for the children during the day, centres must have nutrition policies in place that cover

▶ the food and/or beverages that the centre provides
▶ the times for snacks and meals
▶ the parents' responsibilities
▶ a list of acceptable or unacceptable foods and beverages for parents to use as a guideline in providing the food, taking care to respect families' food preferences
▶ recommendations for environmentally friendly food containers and packaging

Even in these centres supplementary food will be on hand. There may be times when someone forgets a lunch at home or in the car, a child is still hungry after finishing her or his snack or lunch, a parent does not send or cannot afford to send enough food, or a parent consistently sends foods that are high in fat, sugar, and/or salt but low in other nutrients. So it can be more of a challenge for staff when the parents provide food and/or beverages for the children.

 Putting a basket of fruit or other nutritious finger foods out at lunch makes sense. Hungry children can help themselves. This reduces the stigma associated with the children having to ask caregivers for food.

Caregivers want children to have adequate nutrition and to become knowledgeable about food choices. Depending on the child's age, nutrition education is part of the program. As with any issue that caregivers have about children, they need to be sensitive in their approach, handle the issue discreetly, and maintain confidentiality. Food and eating habits are personal aspects of someone's identity, upbringing, and ethnicity, and can be closely connected to self-esteem. Making disparaging comments about a child's lunch or, even worse, throwing the lunch or part of it away, are both unacceptable and disrespectful practices. These practices will not make the parents receptive to talking with caregivers.

Before approaching parents, caregivers ask themselves a number of questions:

▶ How frequent is the problem and how long has it been happening?
▶ Has the parent experienced a recent emotional or financial setback that may temporarily affect their everyday life?
▶ Are the food products that are of concern ones that the caregivers are familiar with? If not, find out more about the food and its preparation. It may be nutritious after all, and it can be an opportunity for new foods to be integrated into the program.

 A child is a vegetarian and her lunches don't have milk or meat. Because you are unfamiliar with the principles of vegetarianism you assume that she isn't getting the protein or calcium she needs. Some plant sources of calcium (e.g.,

almonds, tofu) may be part of the child's daily mainstay. Educating yourself about vegetarianism and asking the parents to explain their family's diet helps you do this. As for the parents, you have demonstrated an interest in their child and they are pleased that they have knowledge and skills to share with you.

WAYS TO PROVIDE ENOUGH NUTRITIOUS FOOD

Children and adults need to eat breakfast to obtain the food energy to work, learn, and play. Many young children go to bed between 7:30 and 9:30 p.m. With the exception of infants, who wake up for a bottle or nursing, children wake up in the morning having fasted for 10 to 12 hours. The demands that rapid growth, development, and everyday activities place on a child's body make it important that he or she eats enough nutrients to fuel growth and activity for several hours.

Morning Snacks Many programs offer a flexible time for morning snack. They recognize that offering the snack at a designated time for all children cannot meet the individual nutritional needs of children.

One child may be out of bed as early as 6:00 a.m., eat breakfast, and leave for the centre. She will be ready for snack before 9:30 a.m.

Regular snacks provide a necessary and positive contribution to a child's food intake. Morning snacks that include foods from three of the four food groups provide the children with essential nutrients. They should be dentally acceptable. The snack could be available for a set period—for example, from 7:30 to 9:30 a.m.—rather than offered as a group snack. Children then have control over when to eat, and can

respond to their body rather than to a time imposed by the program. Because they have a smaller stomach growing children need the opportunity to refuel (if they choose to) every two to three hours. It is also helpful for relatively stable blood sugar levels, rather than dropping low ("I'm starved") and then soaring high ("I'm stuffed") due to ravenous eating.

Dietitian-nutritionists are sometimes concerned that if there aren't set times for eating, children will develop grazing habits—eating constantly with no awareness of body signals for hunger. Having flexible morning snack enables children to eat when they are hungry (and not ravenous) and adequately addresses dietitian-nutritionists' concerns. Obviously, the snack would not be available between 9:30 and 11:30 a.m. or noon, when lunch is served.

Keeping in mind that children have individual body rhythms, just as do adults, there are those who do not eat breakfast, for a variety of reasons:

▶ Some children may not enjoy eating or drinking as soon as they get up in the morning.

▶ There may be no time to eat during the morning rush to get out of the house and drop everyone off. Time pressure on families is a significant reason for children's being hungry in the morning.

▶ Children who have not had a good night's sleep may not have an appetite for several hours after they wake up.

▶ Some children will have eaten only part of their breakfast at home or on their way to the centre. And they will need to finish it or have the morning snack to supplement it when they arrive at the centre. Other children may have eaten a doughnut or Danish on the way to the centre, which provides some quick energy but not the nutrients needed for a morning's activity.

▶ Some families just don't have the food available for breakfast every day. The problem may be more acute at the end of the month, when there is little or no money left in the budget.

▶ Some parents who don't eat breakfast themselves may not see the importance of providing breakfast for their children. Or because of the parents' modelling, the child refuses to eat breakfast.

Morning snacks can be simple yet nourishing. Children who eat a nourishing breakfast at home probably want less of each food, or fewer of the items.

Here are a few simple snack ideas that include three of the four food groups. These snacks are easy to prepare even in centres with limited kitchen facilities:

▶ cold or hot low-sugar cereal, milk, and fruit (fresh or canned in its own juice)
▶ pita bread with hummus and fruit or vegetable juice
▶ cottage cheese with fruit and whole-grain crackers
▶ melted cheese, tomato, and alfalfa sprouts on unbuttered whole-grain toast
▶ banana egg pancakes (blend one ripe banana with two eggs and grill the small pancakes on a non-stick griddle) and milk
▶ blender drinks (e.g., milk or yogurt and fruit or juice; eggs must not be used in blender drinks because of the risk of salmonella food poisoning)
▶ scrambled tofu (soybean curd) on whole-grain toast with fruit
▶ almond butter on crackers with fruit
▶ yogurt with fruit and wheat germ

CHILD NUTRITION PROGRAMS

Many elementary schools have developed breakfast programs because children were arriving at school hungry and unable to concentrate on their work. Some centres located within such schools have been able to utilize these programs as well. Communities are recognizing the contribution of nourishing food to children's everyday well-being and are responding with child nutrition programs across the country. Some are sponsored by government, nongovernmental agencies, nonprofit organizations (e.g., Breakfast for Learning, Canadian Living Foundation), and business. Then there are food banks. These are not solutions to large-scale problems, but they at least reduce children's day-to-day hunger and ultimately have a positive effect on well-being, including the ability to learn. Child nutrition programs are responsive to the communities served, since they may be delivered in a variety of ways, and may be part of an overall plan involving community kitchens or gardens.

FoodShare's Coalition for Student Nutrition, an Ontario-wide network of individuals and agencies committed to better nutrition for children, has developed eight guiding principles for a child nutrition program (reprinted with permission from Coalition for Student Nutrition, FoodShare, Toronto):

▶ nutritious and safe food, regardless of family income
▶ accessible and non-stigmatizing programs that are universal and flexible, not replacing welfare reform
▶ community-based and administered in a way that respects the individuality of the community and addresses its unique needs
▶ culturally appropriate so that it is sensitive to and respectful of individual and community diversity
▶ empowerment of children and families so that parents are not made to feel that their role in the raising of their child is being taken away from them
▶ nurturing, ensuring a warm, caring environment in which children can participate in the program
▶ financial stability to ensure continual funding
▶ education of the public on creative ways in which children can be adequately and properly nourished, both in school and at home

Menu Planning

Menus may be prepared in centres by any of the following people:

▶ the director
▶ the caregiver(s)
▶ the cook
▶ the dietitian-nutritionist, who may be available for centres affiliated with a workplace with a cafeteria, a hospital, or a community college with a dietitian-nutritionist or an instructor from restaurant/food services programs

Each of these options brings strengths and weaknesses.

 ▶ The expertise of a dietitian-nutritionist is a definite asset. However, if the same menu is used in a number of centres, there is no opportunity to respond to individual aspects of the community in which each centre is located.
▶ A knowledgeable cook can get immediate feedback from the children on how they feel about the food. A cook can be creative with the menu and see what works and what doesn't.
▶ When meals are catered, the menu plan is probably written by the caterers, but one hopes that ongoing feedback from the centre is part of the process and that the caterers are responsive. Of course, if they aren't, the centre can take its business elsewhere!

Effective menus reflect a variety of foods that are developmentally appropriate, take into account ethno-cultural recipes, have little repetition of recipes during the four- to eight-week rotation, and introduce new foods and recipes regularly, including foods that children are learning to prepare and eat. Caregivers' ability in reading and developing menus is beneficial for a number of reasons:

▶ they identify the menus that are adequate in terms of nutrition, appeal, and variety

▶ they know how menus can be corrected, improved, or made more creative, especially when younger children turn away from their food and older ones comment, "Not that again!"

▶ they suggest the appropriate substitutions for food(s) when a child is allergic. Serving foods as similar as possible to those that the other children eat is ideal to normalize children with allergies.

▶ they work within the nutrition budget and identify food wastage or unnecessary spending

ADVANTAGES OF ROTATION MENUS

Menus are planned on a rotational basis for periods of four, six, or eight weeks. Four weeks is a short period of time, which means that every fifth Monday the cycle starts again. Children are likely to become bored with the lack of variety in this case. Longer rotation cycles offer greater variety in foods, and no one has to eat the same recipe more than a few times every six or eight weeks. Not many of us could say that about our cooking at home!

Developing four six-week rotation menus, one for each season, has several advantages:

▶ You can take advantage of the fresh produce that is available in season at its lowest prices and, in the summer, food that is grown locally or regionally. Perhaps some vegetables can be grown by the children (depending on your geography and growing season).

▶ The six-week menu would be rotated only once, since each season lasts three months.

▶ You can serve foods that are more popular in certain seasons, such as soups in winter and cold plates in summer. Of course, favourite dishes (e.g., spaghetti) can be part of every rotating menu—once or twice in six weeks for the favourite foods is not too often!

▶ The six-week menu provides a vehicle for introducing new foods to children. It is in the children's best interests to plan a balance of familiar foods and new foods.

GETTING DOWN TO WRITING MENUS

The prospect of facing a page of blank squares and knowing that you must fill those and five more pages with exciting recipes can be somewhat daunting. Like other skills, planning menus takes experience to develop. A good place to start is by critiquing menus that you find in books or centres during your placements. (See Appendices 4.4 and 4.5, pages 297–98.) Consider the following suggestions:

1. *Begin with a number of resources at your fingertips.* The most important one is *Canada's Food Guide to Healthy Eating*, followed by any guidelines for healthy snacks, simple recipes, lists of different vegetables, fruits, juices, breads, and so on that the program has access to.
2. *Know the number of snacks and meals that are served each day.* Programs that are six hours per day or longer should offer foods that constitute at least 50 percent of the *Canada's Food Guide to Healthy Eating* daily requirements. As a rule, the two snacks and one meal combined consist of a total of *at least* three servings from grain products, three servings from the vegetables and fruit group, one to two servings from milk products, and one to two servings from meat and alternatives.
3. *A menu-planning format applies to children over 12 months of age.* As students, you will gain a fundamental understanding of menu planning, which provides you with the basis for adapting menus to the age group that you will be working with.

There may be concerns about foods that can cause choking in younger children. Caregivers working with children under 12 months of age work directly with the parents to ensure that the nutritional needs of the infants are met, including the introduction of semisolid foods.

Steps to Follow for Each Week's Menu
▶ Begin by choosing foods for the five lunches:
  1. Select the meat and alternatives.
  2. Select the grain products that would complement the meat and alternatives.
  3. Select the vegetables and fruit.
  4. Add the milk or a milk product.
▶ Next, choose foods for the morning snacks:
  5. Select foods from three of the four food groups. (See Morning Snacks, page 267.)
▶ Then choose foods for the afternoon snacks:
  6. Select foods from two of the four food groups. (Children's nutritional requirements are usually lower in the afternoon than in the morning.)
▶ Evaluate your week's menu with the menu-planning checklist. (See Table 4.9, page 273.)
▶ Finally, because you are developing a rotational menu, the four, six, or eight weeks of menu plans should be checked for repetition of recipes, for the introduction of at least one new food or recipe a week, and against the food budget.

TABLE 4.9 MENU PLANNING CHECKLIST	YES	NO
Nutritional requirements: • grain products – at least three servings • vegetables and fruit – at least three servings • milk products – at least one serving • meat and alternatives – at least one serving • drinking water – availability at all times is encouraged		
Menus are varied, interesting, and creative (e.g., variety of colours, shapes, textures, tastes). Natural colours of fruit and vegetables, especially when raw, are appealing; a single colour on a plate is not appetizing. Meals should have a variety of shapes and textures to appeal to children's sense of sight, taste, and hearing. Experimenting with new foods, ethno-cultural recipes, and different herbs and spices encourages children to explore a variety of flavours. Be careful not to serve two strong-tasting foods together.		
Menus are planned and served with children in mind (e.g., some finger foods, child-sized servings, age-appropriate dishes and utensils). Preschoolers and school-agers have opportunities to serve themselves.		
Snacks are low in sugar and are nutritionally acceptable.		
Desserts, if provided, are a nutritional part of the meal (e.g., fruit, yogurt, homemade puddings).		
Real, unsweetened fruit juices are provided—not fruit drinks with added sugar or sweetener.		
Foods that have been through a number of food processes or have several additives are not served (e.g., instant potatoes, pudding mixes, processed meats).		
Foods served for celebrations and holidays are nutritious and fun.		
All allergies have been considered while planning menus and at the time of serving meals and snacks.		
Menus are posted in an obvious place for parents to read.		
The posted menu corresponds with what is actually served.		

Food Safety

 OBJECTIVE   To outline ways to reduce the risk of choking, to prevent food-borne illnesses, and to use a microwave oven safely.

This section includes three safety issues relevant to food and children: choking, food-borne illnesses, and microwave ovens. Children are at risk of choking on food when pieces of food are too large or because they are not concentrating on what they are doing (e.g., talking while they have food in their mouth, eating while running around). Providing nutritious food for children goes beyond purchasing it and menu planning. It is of utmost importance that food is safely stored, handled, prepared, and served. Because the immune system of young children is not yet mature, they are even more vulnerable to food-borne illnesses than are adults. Microwave ovens are great timesavers in centres. Although using a microwave at work is basically the same as using one at home, be especially careful when warming bottles of milk or baby food.

Reducing the Risk of Choking

As children grow and develop, they improve their ability to eat a variety of foods. They start with liquids and move to foods that are puréed, to minced or chopped, and finally they are able to bite off and chew solid pieces of food. The risk of choking is high whenever children are given foods that are not developmentally appropriate. As well, children and adults can choke on food when they have food in the mouth and are laughing or crying, when they put pieces in their mouth that are too big, or when they are eating too quickly. For this reason, *all children must be supervised when they are eating.* Caregivers should be formally trained in handling emergencies, including choking.

Caregivers can follow simple guidelines in food preparation to significantly reduce the risk to children. Hard, small, and round foods, whether smooth or sticky, can block a young child's airway (Canadian Paediatric Society et al. 1998, 31). Caregivers should never serve the following foods to children under 4 years of age:

▶ popcorn
▶ hard candy
▶ raisins
▶ whole peanuts and other nuts
▶ foods on toothpicks or wooden sticks
▶ fish with bones

Some foods need special preparation:

▶ Spread nut butter thinly on crackers or bread. Never permit children to eat it straight from a spoon or finger. For many children under 4, thin nut butter with juice or milk. (Note: Many programs are now "peanut-free" environments, due to life-threatening allergies, but may allow other nut butters—e.g., cashew, almond. In fact, at least one province/territory's child care regulations now prohibit food products containing peanut products to be served to children under the age of 3.)

▶ If meat or vegetarian wieners are served, dice them for children under 4 and cut them down the middle for older children.

▶ For children under 4: grate or finely chop raw carrots and hard pieces of fruit, cut grapes into at least four pieces, remove pits from fruit, and remove all bones from fish (Canadian Paediatric Society 1996, 352–53).

Food Safety Practices

Food-borne illnesses are usually caused by bacteria or by toxins produced by bacteria. Some types of food-borne illnesses are very serious—e.g., *Clostridium botulinum* (or botulism) is rare but can be deadly—while others (e.g., *Clostridium perfringens*) produce symptoms such as mild abdominal pain, diarrhea, and nausea, and usually last a day or less. What we may have assumed was a 24-hour flu may actually have been food poisoning. Infants and young children are vulnerable to food-borne illness for many reasons, including body size and immature systems. Honey is a risk factor for infant botulism and should not be fed to infants under 12 months old. Centre staff have been directed to avoid raw eggs and foods containing them because of the risk of salmonellosis (caused by bacteria transmitted from hen to eggshell) (Canadian Paediatric Society et al. 1998, 30).

Because the food we eat isn't sterile, some bacteria are always present. Food provides an ideal environment for bacteria to multiply or produce toxins. Bacteria thrive in warm and moist environments and need something to eat. Given time enough to multiply or produce toxins, bacteria occur in food in numbers large enough to cause food poisoning. Certain foods present a higher risk for food-borne illnesses:

▶ most of the high-protein foods such as meats, fish, and eggs
▶ custards and cream fillings
▶ salads with mayonnaise
▶ gravies and sauces

It is not surprising that summer picnics with sandwiches that have meat or egg fillings or devilled eggs, combined with poor refrigeration or cooling and the warm sun, can cause food poisoning. The bacteria are in their glory: absolutely perfect conditions for them to thrive!

Food becomes unsafe to eat when we do one or more of the following things:

▶ practise inadequate personal hygiene
▶ use dirty equipment or cooking surfaces (e.g., counters, playroom tables)
▶ handle and prepare food improperly

▶ serve food that has spoiled
▶ store food improperly
▶ do not control infestations of insects or rodents

The following is only a preliminary discussion of food safety, though it includes the essentials of what students and new graduates need to know when working in centres. However, caregivers who are responsible for cooking or persons who are hired as cooks should take a formal food-safety course. Information about these courses is available through any public health agency. In accordance with the public health inspectors' food protection guidelines, centres must develop and implement safe kitchen and food-handling practices.

Personal Hygiene

Effective hand-washing is essential both before and after handling food in any way, as well as during food preparation when handling different types of food (e.g., after handling raw meat, wash your hands before you touch any other food). In addition, follow these hygiene practices:

▶ Keep your hair clean and, if it is long, tie it back.
▶ Avoid chewing gum, because saliva easily falls on the food or cooking surfaces.
▶ Wear an apron to prevent bacteria from your clothes getting into food.
▶ Do not prepare or serve food to children when you know you have an infectious illness.
▶ If possible, avoid kitchen duties and feeding children if you are also responsible for changing diapers that day.

COOKING EQUIPMENT AND SURFACES

Used bowls, utensils, cutting boards, and counters have bacteria on them. If they are not cleaned and sanitized properly, the bacteria remain on the surfaces and get into food. How can we prevent this cross-contamination?

► Cleaning and sanitizing procedures must be posted. Daily and weekly schedules include all food contact surfaces, utensils, dishes, pots, and equipment (e.g., mixer, fridge, microwave oven).

Clean and sanitize cutting boards and knives that have been used for raw meat or poultry immediately after use. Assume that all raw meat and poultry has bacteria present (e.g., salmonella in chicken and raw eggs), which will be killed with thorough cooking. Cleaning and sanitizing prevent the cross-contamination of food that comes in contact with the contaminated board or knife. What might happen is that the bacteria land in a food that doesn't need to be cooked, and the food is left at a temperature that allows the bacteria to multiply and cause food poisoning. Separate cutting boards should be used—one for raw meat, another for everything else.

► Counters and food preparation areas must be cleaned and sanitized before and after preparing food.
► *Tables that are used for playing and eating must be cleaned and sanitized before and after eating.*
► Follow the dishwashing routine to ensure clean dishes and utensils.
► Discard cracked dishes, cups, and glasses, since cracks trap bacteria. If a utensil, plate, or cup drops to the floor, place it with the dirty dishes.

SAFE FOOD HANDLING

The way we handle food affects its safety. One of the most important factors in handling food is the food's temperature. The general rule is "keep hot foods hot and cold foods cold." In other words, foods that are either piping hot (above 60°C [140°F]) or refrigerator cold (below 4°C [39.2°F]) are out of the "danger zone." This zone is the temperature range in which bacteria thrive, and it includes our normal room temperature (20° to 22°C [68° to 71.6°F]). High-risk foods should never be kept at room temperature for more than two hours (Health and Welfare Canada 1993a, 9).

It may seem like a waste to throw out food when you are unsure that it is still safe to eat, but the risk you take in serving it is too great. If children or adults eat contaminated food, they may experience discomfort, mild or serious illness, or, even death. Clearly, summer outings and picnics must be well planned with food safety in mind.

Using an insulated container to transport food and freezing the sandwiches so that they are thawed but not lukewarm by lunch time are safe strategies. Select foods that are low-risk.

Thawing meat or poultry must be done carefully, by ensuring that the food does not reach room temperature if possible. All frozen food should defrost in the refrigerator unless the microwave oven is used. Keep the thawed meat in the fridge until you are ready to cook. This cold temperature prevents the bacteria from multiplying quickly.

Organize preparation times so that all the foods are ready at approximately the same time. This way, you avoid situations where some foods are starting to cool while others haven't finished heating. Because children do not like their foods really hot, centres often have all the food ready 10 to 15 minutes before serving the children. This period is long enough to let the food cool a bit but short enough to prevent bacteria from multiplying. For infants and toddlers, cool the food quickly by stirring. Other important suggestions follow:

▶ Use a meat thermometer when roasting poultry and meat to ensure that the internal temperature reaches the specified cooking temperature. When the outside of meat is cooked, the inside may be still harbouring live bacteria.

▶ Keep your fingers on the outside of clean cups and bowls and hold clean utensils by the handles.

▶ Rinse fruit and vegetables thoroughly before using them. If you suspect the use of pesticides or waxes, scrub under warm water (you may want to use a little dish soap) or peel off the skin.

▶ Never transfer food from one child's plate to another's.

▶ Taste food with a spoon that you have not used for stirring and use a new one if you taste again.

▶ Use serving utensils whenever possible, but don't go overboard by using tongs to pass out crackers and slices of bread.

▶ Discard food left on children's plates.

▶ Wipe the tops of cans before you open them.

FOOD SPOILAGE

We've all turned our nose away from a container that smells of sour milk. We can feel the green slime in the bottom of the bag of lettuce or see mould growing on food left at the back of a fridge. Yet we can't always tell when food has spoiled. And often food that causes food poisoning looks, tastes, and smells fresh. Beyond cooking and serving food safely, other preventive practices can be considered to ensure that no one eats spoiled food:

▶ Buy food from a reputable store or supplier.

▶ Refuse to buy or accept foods that are rotting or have passed the expiry date on the label. Refuse cans with large dents that could have broken the seal. Refuse cans that leak or whose ends bulge.

▶ Never use home-canned foods in centres, even if you eat them at home. The biggest risk of botulism poisoning in this country involves home-canned (in Mason jars) vegetables or meat (Health and Welfare Canada 1993a, 13).

▶ Never use unpasteurized milk, even for cooking.

▶ Never give raw eggs in any form to children to eat because of the risk of ingesting salmonella bacteria (e.g., eggnog, raw cookie dough, caesar salad dressing). Avoid purchasing cracked eggs.

▶ Remember the saying "When in doubt throw it out" whenever you are unsure about whether to use or serve a food.

SAFE FOOD STORAGE

Safely storing uncooked foods and leftovers is one more way to prevent bacteria from multiplying quickly. Here are the basic guidelines for food storage:

▶ Regularly check the thermometer (that centres are required to have) in the fridge to ensure that it is set at the right temperature.

▶ Store meat and poultry in containers to prevent blood or juice from leaking onto other foods.

▶ Write the date on leftovers and use within three days or discard.

▶ Store non-perishable foods in airtight plastic containers with a label and the date they were filled. Keep containers off the floor and in a well-ventilated space that is cool and dry.

▶ In the cupboards and the fridge, place newer containers of food behind the older ones, ensuring that you use older foods first.

Assessing the situation:

Evaluate the safety of the following situation. Is it safe? Provide reasons for your decision.

Scenario: You notice a pot of spaghetti meat sauce sitting on the kitchen counter early one afternoon (spaghetti is on the menu for tomorrow). You ask the cook whether it should be in the fridge. She answers, "I'm letting the sauce cool down first because it has to be at room temperature before it goes into the fridge. Otherwise it will go bad."

CONTROLLING INSECT AND RODENT INFESTATION

Insects (e.g., flies, cockroaches, ants) and rodents (e.g., mice, rats) carry germs and spread them wherever they go. An infestation of insects in food (e.g., ants in a container of flour) means the food is spoiled and must be discarded. Few centres have rodent problems, but those that do must consult with their local public health inspector and an exterminator to eliminate the problem immediately. Insects, however, are an ongoing concern. Flies and ants are widespread. In some areas, cockroaches commonly inhabit buildings. Controlling insects inside centres presents a challenge because insecticides, though they get rid of insects, also have the potential to contaminate food, surfaces, toys, and so on. However, non-chemical alternatives are available. Public health inspectors advise centres on types of products and may suggest a "people-friendly" insecticide first.

Rather than have to deal with insect or rodent infestations once they are under way, centres can take the following preventive steps to make the centre less attractive for pests in the first place:

▶ Store food properly (i.e., in air tight containers, dry places)
▶ Don't leave food on counters or tables.
▶ Clean and sanitize cooking and eating surfaces so that crumbs are removed.
▶ Sweep the floor after children eat (cockroaches eat dust and food particles).
▶ Avoid storing food under a sink.
▶ Check boxes and other containers that are brought into the centre—cockroaches like to travel!
▶ Maintain screens and other barriers that insects might try to get through.
▶ Close off spaces around pipes under sinks, and close cracks and holes in doors and walls to the outside.
▶ Act quickly when you notice the first few insects.
▶ Rinse out recyclables before they are placed in the blue box.
▶ Compost appropriate kitchen scraps outdoors, if possible.
▶ Properly store and empty garbage both inside and outside the centre. Keep the area around garbage cans free of litter and spills.
▶ Line all garbage cans with plastic bags and have snug-fitting lids. Preferably, indoor containers should open with a foot pedal. Open wastebaskets should be kept out of children's reach. Containers should be emptied at least once a day—more often if there are problems with odours (e.g., in diapering area).

Microwave Oven Safety

Microwave ovens are commonplace in homes, staff rooms in workplaces, cafeterias, and centres. Although they are convenient and easy to use, they can be hazardous if used improperly. To ensure the safe preparation of foods, the following guidelines are recommended:

► Only use microwave safe containers, preferably non-plastic containers. Plastic food wraps, which are made with nonylphenols, are of concern when heated.
► Stir and test all food coming out of the microwave oven to prevent scalds. Food heats unevenly, resulting in hot spots in the food. As well, the food can be very hot while the container remains cool.
► Keep the microwave clean of spills and splatters to prevent germs from contacting the food that is left inside.
► Ensure that school-agers who use the microwave oven to warm lunches and snacks do so safely.

WARMING BOTTLES

Placing the infant's bottle in a container of hot tap water or an electric bottle warmer is more than sufficient to do the job, but it does take a few minutes. So the microwave oven often becomes the preferred warming method. Yet the risk of scalding infants from formula heated in the microwave oven is a real concern. Health professionals do not recommend using microwave ovens for this purpose. But if you do, consider the following suggestions:

► As with all microwaving, the container must be microwave-safe, and there are issues for both glass and plastic bottles. If plastic bottles are used, those that have become crazed need replacing because the hairline cracks trap milk and germs. Since glass absorbs microwave energy, the glass bottle can crack or explode. In the case of bottles with disposable plastic liners (bags), caregivers must read the instructions on the manufacturer's label regarding use in microwave ovens. It is likely that the manufacturer does not recommend placing plastic liners in microwave ovens. The safest alternative is to microwave in a glass container (e.g., measuring cup) and then transfer warmed milk to the bottle.
► Remove the cover and nipple from the bottle before putting it into the microwave. This allows heat to escape and prevents steam from collecting under the nipple.
► Do not heat a 120 mL (4 oz.) bottle for more than 30 seconds or a 240 mL (8 oz.) bottle for more than 45 seconds at full power.
► Put the nipple back on the bottle and then invert the bottle 10 times. Microwaves vibrate the molecules, especially water, fat, and sugar, and the friction creates temperatures within the bottle that vary at the top, bottom, sides, and centre of the formula. Mixing is necessary to ensure that there are no hot spots to scald the child during feeding. Handle the nipple along the edge that fits onto the bottle, and avoid touching the part of the nipple that the child sucks.

► Always test several drops of the formula on the top of your hand (not on the inside of your wrist). The formula should feel cool. You are trying to take the chill off the formula, not trying to heat it up. When the formula feels warm, it is higher than your body temperature and may be too hot to feed to the child (Clark 1993, 3).

Revisiting the Health Promotion Action Plan

Referring to the *Action Blueprint for Health Promotion* introduced in Unit 1, the following are examples of possible actions relating to our food system.

Individual Problem-Solving and Self-Reliance
► Use the Additives of Questionable Safety list when grocery shopping to minimize the use of potentially unsafe additives. (See page 296.)
► Select organic meat and produce, if possible.
► Become aware of fat, sugar, and salt content of foods and try to keep *Canada's Food Guide to Healthy Eating* in mind when making food choices.
► Buy foods that are less processed.
► Buy foods with a minimum of packaging.
► Buy produce and other foods grown in Canada.
► Involve children in nutrition experiences.

Collective Self-Help
► food cooperatives
► food share programs

Community Action
► community kitchens
► advocate for improvements at local supermarkets
► student nutrition programs

Societal Change
► government support for stricter laws in reducing the use of chemical fertilizers and pesticides
► involvement in nongovernmental agencies advocating for changes in legislation, such as tougher food labelling and packaging laws; new produce grading standards based on the food's nutrition rather than its attractiveness (e.g., *The Supermarket Tour: A Handbook for Education and Action*, by P. White, 1990)
► support for better deals for farmers
► support for organic farming

Conclusion

While parents and caregivers cannot ensure that individual children develop good eating habits for a lifetime, they can provide children with

▶ an adequate variety of nutritious foods that are safe to eat
▶ an environment that fosters or encourages healthy attitudes toward food and eating
▶ a model for healthy eating habits

From infancy, the right of children to decide how much to eat and what foods to eat in an emotionally respectful environment takes priority in child care programs. The five principles to healthy eating guide us to eat well and lead physically active lives.

WHAT'S YOUR OPINION?
TO RISE TO THE CHALLENGE OR NOT?

At this centre, the parents provide lunches for their children and the staff warm foods in the microwave oven, as required. Caregivers have observed that one toddler's lunch routinely consists of highly processed foods. A typical lunch for Peter is a cut-up wiener or piece of salami, French fries, and a store-bought dessert (e.g., cupcake with icing). Vegetables or fresh fruit are rarely provided for Peter. The most natural and nutritious part of the meal is the milk provided by the centre. When a caregiver speaks with the parents about the lunches and about providing more variety, his mother tells her that those are the only foods that Peter will eat. The caregiver explains that Peter eats the variety of foods that the centre provides for snacks each day. At a staff meeting, one of the other caregivers suggests that no further action be taken about Peter's lunches.

If you were working in the centre, how would you feel about this situation? Has this situation been resolved to your satisfaction and in the best interests of the child? Support your position.

▶ **A S S E S S   Y O U R   L E A R N I N G**

Define terms or describe concepts used in this unit.
- nutrition
- factors that shape eating habits
- food insecurity
- nutrients and functions
- *Canada's Food Guide to Healthy Eating*
- food groups
- vegetarianism

- complementary protein
- food processing
- nutrition labels
- food additives
- food jags
- positive eating environments
- advantages of breast milk
- formula

- semisolid foods
- overeating
- undereating
- menu planning
- food safety
- risks of choking
- food-borne illness

Evaluate your options in each situation.

1. The practice at your centre placement is for the caregivers to serve food and to insist that the preschoolers eat everything. There have been a number of power struggles lately, and lunch time has become an unpleasant experience for everyone. The staff have asked you for suggestions.

2. The parents of an active, healthy 8-year-old tell you that they are concerned about their daughter's weight and insist that she be given only one serving of each food at mealtimes. Also, for snacks she is to have only fruit and vegetables.

3. Although the preschoolers eat in small groups at tables, there are a number of groups in the room. The noise level can get high, creating a less-than-calm eating environment, especially for children who are easily distracted.

4. An 18-month-old who has been in the centre for three months will eat only jarred (or puréed) baby food that his parents provide. He refuses the more textured food that the centre serves. Related to this, caregivers are concerned that his language development is being affected. The parents are worried that if they don't provide puréed food, their son will go hungry.

5. You're planning a day-long summer trip to a park with all the infants, toddlers, and preschoolers. Your responsibility is to make arrangements for the food and beverages.

▶ R E S O U R C E   M A T E R I A L S

Organizations

Allergy Asthma Information Association, 30 Eglinton Avenue W., Suite 750, Mississauga, ON L5R 3E7. Tel. (905) 712-2242, fax (905) 712-2245 (or contact provincial office).

Canadian Restaurant and Food Services Association, Allergy Aware Program, 316 Bloor Street W., Toronto, ON M5S 1W5. Tel. (416) 923-8416, national toll-free: (800) 387-5649.

FoodShare Metro Toronto, 238 Queen Street W., Toronto, ON M5V 1Z7. Tel. (416) 392-1629, fax (416) 392-6650. (Available as a resource for any group in Canada interested in school nutrition programs, whether for breakfast, snack, or lunch.)

La Leche League of Canada, National Office, 18C Industrial Drive, Box 29, Chesterville, ON K0C 1H0. Tel. (613) 448-1842, fax (613) 448-1845. (Support groups in various cities across Canada.)

Pollution Probe, 12 Madison Avenue, Toronto, ON M5R 2S1. Tel. (416) 497-8169.

Printed Matter

Additive Alert! What Have They Done to Our Food? A Consumer's Action Guide (1994), by Pollution Probe (McClelland & Stewart).

All Shapes and Sizes: Promoting Fitness and Self-Esteem in Your Overweight Child (1994), by T. Pitman and M. Kaufman (HarperCollins Publishers).

The Caboodle Cookbook: Quality Cooking for, with or by Kids (1990), by J. Cestnik and L. Cestnik (Caboodle & Company).

Child of Mine: Feeding with Love and Good Sense (1991), by E. Satter (Bull Publishing).

Cook and Learn: A Child's Cook Book: Pictorial Single Portion Recipes (1981), by B. Veitch and T. Harms (Addison-Wesley Publishing).

Cooking Vegetarian (1996), by V. Melira et al. (Macmillan Canada).

Creative Food Experiences for Children (1990), by M.T. Goodwin and G. Pollen (Center for Science in the Public Interest).

Feeding Your Baby in the Nineties: From Conception to Age Two (1992), by L. Lambert-Lagacé (Stoddart Publishing Co.)

Feeding Your Preschooler: Tasty Nutrition for Kids Two to Six (1993), by L. Lambert-Legacé (Stoddart Publishing Co.).

Food to Grow On: Give Your Kids a Healthy Start in Life (1994), by S. Mendelson and R. Mendelson (HarperCollins Publishers).

Having Fun with Healthy Foods: A Daycare Menu Planning Manual (1993), by Department of Health, Nova Scotia.

How to Get Your Kids to Eat . . . But Not Too Much (1990), by E. Satter (Bull Publishing).

I'm Hungry: Your Guide to Nutritious and Tasty Food for Young Children (1987), by E. Brownridge (Random House).

Kids Can Cook: Vegetarian Recipes Kitchen Tested by Kids for Kids (1987), by D.R. Bates (Book Publishing Company).

Kids Cook: Fabulous Food for the Whole Family (1992), by S. Williamson and Z. Williamson (Williamson Publishing Co).

Kinder-Krunchies: Healthy Snack Recipes for Children (1982), by K.S. Jenkins (Discovery Toys).

Learning from Cooking Experiences: A Teacher's Guide to Accompany 'Cook and Learn' (1981), by T. Harms (Addison-Wesley Publishing).

Meals without Squeals: Child Care Feeding Guide and Cookbook (1991), by D. Berman and J. Fromer (Bull Publishing Company).

More Than Graham Crackers: Nutrition Education & Food Preparation with Young Children (1980), by N. Wanamaker et al. (National Association for the Education of Young Children).

The No Leftover Child Care Cookbook: Kid-Tested Recipes and Menus for Centers and Home-Based Programs (1992), by J. Dunkle and M. Shore Edwards (Redleaf Press).

Nutrition for Healthy Term Infants (1998), by the Canadian Paediatric Society et al. (Public Works and Government Services Canada). Web site: www.he-sc.gc.ca).

Nutrition in Infancy and Childhood (1993), by P.L. Pipes and C.M. Trahms (Mosby-Year Book).

Promoting Nutritional Health during the Preschool Years: Canadian Guidelines (1989), by the Network of the Federal/Provincial/Territorial Group on Nutrition and National Institute of Nutrition.

"Sharing Ideas about Breast Milk Expression, Storage and Feeding," in *Well Beings: A Guide to Promote the Physical Health, Safety and Emotional Well-Being of Children in Child Care Centres and Family Day Care Homes* (1992), by the Canadian Paediatric Society (Creative Premises).

Starting Right: A Nutritional Guide for Your Child's First Three Years from the Canadian Paediatric Society (available from H.J. Heinz Company of Canada, 5650 Yonge Street, 16th Floor, North York, ON M2M 4G3; national toll-free: 1-800-268-6641).

The Supermarket Tour: A Handbook for Education and Action (1990), by P. White (Ontario Public Interest Research Group).

Super Snacks: Seasonal Sugarless Snacks Recipes for Young Children (1992), by J. Warren (Warren Publishing House).

Through the Seasons: Hands-On Cooking (1991), by K. Faggella (First Teacher Press). (Pre-K to Grade 2.)

Vegetarian Baby: A Sensible Guide for Parents (1991), by S. Yntema (McBooks Press).

Vegetarian Children: A Supportive Guide for Parents (1987), by S.K. Yntema (McBooks Press).

▶ **B I B L I O G R A P H Y**

Birch, L.L. (1992) "Children's Preferences for High Fat Foods." *Nutrition Reviews* 50(9):249–55.

———— (1991) "The Variability of Young Children's Energy Intake." *New England Journal of Medicine* 324(4):232–35.

Boston Children's Hospital (1987) *Parents' Guide to Nutrition.* Massachusetts: Addison-Wesley Publishing.

Canadian Paediatric Society (1996) *Well Beings: A Guide to Promote the Physical Health, Safety and Emotional Well-Being of Children in Child Care Centres and Family Day Care Homes.* Toronto: Creative Premises.

Canadian Paediatric Society et al. (1998), *Nutrition for Healthy Term Infants.* Ottawa: Public Works and Government Services Canada.

Clark, L.L. (1993) "The Use of the Microwave Oven for Heating Bottles of Milk." *In-Touch* 11(2) (summer):3–4.

Czajka-Narins, D.M., and E.S. Parham (1990) "Fear of Fat: Attitudes toward Obesity: The Thinning of America." *Nutrition Today*, Jan./Feb.:26–32.

Deverell, J. (1998) "Are We Buying Better Health with Vitamins, Herbals?" *Toronto Star*, 14 August, E1, E5.

Driedger, S.D. (1997) "Eating Right—New Research Points the Way to Proper Diet for Health-Conscious Canadians." *Maclean's*, 27 October, 50–61.

Eastern/Interlake Home Economists (1994) "Learning from Labels." *Family Connections*. Selkirk: Manitoba Agriculture, fall:10–11.

Evers, S. (1995) "Nutritional Isseus for Low-Income Children." *RAPPORT* 10(4)(fall):5–7.

Figtree, D. (1992) *Eat Smart: A Guide to Good Health for Kids*. New York: New Win Publishing.

Gibson, R.S., et al. (1993) "Dietary Fat Patterns of Some Canadian Preschool Children in Relation to Indices of Growth, Iron, Zinc, and Dietary Status." *Journal of the Canadian Dietetic Association* 54(1):35–37.

Guy, K., ed. (1997) *Our Promise to Children*. Ottawa: Health Canada.

Health Canada (1993a) *Food Safety—It's All in Your Hands*. Ottawa: Minister of Supply and Services.

———— (1993b) *Nutrition Recommendations Update … Dietary Fat and Children*. Ottawa: Supply and Services Canada.

———— (1992a) *Canada's Food Guide to Healthy Eating*. Ottawa: Supply and Services Canada.

———— (1992b) *Food Guide Facts: Background for Educators and Communicators*. Ottawa: Supply and Services Canada.

———— (1992c) *Using the Food Guide*. Ottawa: Supply and Services Canada.

———— (1990) *Action towards Healthy Eating: Canada's Guidelines for Healthy Eating and Recommended Strategies for Implementation*. Ottawa: Supply and Services Canada.

Health Canada (1995) *Canada's Food Guide to Healthy Eating: Focus on Preschoolers*. Ottawa: Supply and Services Canada.

Javernick, E. (1988) "Johnny's Not Jumping: Can We Help Obese Children?" *Young Children* 43(2):18–23.

Kneen, B. (1987) "A Global Glut of Grain." *The Ram's Horn* 38 (Feb./Mar.):4.

Lambert-Lagacé, L. (1993) *Feeding Your Preschooler: Tasty Nutrition for Kids Two to Six*. Toronto: Stoddart.

———— (1992) *Feeding Your Baby in the Nineties: From Conception to Age Two*. Toronto: Stoddart.

Lawless, H. (1985) "Sensory Development in Children: Research in Taste and Olfaction." *Journal of American Dietetic Association* 85:577.

McIntyre, L. (1994) "Lessons from Child Nutrition Programs across Canada." *NutriAction '94: Conference Proceedings*. Toronto: FoodShare Metro Toronto.

McKay, S.E. (1993) *The Picky Eater: Recipes and Survival Tips for Parents of Fussy Eaters*. Scarborough, ON: Today's Parent Book, HarperCollins Canada.

Melina, V., et al. (1994) *Becoming Vegetarian: The Complete Guide to Adopting a Healthy Vegetarian Diet*. Toronto: Macmillan Canada.

Mongeau, E. (1998) *The Role of Dairy Products in the Canadian Diet*. Ottawa: Canadian Agri-Food Research Council.

Newman, T.B., et al. (1990) "The Case against Childhood Cholesterol Screening." *Journal of the American Medical Association* 264(23):3039–42.

Ontario Milk Marketing Board (1992) *Good Beginnings: A Nutrition Education Program for Early Childhood Educators*. Mississauga, ON: Ontario Milk Marketing Board.

Ontario Ministry of Health (1994) *Healthy Eating Manual*. Toronto: Queen's Printer for Ontario.

Parcel, G.S., et al. (1989) "School Promotion of Healthful Diet and Physical Activity: Impact on Learning Outcomes and Self-Reported Behaviour." *Health Education Quarterly* 16(2):181–99.

Pelchat, M.L., and P. Pliner (1986) "Antecedents and Correlates of Feeding Problems in Young Children." *Journal of Nutrition Education* 18:23–29.

Penner, D. (1988) *Guidelines for Effective Native Nutrition Education*. Ottawa: Health Promotion Directorate, Health and Welfare Canada.

Pitman, T., and M. Kaufman (1994) *All Shapes and Sizes: Promoting Fitness and Self-Esteem in Your Overweight Child*. Scarborough, ON: HarperCollins.

Pollution Probe (1994) *Additive Alert! What Have They Done to Our Food? A Consumer's Action Guide*. Toronto: McClelland & Stewart.

Rice, C. (1988) "Society's Obsession with Thinness." *Bulletin*, The National Eating Disorder Information Centre (Feb.) 3(1):1–3.

Satter, E. (1990) *How to Get Your Kid to Eat … But Not Too Much*. Palo Alto, CA: Bull Publishing.

Shea, S., et al. (1992) "Variability and Self-Regulation of Energy Intake in Young Children in Their Everyday Environment." *Pediatrics* 90(4):543–46.

Sheinin, R. (1990) "Body Shame: Body Image in a Cultural Context." *Bulletin*, National Eating Disorder Information Centre (Nov.) 5(5):1–3.

Singleton, J.C., et al. (1992) "Role of Food and Nutrition in the Health Perceptions of Young Children." *Journal of the American Dietetic Association* 92:67.

Stanek, K., et al. (1990) "Diet Quality and the Eating Environment of Preschool Children." *Journal of the American Dietetic Association* 90:1582.

Stephen, A.M., and M.J. Deneer (1990) "The Effect of Dietary Fat Reduction on Intake of Major Nutrients and Fat Soluble Vitamins." *Journal of the Canadian Dietetic Association* 51(1):281–85.

United Nations (1990) *Assessing the Nutritional Status of Young Children*. New York: Department of Technical Co-operation for Development and Statistical Office.

Wardle, F., and N. Winegarner (1991) "Nutrition and Head Start." *Children Today* 21(1):5–7.

White, P. (1990) *The Supermarket Tour: A Handbook for Education and Action*. Toronto: Ontario Public Interest Research Group.

Whitener, C.B., and M.H. Keeling (1984) *Nutrition Education for Young Children: Strategies and Activities*. Englewood Cliffs, NJ: Prentice-Hall.

World Health Organization (1991) "Diet, Nutrition and the Prevention of Chronic Diseases: A Report of the WHO Study Group on Diet, Nutrition and Prevention of Noncommunicable Diseases." *Nutrition Reviews* 49(10):291–303.

Appendix 4.1

Nutrients: Their Functions and Food Sources

THE ENERGY PROVIDERS	ROLE	FOUND IN
Carbohydrates	supply the body's main source of energy; assist in utilization of fats, spare protein so it can be used for tissue formation	breads, cereals, pasta, potatoes, rice, legumes and lentils, fruits and vegetables and their juices, milk and milk products, sugar
Proteins	build and repair body tissues, including muscles, bones, blood; manufacture antibodies necessary to fight infection	meat, fish, poultry, milk and milk products, eggs, legumes, including lentils, tofu, nuts and seeds and their spreads (e.g., peanut butter), breads and cereals in combination with other protein sources
Fats	provide the most concentrated source of energy, carry fat-soluble vitamins, provide essential fatty acids necessary for normal growth and healthy skin	butter, margarine, cooking fats and oils, salad dressings, meats, poultry and fish, egg yolk, nuts and seeds and their spreads, milk and milk products, avocado, foods prepared with fats and oils such as cookies, pastries, cakes, fried foods

THE FAT-SOLUBLE VITAMINS	ROLE	FOUND IN
Vitamin A	forms healthy skin and membranes, assists in bone growth and tooth development, promotes good night vision, repairs tissues	yellow/orange fruits and vegetables, dark-green leafy vegetables such as spinach, egg yolk, cheese, milk, butter, and margarine
Vitamin D	regulates calcium and phosphorus absorption and utilization in formation and maintenance of bones and teeth	fortified fluid, evaporated or powdered milk and margarine, tuna, salmon, sardines. Vitamin D is the "sunshine vitamin" and is available through exposure to ultraviolet rays.
Vitamin E	prevents oxidation of fat in tissues, especially important in red cell membranes and lungs	vegetable oils, margarine, whole-grain cereals, wheat germ, bean sprouts, nuts and seeds and their spreads

(appendix continues on next page)

WATER-SOLUBLE VITAMINS	ROLE	FOUND IN
Thiamin (Vitamin B$_1$)	helps release energy from carbohydrates; enables growth and repair of tissues, especially nerve and muscle; aids in maintaining normal appetite	whole-grain or enriched breads, cereals, and pasta, milk and milk products, pork, nuts and seeds and their spreads
Riboflavin (Vitamin B$_2$)	assists in release of energy, aids cell division and promotes growth and repair of tissues, maintains healthy skin and eyes	milk, yogurt, cottage cheese, whole-grain or enriched breads, meat and poultry
Niacin (Vitamin B$_3$)	helps release energy from carbohydrates, protein, and fats; assists in the synthesis of fat; maintains healthy skin, gut, and nervous system	whole-grain and enriched bread, cereals, and pasta, peanut butter, meat, fish, poultry, legumes, milk, cheese
Vitamin B$_6$	assists in protein, carbohydrate, and fat metabolism, promotes normal functioning of central nervous system	chicken, fish, whole-grain breads and cereals, egg yolk, bananas, avocados
Folate	aids red blood cell formation and protein metabolism	dark-green leafy vegetables, broccoli, Brussels sprouts, oranges and orange juice, bananas, milk and milk products, wheat germ, cereals enriched with folate
Vitamin B$_{12}$	promotes normal blood formation, maintains healthy nervous tissue, aids in protein synthesis	meat, fish, poultry, milk and milk products, eggs
Vitamin C	strengthens connective tissue, bones, skin, muscles, teeth, blood vessels; promotes normal nerve function; enhances absorption of iron	citrus fruits, vitaminized apple juice, dark-green leafy vegetables, green and red pepper, tomatoes, broccoli, potatoes, strawberries

THE MACROMINERALS	ROLE	FOUND IN
Calcium	builds and maintains strong bones and teeth, promotes normal blood clotting and healthy nerve function	milk and milk products, salmon and sardines with bones, dark-green leafy vegetables, broccoli, soya milk, tofu
Phosphorus	aids in formation and maintenance of strong bones and teeth, transportation of nutrients and regulation of energy balance; helps maintain body's acid balance	meat, fish, poultry, eggs, milk and milk products, soya milk, tofu, whole-grain breads and cereals
Magnesium	helps in formation and maintenance of strong bones and teeth, transmission of nerve impulses and release of energy	dark-green leafy vegetables, legumes, seafood, milk and milk products, cereals

(appendix continues on next page)

THE MICROMINERALS	ROLE	FOUND IN
Iron	combines with protein to form hemoglobin, the part of red blood cells that transports oxygen and carbon dioxide, and also myoglobin, which provides oxygen to cells	meats, fish and poultry, whole-grain or enriched breads, cereals and pasta, iron-fortified infant cereals, dark-green leafy vegetables, dried fruits such as raisins
Fluoride	facilitates formation and maintenance of decay-resistant teeth	fluoride-containing water and foods prepared in it, toothpaste
Zinc	functions as part of several enzymes involved in many diverse metabolic roles necessary for growth, development, and energy release	meat, poultry, fish, whole-wheat breads and cereals, legumes, lentils, nuts and their spreads
Iodine	aids in production of thyroid hormones, which regulate energy metabolism and growth rate	iodized table salt, seafood, vegetables depending on regional iodine content of soil and water

DIETARY FIBRE	ROLE	FOUND IN
	indigestible material, which promotes normal elimination of waste from the colon and may have other physiological effects	whole-grain breads and cereals, legumes, fruits, and vegetables

WATER	ROLE	FOUND IN
	the main constituent of the body; necessary for transporting nutrients, promoting metabolic processes, regulating body temperature, eliminating body waste	tap water, beverages such as milk and juices, soups and a wide variety of foods, especially fruits and vegetables

Source: Reprinted with permission from *Promoting Nutritional Health during the Preschool Years: Canadian Guidelines*, Network of the Federal/Provincial/Territorial Group on Nutrition and National Institute of Nutrition (1989), 29–32.

Appendix 4.2

Health Canada   Santé Canada

CANADA'S

Food Guide

TO HEALTHY EATING

Enjoy a variety
of foods from each
group every day.

Choose lower-
fat foods
more often.

Grain Products
Choose whole grain
and enriched
products more
often.

Vegetables & Fruit
Choose dark green and
orange vegetables and
orange fruit more often.

Milk Products
Choose lower-fat
milk products more
often.

Meat & Alternatives
Choose leaner meats,
poultry and fish, as well
as dried peas, beans and
lentils more often.

Canada

Different People Need Different Amounts of Food

The amount of food you need every day from the 4 food groups and other foods depends on your age, body size, activity level, whether you are male or female and if you are pregnant or breast-feeding. That's why the Food Guide gives a lower and higher number of servings for each food group. For example, young children can choose the lower number of servings, while male teenagers can go to the higher number. Most other people can choose servings somewhere in between.

Grain Products
5-12
SERVINGS PER DAY

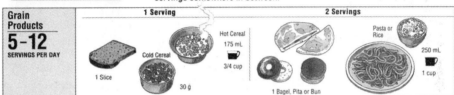

1 Serving — 2 Servings
1 Slice
Cold Cereal — 30 g
Hot Cereal 175 mL — 3/4 cup
1 Bagel, Pita or Bun
Pasta or Rice — 250 mL — 1 cup

Vegetables & Fruit
5-10
SERVINGS PER DAY

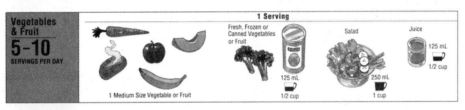

1 Serving
1 Medium Size Vegetable or Fruit
Fresh, Frozen or Canned Vegetables or Fruit — 125 mL — 1/2 cup
Salad — 250 mL — 1 cup
Juice — 125 mL — 1/2 cup

Milk Products
SERVINGS PER DAY
Children 4–9 years: 2–3
Youth 10–16 years: 3–4
Adults: 2–4
Pregnant & Breast-feeding
Women: 3–4

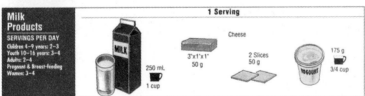

1 Serving
MILK — 250 mL — 1 cup
Cheese — 3"x1"x1" 50 g
2 Slices 50 g
175 g — 3/4 cup

Other Foods

Taste and enjoyment can also come from other foods and beverages that are not part of the 4 food groups. Some of these foods are higher in fat or Calories, so use these foods in moderation.

Meat & Alternatives
2-3
SERVINGS PER DAY

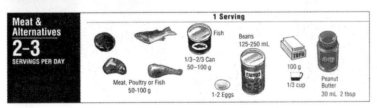

1 Serving
Meat, Poultry or Fish 50-100 g
Fish 1/3–2/3 Can 50–100 g
1-2 Eggs
Beans 125-250 mL
TOFU 100 g — 1/3 cup
Peanut Butter 30 mL 2 tbsp

Enjoy eating well, being active and feeling good about yourself. That's VITALIT

© Minister of Supply and Services Canada 1992   Cat. No. H39-252/1992E   No changes permitted. Reprint permission not required.
ISBN 0-662-19648-1

Appendix 4.3

Additives of Questionable Safety

The following additives are considered to be of questionable safety. Refer to this list when reading food labels and avoid buying foods that contain these additives. For more information on the safety of particular additives, refer to *Additive Alert* (Pollution Probe, 1994).

acacia gum (gum arabic)
allura red (U.S. red dye no. 40)
alum
aluminum potassium sulphate
amaranth (U.S. red dye no. 2)
artifical colour
artificial flavour
aspartame (Nutrasweet, Equal)

benzoic acid
BHA
BHT
brillant blue FCF (U.S. blue dye no. 1)
brominated vegetable oil
1,3-butlyene glycol

caffeine
calcium aluminum silicate
calcium carrageenan
calcium disodium EDTA
calcium furcelleran
calcium silicate
caramel
carbon black
carboxymethyl cellulose
carrageenan
citrus red no. 2
cochineal

dichloromethane
disodium EDTA
disodium inosinate
disodium guanylate

erythrosine (U.S. red dye no. 3)

fast green FCF (U.S. green dye no. 3)
flavour
furcelleran

guar gum
gum arabic
gum tragacanth

hydrolyzed vegetable protein

indigotine

karaya gum

MSG (monosodium glutamate)
magnesium aluminum silicate
magnesium silicate
methylene chloride (dichloromethane)
mineral oil
monoammonium glutamate
monopotassium glutamate
monosodium glutamate (MSG)

natural colours
natural flavours
nitrate
nitrite
Nutrasweet

paprika
ponceau sx (U.S. red dye no. 4)
potassium aluminum sulphate (alum)
potassium bisulphite
potassium bromate
potassium metabisulphite
potassium nitrate (saltpetre)
propyl gallate
1,2-propylene glycol (1,2-proanediol)

shellac
sodium aluminum silicate
sodium benzoate
sodium bisulphite
sodium carboxymethyl cellulose
sodium dithionite
sodium metabisulphite
sodium nitrate (soda niter)
sodium nitrite
sodium silicate
sodium sulphite
sulphurous acid
sunset yellow FCF (U.S. yellow dye no. 6)

tartrazine (U.S. yellow dye no. 5)
tragacanth gum (gum tragacanth)
turmeric

xylitol

Appendix 4.4

Lunch Program Menu

Monday	Tuesday	Wednesday	Thursday	Friday
• tomato & rice soup • tuna sandwiches • cucumber rounds • oranges	• Jamaican beans & rice with roti • celery & carrot sticks • apples	• cheese & potato perogies • garlicky green beans • tomato wedges • apples	• pineapple meatballs • brown rice • peapod & carrot stir-fry • bananas	• lentil burger in pita pockets • salad • baked potato wedges • ice cream
• macaroni & cheese • spinach salad • watermelon	• beefy Spanish rice casserole • broccoli (raw & cooked) • cantaloupe	• spaghetti • garlic bread • caesar salad • pears	• chicken with teriyaki vegetables • brown rice • honeydew melon	• P.D. Day
• scrambled eggs in pita pockets • oven-baked potato wedges • green pepper sticks • oranges	• lasagna • garlic bread • garden salad • apples	• oven-fried lemon chicken • corn • carrot & raisin salad • oranges	• three-cheese pasta • garden salad • strawberries	• chicken, rice & bean soup • cheese sandwiches • apples
• Santa Fe beans • garden salad • apples	• tofu sausages • mashed potatoes with parsley • broccoli (raw & cooked) • strawberries	• cheesy-bean burritos • caesar salad • cantaloupe	• chicken curry • brown rice • cauliflower & broccoli (raw with yogurt dip) • pears	• pizza • vegetable sticks • bananas
		• chicken cacciatore • garlic bread • salad • oranges	• fish sticks • fries • zucchini carrot bake • watermelon	

Note: Milk and water are provided at lunch.

Source: Adapted with permission from Ferncliff Day Care and Fern Avenue Public School, Toronto, ON.

Appendix 4.5

Menu for Preschoolers and School-Agers

	Monday	Tuesday	Wednesday	Thursday	Friday
A.M. Snack	• banana-egg pancakes topped with crushed pineapple	• fresh fruit salad with yogurt and granola	• hot cereal and milk • orange and grapefruit sections	• egg salad on corn bread • grape juice	• banana split in middle with peanut butter filling • fruit juice
Lunch	• soybean burgers • oven-baked potato wedges • spinach and carrot salad with feta cheese dressing • apple slices • milk	• pad Thai (sweet & sour rice noodles with chicken, tofu, and bean sprouts) • crunchy coleslaw • milk	• Jamaican roti (chick-peas, potato, spinach rolled in flatbread) • coconut rice & peas • fried plantain • milk	• minestrone soup (beans, vegetables, and ABC noodles) • rice crackers with colby cheese • kiwi circles • milk	• tacos (hard tortillas or pita with refried beans, cheese, lettuce, tomato, guacamole) • seedless red & green grapes • milk
P.M. Snack	• raisin-bran muffins • celery sticks • milk	• tea biscuits • pear slices	• raw broccoli & cauliflower spears • individual yogurt dilly dip bowls	• bannock with apple butter • tomato-vegetable juice with celery sticks	• hummus (chickpea & sesame pâté) • mini pitas • fruit juice

Notes:
(1) Water is available with all snacks and meals.
(2) Preschool and school-age children are involved in preparing food and serving themselves as often as possible.
(3) Some adjustments to the food selections and preparation if this menu were to be used with toddlers. Infants will have individual menus to best meet their stage of development and specific dietary needs.

Source: Adapted with permission from Rory Magill, Wakefield, PQ.

Unit 5

Safety Promotion

Unit 5: Safety Promotion

An integral part of growing up is trying new things in order to become competent. Whether it is learning to walk, ride a bike, cut with a knife, or draw with a crayon, acquiring a new skill is a learning process. As such, it may take a child a number of attempts before he or she masters the skill. Do you remember learning to ride a bike? You probably fell off more than once! Minor scrapes, bumps, and bruises are a normal part of childhood.

It is a tremendous responsibility to ensure children's safety in centres but not an insurmountable one. We do not want to design a risk-free environment. The goal of safety promotion in centres is to find a workable balance between a safe and a challenging child care program. Children who are not physically challenged are understimulated. This understimulation can have the following consequences:

▶ The children stop seeking challenges, which affects their development and self-esteem.

▶ They turn to or against their peers for stimulation, which often results in antisocial and hurtful behaviour.

▶ They direct their natural desire for trial-and-error learning to times and places in which the risks may be much greater (e.g., toddlers climbing up on bookshelves or from chairs onto counters rather than using developmentally appropriate climbing equipment under adult supervision).

Quality child care programs safely offer children the physical and human resources to experience challenges and learn from them (Greenman 1988, 77–78). Caregivers will pay attention to the four components of safety promotion: training, physical environment, supervision of children, and safety rules. Before discussing how to promote safety, we'll look at childhood injuries from the perspective of the five W's: who, why, where, when, and what.

The Five W's of Safety

 OBJECTIVE   To describe the nature of childhood injuries and factors that increase risk.

An important role for caregivers is to design and implement injury prevention strategies in centres. To develop policies and strategies that are relevant, practical, and effective, caregivers first understand the nature of childhood injuries and factors that increase risk. Caregivers also draw on their knowledge of children's development and how that affects the types of injuries experienced at different ages.

Who

Safety is an important consideration in everyone's life. An average day includes activities with an element of risk: showering, shaving, eating peanut butter on toast for breakfast, navigating the ice-covered front steps of the house, crossing the street, and driving to work. Children face potential risks in their daily lives too. "Of all preschoolers who die, 40% die of injury-related causes" (Canadian Institute of Child Health 1994, 53). Some children's injuries are the same as adults'. Others are directly related to children's growth and development and becoming competent at small and large motor skills. Learning to crawl, walk, climb, ride a bike, or use scissors involves risks, and children sometimes fall or cut themselves while developing these skills. Nonetheless, we can't prevent injuries by stopping children's growth or development any more than our parents could prevent ours.

We will not use the term "accident" in this unit, as it implies that an event was due to bad luck or fate and that nothing could have been done to prevent it. McKay (1994,1) suggests that we consider that there are no airplane "accidents." Instead, they are "crashes," with investigations into the reasons and responsibility. The word "injury" is used here, as in current safety publications, since *injuries are preventable*. Some statistics on children's injuries in Canada:

▶ Injuries account for 40 percent of deaths for 1- to 4-year-olds, 49 percent of deaths for 5- to 9-year-olds, and 64 percent of deaths for 10- to 14-year-olds. The leading cause of all of these deaths is motor vehicle collisions (Statistics Canada, cited in Canadian Institute of Child Health 1994, 44, 46, 61, 64, Public Works and Government Services Canada, 1997, 58).

▶ Injuries due to falls are the leading cause of hospitalization for children aged 1 to 14 years (Statistics Canada, cited in Canadian Institute of Child Health 1994, 50, 69, 70, Public Works and Government Services Canada 1997, 134).

▶ Injuries kill over 500 children under the age of 14 years and hospitalize another 40 000 (Safe Kids Canada 1994, 2).

▶ Injuries are the cause of 3 percent of all deaths for infants under 1 year of age, of which more than one-third are caused by suffocation (Statistics Canada, cited in Canadian Institute of Child Health 1998, 20, 23).

▶ Injuries resulting in death are 1.8 times higher among preschool boys than among preschool girls. For ages 10 to 14 the injury death rate is twice as high for boys as girls (Statistics Canada, cited in Canadian Institute of Child Health, 1998, 44, 62).

Why

Individual differences in temperament may explain why one child is more of a risk-taker, less fearful, more adventurous, and more inquisitive than another. Risk-takers are more likely to be in situations that put them at risk of injury. Gender differences play a role in injuries because boys are often involved in more physically challenging activities. Gender differences in this respect are not yet fully understood. A Canadian study is examining three possible factors: risk perception, peer influence on risk-taking, and parental responses to children engaging in risky behaviour. Regardless of individual, gender, or family response differences, caregivers must maintain levels of supervision appropriate for the activity, the equipment being used, and the age of children. However, caregivers' supervision cannot be centred only on the adventurous children, and boys in general, since all children are susceptible to injuries.

Children learn through exploration. Together with maturation, children reach developmental milestones. *Understanding children's growth and development is essential in anticipating injuries and thus preventing or reducing their severity.* The physical and cognitive developmental immaturity of younger children increases their risk of injury compared to that of older children and adults. Here are some of the reasons why:

▶ Children go through such rapid growth spurts that sometimes their sensory perception doesn't keep up (e.g., a child gets taller, but she senses that she is shorter and misjudges her height with the monkey bar and bangs her head).

▶ Children have yet to learn how to control impulses. Children are unaware of the potential harm they are placing themselves in when they do whatever comes to mind (e.g., running into the street to retrieve a ball, leaning over into a pail of water, following peers to the highest level of the climber where they aren't physically able to handle the challenge).

▶ Children learn through trial and error. When children's environments are not developmentally appropriate and challenging, their experiments involve activities that can be dangerous (e.g., a toddler trying to walk up the chute of a slide because no climber is available).

▶ Children under 3 years of age are usually not aware of others' safety and may contribute to the harm of others (Greenman 1988, 76).

Starting with infants and toddlers, we'll examine aspects of children's growth and development as they relate to safety.

Infants

▶ are learning to roll over from front to back, which puts them at risk of falling from heights (e.g., change tables, counters, furniture) or suffocating if placed on a soft or buoyant surface. They may roll onto their tummy, but then, because unable to roll back, smother themselves when their face is buried in a pillow or adult water bed.

Infants and toddlers

▶ are developing stronger grasps and those who can stand, crawl, or walk put themselves at risk of:
  ▷ falling down stairs
  ▷ pulling on an appliance cord hanging down the front of a counter
  ▷ grabbing a cup of hot tea from a table
  ▷ becoming tangled in drapery cords and strangling
  ▷ pulling off small parts from a toy and choking
▶ have not yet developed an awareness of potential harm. Toddlers will run in front of a moving swing. At this age, most children love playing in water and are not able to discern the difference between supervised water play and playing in the toilet water alone.
▶ have a tendency to put everything in their mouth (sensorimotor learning), which puts them at risk of poisoning and choking.
▶ are active explorers and thus are prone to bumps, bruises, and scrapes from losing their balance and attempting new tasks.
▶ are often like little whirlwinds, because their quest for learning about their world leaves little time for caution.

Preschoolers

▶ are adept at running, climbing, and pedalling a tricycle by the time they are 4. They are becoming more competent and confident on playground equipment and are looking for new and advanced challenges (e.g., climbing even higher up the climber, jumping off the swing while it is still moving).

▶ are in the preoperational stage of cognitive development. As a result, they are unable to judge the speed of a car, the height of the climber's fire pole, or the danger of deep water or matches. They also are unable to clearly distinguish between reality and fantasy. Many children watch television, especially cartoons, which focus on invincible superheroes. These shows may lead some preschoolers to believe that they too can leap from high places or fly.

▶ want and need to have increasing levels of independence, but with this comes risk (e.g., a child can't learn to cut with a knife without using one, so she may cut herself even when using a dull one).

School-agers

▶ are developing competencies in many areas and need to be given more independence and responsibility. Issues concerning children's personal safety arise both at home and in the school-age program. In school-age programs there are fewer caregivers per child (a higher staff–child ratio), resulting in less direct supervision. Children are required to use their own decision-making skills and judgments in various situations—leaving the playground to go into the school to use the bathroom, riding a bike to school, using a neighbourhood playground in the evening without a parent. Before delegating new responsibilities to a child, adults must consider the child's age, level of maturity, track record, and reliability, as well as the inherent safety risks within the school, centre, or neighbourhood.

 A child who takes off her bike helmet after rounding the corner and does not stop at stop signs is not permitted to bicycle to school until she demonstrates that she can follow safe cycling practices consistently.

▶ are paying more attention to interacting with their peers than to what they are actually doing (e.g., a child is so busy talking to his friend on the ground that he doesn't notice that he has moved to the edge of the climber), so physical injuries often result. On the other hand, children can get so involved in an activity that they are oblivious of everything around them (e.g., during a game of tag, a child is so determined not to be tagged that while running away she runs into someone else).

Aside from injuries attributable to these growth and development factors, children are injured from both the use of developmentally inappropriate or poorly maintained equipment and the lack of adequate supervision or rules.

Where

Houses and apartments are designed for adults. Most children spend more time at home than they do in centres, so it is not surprising that children are more often injured at home. Compared to other environments, centres are less dangerous places for children.

Yet, these facts do not mean that we can be complacent about safety at centres, because injuries happen there too. Children can slip in spills from a water table, pinch their fingers in a door, and run into each other. "In a review of 400 consecutive reported [child] care injuries, a Manitoba study found that the playground is the site of the highest number of injuries. Most of these mishaps were falls. The problem did not arise from a lack of supervision, but rather from the physical environment itself. Many playgrounds do not have adequate [impact-]absorbing surfaces under play equipment" (Stanwick 1993, 23). School-age children in particular are at risk of falling on stairs because of frequent use in many school buildings and the likelihood of going up and down unsafely (e.g., taking two stairs at a time, jumping down, not using the handrail).

Almost 42 percent of playground equipment injuries occurred in public playgrounds and parks, while 33.9 percent were in school and centre playgrounds. Particular playground equipment was associated with injuries for the following age groups:

	Slides	Swings	Climbers
1–4-year-olds	34%	30.5%	24.1%
5–9-year-olds	20%	20%	46.9%
10–14-year-olds	19%	29.5%	37.6%

On climbers, children lost their balance or grip on a bar. Many falls from slides occurred when children stood on the top, lost their balance, were pushed off the ladder, or landed badly at the end of the slide (and suffered a twisted foot or ankle, for example). Children sustained injuries as a result of falls while swinging from or jumping off while the swing was still in motion. Passersby have been struck by moving swing seats (Public Works and Government Services Canada 1997, 202–3).

When

Injuries can happen at any time. But there are particular situations or conditions in which the likelihood of injury increases. Childhood injuries in centres often happen:

▶ when children are tired or hungry
▶ when children new to the program are not fully aware of the environment or don't know how to use play equipment safely

▶ when caregivers relax their level of supervision (e.g., while talking among themselves in the playground), or overestimate a child's abilities, or do not anticipate potential consequences of an activity or a child's behaviour

▶ when caregiver–child ratios are not adequate for the activity, whether it is cooking with children or going for a walk

▶ when the daily routine is disrupted (e.g., a familiar caregiver is absent and the care routine and level of supervision are affected)

▶ when a new piece of play equipment arrives and the children become too excited and preoccupied to follow safety rules

▶ when field trips introduce children to unfamiliar situations and unexpected hazards

What

Every year children in Canada are killed or permanently disabled by six types of injuries: motor vehicle collisions and traffic mishaps, drowning, burns, choking, suffocating and strangling, falls, and poisoning. From the caregivers' perspective, these injuries are not of equal relevance in their day-to-day work.

In centres, choking and falls are of course much more likely than motor vehicle collisions. Caregivers must be aware of choking during snacks and meals. They must be prepared for falls all the time. And even though caregivers will not be thinking of car mishaps during the day, they can help children learn traffic rules when they are riding tricycles (e.g., by staying on the right side of the path and putting up a stop sign at path intersections) or when they are out for walks.

Increasing our awareness of the major causes of childhood injuries and death can have a significant and positive impact on safety promotion at home and at work.

The next section begins with an overview of the six types of childhood injuries. It concludes with a table outlining how caregivers can reduce the risks of injuries in centres and help children develop lifelong safety habits. (See Table 5.1, page 315.)

Motor Vehicle Collisions

Traffic-related injury, including injuries to passengers in vehicles, pedestrians, and cyclists, is the number one safety issue for Canadian children. According to Safe Kids Canada, over 20 000 children under age 14 are injured by automobiles each year and one-third are automobile passengers (Safe Kids Canada 1994, 1). Most of these injuries were the result of parents either not using or improperly using child safety seats and seat belts. According to a survey by Transport Canada, only one-third of babies under one year, and less than half of all preschoolers, were restrained properly in vehicles (Transport Canada, cited in Canadian Institute of Child Health 1994, 36, 52). Many pedestrian and cyclist injuries resulted from individuals not obeying traffic rules (e.g., jaywalking or crossing against a traffic light). Cyclists' injuries tended to be more serious when safety equipment (e.g., helmets) was not worn. (See Table 5.1.)

About eight children are killed every year in Canada by their school bus. This happens when the child disappears out of sight in front of the bus and the bus pulls away. Some children are hit by another vehicle passing the bus as the child crosses the road. Centres that have children who come and go on buses must supervise the children directly.

Drowning

Drowning is the second leading cause of injury death for children aged 1 to 9, and is the fifth for children aged 10 to 14 (Statistics Canada, cited in Canadian Institute of Child Health 1994, 45, 63, 64). Few drownings or near-drownings occur in centres. Still, young children can drown in as little as 4 cm (1½ ins.) of water, which means that caregivers must supervise young children around water and help them develop a respect for it. In order to promote children's independence in toileting, many preschool centres are designed with an open door that leads from the playroom to the washroom. Caregivers should remember that children under 3 years (and some children older) need adult supervision in the washroom to assist with hygiene and ensure safety around the toilets, in particular to prevent drowning. (See Table 5.1.)

Burns

Between 1986 and 1990, burns were tied as the second leading cause of injury death for children aged 1 to 4, and the third for 5- to 14-year-olds (Statistics Canada, cited in Canadian Institute of Child Health, 45, 63, 64). There are four types of burns: contact burns, scalds, electrical burns, and chemical burns. In child care programs, children's burns usually result from scalding by hot tap water, soups, or beverages (including burn injuries to the mouth from microwaved bottles), and contact burns from hot metal such as slides. (See Table 5.1.)

CHOKING, SUFFOCATING, AND STRANGLING

Choking results from inhaling or ingesting food or objects that obstruct the person's airway. Suffocation or strangulation occurs when external forces (such as a pillow over the face or a dangling scarf wound tightly around the neck) prevent air from entering the lungs. If a person is deprived of oxygen for four minutes, brain damage can occur. Between 1985 and 1990, suffocation was the fifth leading cause of injury death for children aged 1 to 4, and the fourth for 5- to 14-year-olds (Statistics Canada, cited in Canadian Institute of Child Health 1994, 45, 63, 64). Caregivers must focus on food, unsafe eating behaviour, and toys that can cause choking. Latex balloons (often used in celebrations) should be banned from centres, as they are a major choking risk. They have been banned from all children's hospitals in Canada. The use of Mylar balloons is safer; however, once deflated, Mylar balloons must be discarded safely just like plastic bags. Strangulation can result when clothing becomes caught on slides and climbers, and the child's head or clothing gets trapped in play equipment. (See Table 5.1.)

FALLS

Falls are by far the most common cause of injury in child care environments—not surprisingly, because they can happen anywhere at any time! Of all hospitalizations due to injuries, falls account for 29 percent for 1- to 4-year-olds, 42 percent for 5- to 9-year-olds, and 29 percent for 10- to 14-year-olds (Statistics Canada, cited in Canadian Institute of Child Health 1994, 50, 69, 70).

Falls in centres can happen both indoors and outdoors. While most falls result in minor injuries like cuts, scrapes, or sprains, others can be serious or even life-threatening, causing broken bones, head injuries, and internal or external bleeding. Playground falls are common and can be serious, especially if the child falls onto an inadequate protective surface. And, like adults, children trip on stairs, mats, loose carpets, toys, and other objects and slip in spills of water or sand. (See Table 5.1.)

Riding toys, tricycles, and walkers can contribute to childhood injuries. According to the Canadian Hospitals Injury Reporting and Prevention Program (CHIRPP) (1998), 7.5 percent of the injuries from tricycles happened in centres between 1990 and 1996. The number one cause of serious head injuries in school-age children is a fall from a bicycle when not wearing an approved bike helmet. One study showed that wearing a helmet reduced the incidence of head injuries by 85 percent (Thompson et al. 1989). Eighty to 90 percent of school-age children own bikes, and a survey in Quebec indicates that 95 percent of children in Grades 4–6 ride a bike at least once a week (Public Works and Government Services Canada 1997, 108). Of the bicycle injuries reported to CHIRPP in 1993, only 10 percent involved children who were wearing a helmet at the time of the mishap. However,

the increasing use of helmets in the past few years represents a major improvement in the safety-related behaviour of Canadian children and youth (Public Works and Government Services 1997, 113). Safety campaigns in Quebec and Ontario were not as successful in socioeconomically poorer communities and rural communities. The cost of helmets must be considered in future educational campaigns (Public Works and Government Services 1997, 108).

The main reason for both tricycle and bicycle injuries was that children hit something while they were riding. Children most frequently received injuries to the head and neck (e.g., cuts, scrapes, dental damage, concussions, fractures) as well as cuts, bruises, abrasions, dislocations, sprains, and fractures of legs and arms. How can caregivers reduce the number of cycling injuries in centres and help children learn lifelong safety habits? Caregivers are encouraged to consider including the following practices in their policy:

- ▶ Have children wear bike helmets on riding toys and tricycles so they see them as a natural a part of riding.
- ▶ Ensure that riding paths are designed so that children can't crash into objects.
- ▶ Ensure that children are actively supervised.
- ▶ In school-age programs, staff should develop a policy for bikes, in-line skates, and skateboards that stipulates that children travelling to their programs wear helmets and other safety equipment recommended for each activity. Parents may not support your position, but while the children are under your supervision you can either have them wear the safety equipment or prohibit the activity. When helmets become required by law in your province/territory, you can enforce the law. In the case of in-line skating, an activity that is becoming very popular, CHIRPP (1998) data indicate that of the 1046 injuries reported, the vast majority were to children in the 10–14-year-old-age range, with 42.3 percent of those children sustaining fractures and 74.9 percent reporting no protective equipment worn at the time of injury.

Currently, it is unlikely that you will find many centres with toddlers and preschoolers wearing helmets on the riding toys and tricycles. Some families find the cost of new or used safety equipment prohibitive. Perhaps centres could canvass families or the neighbourhood for equipment no longer in use. This equipment could be swapped or given to individual families. In the area of bike safety, national organizations provide support and education. (See Organizations, page 373.) Caregivers who travel to work on bikes are encouraged to wear a helmet, not only for their own safety but also to model safe behaviour to children. Legislation requiring bike helmets is mandatory in several provinces and under consideration in other provinces/territories.

Poisoning

Poisoning is rarely fatal but can result in serious illness. It is a common pediatric emergency that can be a traumatic experience. In fact, poisoning is the second leading cause of injury hospitalization for preschoolers (Statistics Canada, cited in Canadian Institute of Child Health 1994, 50). Poison-proofing is the term commonly used to describe the process of identifying and keeping potentially hazardous products out of children's reach. However, it's important to recognize that poison-proofing is an ongoing process, not a one-time thing (e.g., in a centre you have products locked away, but parents put purses and diaper bags on the floor that may contain products that children can access). It's logical that poisonings happen much more often in children's homes. Centres usually don't have many hazardous products (pesticides, paints, gasoline, medications, nail polish and remover, ashtrays and cigarettes, alcohol, etc.), and the ones they have are locked out of the children's reach (as part of the poison-proofing at the centre). Almost any substance taken in sufficient quantities can be a poison. (See Table 5.1.) Poisoning can occur when someone

▶ eats or drinks a hazardous product
▶ touches or spills a product on the skin and the chemical is absorbed through the skin
▶ breathes in fumes of liquids

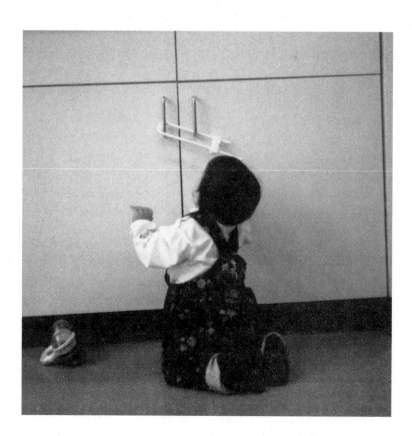

TABLE 5.1   IMPLEMENTING PREVENTION STRATEGIES

FALLS

Infants and Toddlers				Preschoolers			School-Agers						
Birth	12 mths.	18 mths.	24 mths.	3 yrs.	4	5	6	7	8	9	10	11	12

off furniture, change tables, counters (1)

out of highchairs, cribs, strollers (2)

out of windows (3)

down stairs (4)

riding toys, tricycles, bicycles, and in-line skates (5)

playground equipment (6)

slip or trip on water, ice, sand, toys, carpeting, extension cords (7)

CHOKING, SUFFOCATING, AND STRANGLING

Infants and Toddlers				Preschoolers			School-Agers						
Birth	12 mths.	18 mths.	24 mths.	3 yrs.	4	5	6	7	8	9	10	11	12

suffocate on pillows, mattress, and adult waterbeds (1)

strangling in blind and drapery cords dangling in the crib or bed, pull toys, soother strings (2)

choke on small toys (<4 cm in diameter), toy parts that can be pulled off (e.g., buttons, clothing) (3)

choke on latex balloons, suffocate from plastic bags (e.g., dry-cleaning bags) (4)

choke on foods (5)

suffocate when loose scarves and hoods get caught on playground equipment (e.g., slides) (6)

choke when eating too quickly or talking, laughing, or running while eating or eating large pieces of food (7)

(table continues on next page)

TABLE 5.1 IMPLEMENTING PREVENTION STRATEGIES (continued)

DROWNING

Infants and Toddlers

Birth	12 mths.	18 mths.	24 mths.

Preschoolers

3 yrs.	4	5

School-Agers

6	7	8	9	10	11	12

- wading pools and swimming pools (1)
- puddles, pails, or large containers of water (2)
- creeks, rivers, lakes, oceans (3)

MOTOR VEHICLES

Infants and Toddlers

Birth	12 mths.	18 mths.	24 mths.

Preschoolers

3 yrs.	4	5

School-Agers

6	7	8	9	10	11	12

- not in proper child restraint seats (1)
- run or play on the street (3)
- lack of or improper use of seat belts (2)
- riding bicycles on the street (4)

POISONING

Infants and Toddlers

Birth	12 mths.	18 mths.	24 mths.

Preschoolers

3 yrs.	4	5

School-Agers

6	7	8	9	10	11	12

- consumes potentially hazardous substances such as cleaning products; alcohol, medications (e.g., vitamins); certain flowers, plants and berries; perfume, nail polish and remover (1)
- eats cigarettes and the butts (2)
- on a dare to seek approval from peers, drinks or eats an unknown fluid or substance that is hazardous (3)
- drugs or alcohol overdose (4)

BURNS

Infants and Toddlers

Birth	12 mths.	18 mths.	24 mths.

Preschoolers

3 yrs.	4	5

School-Agers

6	7	8	9	10	11	12

- scalds from hot tap water, beverages, soups (1)
- burns from stoves and ovens, heat radiators, fireplaces, wood stoves (2)
- sticking objects in electrical outlets, chewing on electrical cords (3)
- metal buckles and vinyl-covered car seats exposed to the sun (4)
- metal slides exposed to the sun (5)
- playing with matches or lighters (6)
- using the stove or electrical appliances while cooking (7)

(table continues on next page)

TABLE 5.1 IMPLEMENTING PREVENTION STRATEGIES (continued)

The following suggestions appear in the order in which the risk factors are listed in each category.

FALLS

1. Always keep one hand on the child during diaper changes. Never put children on counters or tables even when they are in a baby chair/seat. Until children are able to climb on and off chairs, sofas, etc., never leave them there unattended.

2. (See Table 5.2, page 326.) Do not use walkers.

3. Keep furniture away from the windows. Windows should be secured with screens or stops or grills to prevent opening more than 10 cm (4 ins.).

4. Secure safety gates on all stairwells (top and bottom) that infants and toddlers can access without an adult. Safety gates must be screwed securely into the wall (do not use pressure-type gates). Install handrails at children's height. Good lighting. Keep stairs clear of toys, shoes, clothing, etc. Model safe behaviour on the stairs. Supervise young children using stairs.

5. Actively supervise children. Establish developmentally appropriate rules for riding toys. Create safe riding paths. Begin using bike helmets for children on riding toys and tricycles. Encourage parents to enroll school-age children in bicycle safety courses. Establish a centre policy covering school-age children riding bicycles and using in-line skates while in the child care program, including parental permission and the use of recommended safety equipment.

6. Actively supervise children. Help children learn the appropriate use and safety rules for play equipment. Regularly check and maintain play equipment and protective surfaces. Ensure natural surfaces are topped up seasonally and as needed. Document the regular maintenance checks.

7. Immediately wipe up spills of water (e.g., water table). Keep sidewalks and stairs clear of ice and snow. Sweep up sand on floor under sand table. Keep toys off walkways in the rooms. Do not use scatter rugs. Do not run extension cords across floors where people walk or under carpeting (fire hazard).

CHOKING, SUFFOCATING, AND STRANGLING

1. Do not provide pillows in cribs for infants under 1 year old. Remove plastic wrapping from crib mattresses. Never use garbage bags as mattress covers. Do not hang mobiles over the cribs. Keep plastic bags out of children's reach.

2. Strings on soothers and pull toys must not be longer than 15 cm (6 ins.).

3. Avoid giving children under 3 years objects smaller than 4 cm (1 1/2 ins.). Check their toys for small parts that can be easily removed.

4. Ban the use of latex balloons in centres. Safely discard deflated foil balloons, because they can suffocate young children.

5. Know which foods can cause choking in children. (See Reducing the Risk of Choking, page 274.)

6. Tie and tuck scarves into coats. Ensure hoods are fastened snugly. Clothing manufacturers are redesigning hoods that fasten with Velcro rather than drawstrings. Have a policy prohibiting drawstrings on clothes. Do not permit children to wear dramatic play clothes on play equipment.

7. Prohibit the attachment of ropes, strings, cords, skipping ropes, etc., to play structures. Use only climbing ropes that are designed and manufactured for play structures.

8. Encourage children to eat slowly and chew properly. Model safe eating habits.

DROWNING

1. Never leave children unsupervised in the pool, regardless of their age. Empty portable wading pools immediately after use and store upside down. Teach children water safety.

2. Actively supervise infants, toddlers, and preschoolers in the washroom. Check playground for stagnant puddles of water. Keep diaper pails out of children's reach. Never keep pails or basins filled with water or cleaning solutions near children.

3. Teach children to respect water, not to play near creeks and rivers, not to go on the ice in the spring. Canals, rivers, and lakes used for ice skating must be safe to use. Boats used to transport children must have appropriate-sized approved flotation device for each child and adult.

(table continues on next page)

TABLE 5.1 IMPLEMENTING PREVENTION STRATEGIES (continued)

MOTOR VEHICLES

1 & 2. When centres provide transportation for children, appropriate child restraints or seat belts must be used. If caregivers are aware of parents not using proper restraints for their children, be advocates for children (e.g., encourage or assist parents in obtaining and using the restraints). Safety education with preschool and school-age children includes the buckle-up message.

3. Actively supervise children. Ensure that gates and fences around the playground are maintained. Reinforce the message that very young children are never to run onto the street or cross it without holding an adult's hand. Help preschoolers and school-agers learn traffic safety and laws.

4. Help children learn bicycle safety rules and ensure that children wear bicycle helmets. Model safe bike riding.

POISONING

1. Regularly identify and remove potentially hazardous products in the centre and playground. Keep all medication locked and out of reach of children. Keep first-aid kits out of reach. Staff and parents must keep purses, knapsacks, and diaper bags off the floor and out of children's reach. Post the poison control centre's phone number by every phone. Teach children not to eat plants or berries without checking with an adult first.

2. Enforce the no-smoking policy in centres. Caregivers who smoke outside must not leave cigarette butts on the ground where young children can pick them up. Ashtrays must be carefully emptied and kept out of reach.

3 & 4. Provide education opportunities on drug and alcohol abuse for school-age children and parents (e.g., invite a guest speaker).

BURNS

1. Younger children must be supervised around water at all times. Ensure that the temperature of the hot water from faucets does not exceed 43°C (110°F). Hot beverages or fluids are not permitted in the play area, nor may staff drink them while holding children.

2. Kitchens must be inaccessible to unsupervised children. Children must be supervised during all cooking activites. All sources of heat (e.g., radiators, hot-water pipes, registers) accessible to children must not exceed 43°C (110°F). Install physical barriers around fireplaces, wood stoves, furnaces, hot-water heaters if children have access to them.

3. Cover all unused electrical outlets with plastic outlet covers. Electrical cords should be out of children's reach.

4. Cover car seats, child restraints, and strollers with a blanket or towel to shade them from the sun. Older children and caregivers should be in the habit of checking vinyl seats and belt buckles before getting in the vehicle.

5. Place metal slides in shaded areas or plant trees or erect a structure that provides shade. As a short-term remedy, use metal slides in the morning before it gets too hot. If possible, pour cold water to cool the metal; there may be days when the slide is closed.

6. Matches and lighters must never be within children's reach. Keep purses, diaper bags, knap sacks, etc., off the floor and out of reach. Children can learn the fire message, "Stop, drop, and roll."

7. See Cooking with Children, page 506.

How Can We Promote Children's Safety?

OBJECTIVES   To understand the importance of training, including emergency training in safety promotion.
To identify strategies in an ongoing evaluation of the indoor and outdoor environment.
To view active supervision as an essential component in injury prevention and to identify the various factors that affect the level of supervision.
To understand the limited role that safety rules play in injury prevention and describe the essential considerations in developing and adapting rules for each age group.

The challenge for caregivers is to provide an environment that is not only developmentally challenging but is also as safe as possible so that children can be physically active and gain new skills. Caregivers and parents recognize that bumps, scrapes, and bruises are a normal part of growing up. Children are inevitably injured when using play equipment. However, the likelihood of broken bones and head or internal injuries is minimized if the equipment is developmentally appropriate, the protective surfaces are adequately maintained, the children use the equipment properly, and the caregivers actively supervise their activities. By modelling safe but not overly anxious behaviour, adults help children develop an awareness of safety. The adage "Do as I say, not as I do" does not apply to safety, nor to anything else, for that matter. Children will adopt adults' behaviour, whether it is appropriate or not.

e.g.   It is much more likely that children will learn safe pedestrian behaviour when they see the adults using the crosswalks (flashing the lights and pointing), waiting for walk signs, stopping to look both ways before crossing the street, and not walking between parked cars. The opposite can also be true. If children see adults breaking safety rules that they have been told to follow, they will not see how these rules apply to their own safety.

Caregivers' observation skills are continually tested in terms of identifying the following elements to ensure children's safety:

✔ changes in children's physical and cognitive abilities
✔ the need for changes in the play area's design or layout
✔ hazardous equipment and playing surfaces
✔ inappropriate use of equipment
✔ tired or hungry children
✔ questionable use of safety rules or levels of supervision for specific activities

We use scenarios throughout this section to illustrate how caregivers can anticipate and prevent serious childhood injuries. Caregivers' understanding of children's development is an integral component in injury prevention.

 You would not permit a toddler to use the school-ager's slide any more than you would permit a 10-year-old to drive. Although the toddler might manage to climb the steps and sit down before sliding, he could fall at any time. Moreover, the slide itself is designed for children much larger than a toddler and has spaces between the steps and at the top that toddlers could fall through. Similarly, although the 10-year-old could reach the gas pedal and drive a car in a straight line, she is incapable of handling potential road hazards. In both of these examples, the children are neither physically nor cognitively ready to accomplish these tasks.

The following four components are interconnected and one or more can either cause or prevent injuries:

▶ training
▶ physical environment
▶ supervision of children
▶ safety rules

 ▶ The climber is developmentally appropriate but the protective surface is not maintained. The children understand the safety rules for using the climber, and a caregiver is assigned to supervise the children. A child loses her balance on the ladder and falls to the ground. The child suffers a mild concussion because the protective surface was not up to standard.

▶ Children are playing too close to the swings. However, because the caregiver observed and anticipated that a child might be hit by a moving swing, she moved the children to an appropriate area and reviewed the safety rules with them.

Training

Once you complete your early childhood education training, you will be equipped with entry-level skills and knowledge. No one should expect you to be ready or willing to accept a supervisor's role. However, you will be able to take an active role in safety promotion because you will know the fundamental principles of child development and how to integrate them with your observation skills. Your knowledge and abilities in injury prevention will be enhanced as you improve your observation skills through work experience. Promoting safety in the child care program involves positive attitudes, knowledge, and behaviour. Your commitment to seeking up-to-date information about safety, putting this information into practice, and modelling safe behaviour yourself are all part of your responsibility. Training opportunities may be on-the-job, or through courses, conferences, and possibly ongoing committee work or networking.

One possible consequence of injuries is the need for caregivers to administer first aid to children. Although regulations vary across Canada, all child care regulations stipulate that a specified number of the caregivers in a centre must have current first-aid certificates. First-aid techniques cannot be learned solely from a book. Try putting on a sling properly from looking at a picture! It's not as simple as it may appear. Caregivers must know how to manage choking in children and adults, and how to apply first aid. Ideally, ECE training programs ensure that their students take a standard first-aid course applicable to children and receive a certificate from a first-aid training program recognized by their child care office. Every student is strongly encouraged to obtain certification in cardiopulmonary resuscitation (CPR), including infant/child CPR. Certification in first aid and CPR not only demonstrates your professional commitment to safety but is an important and relevant skill on a résumé.

Physical Environment

Children's safety should be one of the main priorities when designing and furnishing centres. When prioritizing steps in promoting children's safety, the physical environment tops the list (ahead of supervision and safety rules). Regardless of the level of adult supervision or children's own awareness, children are at undue risk when the environment itself is inherently dangerous. Safety features should include the safe placement of electrical outlets and heating radiators/vents or electric baseboard heaters, safety glass in doors and the windows that separate rooms, doors that won't crush fingers, handrails on stairs for children, and hot-water temperatures that won't scald. These and other safety features such as smoke alarms and carbon monoxide detectors are the concern of the child care office, centre director, and board of directors. We focus here on the safety issues that have the most relevance to caregivers in their day-to-day work.

Infants and toddlers are rapidly changing and learning new skills. Caregivers draw on their knowledge of growth and development and observation skills to identify changes in each child and in the social relations among the children as a group. In response, caregivers may have to adjust the overall layout of the play area and frequently remove or add new and more challenging play material and equipment to meet individual children's next stage of development. Greenman has repeatedly seen toddler programs that were sterile environments devoid of large motor challenges. These inappropriate settings can result in children withdrawing, becoming aggressive (e.g., biting), or physically challenging themselves in inappropriate ways. "The net effect is often that the potential for harm is not reduced, only the source of harm is redirected" (Greenman 1988, 77).

Assessing the situation:
How could you prevent the following injury?
Scenario: A 10-month-old boy is learning to climb and he is particularly fond of climbing on the box that covers the heat radiator in the playroom. On one attempt, he falls backward onto his bottom and bangs his head on the floor.

Organizing the centre's indoor space provides opportunities for caregivers to prevent injuries for all age groups:

▶ In planning the room arrangement, caregivers need to consider the traffic areas so that paths lead children between activity centres rather than through them, without creating congestion.

▶ Provide areas with enough space for children to explore material and that other children don't have to walk through.

▶ Establish boundaries by using shelves or dividers and carpeting to your advantage, to break up open spaces that children would run in.

▶ When considering where to place the table and chairs in the playroom, allow enough space for the chairs to be pulled out while the children stand and sit during an activity and for a clear walkway behind the chair. (The walkway will reduce the likelihood of children tripping on chair legs.) This rule applies also to easels.

▶ Provide storage units and organize the space so that children can return materials and supplies. Add pictorial labels to shelves, boxes, and so on, to guide children in putting toys and material away during cleanup.

▶ Secure all shelving so that it cannot be tipped over. Limit the heights so that caregivers can view the room.

▶ Put the block area away from the traffic area.

▶ Choose round or curved tables rather than straightedged tables.

▶ For the water and sand tables:
  ▷ Place them on tile floor for easy cleanup (i.e., children and staff can slip in spilled water and sand).
  ▷ Keep cleanup tools handy at children's level (e.g., dustpan, broom, mop).
  ▷ Sand on the floor should either be discarded or put into the outdoor sandbox.

FURNITURE

Furniture should meet the needs of both the children and the adults. Tables, chairs, cots, activity centres, bookshelves, and so on must be durable and of a size that suits the children who use them. However, centres are also workplaces, so they must also meet the physical needs of the adults who work in them. Adult chairs should be available in the eating area and comfortable chairs or sofas in the play area for care-givers to read books, cuddle children, and feed infants. Yet we can't forget that the adult-sized furniture must be child-safe.

▶ A 15-month-old boy is crawling around a rocking chair at the same time that a caregiver is giving an infant her bottle. The boy's fingers become caught under the runner.
▶ A preschooler uses the levered handle for the recliner's footrest and her hand gets caught in the metal mechanism when she closes it.

From the standpoint of safety, much of the furniture manufactured for infants must meet the safety criteria established by Health Canada's Product Safety Branch. Their publication *Is Your Child Safe?* assists caregivers and parents in purchasing used furniture that meets the safety standards. Did you know that it is against the law to sell an old crib (made before September 1986) that does not conform to these standards?

With the cribs, highchairs, strollers, and possibly playpens in place in centres, what are the practices needed to ensure children's safety on a daily basis? (See Table 5.2, page 326.)

What about the ever-popular walker? Between 1990 and July 1994, almost 1000 children were injured using walkers, as reported by the Canadian Hospitals Injury Reporting and Prevention Program (CHIRPP), in which only 15 hospitals participated. Since 1989 manufacturers have voluntarily ceased selling walkers in Canada. Yet parents continue to buy them at garage sales, borrow and lend them, or buy them in the U.S. As walkers are becoming more difficult to obtain in Canada, the number of injuries reported by CHIRPP is decreasing. (Only 451 were reported in 1996.) It is unfortunate, though, that 451 babies in that year sustained traumatic experiences, including 336 fractures and numerous head injuries.

Walkers give infants a vehicle that can propel them at speeds that they are unable to handle. Adults are surprised at just how fast a baby can pick up speed in a walker, which often makes it impossible for an adult to stop the child before she or he tips over or crashes down the stairs. Since the infant is off the floor, he or she can reach cords and objects off low tables, which may lead to burns, poisonings, and other injuries.

Further, walkers put infants in an upright position, though many of them may not be able to sit unsupported. Infants' physical development evolves through a series of stages in which each stage prepares them for the next. Walkers not only confine children but also prevent them from moving naturally using their developing skills and abilities. *There is absolutely no reason for caregivers to provide infants with walkers.* Quality child care provides good modelling for parents. Walkers in centres should be banned; otherwise, parents get the impression that walkers are appropriate equipment for babies. New ideas and designs in furniture and play equipment must be evaluated for safety on an ongoing basis.

INDOOR PLAY EQUIPMENT

Centres provide children with play materials, equipment, and toys manufactured for children. Play materials can also be inexpensive objects found around the house—empty plastic containers, wooden spoons, measuring cups, blankets, scarves and hats, used clothes, pillows, cardboard boxes, pieces of wood, sand, and water. Toys and materials must be developmentally appropriate to ensure the safety of the particular age group using them. Toys for school-age children, for example, often have small pieces and removable parts, such as doll clothes and accessories or limbs, that can be pulled off and might choke younger children. Paints, glues, and coloured paper must be non-toxic to protect children who get them in their mouth.

Each day, caregivers inspect toys for the following:

✔ broken parts or pieces; when found, they are repaired or put safely in the garbage
✔ torn seams on dolls that could permit stuffing to come out
✔ chipped paint, rusting metal, etc.
✔ sharp or splintered edges
✔ exposed hinges or pinch points between moving parts
✔ frayed rope

Outdoor Play Equipment

The outdoor environment in the child care program is filled with joy and learning, especially when it is designed to meet the needs and interests of the children and when caregivers give the outdoor curriculum the ongoing attention it deserves. The play-based nature of the outdoor environment provides opportunity to enhance all areas of the child's development, such as physical (gross and fine motor, body awareness, spatial awareness, directional awareness, balance, perceptual-motor), problem-solving, language, pro-social development, creative expression, and of course self-esteem (Frost 1992, 25-49). Outdoor play can enhance physical agility and fitness, stress reduction through games, imagination—the list is almost endless. Many resources are available to support caregivers' awareness and planning of the outdoor curriculum, which is essential to a quality early childhood education program.

We must focus on the safety aspects of the outdoor environment due to the reality that most serious injuries in child care programs occur on the playground. The Canadian Standards Association (CSA) standards are intended to promote and encourage the provision and use of outdoor play spaces that are well designed, well maintained, innovative, and challenging for children (Canadian Standards Association 1998, xii). Wherever possible, the standards indicate modifications to the development of play spaces and equipment in order to make them accessible to children with a range of special needs.

The CSA suggests a range of environments and equipment for play activities, dividing the age groups into preschool (18 months–5 years old) and school-age (5–12 years old), recognizing 5 as a transition year for physical growth and development and the fact that as children get older, their abilities, interests, and needs change. Caregivers are responsible for ensuring that children safely use equipment designed for appropriate age and ability levels (see Table 5.3 and Table 5.4).

In the vast majority of playground injuries, two characteristics of the environment have a major influence on the severity: the quality of the cushioning material and the height the child falls from. The ground space under and around each piece

TABLE 5.2	PROTECTIVE SURFACING MATERIALS			
MATERIALS	**CHARACTERISTICS**	**ADVANTAGES**	**DISADVANTAGES**	**MAINTENANCE**
Sand	• Clean, washed • Non-packing	• Excellent impact-absorption qualities • Pleasing appearance • Drains well • Durable • Responds well to exposure to sun and rain	• Can get into user's eyes, hair, and shoes • Cannot be used with wheelchairs • Effectiveness reduced when wet, frozen, or combined with soil or foreign matter • Can conceal insects, animal excrement, and dangerous sharp items (e.g., nails, glass) • Higher ongoing maitenance cost	• Regular inspection required since depth reduced by wind and activities of users • Needs to be raked and turned over periodically • Foreign matter should be removed • Needs to be periodically replenished/replaced
Pea Gravel Metering Stone alluvial deposits of rounded particles approximately 9 mm (3/8") diameter	• Clean • Rounded • Free of soil	• Good impact-absorption qualities • Attractive texture • Drains well • Durable • Does not blow around • Responds well to sun and rain • Less attractive [than sand] to animals • Not muddy in wet weather or dusty in dry weather • Effectiveness not reduced when wet/frozen	• Can be put into ears and mouth • Cannot be used with wheelchairs or other mobility aids • Can be thrown or scattered • Can conceal insects and other dangerous and sharp items • Potential formation of "hard pan" under travelled areas • Higher ongoing maintenance cost	• Regular inspection to check depth • Foreign matter must be periodically removed • Needs to be periodically replaced or replenished • Needs periodic breakup and removal of "hard pan"

(table continues on next page)

TABLE 5.2	PROTECTIVE SURFACING MATERIALS (continued)		
MATERIALS	**CHARACTERISTICS**	**ADVANTAGES**	**DISADVANTAGES**	**MAINTENANCE**

MATERIALS	CHARACTERISTICS	ADVANTAGES	DISADVANTAGES	MAINTENANCE
Wood/bark chips or combination	• Well-prepared, dried • Need to ensure check of source for safe materials • Coniferous chips more durable	• Attractive texture • Resilient • Drains well • Fairly durable • Users don't play with the material • Mildly acidic composition retards insects or fungal growth	• Can compact when wet, frozen, or pulverized • Slowly decomposed and powdered by ongoing play action • Can harbour animal excrement, sharp or dangerous foreign matter • Can be ideal for microbial growth when wet • Can be ignited • Can cause splinters • Easily removed—can float away during rainstorms	• Requires regular inspection • Needs to be periodically replenished or replaced • Needs to be packed and turned over periodically
Unitary (manufactured) surfaces	• Varying thicknesses and colours • Must be used at suitable thickness, and be well-anchored and installed • Wide variation in available surfaces	• Effectiveness not likely to be impaired as severely when frozen • Consistent impact qualities • Easy to clean • Drains well • Pleasing appearance • High level of accessibility • Material not displaced or removed by user • Durable • Lower maintenance costs over long term	• Subject to vandalism • Can be flammable • Can become hard over time • Wide variation in quality and durability • Higher initial cost	• Requires regular inspection

Note: The depth of the surface material will depend on the potential critical height and the resiliency of the material.

Source: Reprinted with permission from *Children's Playspaces and Equipment*, Canadian Standards Association (Etobicoke: CSA, 1998), 199.

of equipment, called the encroachment area, must have a surface that cushions a child's fall as much as possible. The encroachment areas help protect not only the children using the equipment but also those walking by. Whenever possible, the areas should be clearly marked off to create pathways that can be followed by children and staff. This should prevent anyone from getting hit by a swing, by a child jumping off the climber, or by someone coming off the end of a slide.

Spacing of equipment is another factor in the design of a safe playground. The CSA (1998, 63–67) requires at least:

► 1.8 m (6 ft.) of space around stationary equipment
► 5.4 m (18 ft.) of space between moving equipment (e.g., swings, slide chutes)
► 1.8 m (6 ft.) of space between any piece of equipment and the playground's perimeter

A child can receive a fatal head injury from falling just 30 cm (12 ins.) onto protective surfacing/concrete. CSA standards specify the types of materials that can be used for each piece of equipment and how deep these materials must be. Sand, pea gravel, or wood bark chips are used. Some centres use synthetic (manufactured) materials as the cushion material in playgrounds. This material, made from recycled tires, comes in sheets of various thicknesses and allows for water drainage. The best-suited material depends on the specific piece of equipment, the age of the children using it, weather conditions, availability, and cost (e.g., sand that is constantly soaked by rain loses some of its impact-absorbing quality, so pea gravel that allows water drainage may be a better choice). Table 5.5 (page 333) elaborates on the various materials used as protective surfaces. The material most suitable may also depend on the focus of the play space. For example, if a centre has a vision to develop an outdoor space that is as natural an environment as possible, sand or wood chips are obviously more compatible with this vision.

Cushioning materials are critical safety features, but there is a height from above which a child in a fall is likely to sustain serious injury. A fall from a height greater than 1.5 m (5 ft.) could be fatal even if there were 22 cm (9 ins.) of pea gravel covering the encroachment area (Safe Kids Canada 1997, 5). Challenging, enjoyable playgrounds offer a wide range of experiences; they do not place the emphasis on the limited challenges that the height of the equipment offers to children.

Over time, equipment shows the effects of daily use and weathering. Walking and running pack down some protective surfaces (e.g., sand). Whatever material is used must be maintained to ensure that it is fulfilling its purpose. For these reasons, caregivers are responsible for regularly checking the surfaces and maintaining the equipment. Centres that use public or school playgrounds cannot assume that the equipment is inspected regularly. Caregivers should check the equipment and promptly report problems and concerns. The next time you walk by a school or public playground, stop and examine the condition of the protective surfacing under the climbing equipment. You may have legitimate cause for concern for children's safety!

A public school playground committee comprising parents from the school and the centre asked the school board for a safety inspection of the large play structure used by children from the school, centre, and neighbourhood. To everyone's shock and disbelief, 18 faults with that one piece of climbing equipment were found. Recommendations included adding more cushioning material to the protective surface, resetting bolts in wooden decks, and replacing the rungs on a ladder. Any of these faults could contribute to children's injuries.

Depending on the problems with equipment, caregivers decide whether children can use a particular piece of equipment. Ultimately staff are responsible for the children's safety. Staff are accountable if they knowingly permit children to use defective equipment or if it is shown that an apparent defect was not identified. In addition, caregivers take children off-site to other playgrounds and need to be able to assess the safety of that environment. Placing children at risk in an inherently unsafe environment, regardless of the level of supervision, is not ethically acceptable and can affect liability.

Assessing the situation:
What were the potential risks that caregivers should have identified and what should have been done to prevent the injury and any further injuries?
Scenario: One winter day, an 8-year-old girl is playing on the climber in the school playground. Her hands slip from the rungs and she falls to the ground.

TABLE 5.3	USING INFANT AND TODDLER EQUIPMENT SAFELY

EQUIPMENT SAFETY PRACTICES

Cribs	• The railing must be up and secure after putting the child in to sleep. • Bumper pads and large stuffed toys should not be in the crib once the child can stand up inside so that neither can be used by the child to climb over the side. • Never provide an infant with a pillow in the crib because of the risk that the infant will be unable to roll her face off a pillow to avoid suffocation. • To prevent strangling, blind and drapery cords must be secured away from cribs. Strings attached to mobiles and crib gyms must not be within children's reach (lying or standing).
Highchairs	• Never leave children unsupervised. • Always use the safety belts, but don't assume that children can't wiggle out or unfasten them. • Ensure that the child's fingers, hands, and head can't be trapped when putting on or taking off the tray. • Help children learn that they must always sit down and that standing is not permitted. • Check that all locking mechanisms are secured, ensuring that the chair doesn't collapse. • Don't place chairs near doorways, stoves, fridges, or walls where children could tip the chair over by pushing against it with their feet. • When chairs are not in use, keep them out of reach of children to prevent toddlers from trying to climb on them.
Strollers	• Never leave children unsupervised. • Check that all locking mechanisms are secure, ensuring that the stroller doesn't collapse. • Check all the brakes. • Use brakes when children are getting in and out or when parked with children inside. • Watch that hands and fingers are clear before reversing the handle. • Always use the safety belts, but don't assume that children can't wiggle out of or unfasten the belt. • Don't overload the handles with knapsacks, bags, etc., that can cause the stroller to tip. • Help children learn that they must always sit down.
Playpens*	• Ensure that the sides are up and secure. • Avoid large stuffed toys and boxes, etc., that children can use as steps to climb over the side. • To prevent strangling, blind and drapery cords must be secured away from playpens; mobiles and crib gyms with strings must not be within children's reach (lying or standing). • Keep playpens out of direct sunlight, as hot vinyl might burn the child's skin. • Check the vinyl mattress or railings for tears that children could bite off and choke on. • Do not use for children who either are tall enough or weigh enough to crawl over or tip over the playpen.

* When not sleeping, infants and toddlers must have the freedom to explore, play, and socialize in environments that are safe and secure. The routine use of playpens is discouraged for children of any age. Some centres use them for young infants outside or as a temporary safe place before returning children to the play area after diapering.

Source: Adapted from the Canadian Paediatric Society, *Well Beings* (Ottawa: Canadian Paediatric Society, 1996), 408–17.

TABLE 5.4 SUGGESTED FACILITIES/EQUIPMENT FOR PLAY ACTIVITIES For children from 18 months to 5 years old	
SUGGESTED	**FACILITIES AND EQUIPMENT**
Physical play	• a hard-surface route, preferably a large or circular one for wheeled toys • facilities and space for large-muscle activities such as climbing on equipment • soft open space for running or ball games (the space for physical play may approximate 40% of the space in a playground)
Social play (play together in small groups)	• playhouse and other structures to encourage imaginative play • landscaped enclosure • table and benches or chairs
Manipulative cognitive play (to create, manipulate)	• sandbox • water play such as spray pad • natural area • pots and pans • outdoor blocks, boards • outdoor drawing board
Quiet retreat play (to rest, imagine, or watch)	• enclosure, landscaped or fenced • table with seating • perch or hideaway
Physical play (a) games with balls or aerial objects (such as Frisbee, ball hockey, or kite-flying)	• open and level space of grass or hard surface, uninterrupted by trees or electric wires; enclosure, fence, or berm • seating at periphery
(b) ground-related games using the **whole body** (such as tag, roller-skating)	• open, level hard-surface area, or grassy area, not necessarily flat; enclosure, fence, or berm • seating at periphery
(c) strategy games requiring smaller **spaces** (such as marbles, hopscotch, or tetherball)	• protected small areas 1–3 m^2 (25 sq. ft.) • smaller hard-surface or grass areas
(d) activities that challenge dexterity and muscular control	• climbing structures, balance bars, swings
Manipulative cognitive play	• loose materials such as blocks, boards, sand, water sprays, natural areas (some of these activities require supervision; see relevant sections of CSA standards for details)
Social play	• table and seating, table games, sheltered space, natural area

(*table continues on next page*)

TABLE 5.4   SUGGESTED FACILITIES/EQUIPMENT FOR PLAY ACTIVITIES (continued)

SAND PLAY AREAS FOR ALL AGES

Size. The sand area should be large enough to encompass activities by several groups of children without interference. The total sand play area should be in proportion to the size of the overall play area. Where there are likely to be large numbers of children of varying ages, the total area for sand play may be divided into several smaller sand play areas. A 2 x 2 m (4 m²) (40 sq. ft.) sand area can be a comfortable cognitive sand play area for a group of up to 10 children. A minimum total sand play area of 6 x 7 m² (65 x 75 sq. ft.) is desirable in public parks and other public play areas. (This total should not include impact sand in the equipment area.) Sand play is a very popular play experience for children of all ages, and the play area design should maximize the total amount of space for sand play.

Types of Sand. The sand for creative play should pack together for moulding. Thoroughly washed brick sand, or an equivalent, such as seaside sand, should be used. Blow sand should not be used. The sand should be free of organic material, dirt, clay, silt, iron, asbestos, and other contaminants.

Depth of Sand for Play. The sand depth should allow for major excavations by the child, without disturbing the foundations and drainage. A minimum sand depth of 200 mm (8 ins.) is recommended. The preferred depth of sand is 450 mm (18 ins.).

Source: Adapted with permission from *Children's Playspaces and Equipment* (Etobicoke: Canadian Standards Association, 1998), 209, 211.

TABLE 5.5   SOME ELEMENTS THAT MAY APPEAR IN A SUPERVISED PLAY AREA

Shelter
Consideration should be given to providing some protection from sun and inclement weather. Creative play activities and fine motor activities can also be provided in such shelters. The design should be such that children can be easily supervised.

Storage
Some storage space is required on most supervised playgrounds. This should be a secure space for maintenance, materials, and equipment storage. If the design of the storage area allows for play use by children, there should be no possibility of children being trapped inside. The supervisor should be able to lock the door in an open position as well as lock it shut.

Water: Types of Water Play Areas
When possible, play areas should provide access to water to promote creative, social, and intellectual (cognitive) development. Play facilities that encourage playing with water are recommended. These could take the form of play streams, water channels, faucets, or manual pumps.

Loose Materials
Loose materials are an essential ingredient for creative play and should be provided wherever possible. They should be provided in a supervised area with defined limits, such as an enclosure. A flat area, separated and protected from physical play activities that may interfere, should be provided. Recommended loose materials include the following:
(a) hollow wooden blocks or large unit blocks and boards (20 × 200 mm) in various lengths. The suggested dimensions for the hollow wooden blocks are 200 × 200 × 200 mm and 200 × 200 × 400 mm. These should be stable enough to allow children to build small-scale spaces. All edges should be rounded, and the blocks or boards should possess the characteristics of a safe toy for young children. They should be finished for outdoor use and suitable in size, weight, and bulk for handling by small children;
(b) containers of all kinds
(c) blankets, rugs, pieces of cloth, old clothes for dress-up
(d) wagons and other wheeled toys, including wheelbarrows
(e) paper and craft materials
(f) balls and other objects
(g) bolsters, cushions, and other soft and foam objects
(h) play parachutes and other elements for cooperative games
Handles and grips on items should be appropriate for young children, to allow secure gripping and manipulation. Other loose materials to be used outside the specified creative play area may also be offered. These can include props to encourage role play and dramatic play by young children and tools and hardware for activities of older children.

Garden Plots
Where possible, garden plots should be made available to school-age children. Supervision is necessary for the distribution of gardening tools and for watering. A knowledgeable adult can provide useful training for the children in good gardening techniques.

Source: Reprinted with permission from *Children's Playspaces and Equipment* (Etobicoke: Canadian Standards Association, 1998), 177–79.

She is admitted to the hospital's emergency department with a broken arm. The protective surface under the climber is covered with ice. Note that another child had to run to tell a caregiver that the girl was lying on the ground.

Conducting Safety Checks

Caregivers' observations obviously play a significant role in preventing injuries throughout the day. Children, activities, issues, concerns, and other distractions will prevent any caregiver from identifying every potential safety risk in the environment. For this reason, regular safety checks are an essential component of injury prevention. Each day, the first caregiver who arrives in the morning, preferably before the children arrive, will walk through the centre and playground looking for items that must be attended to immediately. This could include replacing a burned-out light bulb in the stairwell, securing a blind cord that is hanging down the wall, putting the plastic outlet covers in unused electrical outlets, or removing cat feces from the outdoor sandbox. As well, cupboards may have been left unlocked or hazardous products left out on a counter or floor when the centre was cleaned the night before.

Before children go out to the playground each morning, caregivers need to conduct a quick check, looking for garbage, sharp objects (e.g., broken glass, discarded needles), discarded condoms, animal feces, puddles of water, ice on the protective surfaces, or wood chips that have been scattered by the wind or through use.

Like our homes, centres experience considerable wear and tear. Ideally, centre directors design standard checklists that are relevant to their particular building and playground. Weekly, monthly, and yearly safety checklists can be used to identify hazardous items, faulty equipment, and general maintenance requirements. Safe Kids Canada, in consultation with the CSA, has produced a video and booklet entitled *Child's Play—A Playground Safety Guide for Daycares, Schools, and Communities* that will help centre staff identify and correct potential safety hazards. See Resource Materials, page 373. Refer also to *Well Beings* (Canadian Paediatric Society, 1996, 971–97).

Documenting these checks and subsequent actions is part of an overall risk management program that also reduces the risk of legal liability. Safe Kids Canada (1997, 6) suggests three classes of potential hazards:

▶ Class A: a condition that could cause major injury or fatality, and *needs* to be corrected *immediately* (e.g., an entanglement point on a slide)
▶ Class B: a condition likely to cause serious injury with temporary disability, and needs to be corrected as soon as possible, before next scheduled inspection (e.g., sand needs topping up under a climber)
▶ Class C: a condition likely to cause minor injury, or that doesn't meet CSA standards, and may need long-term planning or budgeting

Reference must be made to the CSA's publication whenever a playground evaluation, a new playground, or changes or additions (i.e., retrofitting) are under consideration to make the most informed decisions and reduce the risk of legal liability in the event of an injury.

Supervision of Children

Child care regulations have established minimum caregiver–child ratios and maximum group sizes for the different age groups. Do you know your province or territory standards? Refer to your child care regulations to complete the following information:

Caregiver–Child Ratio	Group Size
infants: ___ : ___	
toddlers: ___ : ___	
preschoolers: ___ : ___	
school-agers: ___ : ___	

You may find it interesting to compare these figures with those recommended by both the Canadian Child Care Federation and the National Association for the Education of Young Children, which can be found in *Well Beings*. Note that the definitions of age groups may differ from those in your child care regulations.

Adequate staffing is essential in the supervision of children. Children are naturally curious and often do not understand the potential dangers or consequences of their actions. Combine this fact with the excitement that children feel who are having fun or trying something new, and the potential for children to forget safety rules or use equipment unconventionally is much higher. While supervising children, caregivers should *always* assume that children can do more today than they could do yesterday. The comment "I didn't think he could roll over yet, so I thought it was safe to leave him on the diaper change table for a few seconds!" indicates the caregiver's inability to apply developmental theory to child care practice. This comment points out that she did not follow a very basic safety practice with infants and toddlers. In some ECE training programs, this student's behaviour would be grounds for expulsion. Making assumptions about children's abilities can lead to injuries. Therefore, *caregivers must actively supervise children.*

Afternoon naps usually begin after lunch, when children are naturally tired and have full tummies. This is the time when caregivers take their own lunch breaks. With some staff off for lunch, there are fewer caregivers working unless additional adults come in to cover during these times. Here is the challenge: How do the remaining caregivers adequately supervise all the children? Both those children who are napping and those who are up playing require supervision. For preschoolers, the nap and play areas are usually in the same room, which facilitates supervision. However, for infants and toddlers the nap room is usually separate from the play area. As well, infants and toddlers typically sleep at different times during the day and for extended periods. Caregivers regularly go into the nap room to check on, resettle, or bring out the children who have awakened. Baby monitors are an inexpensive but valuable piece of equipment for caregivers to use *in addition to regular supervision*. What program could support having a caregiver in the nap room most of the day? As an aside, position young infants on their backs or sides to sleep. Research has indicated a link between sleeping on the tummy and sudden infant death syndrome (SIDS). Once children can reposition themselves while sleeping, this practice is not applicable.

DURING INDOOR PLAY

Equipment, toys, supplies, furniture, storage, and physical space should be designed and developmentally appropriate for the children using them, so that much of the caregivers' supervision is focused on facilitating play and guiding children's prosocial behaviour. From the standpoint of injury prevention, the level of supervision depends on the inherent risks of the activity, the ages of the children, and the applicable rules.

▶ Infants and toddlers must never be left alone during water play. Yet preschool children would not necessarily need a caregiver to be directly at the water table at all times.

▶ Preschoolers and school-agers involved in woodworking must be supervised directly.

▶ A small group of school-agers are playing a board game in the hall. Though they are out of view, you know where they are; they are still within earshot.

DURING OUTDOOR PLAY

Outdoor play presents caregivers with unique supervisory challenges because of the greater risk of injury from increased physical activity and a less structured environment. Outdoor play needs to be scheduled when all caregivers are working rather than when some are away at lunch or on a break. Outdoor play time is not a time when staff can be distracted by talking together. The outdoors provides children with a much less confined place in which to play. The equipment is physically challenging and some pieces, such as the climber, have inherent dangers because they enable children to reach distances metres off the ground. And children must be protected from people who pose a potential threat, including parents without custody and strangers.

Ideally, the layout of the area provides and encourages smaller groups of children to gather throughout the playground (e.g., sandbox, garden plot, water table, painting easels, places in the shade, swings, slides, climber) rather than congregate in one or two areas. Caregivers should spread out throughout the playground and move among the play spaces for which they are primarily responsible. Equipment, especially the climber, should have one caregiver who is directly responsible for supervision. Another person could supervise children on the swings and slide. Tubular slides present special safety concerns because the tube blocks caregivers' view of children sliding down. Furthermore, a child's clothing, hood, or scarf could become caught and cause strangulation. This is why centres should have a policy that bans drawstrings on hoods and that requires scarves, if worn, to be tucked into the coat. As well, caregivers must be vigilant in ensuring that skipping ropes, cords, ropes, and so on, have not been tied to play structures and, when found, are taken down immediately. A centre policy should spell out that only ropes designed for climbing should be attached to such structures.

Outdoor play is a time for preschool and school-age children to choose the activities they will take part in. While these older children do not always need caregivers to take as active a role in their activities, caregivers should not be any less involved in supervising what the children are doing.

For infants and toddlers, caregivers cannot let their guard down for a second. Infants who haven't yet learned to creep or crawl can sit on a blanket with toys and books. But once they can travel, there is no end to what they can do. Take a close look at what young children can find in the grass and soil. A puddle of water could drown a young child. A stone could cause choking. However, these potential risks should not exclude these children from outdoor play. Even very young children can begin to learn what they can and cannot safely put in their mouth, with caregivers' guidance.

Beyond the regular level of supervision, more vigilant supervision is required at certain times, such as when a new piece of equipment is added to the playground. At first, this piece of equipment will be more popular and children will need extra supervision until the novelty wears off. Children need time to become familiar with any necessary safety rules; children aged 4 and older can be involved in developing them. Field trips are also times when additional supervision is required. Centre

directors generally arrange for volunteers, often parents, to provide extra adults to improve the adult–child ratio. (See Walks and Field Trips, page 357.)

Assessing the situation:
Identify the issues that caregivers could learn from this scenario and what they need to consider in planning the next field trip to prevent injuries.
Scenario: On a field trip to the zoo, a group of 24 preschoolers and three caregivers take time out to use the small playground. While there, two children crash into each other and another child is hit by someone on the swing.

PREVENTION OF MISSING CHILDREN

Caregivers must know the whereabouts of all children at all times. Preventing children from wandering away from the group on a field trip or out of the playground is far easier than trying to locate a child after he or she has gone missing—and easier than suffering the emotional consequences experienced by the child, other children, caregivers, and of course the parents.

Implement the following measures to ensure children's personal safety:

▶ Maintain a daily attendance record that provides caregivers with a head count and tells them quickly who is absent or who has already gone home with his or her parent.

▶ Secure all exits from the centre and ensure that young children cannot open them.

▶ Control entry into the centre with a security system, which in some regions in Canada may involve simply locking the outside doors.

▶ Lock the playground gate when children are outside and have one caregiver responsible for conducting regular head counts.

▶ Establish the steps to follow if a child goes missing from the centre, the playground, or a field trip. Design a search plan for the centre, playground, and surrounding neighbourhood. Centre staff may find it useful to contact an agency that deals with missing children, or the local police department, to assist them in developing a plan that meets their needs. (See Planning Successful Field Trips, page 357.)

Safety Rules: A Learning Process

Most of us don't consciously think about the fact that our daily lives are governed by rules. Yet we don't plug in the electric radio near the bathtub. We follow traffic laws while driving and understand the consequences if we are stopped by the police. And we read the instructions before connecting a propane tank to the barbecue—or at least we should!

Society must have rules so that people can coexist. We cannot get a driver's licence until we are 16 years old or older. Society has determined that by that age, we are physically and cognitively ready to operate a vehicle, understand and follow the traffic laws, and accept the serious responsibility of driving.

Adults guide children with rules necessary for their own safety and the safety of others and that respect shared property. The ultimate goal is to learn to behave responsibly and to develop self-control during childhood. To promote this development we try to provide children with a child care environment that respects their need for autonomy and independence, their need to have some control over their world. The process of learning takes time. Children gradually gain more independence and responsibility based on their level of cognitive, physical, emotional, and social development. Children start to learn to follow rules with a simple rule for an activity, and gradually they work toward an understanding of rules that are more complex. This process enables older children to learn problem-solving and decision-making skills based on their own safety and their respect for others and property. At this point they rely on the attitudes, knowledge, and skills that they have developed and less on adult guidance and supervision. Rules learned in childhood pave the way for lifelong patterns of behaviour.

A caregiver guides a toddler to pedal her riding toy along the path. As a preschooler, the child learns to not ride double on tricycles, to slow down on the curves of the path, and to wear a bike helmet. As a school-age child, she attends a bicycle safety course and rides to and from school. By the time she is a teenager and young adult, she is capable of making her own decisions about riding bikes and can transfer this knowledge and these skills to driving a vehicle.

Whose Need for Control?

Most of us, children included, want to enjoy the feeling of independence and a sense of control over our lives. Consequently, young children often say, "You're not the boss of me," in response to an adult's power over them. Children react this way for one of two reasons. First, they naturally want to be in complete control, so the rules imposed by adults are considered to be an infringement on their freedom and desire for independence. Nurturing caregivers recognize this but also know that a secure environment for children includes consistent expectations. The second reason is that the children are legitimately reacting to adults who are inappropriately using their own need for power to control children. When caregivers are in a power struggle with children, they must always ask themselves whether a particular rule is really in the children's best interest or is simply a way to control them. *Caregivers who have overwhelmed children with rules for absolutely everything have set themselves up for countless power struggles with children.* In the long term, this practice increases the potential for making children feel incompetent and lacking in the confidence to make independent decisions.

There are always situations that require caregivers to act immediately, regardless of the child's response, because the child or others are in danger. Following the incident, the caregiver can then talk with the child about what has happened and help him or her understand the reasons behind the safety rule.

- A toddler stands up to run down the slide.
- Two children are fist-fighting.
- A school-age child is jumping from the top landing of the stairwell.

Often, caregivers observe a child breaking a safety rule but putting no one in danger. To prevent a power struggle with the child, the caregiver takes a moment to reflect on the intent of the rule rather than react immediately:

- Should the rule be adapted or eliminated because the child's skills and abilities have increased?
- Has the rule any foundation? If not, it should be eliminated.

Meeting to evaluate the safety rule enables caregivers to validate their assumptions about the rule by considering the children's changing skills and abilities, the activities and inherent risks, the condition and maintenance of equipment, and the children's responses to the rules. This can also be an opportunity to evaluate other rules and to revise or eliminate unnecessary ones. Whenever possible, children should be included in developing and evaluating rules for specific activities. These are opportunities for children to begin learning to look at the bigger picture around safety, developing observation skills, identifying risks and anticipating possible outcomes, understanding the rationale behind the rule, and so on. A potential danger to children are our own attempts to protect them. If they can't understand the rationale for rules, or if the rules are unbending, we could be setting up children for injuries. They will be denied experiences to build their decision-making skills, develop their confidence in their ability to think for themselves, and consider the reasons for their being asked or pressured to do something by others.

GUIDELINES FOR SAFETY RULES

Whenever you are in the process of developing safety rules, remind yourself that *rules do play a role in injury prevention, but they should not be the primary preventive. Rules alone cannot ensure children's safety.* Caregivers will consider the following elements in developing rules:

- ▶ the age of children
- ▶ whether the activity is developmentally appropriate
- ▶ the potential risks in the activity or play equipment and possible outcomes
- ▶ the design of the physical environment
- ▶ the level of supervision and modelling
- ▶ previous injuries related to this activity

Obviously, if an activity is not developmentally appropriate, it should either be adapted or cancelled. A long list of rules does not ensure injury prevention. In many instances, rules are unnecessary or can be reduced in number when the prevention strategies have been implemented.

- ▶ Before permitting children to use the climber in a neighbourhood playground for the first time, caregivers check that the climber is developmentally appropriate and well maintained. They will be sure that there are enough staff available to supervise the climber and the remainder of the playground before developing rules for the preschool children.
- ▶ A 3-year-old can say, "Stop, look, and listen before you cross the street." However, even though she does that when she is with you, you cannot assume that she is able to cross the street safely alone.

No one list of safety rules fits every child care program's requirements. Rules depend on the philosophy of the centre, the age of the children, and also the particular group of children, types of equipment, design of the physical indoor and outdoor space, and so on. Rules are ever changing, requiring an ongoing awareness for appropriateness and utility. It is better not to have a rule than to have one that has lost its value. Similarly, it is better to have fewer rather than more rules.

You are invited to participate in an activity, but before you begin you are presented with this list of rules:

▷ Don't run.
▷ Don't eat during the activity.
▷ Stay away from the red area.
▷ Keep your hands to yourself.
▷ Keep your voice down.
▷ Keep your shoes on.
▷ Don't climb on the furniture.
▷ Put everything away when you're done.

Now close your eyes and recite all the rules you have just read. Then repeat them tomorrow morning without reading the list. Unless you have a photographic memory, you probably will not remember more than one or two rules either now or tomorrow. How then can we expect children to remember and follow a list of rules for each piece of play equipment and activity? How many of these rules are stated in positive terms?

It is often easy to come up with many rules for using equipment or other activities. When a piece of equipment or activity has more rules attached than are essential, they may reduce everyone's enjoyment, cause children to become frustrated, and may in fact be either unsafe or developmentally inappropriate. Caregivers who continually restate the same rule many times a day probably should re-evaluate either the rule or the activity. Limit the number of rules by prioritizing what is most important for the children's safety. To ensure that safety rules are appropriate and effective, think about the following criteria:

▶ Consider children's development. (A rule that expects toddlers to share is frustrating for everyone, yet older preschoolers can be expected to share. Instead, positively reinforcing toddlers when they do share helps to promote sharing.)

▶ Rules are stated in positive terms. They focus on what children can do rather than what they can't do.

▶ Rules are stated in clear and simple language, especially those for younger children.

▶ Rules are realistic, with enough freedom to encourage creative play but enough restrictiveness to prevent unsafe behaviour.

▶ Rules are consistently enforced using gentle reminders and positive acknowledgment when children follow them. Threats, yelling, sarcasm, or any other tactics that can scare, intimidate, or embarrass children should *never* be used—this is emotional abuse. Children who have difficulty following important safety rules, even after being reminded, should be removed from that particular activity with an explanation of why removal is a logical consequence.

"Sand can get in children's eyes when you throw it. You need to find something else to do right now." However, give the child the opportunity to return to the activity later, which demonstrates your confidence in the child's ability to follow the rule.

▶ Rules are modelled by caregivers. Modelling helps children understand the importance and necessity of rules.

▶ Rules are developed, whenever possible, with the involvement of preschoolers and school-agers. (When a new toy is available, you can ask children what could happen if…? and what would then be important guidelines or rules for using it?)

▶ Rules provide teachable moments to point out sensible safety guidelines.

 When a child or adult trips over a toy, it is an ideal time to mention why the rule about putting toys away before moving to the next activity is important. Yet care must be taken not to constantly lecture or nag children or else they are likely to tune us out!

▶ Rules are reviewed with children before they begin an activity that they haven't done for several months (e.g., woodworking, using the riding toys outside now that the snow has melted).

I. Rules and Ball Play

Let's use ball play to demonstrate some possible rules for children in different age groups and how the type and number of rules would evolve.

Infants and Toddlers

Ball play involves exploring, throwing, or rolling balls with little accuracy across a room, in a playground, or to a caregiver. Infants' and toddlers' eye–hand coordination is still developing, they are just becoming aware of cause and effect, and they are not yet ready to share. Therefore, a rule for ball play is usually unnecessary for this age group. Instead, caregivers should provide children with plenty of soft, light, midsize balls to prevent problems. Constant active supervision and guidance are required.

Preschoolers

Between the ages of 2 and 5, children improve their accuracy in throwing balls. They may play simple games with peers, such as pitch and catch, hot potato, or soccer. It is a good idea to continue using softer rubber or inflated balls and ones that are lighter. Appropriate rules for this age group would be ones like these:

▶ Throw the ball to someone, not at someone.
▶ Put away the balls when you are finished so no one trips over them.
▶ Keep balls in the large motor area when playing inside.
▶ When outside, you can bounce the ball on this wall because it doesn't have windows and people won't be walking between you and the wall.

▶ When a ball goes over the fence, an adult will get it.

Obviously, only one or two of these rules would be needed at any one time!

School-Agers

These children develop more complex ball skills, play cooperative and competitive games and sports, and often break up into teams. They may be quite accurate and powerful in throwing balls and using bats. Except for the general guidelines about not harming self, others, or property, rules depend on the particular ball game. While they are learning a ball game like soccer, dodge ball, street hockey, baseball, or volleyball, caregivers can help them develop and understand the safety rules of the game. In baseball, for example:

▶ Play in an area away from other children.
▶ Wear a helmet when at bat.
▶ Put the bat down after swinging. Don't throw it.

In dodge ball, for example:

► Use the light, soft rubber ball.
► Aim below the waist.

II. Rules and Swings

We'll use swings to demonstrate some possible play equipment rules for children in different age groups and how the rules might evolve.

Infants and Toddlers

Caregivers usually have to lift children into a swing. Because a caregiver has to be right there with an infant, rules aren't needed. Older infants and toddlers may need rules such as these:

► Hold on with both hands.
► Stay sitting until the swing stops.

Preschoolers

These children are learning to use swings with less direct adult involvement. There is quite a difference between the ablility of a 2-year-old and that of a 5-year-old on swings. The following examples are more appropriate for children who have become competent on swings and can use them independently:

► Stop the swing completely before getting on or off.
► Look carefully when walking in front of or behind moving swings.
► Only one child may be on the swing at any time.

School-Agers

Most children who are still interested in swings are already competent to use them the regular way and find new and challenging ways to swing (e.g., shimmying up the swing poles, twisting the chains and letting them spin out, jumping off a moving swing, standing on the seat). Some rules for swings may be:

► Only one child on the swing at any one time.
► Make sure that no one is near when you jump off.

School-age programs may permit more innovative uses of swings depending on a number of factors such as skill levels of the particular children, condition of the protective surface, and whether younger children are using the playground at the same time. Think how you might handle a question from preschoolers about why older children are allowed to jump off swings but they aren't. Remember, rules are not static: they can change with children's development or the situation.

 e.g. Children are permitted to jump off moving swings. During a safety check of the playground, the caregiver sees that the sand underneath the swings is hard-packed. To prevent an injury, until the sand is worked up, children are asked to wait until the swings stop moving before getting off. Children will understand the reason why and that this rule is only temporary.

What's the Rest of the Story?

 OBJECTIVES To describe safety issues related to seasonal changes.
To discuss the principles and practices in planning and conducting field trips.
To be aware of situations in which child protection is a concern.

The remainder of this unit is devoted to other safety-related issues that caregivers should consider. Some of these pertain to safety on a daily basis, such as protecting children from the seasonal elements and going for walks; others are of a more general nature, such as injury reports and responding to emergencies.

Being Outdoors Safely: Summer and Winter

Can you imagine living in a place where the weather is always the same? Maybe you can if you're reading this unit in the middle of winter with a wind chill of –34°C (–29°F)! Canada's changing seasons provide us with wonderful opportunities to participate in a variety of activities and sports, but the hot and cold weather pose certain safety considerations.

SUMMER

The suntan remains popular—a symbol associated with health, active living, and attractiveness. After a long winter, the allure of the sun can be overwhelming, especially when one feels the warmth on the face and skin. In the past few years, however, there has been a concerted effort to educate the public about the dangers of sun exposure. Pamphlets, magazine articles, and television commercials outline the relationship between ultraviolet (UV) radiation and skin cancer (e.g., melanoma), eye damage, and premature aging of the skin. Did you know that sun tanning machines produce the same wavelength of light as the sun and cause the same damage (Canadian Cancer Society 1993)?

Skin cancer is the most common type of cancer, but fortunately the cure rate is over 90 percent. The Canadian Cancer Society estimates that around 16 000 new cases of skin cancer are diagnosed each year and that there were 58 500 cases of non-melanoma skin cancer in 1994. Malignant melanoma, which accounts for one of three types of skin cancer, is relatively uncommon but occurs in younger people more often than the other types (National Cancer Institute of Canada 1994, 10; Canadian Cancer Society n.d., 2, 5, 10).

How do caregivers protect themselves and children while outside during the summer? They can begin by *limiting or avoiding outdoor play and walks between 11 a.m. and 2 p.m.* (Peak hours may vary by an hour one way or the other). However, if children are to get outside even twice a day, a compromise needs to be reached: shade must be available, fluids offered, and sunscreen, hats, sunglasses, and clothing must be used. Children are more sensitive to UV exposure than adults because children have thinner skin, and on average they spend more time outdoors than adults. Two or more serious sunburns as a child or adolescent significantly increase the risk of getting skin cancer later (Health Canada 1998).

About 30 minutes before going outside, caregivers should *liberally apply sunscreen lotions* with a sun protection factor (SPF) of at least 15. Remember to apply lotion above where shorts and sleeves stop, since they ride up the legs and arms while the children are playing, and also to the top of the children's feet when they are wearing sandals. When children are very active and sweating, lotion should be applied more often to give 100 percent UV protection. Children using wading pools or sprinklers either need to wear a waterproof sunscreen or to have regular sunscreen reapplied when they get out of the water. As added sun protection, children can wear T-shirts over their bathing suits to protect their shoulders, back, and chest.

Centres may prefer to use communal bottles of lotion, since it is much faster to do one child after another than to use 20 different bottles of lotions and try to keep them all straight. As well, all the bottles must be kept out of reach of children. In these centres, staff check with parents to ensure that they approve of the type that is used. Some children may have a skin reaction to a particular brand of sunscreen, most often ones that contain PABA. Caregivers do not have to wash their hands after each application. Not only is this time-consuming, but the risk of spreading infection through sunscreen is negligible even when someone has a cut or scrape, because these should be covered with either clothing or a Band-Aid. The only time that hand-washing may be warranted is when a child has an allergy to the sunscreen brand used by the centre; then the caregiver would need to wash off the centre's lotion before applying this child's own. Older preschoolers should be learning to apply their own lotion. These children need supervision to ensure that they don't get lotion in their mouth or eyes and that they adequately cover all exposed skin. By the time they are school-age, most children should be responsible for this task. Remember, it takes about 10 minutes for unprotected skin to sunburn in the summer sun. Therefore, a lotion with a SPF of 15 provides children with 150 minutes of protection. Don't forget that sunscreen should be applied in the early spring and also late into the fall. Choose lotions that

▶ don't contain alcohol (which may sting skin and eyes)
▶ are unscented (will not attract insects)
▶ don't contain PABA

Everyone should *wear hats*, preferably with a wide brim that shades face, ears, and neck. Some children don't like wearing hats but may be more likely to wear baseball caps, which are very popular. Don't forget to put sunscreen on their ears and the back of their neck. Child-sized shatterproof *sunglasses* with 100 percent UV protection are now available at low prices; parents should be encouraged to provide their child with a pair. Although many toddlers and young preschool children may not keep them on, we are at least introducing them to the idea. Ideally, children wear long-sleeved shirts and long pants, although this seems impractical when it is very hot and/or humid. Whatever clothing is worn, it should be loose-fitting and cool to help reduce sweating.

Ensure that *shade* provided by trees, table umbrellas, awnings, or other structures is accessible to children to play in. Children should be encouraged to come into shade every half-hour while outside. Wading pools should be placed in the shade. *Sunscreen is not a replacement for shade*.

Physical activity in hot weather puts children at risk of becoming dehydrated because the body loses water through sweating. *Offer water* to children before they go outside and encourage them to drink water several times while outside and again after they are back inside. Pay particular attention to children who are using the play

Interesting Facts about the Sun

► *Fiction:* A tan is healthy. *Fact:* A tan indicates that your skin is already damaged.
► *Fiction:* A tan protects me from the sun. *Fact:* A dark tan on a white person offers an SPF (sun protection factor) of about 4. An SPF of 15 is recommended when skin exposure is unavoidable.
► *Fiction:* Black skin protects me from the sun. *Fact:* People with black skin can get sunburns and skin cancer. Black skin gives an SPF of 8 at most.
► *Fiction:* You can't get burned on a cloudy day. *Fact:* Up to 80 percent of the sun's rays can penetrate light clouds, mist, and fog.
► *Fiction:* You can't get burned if you're in the water. *Fact:* Water offers minimal protection. Water surface reflection can intensify the sun's rays on your skin.
► *Fiction:* Baby oil is a good sun lotion. *Fact:* Baby oil may intensify the effects of the sun and may cause skin to burn faster.

Source: From *Facts About the Sun. The Sun, Your Baby and You: A Parent's Guide to Sun Protection* (1992), Health Canada: Minister of Supply and Services Canada. Reproduced with permission of the Minister of Public Works and Government Services Canada, 1999.

equipment and running around, as they will be losing more water through sweat. Children can be dehydrated and not complain of thirst.

Remember how germs are spread and do not use a communal drink bottle or shared cups. If you don't have access to running water outside, bring out a jug and enough cups for everyone.

Infants should

▶ *be shaded from the sun at all times.* Not only is their skin protection system not fully developed, but for most of their first year they cannot move out of the sun on their own. And they can't tell you when they are getting too hot or thirsty.

▶ get plenty of fluids even if they are just lying on a blanket in the shade. Young children can become *dehydrated very quickly* because they have more surface area (skin) to body mass as compared to adults. Signs of dehydration and treatment are discussed in the section on diarrhea. (See page 178.)

▶ wear T-shirts over their bathing suits when they are in the wading pool.

▶ not, when under the age of 6 months, have sunscreen applied, because they may put lotion-covered hands or feet in their mouth. Also, the lotion may irritate their skin.

▶ whenever possible, be dressed in loose-fitting clothes that have long sleeves and pants (or long-sleeved cotton jumpers) and should wear hats.

Certain medications can cause skin reactions such as rashes, swelling, blisters, or redness that look like an exaggerated sunburn. Photosensitivity reactions are relatively common. Symptoms can appear immediately once the skin is exposed to sun or several hours after exposure has ceased. Interestingly, symptoms may develop only on skin that wasn't covered by clothing or may appear anywhere on the body. Symptoms can last for several days, even after the prescription is completed. Some of the commonly prescribed medications that can cause photosensitivity are some antibiotics, antihistamine creams, oral contraceptives (the pill), and sunscreen containing PABA. Some of the medications prescribed for the management of diabetes, cystic fibrosis, and mental health disorders can cause photosensitivity reactions. (See Administering Medication, page 186.)

Do you ever hear adults say to children, "Just do what I say because I'm the parent" or "I don't have to do that because I'm the adult"? Take a moment to think about the behaviour that caregivers model if they sunbathe, compliment one another on their tan, or refuse to wear hats and sunglasses or to apply sunscreen at work. The adult who tells children that they must do things because he or she told them so is, in fact, controlling children.

UV Index and the Humidex   Ozone is a 20-kilometre-thick layer of gas surrounding the earth 15 to 35 kilometres above the surface. Ozone filters out most of the sun's ultraviolet (UV) rays so that they don't reach the earth (Environment Canada 1992, 2). Basically, the more UV rays we are exposed to, the faster our skin is damaged. Cloudy days don't necessarily protect us from UV rays. The darker and thicker the clouds, the more UV rays that are blocked. Fluffy and thin clouds don't block UV rays, and UV rays that are reflected off bright surfaces (e.g., sand, concrete, water, snow) increase our exposure. In Canada, people living at higher elevations (e.g., mountains) get more UV rays because the air is cleaner and thinner. And UV exposure increases the closer you are to the equator, so there will be more in Southern Ontario than in the Arctic (Environment Canada 1993).

UV rays are strongest in the summer, but during other seasons too caregivers need to be aware of UV rays (e.g., a sunny winter day in the Rockies). In the summer, the weather reports usually provide the UV index for the day. UV is measured on a scale of 10, with 10 indicating the shortest sunburn time, typically on a sunny summer day. Tables 5.6 and 5.7 put the UV index into practical and relevant terms so that caregivers can prevent skin damage to children and themselves.

Depending on where you live, you may be used to hearing weather reports on the radio or television include not only the day's temperature but also the UV index and the humidex (e.g., "It's 32°C today, but the relative humidity makes it feel like 42°C"). The more moisture there is in the air, the less sweat evaporates off skin,

TABLE 5.6   WHAT DOES THE UV INDEX MEAN TO ME?

UV INDEX	CATEGORY	SUNBURN TIME
over 9	extreme	less than 15 minutes
7–9	high	about 20 minutes
4–7	moderate	about 30 minutes
0–4	low	more than 1 hour

When the UV index is over 9, UV-B is extremely strong and you will burn in less than 15 minutes. (Sunburn times are for light untanned skin; the times are somewhat longer for those with darker skin.) Even if you do not get a burn, you may still be damaging your skin.

Source: Environment Canada, *UV AND YOU: Living with Ultraviolet* (1993). Reproduced with permission of the Minister of Supply and Services, 1995.

TABLE 5.7   THE UV INDEX: TYPICAL SUMMER MIDDAY VALUES

CANADIAN COMMUNITIES COMPARED TO THE TROPICS AND THE NORTH POLE	UV INDEX
Tropics	10.0 extreme
Toronto	8.0 (high)
Halifax	7.5 (high)
Edmonton	7.0 (high)
Yellowknife	6.0 (moderate)
Iqaluit	4.8 (moderate)
North Pole	2.3 (low)

Source: Environment Canada, *UV AND YOU: Living with Ultraviolet* (1993). Reproduced with permission of the Minister of Supply and Services, 1995.

which is why people feel hot and sticky when it's very humid outside. Basically, the humidex value is calculated using the temperature and the relative humidity. How does the humidex tell us what it's like outside?

▶ 20° to 29°C (68° to 84°F): It's comfortable for most.
▶ 30° to 39°C (86° to 102°F): Most will feel discomfort, some more than others.
▶ Over 40° (104°): Almost everyone will be uncomfortable. Most activities and work must be restricted.

Caregivers use their discretion when the humidex reading is high to ensure that children playing outside do not become dehydrated or sick. Perhaps outdoor activities could be limited in duration and restricted to quieter play in the shade, or perhaps water play could be made available.

Insects and Repellent To avoid attracting insects, wasps, and bees, avoid serving sweet food and beverages outside and keep garbage containers far from the play area. Exercise caution when a child has an allergy to bees or wasps and be sure that his or her adrenalin kit is outside with the caregivers and the child. Remember that if the insects are prevalent and are biting, the best option may be to keep the children inside or to arrange to use a community centre or school gym to get physical exercise, even if it's only for a few days.

Repellents are used to repel mosquitoes, ticks, fleas, and biting flies. *Repellents are poisonous and must be kept out of reach of children.* Only those with no more than 50 percent deet should be used on children's skin. Do not apply on children under 6 months old. Use clothing or mosquito netting over strollers and carriages, or avoid going outside if the insects are particularly bad. A drop of white vinegar or oil of citronella behind ears, lenses, and wrists may help keep insects away. Remember the following points if you use repellents:

▶ Choose lotions rather than sprays.
▶ Apply *sparingly* and only on exposed skin, not under clothes or diapers, and avoid eyes and mouth.
▶ To prevent children getting the repellent in their mouth, do not apply on their hands and fingers.
▶ Never permit young children to put repellent on themselves or others. Older preschoolers may apply it with supervision and most school-agers should have learned how to apply it safely.
▶ Once children are back inside, wash off the repellent.
▶ Ask the parents' written permission before using repellent.

WINTER

Winter conjures up pictures of chattering teeth, metre-high snowdrifts, and icy roads. Yet winter also has beautiful blue skies, clean crisp air, and snow that sparkles like diamonds. And snow is a wonderful play medium for winter activities and

sports. Children can have great fun in playgrounds even though in most regions of Canada it will be very cold. Getting outside in the winter provides all of us with much needed physical activity, fresh air, and sunlight, which is the best source of vitamin D.

Dressing appropriately for the weather goes a long way toward making winter activities enjoyable and safe. Scarves and hoods can become caught on play equipment, resulting in strangulation. Ensure that scarves are tied, with the ends tucked into the coat or parka, and that hoods are tied snugly around faces. Some clothing manufacturers are now making cordless hoods that fasten with Velcro rather than cords.

Most of our body's heat is lost through our head. Wearing appropriate winter hats, tuques, hoods, and so on is equally important for adults and children in protecting us from chill and our ears from frostbite. Exposed skin freezes in just a few minutes when it is cold enough outside. Noses, cheeks, ears, fingers, and toes are most prone to frostbite. Watch the children to ensure that their hats, hoods, and scarves do not slide out of place and that someone hasn't got a boot full of snow.

Watch for children who take off their mitts when using play equipment. Toddler snowsuits often come with mitts (without thumbs) that snap onto the cuffs. Toddlers quickly become frustrated with mitts and pull them off because they can't do anything with their hands. Parents should be encouraged to provide toddlers with non-slippery mittens with thumbs. Unless the mitts or gloves are leather, they get wet quickly during play. Wet mitts not only chill children's hands but also increase the likelihood of frostbite. Centres may have mitt-drying racks or ask parents to send two or three pairs of mitts each day so that children have a dry pair to wear during the afternoon.

As discussed in the section on summer safety, caregivers have a professional responsibility to dress appropriately for the weather conditions when supervising outdoor play. If it is cold enough for children to be wearing hats, mitts, winter boots, and zipped-up coats, caregivers should wear the same. This is not only to model the behaviour for the children but also to protect themselves from chill and frostbite.

Children may complain that they are cold or wet. Obviously, if they are wet they have to go indoors and change into something dry before going back outdoors. However, some children will tell you that they are cold from the moment they step out the door. Often they need to be encouraged to start moving around so that they warm up. Caregivers can help them by moving around themselves and inviting children to join them. Yet after being outside for some time, some children will be cold and should go inside to warm up.

We often begin our winter mornings by listening to the day's temperature and wind-chill factor. The Canadian Paediatric Society (1996, 449) suggests that children remain indoors under the following conditions:

▶ when the temperature is below −25°C (−13°F), regardless of the wind-chill factor, or

▶ when the wind-chill factor is reported as 1625 or higher or as −28°C (−15°F) or below, regardless of the temperature.

Some child care regulations stipulate an outdoor temperature below which it is deemed too cold for children to play outdoors. Obviously in some regions of Canada, people are accustomed to long, cold winters and have appropriate winter clothing to minimize the amount of exposed skin. In other regions, where cold weather occurs less frequently, children may have to remain indoors for several consecutive days. Centre staff may want to explore options within the community that would provide space for children to be physically active every day.

Catching falling snowflakes on our tongue is a lot of fun. Blankets of fresh white snow are inviting to eat. Yet children should be discouraged from eating *fallen* snow (on the ground, fences, benches, etc.) or licking icicles, which can be contaminated with dirt or pollution or animal/bird feces or urine. On milder days it's hard for any of us to resist picking up snow and making snowballs. Children naturally want to throw balls and snowballs are no exception. However, people can easily be injured by snowballs that are thrown too hard or that contain stones. Perhaps you can reach a compromise on snowballs. Designate a wall (without windows) or a tree that snowballs can be thrown at, although you will still have to supervise to ensure that children do not throw balls at one another. Children can also be encouraged to build walls, animals, people and so on, with snow.

It would be hard to find an adult who grew up in Canada who didn't try to stick his or her wet tongue on cold metal, contrary to parental warnings. So you won't be surprised if some children freeze their tongue to metal objects and perhaps suffer a painful injury.

Frostbite occurs when the skin and underlying tissue gets frozen. Frostbite may not always be painful, but the skin or patch of skin (e.g., nose, cheeks) looks white, and in advanced cases may be blistered.

You will need to know what to do when a child's tongue becomes stuck to metal:

First Aid

1. Try to prevent the child from pulling away from the metal.
2. Blow hot breath onto the stuck area or pour warm water onto the object.[1] Gently release the child.
3. If bleeding occurs, such as on the tongue, grasp the tongue with folded sterile gauze and apply direct pressure[2] (Canadian Paediatric Society 1996, 237).

[1]An experienced caregiver suggests putting a small container filled with hot tap water in a coat pocket before going outside. The water will cool off and it is immediately available.
[2]This is just one more reason why a first-aid kit must always be brought out to the playground.

You will need to know what to do if frostbite occurs:

First Aid

1. Carefully handle and re-warm the area only if there is no chance of a re-freezing before returning to a warm place.
2. If you are outside, warm extremities by holding them in someone's armpits. Warming ears and noses with a warm palm is enough for mild freezing.
3. Treat deeper freezing by holding the extremity in warm water (40.5°C to 43.3°C [105°F to 110°F]) for 20 minutes.[1]

[1]Children should be seen by their doctor or an emergency room physician to ensure that there is no permanent skin damage (Canadian Paediatric Society 1996, 236).

Activities in the Winter   Winter sports such as skating, tobogganing, and skiing all have the potential to cause injuries. To reduce the risk of injury, caregivers must ask themselves five safety questions when they are planning winter sports:

1. Is this activity developmentally appropriate for the children?
2. Is the location designed for children to use (e.g., the height of the tobogganing hill) and are there potential hazards—trees, walking paths, ditches, or a road—at the bottom of the hill?
3. What are the potential dangers? How can they be reduced or eliminated?
4. What safety equipment must children wear? Is there enough equipment for each child?
5. Can we recruit enough staff or volunteers for supervision?

For example, toboggans and sleds are dangerous if improperly used, and can cause head, pelvic, and back injuries. Consumer and Corporate Affairs Canada (1993) has issued a bulletin that includes the following advice:

▶ avoid sliding near roads, driveways, trees, poles, rocks, and water
▶ make sure children wear protective helmets
▶ stay seated and don't overload toboggans or sleds
▶ remove all scarves and drawstrings
▶ climb the hill to the side, away from others sliding down
▶ be extra careful on icy hills—children will go faster than they expect

We can get sunburned in the winter, too, because snow and ice reflect the sun's rays. Sunscreen and lip balm with SPF should be used when children are outdoors for several hours. The lotion helps protect the skin from windburn.

Walks and Field Trips

Children need to expand their world in many ways and directions, and walks and field trips provide opportunities for learning and enjoyment. Yet unfamiliar surroundings increase the opportunity for injuries, especially for children. Whether caregivers are taking a small group for a walk to the public park or a group of 6- and 7-year-olds to the planetarium by public transit, advanced planning ensures that the outing is safe and developmentally and educationally relevant.

Centres have developed written policies and procedures regarding walks and field trips. Walks are often a regular part of a child care program, as when infants and toddlers go out in strollers or wagons every day. Caregivers at centres without a playground need to walk children to neighbourhood playgrounds daily. In both cases, staff obtain written parental permission for walks at the time of enrollment. Parents then know that their children are frequently being taken off the premises and can discuss any concerns that they may have with the staff.

PLANNING SUCCESSFUL FIELD TRIPS

The key to safe field trips is careful planning. It is important to reiterate the caregivers' responsibility for children's safety at all times. Remember that you need to consider all aspects of the field trip, including

▶ preparing the children and adults
▶ transporting the group to and from the destination
▶ assessing the actual activity and physical environment
▶ evaluating the trip on returning

An itemized list is useful in planning, but caregivers also have to brainstorm to anticipate other issues that may come up and determine how they can prevent confusion or injuries. Organizing the routine walk to the local playground is quite different from busing a group to a conservation area. Posting a checklist for walks

saves time and ensures that caregivers take everything they need. But even a routine walk may present you with a surprise, which requires caregivers to make a decision and ensure the group's safety. You have probably planned an event down to the last detail and then something unexpected happens. That invariably happens on field trips too. Caregivers need to think on their feet and apply their safety knowledge and skills to make responsible decisions.

▶ Finding that half a block of sidewalk has been ripped up, caregivers and toddlers have to walk along the road past the construction to get to the playground. This is not ideal, but the staff carry it out as safely as possible. Responsible caregivers will talk about what happened with the children on returning to the centre, and next time choose a new route, if possible, until the construction is completed.

▶ Two of the parents who had volunteered to accompany your group to the children's theatre presentation announce at the last minute that they are unable to attend. What do you do—cancel the trip, phone around for other volunteers, or...?

Caregivers have some basic but important questions to ask themselves when they plan field trips:

▶ Is the trip developmentally appropriate for the age group? Who benefits by taking infants to a planetarium? For infants and toddlers, it often makes sense to plan simple trips that are close to the centre—a trip to a neighbourhood library, for example.

▶ Is the trip educationally appropriate? Taking a preschool group to the mall because the adults want to shop is irresponsible. Trips that do not relate to the interests and learning needs of the children are also more likely to be unsafe, because bored children of any age tend to look for other stimulation, such as pushing one another or wandering away from the group.

▶ Do the caregivers believe that the children are able to understand and follow the trip's guidelines?

 e.g. Taking a newly formed group of preschoolers on a field trip that requires several rules may be asking for problems. Instead, start with short walks and excursions, helping children to develop an awareness of safety rules, and progress from there.

▶ Have caregivers select a way to quickly identify the members of their group while out in a public place where there may be other groups of children (e.g., T-shirts, smocks, or ball caps all in the same colour or a visible tag with the centre logo and phone number). School-age children don't want to be embarrassed; involve them in the decision of identifiable clothing. Why is it important not to have the child's name on a tag on his or her clothing?

Ensure that one caregiver does regular head counts: before leaving the centre, several times during the trip, before leaving again, and on arrival back at the centre. Centre staff are encouraged to have a recent colour photograph of each child as well as his or her age, height, weight, and eye colour. If a child is missing, a photo and description will be useful. Instamatic photographs work well and the description of the child can be written in the white space under the picture. (See Prevention of Missing Children, page 338.)

▶ Are there enough adults to ensure safety? Make sure to have more than the legislated minimum number of adults—that is, improve on the adult–child ratio and even more so on trips with younger children or children with specific needs. Some centres find it difficult, if not impossible, to recruit volunteers or parents to join them on trips. Staff may take smaller groups of children at a time, over a few days (on visits to the fire station on Tuesday, Wednesday, and Thursday, for example). These centres may have included this model in their field trip policy.

▶ Is there quick access to a phone? Bringing a cell phone is the best solution; if this is not possible, ensure that a phone is nearby in case it is needed.

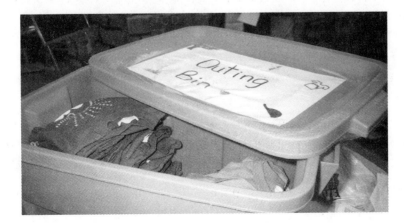

Many centres use a walking rope for children to hold when walking as a group outside the centre's property. Staff believe that by holding onto a knot or handle attached to a rope, the young children are safer. Caregivers assume that they are able to keep track of the children because they are in an orderly line, and that children will not dash off. The use of ropes is a debatable issue among caregivers. We do not, however, support the use of ropes, for a number of reasons:

▶ The use of ropes implies that the caregivers don't believe that the children are competent enough to follow the rules for walks. Toddlers who aren't ready to follow the rules should be in strollers or wagons that they can get out of in order to walk around in a park or playground.

▶ When one child trips, all the children holding on may fall also, which is potentially more hazardous than not having a rope.

▶ Caregivers who rely on the rope as a security measure may not notice when one child lets go.

▶ Holding onto a rope is not a natural way to walk and thus doesn't provide young children with a realistic experience. It also may encourage them to depend on caregivers rather than to develop a natural awareness of their surroundings and safety.

▶ Some people in the community already view child care as an institutional setting. Seeing children walking along the street holding onto a rope may reinforce that negative view of child care.

Environmental Contaminants

We have discussed concerns about UV rays, humidity, and wind chill, but there are many other environmental factors that environmentalists and researchers are bringing to our attention. Since the 1940s hundreds of thousands of new chemicals have been introduced into our world in the name of progress and a better standard of living.

The impact of this chemical onslaught on the environment, wildlife, and humans is alarming and still unfolding. Many toxic substances are classified as neurotoxins, hormone disruptors, carcinogens, and respiratory irritants. Some chemicals fit into more than one of these categories. Cell and reproductive changes are becoming more evident as affected generations develop and reproduce. Largely unknown, however, is the impact of synergy: the effect of chemical combinations to which we are exposed. We all breathe the same air and drink the same water, so these chemicals know no boundaries, and that makes pinpointing their effects even more complex.

Awareness and action by individuals, groups, and governments are the keys to moving away from a destructive path. The discussion here will focus on why children are more vulnerable to environmental contaminants, environmental concerns known to effect children's health, and possible actions using the health promotion action plan framework. (See Revisiting the Health Promotion Action Plan, page 371.) It is beyond the scope of this discussion to describe the many types of toxic substances and their effects. For further information, consult the resources listed at the end of this unit.

CHILDREN'S VULNERABILITY TO ENVIRONMENTAL TOXINS

Although a wide range of opinion exists among professionals regarding the impact of environmental factors on health and safety, there is no doubt that children are more vulnerable than adults to environmental contaminants, both immediately (acute reactions) and in the long term (chronic effects). Some of the reasons for children's increased risk are:

► Children's tissues and body systems (e.g., nervous, respiratory, reproductive, digestive, and immune) are not fully developed and are thus more susceptible to damage. Because their growth is regulated by hormones, many environmental toxins are possible "hormone disruptors" (Chance and Harmsen 1998, S11).
► Children inhale toxins faster than adults, because they breathe more rapidly, have smaller airways, and take in more air relative to their body weight than adults do (South Riverdale Community Health Centre 1997, 4).
► Children eat more fruits and vegetables and drink more liquids in proportion to their body weight than do adults. Therefore, their potential exposure to toxins such as lead, pesticides, and nitrates is greater (Children's Environmental Health Network 1998, 5).
► Young children spend more time close to the ground and often put their hands in their mouth. These actions expose them to toxins in dust, soil, and carpets, as well as to pesticide vapours floating close to the ground (Chance and Harmsen 1998, S9).
► Children absorb nutrients in the gastrointestinal tract more quickly than do adults, and this may increase their susceptibility. For example, because children

have a greater need for calcium, they absorb more of this mineral when it is present in the gastrointestinal tract, but the body will absorb lead instead of calcium if it is present. An adult absorbs approximately 10 percent of ingested lead, while a toddler absorbs 50 percent! (Children's Environmental Health Network 1998, 4).

▶ Children's ability to detoxify and excrete toxins differs from adults'. (Children's Environmental Health Network 1998, 4).

Children who live in poverty are disproportionately at risk of exposure to environmental toxins. These children are more likely to live in industrial areas, closer to smokestacks, garbage dumps, and highways with exhaust fumes. Their home environments are more likely to be improperly designed and poorly maintained buildings, with poor indoor air quality, old paint (which may result in lead exposure), old plumbing, and parking lots backed onto apartment buildings (Chaudhuri 1998, S26).

Environmental Concerns and Children's Well Being

The following section covers the four environmental issues of greatest concern to children's health and safety: air pollution, lead, pesticides, and PVCs (polyvinyl chlorides).

Air Pollution   Air pollution, both indoor and outdoor, can affect respiratory health and influence children's behaviour (e.g., irritability may result from mild reactions to air contaminants). Although there is controversy about the over-diagnosis and the causes of asthma, "there is substantial evidence that asthmatic and non-asthmatic children have significant adverse health responses to many air contaminants" (Raizenne et al 1998, S46). (See Asthma, page 195.)

Indoor air pollutants include such substances as tobacco smoke, carbon monoxide, radon, formaldehyde, mercury, and asbestos. Ironically, these substances were intended to improve quality of life. The presence of some of these substances has resulted in better insulation, decreased ventilation (which has contributed to problems with airtight buildings), increased indoor humidity and higher temperatures, and more furniture and conveniences. The biggest concerns in outdoor air pollutants have been ozone, suspended particles, and sulphur compounds. "Exposure to ozone has been associated with increased asthma rates in children as well as a reduction in lung function, and also causes exercise-related wheezing" (Children's Environmental Health Network 1998, 10).

There are a number of ways to improve indoor air quality and reduce children's exposure to environmental contaminants. One obvious way, which has been successful in public places in Canada, is to ban smoking indoors. Parents and caregivers who have not yet been able to quit smoking need to recognize the importance of smoke-free environments for children.

Other suggestions for improving indoor air quality concern children's exposure to dust and other potentially harmful substances. Ensure that the centre's surfaces, furniture, counters, and shelves are easy to clean and that they *are* cleaned on a regular basis. Use unscented cleaning and laundry products, and encourage staff not to wear perfumes or colognes, which some people are allergic to. Limit the amount of carpet used within a centre. Avoid its use in high-traffic areas where people are wearing shoes or boots and where food or play materials such as paint and play dough are used. Purchase carpeting that is hypoallergenic and cleans well. Ensure that it is vacuumed daily and steam-cleaned regularly. In centres without infants and toddlers, consider eliminating carpeting altogether. Even in those centres with infants and toddlers, other things could be used on the floor instead of carpets (e.g., mats). Window coverings, especially horizontal blinds, tend to trap dust. When selecting window coverings, consider roller blinds. Select fabrics and designs that can be removed and washed easily.

To help protect children outdoors, enforce a no-idling zone during pickup and drop-off times and prohibit smoking close to the centre.

Lead Lead exposure has been associated with serious illness and even death. Scientists now know that even low-level lead exposure can affect a child's brain development and nervous system, leading to possible behavioural and learning difficulties and reduced intelligence (Canada Mortgage and Housing Corporation and Health Canada 1997, 3). It is impossible to avoid lead exposure completely, but safety awareness and precautions limit exposure. A great public health success in the 1970s was the elimination of lead from gasolines. Lead-based paint, found in and on the exterior of older buildings (lead was used as a pigment in paints until shortly after World War II), remains a hazard for many children. Information about how to determine if this is a problem and how to safely remove lead-based paint is readily available.

Exposure to lead in dust and soil is a main concern, because preschoolers are likely to ingest dust and soil on an everyday basis. Houses and apartments and centres situated near industries that have used lead, or situated on busy streets, may contain high levels of lead because lead can remain in the soil for decades and contaminate vegetables grown in that soil. Another source of lead contamination is old lead piping and soldered pipes. Municipally treated drinking water is almost lead-free when it leaves the water plant, but it may pick up lead from the plumbing systems of older houses or apartments or from a lead-containing solder common in newer copper systems. In some areas, plumbing codes now limit the content of lead in solder. Lead accumulates when water stands in the pipes, so the first water out of the tap generally contains the most lead. Running the water for a few minutes can reduce the lead content, and hot water picks up more lead than cold, so use cold water from the tap for drinking, cooking, and making baby formula.

Pesticides Pesticide products registered by the federal government to control pests such as insects, rodents, and weeds have been an ongoing concern because of their obvious toxicity. Recently there have generally been more stringent standards and regulations to prevent acute (immediate) episodes of toxicity, though children may be more liable than adults to experience latent (delayed) effects over the course of their lifetime (Children's Environmental Health Network 1998, 10). Using chemicals to treat our lawns and gardens and to de-flea our pets exposes us to long-term hazards. Insect repellents are likely more hazardous than the bug bite itself (South Riverdale Community Health Centre 1997, 30). A number of health concerns—allergies, hormone disruption, and developmental neurotoxicity, to name a few—have possible associations with pesticides. There is some interest in setting standards to protect children from pesticide residues in foods, and some communities, such as Waterloo, Ont., have become pesticide-free with respect to public parks and gardens.

PVCs PVCs (polyvinyl chlorides) have captured a lot of media attention, nationally and internationally, due to efforts to ban the use of soft vinyl (PVC) mouthing and teething toys and rattles for children between 3 and 12 months of age and weighing less than 8 kg (18 lbs.) (Health Canada 1998). The controversy began in the spring of 1997, when the Danish government reported that high levels of phthalates called DINPs, which are added to vinyl toys to soften them, were escaping from teething rings. As with any other environmental issue, there are two sides, each negating the other's position. The most immediate concern with phthalates in PVCs is that they leach out of the plastic fairly easily and are thought to be hormone disruptors and to interfere with the hormone systems in children; such disruption may have long-term effects on reproductive ability and possibly cause some forms of cancer. The controversy continues, but common sense tells us that if there is concern about a long-term impact on the health of children, caution is warranted. In the fall of 1998, Canada's federal government followed the lead of the European Union and banned the use of phthalates in teething rings and other infant toys.

Plastics have become a significant part of our environment in the last 20 years. One look around (indoors and outdoors) in a child care centre and it is obvious that we have come to depend on plastic toys, equipment, and utensils. It is likely that hazardous substances can be replaced with safer alternatives in the production of plastic products. We may also find that rethinking the use of some plastic products is worthwhile. Suggestions from the Canadian Institute of Child Health (1998, conference material) to reduce children's exposure to hormone disruptors found in PVCs include:

► Never microwave food in plastic containers, as the chemicals leach out. Use glass, china, or ceramic dishes. Baby bottles should be warmed in hot water. Silicone nipples and pacifiers or soothers do not contain phthalates.
► Use fabric teethers when possible.
► PVC mini-blinds contain lead that breaks down and becomes a dust on the surface. Wash this away carefully and often.
► Hard plastics are a better choice than soft, squishy plastics for children who chew on toys.
► Some manufacturers make PVC-free children's toys.

When we consider the vast and still relatively unknown aspects of environmental contamination, we can become overwhelmed and feel powerless to make a difference. However,

> as increasing attention is paid to reducing the production, use and discharge of some of the most toxic substances, it becomes clear that options are available. Motivation to clean up has come from regulations, from economic signals, from consumer demands, and from all in combination. (World Wildlife Foundation 1998, 2)

Being Prepared for Emergencies

Caregivers should have an up-to-date first-aid certificate that equips them with the knowledge and skills

▶ to help them remain calm
▶ to administer basic first aid or at least to ensure that their actions do not make an injury worse while waiting for emergency medical services (EMS: dial 911)
▶ to use the supplies in a first-aid kit
▶ to know when to call emergency medical services

Throughout your ECE training you will work in centres, and one of your first tasks when starting in a new centre will be to familiarize yourself with its emergency policy and procedures and take part in fire drills. Be sure you know where the following are located in the centre:

✔ emergency exits and posted evacuation routes (centre's floor plan with exits indicated)
✔ first-aid kits
✔ fire extinguishers and fire alarms (read the operating instructions)
✔ smoke detectors and carbon monoxide detector
✔ emergency phone numbers within the community, as well as the children's parents' numbers
✔ blankets and flashlights

INJURY REPORTS

An injury report should be completed whenever a child or caregiver is injured—even when the injury appears to be minor. Minor cuts can become infected. A head injury may show no immediate observable symptoms, but changes in behaviour can develop hours later. When in doubt, always complete an injury report. Caregivers should also document the injury in the child's file and make reference to the completed injury report. The injury report provided at the end of this unit covers the pertinent information, including the time and date, caregiver's signature, and who was notified. A line drawing is provided so that caregivers can mark where the injury is on the body. (See Appendix 5.2, page 391.)

The primary purpose of the injury report is to serve as a legal document. Clear and succinct documentation is required to report the injury as objectively as possible. Depending on the child's injury and the outcome, these reports may be reviewed by the child care office, police, or lawyers if the question of professional liability or suspected child abuse is raised. A copy of the injury report is usually placed in the child's file.

The report also serves as a tool for staff in developing injury prevention strategies. Caregivers use the report to evaluate a specific

injury or a series of similar injuries in their centre. From this information, caregivers first consider the five W's of safety promotion:

▶ who
▶ why, such as the level of supervision, what the child was doing at the time, and his or her developmental stage
▶ where, such as on a particular piece of play equipment, its general condition, the protective surface, or on a walk or field trip
▶ when, such as the time of day and weather conditions
▶ what happened in chronological order and what was the type and extent of the injury, including what the actual injury looks like (size, colour, location on the body)

Caregivers then consider everything they learned about this incident to determine and implement the necessary changes to prevent similar injuries in the future, or at least to reduce the severity. The following are a few possible alterations either in practice or to equipment:

▶ increase the level of supervision
▶ modify, repair, or remove a piece of play equipment
▶ review the safe use of play equipment with the children
▶ reorganize a particular planned curriculum with children (e.g., reduce the number of steps in a preschool cooking activity and the number of children to better supervise them with cutting and cooking)

▶ eliminate a particular planned event with children (e.g., a field trip to horseback ride with preschoolers)

CHILDREN'S SAFETY AT PICKUP TIMES

Caregivers are responsible for the safety of children until the children leave the premises with their parents or persons authorized by the parents. Centre staff may be faced with a situation in which an unauthorized person arrives to pick up a child, or conditions are deemed unsafe for releasing a child to the parent, or no one comes to pick up the child at the end of the day, or school-agers are permitted to leave unattended.

School-Age Children School-agers range in age from 6 to 12 and their abilities, skills, and need for independence vary.

> According to the National Child Care Study, one-fifth, or over 320,000 children aged 6 to 12 years spend some time alone while their parent(s) works or studies … Almost 30%, or over 93,000 of these children, were between 6 and 9 years of age. (Canadian Council on Social Development, cited in Canadian Institute of Child Health 1994, 71)

Some parents feel that their children are competent and can handle the responsibility of being at home alone and the children may want it that way. Other families feel they have no option but to leave their children at home on their own after school. In response, many communities have a telephone number that children can call if they are lonely, need someone to talk to, or are worried about something. And the community in which you live in Canada may play a role in parents' sense of safety and their level of comfort in having children home alone.

The law requires that parents provide reasonable provision for the safety of children under age 16. However, this law is vague in terms of what is considered reasonable. School-age programs are then faced with the dilemma of creating a policy on the release of school-agers at the end of the day. Centres' policies depend on their philosophy, their setting (urban versus rural), their location within a city, and the parents using the centre. Ultimately, caregivers and parents both want children to gain increasing levels of independence and responsibility. Most adults realize that developing autonomy through opportunities to manage some risk is beneficial for children.

The program can foster autonomy in school-age children by integrating the concept of "intermittent supervision" (Young 1994, 43-44). "While children benefit from a gradual expansion of boundaries, attention must be paid to the abilities of the child and the potential risks present in the environment" (43). When developing an intermittent supervision policy, the program considers issues such as program philosophy, physical layout, and length of time for transitions.

▶ Children move independently from their classroom to the school-age program within the building or outside to a portable.

▶ Children go inside the school to use the washroom and then return to the play-ground.

At the time of a child's enrollment, parents are made aware of this approach to supervision and are given an opportunity to discuss any concerns they may have. School-age programs may require that parents sign a permission form regarding intermittent supervision within the program. There are a number of reasons why children may leave the site without adult supervision: they may walk home from the school-age program, go to an off-site after-school activity, or walk to the corner store on an errand as a way to gain autonomy. But no caregiver would permit unsupervised activities such as these without prior consultation.

Centres work out the specific arrangements for each child with the parents. This agreement is put in writing in the child's file. Before parents permit their children to walk home alone, for instance, school-agers' caregivers and parents determine the child's readiness and safety factors. The following questions should be asked:

▶ Has the child asked his or her parents to let him or her walk home and does he or she understand what it will be like to be home alone? If the child has not made this request, the child is unlikely to be ready for this responsibility.

▶ Does the child's teacher feel that the child is developmentally ready? Teachers can provide parents and caregivers with valuable insights into children's behaviour (e.g., "Every time I step out of the classroom, Tom is doing something that endangers his safety," or "Danny follows guidelines well and demonstrates initiative").

▶ What are the potential risks for the child on the way home from the centre?

▶ What kind of adult supports are available to the child once she or he is at home (e.g., neighbour, clerk in the corner store, telephone helpline for children, telephone access to her or his parents at work)?

Unauthorized Persons   Parents must feel confident that caregivers will not permit an unauthorized person to take their child from the centre. To protect children from abduction, programs require an authorization policy and procedures which ensure that only authorized individuals pick up children. Parents and the centre should have a *written* agreement that lists the people that parents authorize to take their children from the centre. (Some parents will authorize one person only.)

If the list is part of a contract with the parent and an employee releases a child to a person not named in the list, then the centre will not only be in breach of contract but also of their duty under the Day Nursery [Ontario] regulations. If the child is injured, a negligence action (lawsuit) may follow. (Bogoroch-Ditkofsky 1991, Chapter 4, 13)

Staff cannot release a child to anyone who has not been authorized in writing. A parent could not call the centre on the spur of the moment and verbally add a name to the list. However, due to unexpected work responsibilities or travel problems, parents find themselves in situations in which they can't get to the centre in time to pick up the child. A parent may then call and tell the caregiver that a friend will come to the centre even though this person isn't on the authorized list. These situations are grey areas. Caregivers have to be practical and exercise common sense. The parent has called the centre first, and verbally authorized the person for this specific day, and the child knows her or him. It would be unlikely that the staff refuse to release the child to this individual.

There may be times when someone arrives who is not on the list and the parent has not called the centre. Even if the child is happy to see that person and would be comfortable leaving with him or her, caregivers are legally responsible not to release the child to this unauthorized person. In this situation, the caregivers must call the parents. The parent may simply have forgotten to tell the staff that morning. To avoid a similar situation in the future, the parents can add this person's name to the written agreement. The least likely occurence, but the one of most concern, is that this person is in fact attempting to take the child without the parent's permission.

Non-Custodial Parents Many children live in families in which parents are either separated or divorced. Many of these families have workable agreements for child custody and visitation. In cases of joint custody, there usually aren't concerns for the child's safety. However, there are situations in which agreements are not straightforward. From caregivers' perspectives, parents must provide a copy of the custody order and a photograph of the non-custodial parent. If situations arise when the custodial parent releases the child to the other parent, the custodial parent must provide the staff with written permission. All caregivers must be apprised of these custody agreements to ensure that a child is not released to a non-custodial parent without authorization. Caregivers should be cautious if the non-custodial parent arrives on a day other than the one that had been agreed on. Staff can't assume that releasing the child is acceptable to the other parent simply because it's a different day. Parents, not strangers, are responsible for most child abductions.

What do staff do when an unauthorized non-custodial parent insists that the centre release the child to him or her? Caregivers may face a verbal or physical confrontation with this parent. In this situation, staff need to

► calmly ask the parent to move to an area with more privacy (more than one caregiver should be with the parent), or at least have staff move all children away or outside

► have someone call the custodial parent so she or he knows what is happening. Depending on their rapport, the custodial parent may be able to talk to the other parent or quickly come to the centre.

► call the police if the parent loses control or tries to leave with the child

Children in Need of Protection: Intoxicated Parents It may be hard to imagine that parents could actually arrive to pick up their children while intoxicated with alcohol or drugs. Yet it does happen, and caregivers must know how to handle such situations for the safety of the child and parent. Caregivers have a number of concerns:

▶ releasing the child to a parent whom they consider to be incompetent to care for the child
▶ the safety of parent and child on the way home
▶ the safety of others if the intoxicated parent is driving
▶ the child's safety and well-being once they return home, especially if there is no second adult in the home
▶ the potential liability of the centre if staff knowingly allow an intoxicated parent to drive and a motor vehicle mishap occurs

From both an ethical and a legal perspective, caregivers cannot release a child to someone who could cause the child harm. Each situation is different. Each depends on the age of the child, the staff's relationship with the parent, whether the problem is a recurring one, and so on, and as such it is a subjective decision on the part of the staff. The situation could be difficult to handle. Caregivers should

▶ offer the parent coffee and calmly talk about safety concerns for the child and parent (the child should not be present)
▶ ask the parent whether someone could come to the centre and pick them up and ensure that the child is cared for when they arrive home:
  ▷ the other parent, if he or she is actively involved in the child's daily life
  ▷ the authorized adults
▶ in extreme cases, call the child protection agency and discuss the situation with them
▶ if the parent is belligerent or confrontational, or wants to or has already taken the child from the centre and is driving away, call the police and tell them that a drunk driver is leaving the centre with a child

When No One Arrives What happens if half an hour after closing the centre, the parents have not yet arrived and cannot be reached by phone? Staff should try contacting the following people:

▶ the alternate adults listed in the emergency information
▶ people on the authorized list
▶ as a last resort, the child protection agency. They will provide staff with guidance in handling the situation.

Revisiting the Health Promotion Action Plan

The following are examples of what we can do to reduce exposure to and production of environmental contaminants:

Individual Problem-Solving and Self-Reliance

▶ In addition to working smoke detectors, install and maintain carbon monoxide monitors.

▶ Pay attention to air quality advisories and the air quality index. (For daily air quality index readings call 1-800-387-7768.)

▶ Limit activities that contribute to air pollution.

▶ Minimize contact between food and plastics (e.g., microwave in glass containers).

▶ Minimize the use of plastic mouthing toys.

▶ Run the water taps (or water fountain) for a few minutes each morning to reduce the contaminant load, including lead.

▶ Eat pesticide-free foods (e.g., organic fruits and vegetables) when possible.

▶ Use non-toxic repellents to control pests (e.g., dab white vinegar behind ears, knees, and wrists; spray a hot-pepper and water mix on leaves to deter caterpillars).

▶ Minimize the ingestion of toxic chemicals through routine hand-washing.

▶ See resources such as *Hidden Exposures* for further suggestions. (See Resource Materials, page 373.)

Collective Self-Help

▶ Insist on nonsmoking environments.

▶ Test for lead in paint, soil, dust, solder, and drinking water. (See Abotex Enterprises under Resource Materials, page 373.) Share your findings with others in your neighbourhood.

▶ Demand full disclosure when pesticides are used in public places (school yards, parks, roadsides).

Community Action

▶ Interested citizens can meet with the supermarket manager to request organic produce, or start a Good Food Box program. A number of communities in Canada have started programs in which affordable locally grown produce (both organic and non-organic) is made available on a biweekly or monthly basis.

▶ Find out if your community is or is in the process of becoming a pesticide-free zone. If it is not, find out how to advocate for this.

▶ Join or start a group to learn about environmental contaminants and how to reduce them.

Societal Change

▶ Join a national organization that advocates for children's environmental health. The Canadian Institute of Child Health is at the forefront of this important movement.

▶ Advocacy that results in legislated changes benefits everyone. Support the campaign for a clean environment and health protection laws in Canada. The public is encouraged to send messages to key federal officials to continue improving standards through the Canadian Environmental Protection Act.

Conclusion

Since 1980 the rate of hospitalization due to injury has decreased by 24 percent for preschool children and 20 percent for 5- to 14-year-olds (Statistics Canada, cited in Canadian Institute of Child Health 1994, 49, 65). We must remain vigilant and act on behalf of children to decrease the injury rate further in the coming decades. One senseless death of a child is too many. "As long as the design of our technology and our physical and socio-legislative environments does not account for their specific safety needs, children and youth will incur injuries that could otherwise have been avoided" (Minister of Public Works and Government Services Canada 1997, 7). Air bags in cars, for example, are a preventative measure that can be detrimental to young children. Parents and caregivers have an integral role in helping children to learn lifelong safety behaviour. As children grow and develop, the caregivers' role moves from one of protecting children to one of enhancing their understanding of safety, identifying potential risks, and preventing injuries. Our communities and society have an important role in safety promotion through research, education, and legislation based on children's needs.

WHAT'S YOUR OPINION?
TO CLIMB OR NOT TO CLIMB?

If there is a tree to be climbed, there will be children wanting to climb it. Tree-climbing in centre playgrounds continues to be a controversial issue among caregivers, parents, and health professionals. For a class debate, remember to consider the different age groups and types and sizes of trees.

ASSESS YOUR LEARNING

Define terms or describe concepts used in this unit.

- the who, why, where, when, and what of children's injuries
- injury prevention strategies
- Canadian Standards Association
- protective surfaces
- encroachment area
- safety checks
- sun protection factor
- UV index
- frostbite
- wind-chill factor
- considerations for field trips
- emergency preparations
- unauthorized persons

Evaluate your options in each situation.

1. A parent whose youngest child is now a toddler donates the walker that had been used by all her children. She suggests that it would be a welcome addition to your infant room because the younger babies would be more mobile.

2. The daily routine usually ends with outdoor play, and parents pick up their children from the playground. Children need active supervision on equipment, but parents also need the opportunity to speak with a caregiver about their child's day.

3. School-agers on the playground are inundated with a long list of rules and often feel that they have no control. Many children are trying to feel more powerful by deliberately breaking rules when caregivers' backs are turned.

4. The winter has been extremely cold and windy, yet a number of the school-agers are not wearing their boots and hats because "it's just not the thing to do." Before and after school, the children have a choice betweenn staying in and going out to the playground. These same children choose to stay indoors. Some haven't played outside all month.

5. You are on a long summer walk with the preschoolers before lunch and suddenly you remember that none of you is wearing sunscreen.

RESOURCE MATERIALS

Organizations

Abotex Enterprises Ltd., 3031 Wildwood Drive, Windsor, ON N8R 1S7. Tel. (519) 735-8645 or 1-800-268-5323 for nearest retail location. (Suppliers of Leadcheck Swabs.)

Canadian Bike Helmet Coalition Project, Canadian Institute for Child Health, 885 Meadowlands Drive, Suite 512, Ottawa, ON K2C 3N2. Tel. (613) 224-4144, fax (613) 224-4145. (Provides a free Cycle Safe Helmet Campaign Planning Kit: sample helmets, video, etc. Groups may purchase a large quantity of helmets at a discount.)

Canadian Hospitals Injury Reporting and Prevention Program (CHIRPP), Health Canada, 46-LCDC Building, Tunney's Pasture, Ottawa, ON K1A 0L2. Tel. (613) 957-0843, fax (613) 941-2057.

Canadian Institute of Child Health, 885 Meadowlands Drive, Suite 512, Ottawa, ON K2C 3N2. Tel. (613) 224-4144, fax (613) 224-4145.

Canadian Poison Control Centre, Health Sciences Centre, 840 Sherbrook Street, Winnipeg, MB R3A 1S1. Tel. (204) 787-2445, fax (204) 787-4807.

Canadian Standards Association (CSA), 178 Rexdale Boulevard, Rexdale, ON M9W 1R3. Tel. (416) 747-2696 or 1-800-463-6727, fax (416) 747-2473.

Canadian Tire Cycle Safe Helmet Program, Canadian Tire Child Protection Foundation, P.O. Box 770, Station K, Toronto, ON M4P 2V8. Tel. (416) 480-8226, fax (416) 487-6524.

Child Restraint System Testing Program, Occupant Protection Specialist, Transport Canada, 13th Floor, 344 Slater Street, Ottawa, ON K1A 0N5. Tel. (613) 993-6155, fax (613) 998-4831.

KidsCare National Program, KidsCare Coordinator, Product Safety Bureau, Health Protection Branch, Health Canada, Place du Portage, Phase 1, 17th Floor, 50 Victoria Street, Hull, PQ K1A 0C9. Tel. (819) 997-4776, fax (819) 953-3857 (or contact your regional office for materials on product safety awareness for children, parents, centres, etc.).

National Bicycle Safety Foundation, 1823 Harbour Drive, Coquitlam, BC V3J 5W4. Tel. (604) 936-3913, fax (604) 936-3922.

Product Safety Bureau, Chief, Policy, Planning and Information Division, Health Protection Branch, Health Canada, 50 Victoria Street, 17th Floor, Zone 4, Hull, PQ K1A 0C9. Tel. (819) 953-2455, fax (819) 953-3857. (Regulates the sale and advertising of dangerous products and provides consumer information.)

Public Awareness Campaigns, Public Safety Section, Canada Safety Council, 2750 Stevenage Drive, Suite 6, Ottawa, ON K1G 3N2. Tel. (613) 739-1535, fax (613) 739-1566. (Provides information kits, posters, and pamphlets.)

Safe Kids Canada, Hospital for Sick Children, 88 Elm Street, McMaster Building, Room 4019, Toronto, ON M5G 1X8. Tel. (416) 813-7289, fax (416) 813-4986. (Monitors children's injuries and develops prevention programs; Safe Kids coalitions are located across Canada.)

Safety Walk, Manager Playsafe, the War Amps, 140 Merton Street, Suite 530, Toronto, ON M4S 1A5. Tel. (416) 412-0600, fax (416) 297-2650. (Safety kit designed for walks in any environment.)

Safety Workshop Series, Infant and Toddler Safety Association, 385 Fairway Road, Suite 4A-230, Kitchener, ON N2C 2N9. Tel. (519) 570-0181. (Provides an instructor's guide; a four-part workshop covering safety in the nursery, transportation, product safety, and childproofing the home; and resource materials.)

Water Safety Services, the Canadian Red Cross Society, 1800 Alta Vista Drive, Ottawa, ON K1G 4J5. Tel. (613) 739-3000, fax (613) 739-2599. (Produces posters and pamphlets for parents of preschoolers.)

Your Baby's Health and the Environment, Hazardous (Consumer) Products Section, Health Canada, Room 1132, Main Statistics Canada Building, Tunney's Pasture, Ottawa, ON K1A 0C2. Tel. (613) 954-1759, fax (613) 954-7612. (Involved in assessing, managing, and communicating the health risks of chemicals for children from birth to young school-age.)

Printed Matter

Caring Spaces, Learning Places: Children's Environments That Work (1988), by J. Greenman (Exchange Press).

Children's Playspaces and Equipment (1998), by the Canadian Standards Association, 1-800-463-6727.

Hidden Exposures: A Practical Guide for Creating a Healthier Environment for You and Your Children (1997) by South Riverdale Community Health Centre (send cheque or money order for $10—this includes postage and taxes—to Programs Assistant, 1091 Queen Street E., Toronto, ON M4M 1K7).

Is Your Child Safe? (1988), by the Product Safety Branch, Health Canada (Minister of Supply and Services Canada; cat. no. RG23-83/1988).

Keep Them Safe and Child Restraint Information Program, Canadian Automobile Association (CAA), 1775 Courtwood Crescent, Ottawa, ON K2C 3J2 (or contact your region's automobile association).

Max the Safety Cat Program (1986), by the Canadian Institute of Child Health.

An Outdoor Classroom: The Early Childhood Playground (1987), by S.B. Esbensen, (High/Scope Press).

Play and Playscapes (1982), by J.L. Frost (Delmar Publishers).

Selected Papers from What on Earth: A National Symposium on Environmental Contaminants and the Implications for Child Health (1998) *Canadian Journal of Public Health* 89 (supplement 1) (May/June).

Toy Report (annual), by the Canadian Toy Testing Council, 950 Gladstone Avenue, Suite 110, Ottawa, ON K1Y 3E6 (available in bookstores and libraries).

When Child's Play Is Adult Business (1987); *Safe Not Sorry* (1985); *On Your Own* (1989), by the Canadian Institute of Child Health.

Videos

Child's Play: A Playground Safety Guide for Daycares, Schools and Communities (1997), by Safe Kids Canada (video and booklet are available from CSA, tel. 416-747-4044 in the Toronto area or 1-800-463-6727 outside).

Cutting the Risk, Keeping the Magic (1997), by Metro Toronto Community Services.

▶ **B I B L I O G R A P H Y**

Anonymous (1993) "Here Comes the Sun." *Toronto Star* 22 May: B1.

Aronson, S.S. (1984) "Summer Safety and First Aid." *Exchange*, Aug.:13–15.

Avard, D., et al. (1992) "Health Status Indicators and the Legislative Environment," in *Canadian Child Health Law: Health Rights and Risks of Children*, B.M. Knoppers, (ed.). Toronto: Thompson Educational Publishing.

Bogoroch-Ditkofsky, M. (1991) *Daycare and the Law*. Toronto: Umbrella Central Day Care Services.

Brooks, G. (1990) "Drug-Induced Photosensitivity." *Pharmaceutical Journal* 7 (July):19–21.

Canadian Cancer Society (n.d.) *Facts on Skin Cancer*. Toronto: Canadian Cancer Society (pamphlet).

——— (1993 rev.) *Sun Sense*. Toronto: Canadian Cancer Society (pamphlet).

——— (1990) *Skin Sense: Indoor Tanning Is No Safer Than the Sun*. Toronto: Canadian Cancer Society (pamphlet).

Canadian Foundation for the Study of Infant Deaths, Canadian Institute of Child Health, Canadian Paediatric Society, Health Canada (1993) *Joint Statement: Reducing the Risk of Sudden Infant Death Syndrome in Canada*.

Canadian Hospitals Injury Reporting and Prevention Program (1998) *CHIRPP Database: 1990 to July 1996*.

Canadian Institute of Child Health (1998) *Children's Environmental Health*, D. Walker, ed. Proceedings Report from "Linking Research to Practice: A Canadian Forum," October 25–27, 1998.

———— 1994) *The Health of Canada's Children: A CICH Profile*, 2nd ed. Ottawa: Canadian Institute of Child Health.

Canada Mortgage and Housing Corporation and Health Canada (1997) *Lead in Your Home*. Ottawa: Canada Mortgage and Housing Corporation (booklet).

Canadian Paediatric Society (1996) *Well Beings: A Guide to Promote the Physical Health, Safety and Emotional Well-Being of Children in Child Care Centres and Family Day Care Homes*. Toronto: Creative Premises.

Canadian Standards Association (1998) *Children's Playspaces and Equipment*. Etobicoke, ON: Canadian Standards Association.

Chance, G., and E. Harmsen (1998), "Children Are Different: Environmental Contaminants and Children's Health." *Canadian Journal of Public Health* 89 (supplement 1): S9–S13.

Chaudhuri, N. (1998) "The Case for Child Development as a Determinant of Health." *Canadian Journal of Public Health* 89 (supplement 1): S26–S30.

Children's Environmental Health Network (1998) "About Children's Environmental Health: Introduction." Retrieved in January 1999 from the World Wide Web: http://www.cehn.org.

Consumer and Corporate Affairs Canada (1993) *Toboggan and Sled in Control*. Ottawa: Supply and Services Canada.

Environment Canada (1993) *UV and You: Living with Ultraviolet*. Ottawa: Supply and Services Canada (pamphlet).

———— (1992) *Guarding Our Earth Ozone*. Ottawa: Environment Canada (pamphlet).

Esbensen, S.B. (1987) *An Outdoor Classroom: The Early Childhood Playground*. Ypsilanti: High/Scope Press.

Frost, S.L. (1992) *Play and Playscapes*. Albany: Delmar Publishing.

Greenman, J. (1988) *Caring Spaces, Learning Places: Children's Environments That Work.* Redmond: Exchange Press.

Health Canada (1998) *Important Message to Parents and Caregivers of Very Young Children.* Ottawa: Health Canada.

———— (n.d.) *The Sun, Your Baby and You: A Parent's Guide to Sun Protection.* Ottawa: Publications Division, Communications Branch.

Health Protection Branch, Health and Welfare Canada (1991) *Issues: Fun in the Sun.* 2 July.

Hu, X., et al. (1994) "Current Bicycle Helmet Ownership, Use and Related Factors among School-aged Children in Metropolitan Toronto." *Canadian Journal of Public Health* (Mar./Apr.) 85(2):121–24.

———— (1993) "Parental Attitudes toward Legislation for Helmet Use by Child Cyclists." *Canadian Journal of Public Health* (May/June) 84(3):163–65.

Lewis-Webber, M. (n.d.) *Children and Sun Protection: A Practical Guide for Parents and Early Childhood Educators on Sun Protection from Increased Exposure to Ultraviolet Radiation Caused by Depletion of the Ozone Layer.* Winnipeg: M. Lewis-Webber (pamphlet).

McKay, S. (1994) *Safety First.* Ottawa: *Homemaker's Magazine* and Health Canada.

Metro Toronto Community Services, Children's Services Division (1997) *Cutting the Risk, Keeping the Magic.* Toronto: Metro Toronto Community Services.

Minister of Public Works and Government Services Canada (1997) *For the Safety of Canadian Children and Youth—From Injury Data to Preventive Measures.* Ottawa: Supply and Services Canada.

Morris, B.A.P., and N.E. Trimble (1991) "Promotion of Bicycle Helmet Use among School Children: A Randomized Clinical Trial." *Canadian Journal of Public Health* (Mar./Apr.) 82(2):92–94.

National Cancer Institute of Canada (1994) *Canadian Cancer Statistics.* Ottawa: National Cancer Institute of Canada, Health Canada.

Raizenne, M., et al. (1998) "Air Pollution Exposures and Children's Health." *Canadian Journal of Public Health* 89 (supplement 1): S26–S30.

Safe Kids Canada (1997) *Child's Play—A Playground Safety Guide for Daycares, Schools and Communities.* Toronto: Safe Kids Canada.

———— (1994) *Buckle Up Backgrounder* (June).

South Riverdale Community Health Centre (1997) *Hidden Exposures: A Practical Guide for Creating a Healthier Environment for You and Your Children.* Toronto: South Riverdale Community Health Centre.

Stanwick, R. (1993) "Preventing Childhood Injuries in Day Care Settings." Interaction Summer:23–24.

Stephens, K. (1993) "A Tree Climbing Advocate Speaks Out." *Exchange* 7:77–78.

Thompson, R.S., et al. (1989) "A Case Control Study of the Effectiveness of Bicycle Safety Helmets." *New England Journal of Medicine* 320:1361–67.

Wilson, R.A., et al. (1996) "Developing an Environmental Outdoor Play Space." *Young Children*. September: 56–61.

World Wildlife Foundation (1998) "Global Toxic Initiative." Retrieved in January 1999 from the World Wide Web: http://www.worldwildlife.org.

Young, N. (1994) *Caring for Play: The School and Child Care Connection.* Toronto: Direction 2000.

Appendix 5.1

Weekly Safety Checklist

Name of Person Performing Inspection					
Date of Inspection					

INDOORS	**OK**	**ACTION REQUIRED**			
	✔	✔	**Please Specify**	**Date Completed**	**Comments**
PLAY AND SLEEPING AREAS					
There are no long paths that encourage running.	❏	❏			
All exits are clearly marked and free of any obstacles or clutter.	❏	❏			
There is easy access to emergency phones.	❏	❏			
Electrical cords are not within children's reach. Cords are not run under carpeting nor are they in traffic paths or doorways.	❏	❏			
Unused extension cords are unplugged and out of reach.	❏	❏			
Unused electrical outlets have plastic outlet covers.	❏	❏			
Drawers are kept closed.	❏	❏			
Matches, lighters, medicines, cleaning agents, and tools are inaccessible to children.	❏	❏			
Staff and visitors' belongings, purses, and medications are inaccessible to children.	❏	❏			

(appendix continues on next page)

INDOORS	OK	ACTION REQUIRED			
	✔	✔	**Please Specify**	**Date Completed**	**Comments**
Locks on doors can be opened by an adult without difficulty, but not by children.	❏	❏			
Garbage containers have tightly fitting lids, preferably operated by foot pedals. (Lids should not be left up after use.)	❏	❏			
Soiled diapers are disposed of in securely tied plastic bag(s). Soiled diapers and diaper pails must be stored away from children.	❏	❏			
Cat litter boxes are not accessible to children.	❏	❏			
There are no precariously placed small, sharp, or otherwise hazardous objects.	❏	❏			
Furnishings are in good repair and free of sharp edges, splinters, pinch points, or crush points.	❏	❏			
Drapery and blind cords are tied up and secured with safety hooks.	❏	❏			
All storage units are well constructed and stable. Units are anchored to the wall or flooring to prevent sliding, collapsing, or tipping over.	❏	❏			

(appendix continues on next page)

INDOORS	OK	ACTION REQUIRED			
	✔	✔	**Please Specify**	**Date Completed**	**Comments**
All TVs, VCRs, computers, projectors, etc., are secured on stands that ensure no tipping or collapsing.	❏	❏			
■ Supervision					
Children are never unattended and always supervised by enough well-trained staff who can evacuate children in an emergency.	❏	❏			
There is no bottle-propping.	❏	❏			
No toddlers are walking around with bottles or food.	❏	❏			
No running is allowed inside the facility.	❏	❏			
■ Equipment					
Baby carriers are never used as car seats.	❏	❏			
Toys are in good repair and free of sharp edges, pinch points, and splinters.	❏	❏			
No toys accessible to young children have strings or cords longer than 15 cm (6 in.) that can encircle the neck.	❏	❏			
Toys are stored when not being used. (Open shelving is desirable for easy selection.)	❏	❏			

(appendix continues on next page)

INDOORS	OK	ACTION REQUIRED			
	✔	✔	**Please Specify**	**Date Completed**	**Comments**
Toys are age-appropriate and suited to the abilities of the children using them.	❏	❏			
Toys for different ages are stored separately.	❏	❏			
Art materials are properly stored in labelled containers.	❏	❏			
HALLWAYS AND STAIRS					
Stairways are well lit.	❏	❏			
Stairs and stairways are free of stored items.	❏	❏			
Safety gates are at the top and bottom of the stairs, if appropriate.	❏	❏			
Exits are clearly marked.	❏	❏			
Electrical cords are out of children's reach and kept out of doorways and from under carpets. Unused extension cords are unplugged.	❏	❏			
Unused electrical outlets have plastic outlet covers.	❏	❏			
Locks on doors can be opened by an adult without difficulty, but not by children.	❏	❏			
KITCHEN					
Pot handles are always turned toward the back of the stove.	❏	❏			

(appendix continues on next page)

INDOORS	OK	ACTION REQUIRED			
	✔	✔	**Please Specify**	**Date Completed**	**Comments**
Appliance cords are rolled up when not in use. No cords hang over the counter where they could be caught in a cupboard or drawer or be within children's reach.	❑	❑			
Dishes are in good condition and not cracked or chipped.	❑	❑			
Sharp, pointed, or otherwise dangerous cooking utensils (such as knives or glass) are not within the children's grasp.	❑	❑			
Garbage containers have tightly fitting lids, preferably operated by foot pedals. (Lids should not be left up after use.) Do not store containers near a furnace or hot water heaters (fire hazard).	❑	❑			
Cleaning agents are stored in original containers except for bleach, which is properly labelled and kept in a locked cupboard (along with any tools, matches or lighters, and plastic bags) away from any food.	❑	❑			

(appendix continues on next page)

INDOORS	OK	ACTION REQUIRED			
	✔	✔	**Please Specify**	**Date Completed**	**Comments**
All medication is stored out of the reach of children (a locked cupboard or container may be required).	❑	❑			
■ SUPERVISION					
Children are never left unattended in the kitchen.	❑	❑			
WASHROOMS					
Step stools are provided where appropriate for sink and toilet.	❑	❑			
Smaller toilet seats, which fit on top of the toilet, are flush with the toilet's seat. (Seats that would elevate the child high off the floor are not recommended.)	❑	❑			
Cleaning agents are stored in original containers and kept in a locked cupboard out of children's reach.	❑	❑			
Garbage containers have tightly fitting lids, preferably operated by foot pedals. (Lids should not be left up after use.) Garbage containers are emptied daily.	❑	❑			
Plastic bags are stored in a locked cupboard out of children's reach.	❑	❑			

(appendix continues on next page)

INDOORS	OK	ACTION REQUIRED			
	✔	✔	Please Specify	Date Completed	Comments
Soiled diapers are disposed of in securely tied plastic bag(s). Soiled diapers and diaper pails must be stored away from children.	☐	☐			
Any locked door can easily be opened by an adult.	☐	☐			
■ Supervision					
Younger children are never left unattended in the washroom.	☐	☐			

OUTDOORS	OK	ACTION REQUIRED			
	✔	✔	Please Specify	Date Completed	Comments
Traffic/Field Trips/Vehicles					
Staff are aware of who can take a child out of the child care facility.	☐	☐			
Staff are trained in what to do in an emergency: a written plan or procedure is available.	☐	☐			
■ Supervision					
Children directly proceed from vehicle to building and vice versa with no playing in the passenger loading area.	☐	☐			
■ Equipment					
Vehicles are mechanically in order and lights are working.	☐	☐			

(appendix continues on next page)

OUTDOORS	OK	ACTION REQUIRED			
	✔	✔	**Please Specify**	**Date Completed**	**Comments**
No sharp or heavy objects are stored on the back cargo shelf. (They could become missiles in a sudden stop or collision.)	❑	❑			
Each vehicle contains a first-aid kit and the emergency record of every child on board.	❑	❑			
Each vehicle has a list of emergency phone numbers, such as police, fire, hospital.	❑	❑			
PLAYGROUND					
The area is free of litter and sharp objects.	❑	❑			
Furnishings are not broken or overturned.	❑	❑			
There are no stagnant ponds of water.	❑	❑			
Paths are in good order.	❑	❑			
Garbage containers are provided. They are anchored and away from equipment and play areas.	❑	❑			
Poisonous plants are removed from the play area.	❑	❑			

(appendix continues on next page)

OUTDOORS	OK	ACTION REQUIRED			
	✔	✔	**Please Specify**	**Date Completed**	**Comments**
Staff provide clean drinking water in the play area.	❑	❑			
Shady areas are provided.	❑	❑			
The entire playground is structured for quick and easy inspection for good supervision.	❑	❑			
■ SUPERVISION					
Equipment is age-appropriate and does not exceed the abilities of the children using them.	❑	❑			
■ PROTECTIVE, ENERGY-ABSORBING SURFACES					
All play equipment more than 30 cm (12 in.) above ground has at least 25–30 cm (10–12 in.) of cushioning material beneath the structure (more if tall structure). The material extends 1.8 m (6 ft.) beyond the piece of equipment. The material may be sand, pea gravel (.32 cm [1/8 in.] diameter round stones), bark chips, or manufactured surfaces approved by the CSA. (Pea gravel and wood should be avoided in infant/toddler areas.)	❑	❑			

(appendix continues on next page)

OUTDOORS	OK ✔	ACTION REQUIRED ✔	Please Specify	Date Completed	Comments
Protective cushioning surfaces are checked daily to remove foreign objects and materials (e.g., animal feces, garbage, sharp objects). Rake weekly to prevent surfaces from becoming compacted and hard.	❑	❑			
No standing water is on protective surfaces or within play structures.	❑	❑			
Drains are checked for plugging and debris. Plant growth is removed from drains.	❑	❑			
■ ALL EQUIPMENT					
No splinters, cracks, or breaks appear in wooden equipment.	❑	❑			
Equipment is free of sharp edges, protrusions, and cracks.	❑	❑			
No equipment is bent or improperly anchored.	❑	❑			
No parts of the equipment are missing.	❑	❑			
All pinch- or crush-point covers are intact.	❑	❑			
All moving parts function smoothly and are well lubricated. There is no excessive motion or noise and no protective pieces are missing.	❑	❑			

(appendix continues on next page)

OUTDOORS	OK	ACTION REQUIRED			
	✔	✔	**Please Specify**	**Date Completed**	**Comments**
■ SLIDES					
If the slide is made of several sections, there are no gaps, pinch points, or rough edges in the sliding surface.	☐	☐			
■ TUNNELS					
The tunnel material is securely anchored to the ground.	☐	☐			

Sources: Developed in part from *Health in Day Care: A Manual for Health Professionals,* American Academy of Pediatrics (Elk Grove Village: American Academy of Pediatrics, 1987) and *Healthy Young Children: A Manual for Programs*, A. Shapiro Kendrick et al., eds. (Washington, DC: National Association for the Education of Young Children, 1988). Courtesy of the Canadian Paediatric Society, *Well Beings* (Ottawa: Canadian Paediatric Society, 1996), 982–91.

Appendix 5.2

Injury Report

Name of child: _____ Date of birth: _____

Date and time of injury: _____

Parent(s) notified: _____

Describe the injury (you may also use the line drawing of the child to indicate where the injuries are located on the child's body):

_____

_____

Describe how the injury occurred:

_____

_____

Where did the injury occur? _____

If any equipment or product was involved, please describe it:

_____

_____

Was first aid administered?   Yes ❑   No ❑   (If yes, specify)

_____

_____

Who administered first aid? _____

Was any further action taken (e.g., child sent to hospital, to physician, taken home)?

_____

_____

If the child remained at the facility, what was the child's level of participation?

_____

_____

Other comments:

_____

_____

What corrective action should be taken to prevent further injuries of this type?

_____

When was the centre director notified about the injury? Time: _____ Date: _____

Names of staff who witnessed the injury: _____

_____   _____   _____   _____
Reporting caregiver's signature   Date   Parent's signature   Date

(Please use the attached diagram, when applicable.)

INDICATE SITE OF INJURY WITH AN "X."

Source: Courtesy of the Canadian Paediatric Society, *Well Beings* (Ottawa: Canadian Paediatric Society, 1996), 867–69.

(appendix continues on next page)

Name of caregiver: _____   Date: _____

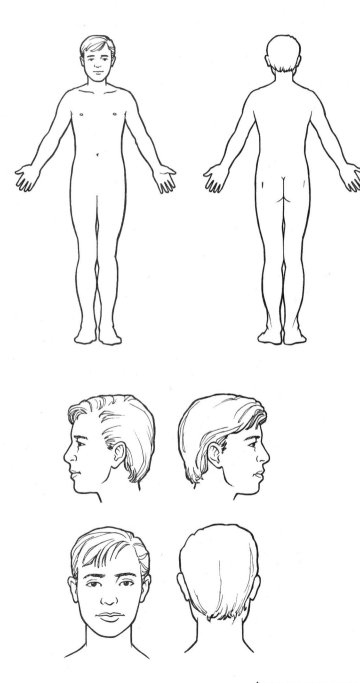

INDICATE SITE OF INJURY WITH AN "X."

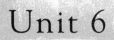

Unit 6

Child Abuse
Prevention

Unit 6: Child Abuse Prevention

Many trained and experienced caregivers identify child abuse as an area in which they need further education. Although it is impossible to know the true extent of child abuse, because much goes unreported, even conservative estimates of the number of reported cases make it likely that caregivers will come in contact with children who are victims of abuse. Participating in continuing education opportunities combined with work experience and collaboration with professionals and agencies enhances your understanding and skills in the area of child abuse.

Since caregivers are frontline professionals and work closely with children, they are in a position to identify children that they suspect are being abused, and are able to activate primary, secondary, and tertiary prevention. In other words, child care programs can contribute to the prevention of child abuse in three ways:

▶ by modelling positive child guidance (primary prevention)
▶ by early identification of suspected child abuse and by reporting suspected abuse, if warranted, to the child protection agency (secondary prevention)
▶ by supporting both children and their families where child abuse has been confirmed (tertiary prevention)

As professionals, caregivers are required by law to report their suspicions of child abuse. Their relationship with children and their families also creates an ethical responsibility to report. These reports make it possible for child protection agencies to provide protection for children who are at either immediate or future risk and to assist the children and their families in recovery.

Failure to recognize and to help stop child abuse can result in serious consequences for children, including long-term emotional and physical problems, and, in extreme cases, death. Another devastating consequence is that adults who were

abused as children may themselves become abusers or be further victimized (e.g., spousal abuse), so the cycle of abuse continues.

Exploring Your Feelings

 OBJECTIVES To identify your feelings about child abuse and how you can deal with them.
To identify your level of openness to family diversity.

As individuals, we need to understand our own feelings about this sensitive and emotional subject. Working with families involves a wide range of philosophies, parenting practices, and lifestyles. Caregivers' openness to diversity in values and customs contributes to their sensitivity and effectiveness on a personal as well as a professional level.

About Child Abuse

Each of you brings different life experiences and spiritual and cultural beliefs to the program. Some people find it incomprehensible that someone could inflict emotional and physical pain on a child, or they may feel anger and hatred for abusers. Others are themselves survivors of child abuse. Even if you were not abused as a child, you probably know someone who was. For survivors, the realm of emotional and physical reaction to child abuse may be overwhelming. Attempting to understand child abuse from a professional rather than personal perspective is challenging. Those of us who have only read or heard about child abuse will still have strong feelings about abuse.

What do we do with all these emotions and responses? You may feel the need to acknowledge and work through your feelings to deal effectively with this issue in your work.

 ▶ You are so angry at the thought of a parent hurting a child that you question your ability to provide further support to the child and family.

▶ As an adult survivor of child abuse, you may feel that this course is the impetus you need to work through the abuse.

Sexual abuse can generate a range of intense emotional reactions. We all experience some reaction when faced with disturbing behaviour. When you read a newspaper article or hear a story on the television or radio about sexual abuse, how do you feel? Perhaps you feel disbelief that anyone could do such a thing to a child. Perhaps you feel anger at the child for not telling someone when it started. It is important for anyone caring for children to explore her or his feelings toward sexual abuse. Our reactions can affect our understanding of sexual abuse and the way we respond to children who have been sexually abused (Institute for the Prevention of Child Abuse 1995, 50).

Obviously, not everyone responds to child abuse in a dramatic or emotional way. However, those who have concerns about their confused feelings or about approaching issues that may not have been dealt with since childhood may find it necessary to talk with a trusted friend or a counsellor. The college's counsellors or an ECE instructor can provide students with names of referrals (social workers, counsellors, or psychologists) and community services.

About Family Diversity

The region of Canada we live in and, more specifically, the location of the centre we work in, may determine the diversity of families' structures, living styles, social and economic situations, ethno-cultural backgrounds, religions, and so on. It is more important to realize that you don't have to adopt someone else's values and beliefs but need to develop a level of understanding and respect for others' values and beliefs.

 While helping preschoolers with their bathing suits for the wading pool, you notice that one child has small circular bruises over his chest and back. When you ask, "How did you get these bruises?" the 4-year-old replies, "Mommy used a spoon to make me better." The child is not upset, and is generally a content child who is always happy to see his mother at the end of the day.

A manifestation of bad wind (a notion derived from Chinese medicine) such as a cough can be released by creating small bruises on the body, commonly effected by rubbing the body with a coin or a spoon or by cupping—that is, by placing a hot cup on the body and letting it cool until the air contracts and draws the skin upward. When bruise lines appear the bad wind has come to the surface and left the body. (Dinh et al. 1990, 194)

In this example, the caregiver may suspect child abuse. Yet by talking with the child and the parent at the end of the day, the caregiver learns more about the family's traditional health practices, and learns that the practice was done in the best interests of the child and with the best intentions. However, every situation is unique. There may be times when caregivers must pursue their suspicions further.

Learning to work effectively with diverse families requires an open attitude and skills. These skills can be developed from

- ▶ the family, in a respectful manner
- ▶ co-workers
- ▶ post-diploma courses and anti-bias workshops

- ▶ relevant agencies in the community
- ▶ literature and videos

To summarize, you must ask yourself two important questions before you can manage suspicions of child abuse in a practical way in child care programs:

1. What are some of the feelings I have about child abuse—such as fears, anger, frustration, sadness—and how can I deal with these in a way that enables me to work effectively with families?
2. How open am I to living styles, values, and parenting practices that are different from my own? In other words, am I able *not* to assume automatically that different practices are wrong or abusive?

Child Abuse

 OBJECTIVES   To define and describe each category of abuse: physical abuse, emotional abuse, sexual abuse, and neglect.
To develop a heightened awareness of the complex consequences of abuse on children.

The definition of child abuse has evolved over time and will continue to do so. Twenty years ago, child abuse was thought to concern mainly children who were severely physically abused. Since then, we have become aware of the high incidence of child sexual abuse and the damaging consequences for children who have been abused emotionally.

Child abuse is always a misuse of power—a person with greater physical, intellectual, and/or emotional power and authority controls a child in a way that does not contribute to the child's health, growth, and development. Abuse or neglect of children can occur within the home, in institutions, and even at the community or societal level:

- ▶ parents or other individuals who physically or sexually abuse children
- ▶ institutional practices that are abusive to children, such as the inappropriate use of physical restraints
- ▶ the devastating physical, emotional, and social consequences for the more than one million children in Canada who live in poverty

Types of Abuse

Generally, child abuse is categorized into four types: physical abuse, emotional abuse, sexual abuse, and neglect. While this categorization can be useful, it implies distinctions that don't always exist. In reality, the four types of abuse do not operate exclusively of one another. In fact, it is common to find that categories of child abuse coexist.

 e.g.   A child who is being physically abused is also abused emotionally or at least suffering emotionally as a result of pain inflicted on her.

PHYSICAL ABUSE

Children who have suffered injuries that were inflicted by parents, older siblings, extended family members, or others have been physically abused. In some cases, abuse occurs only once, but in most situations the child is abused over a period of time. The physical abuse usually becomes more severe over time; the abuser often justifies his or her actions in terms of discipline and may not have initially intended to hurt the child. There are as many types of injuries as there are ways and objects with which someone can physically abuse. Ayoub et al. (1990, 239–42) created four groups of physical injuries that result from physical abuse:

1. *Injuries to the skin and soft tissue underneath include bruises, abrasions (e.g., cuts, scrapes), hematomas (swellings containing blood), bites, and burns.* Bruises or abrasions can be caused by being hit by hands or blunt instruments (e.g., belts, hairbrushes, or rope), or by being kicked. Severe bruising, especially on the buttocks or legs, often results from excessive discipline involving objects such as fly swatters or wooden spoons. Bruises often take on the shape of the object used. Tying children's arms and/or legs together or to a chair or bed can cause burn marks or cuts to wrists or ankles. Dunking children in hot water can cause burns. "Isolated burns on the buttocks, palms of the hands, or soles of the feet are particularly suspicious. Another kind of contact burn is from cigarettes" (Ayoub et al. 1990, 241). (See Figure 6.1, page 404.)

2. *Injuries to the head and central nervous system include bleeding inside the eyes or brain tissue (often from being violently shaken), spinal injuries, and asphyxia (from choking or suffocating).* Shaking a young child, especially an infant, is a common cause of serious injury or death. Adults may not realize that the use of force in a moment of anger can lead to a lifetime of ill effects.

3. *Internal (abdominal) injuries are serious and can lead to death.* Internal organs such as the spleen and pancreas can be crushed or ruptured. A punch or kick to the abdomen can rupture the child's stomach. If a child is thrown, the impact could tear the liver or spleen.

4. *Injuries to the skeletal system can result from shaking, squeezing, or a direct blow.* Actions such as pushing the child down the stairs can result in fractures of the arms, legs, or skull. An infant's skull is thin and pliable, so a blow to the head by a hand or foot can easily cause a fracture.

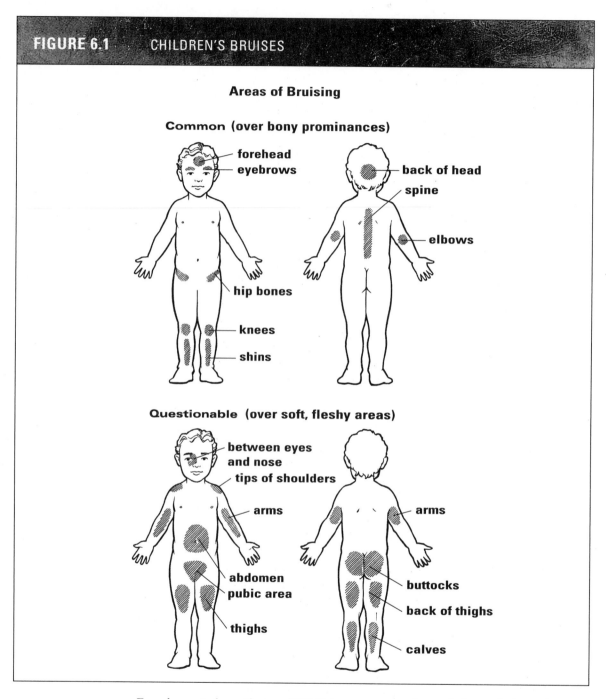

FIGURE 6.1   CHILDREN'S BRUISES

Areas of Bruising

Common (over bony prominances)

- forehead
- eyebrows
- back of head
- spine
- elbows
- hip bones
- knees
- shins

Questionable (over soft, fleshy areas)

- between eyes and nose
- tips of shoulders
- arms
- arms
- abdomen
- pubic area
- buttocks
- back of thighs
- thighs
- calves

Female genital mutilation (FGM) is an extreme form of physical abuse that has only recently come to the attention of the general public in Canada. A three-category classification system is generally used to define the severity of the mutilation—ranging from removing the hood of the clitoris to cutting away all the external sexual organs (i.e., clitoris, labia minora, and all or most of the labia majora). The most severe form is infibulation, which refers to the edges of the remaining tissue of the vulva being sewn together, leaving only a tiny opening for urinating and menstruating that is later cut open for intercourse and childbirth.

The short- and long-term health effects of this practice can be physically, emotionally, and socially devastating to the girls and women, causing excruciating pain and sometimes death. A United Nations study (1994) estimates that FGM has been performed on 114 million girls and women around the world. Often it is done when girls are between 4 and 10 years old, without anesthetic and under unsterile conditions (Clement 1994). The usual rationale for the practice is that it ensures that the girls are suitable for marriage.

There has been global action to prevent further incidents of FGM, and acknowledgment that it is a violation of human rights.

- ▶ In 1985 the British government passed a law banning FGM in Britain.
- ▶ In Canada, FGM violates several Criminal Code provisions and any person performing the mutilation, as well as the girl's parents, could be charged and tried for assault causing bodily harm.

Culture, tradition, and religion are used as the rationale to justify this violent abuse. FGM is practised predominantly in countries in which the religion is Islam. However, it is important to understand that the Koran, the sacred book of Islam, holds no requirement for this practice. Therefore, using religion as a rationale for violence is insupportable. FGM is done traditionally for men to maintain control over women's lives, including their sexual lives.

Many girls and women who come to Canada are victims of FGM. A range of issues may emerge for these girls and women and they must be treated with sensitivity. If you have had this procedure, seek out caring and enlightened physicians and other professionals who will be supportive to your physical, emotional, and social well-being.

Child protection agencies, particularly those in large cities, have developed (or are developing) a policy to respond to victims of female genital mutilation. These policies acknowledge that girls who have already undergone the practice need compassion and support—particularly, culturally relevant support. Child protection agencies aim to protect young girls where there is risk of this physical abuse (FGM is performed illegally here in Canada, and girls are also taken to other countries for the practice). There will be continued concern and more information on this issue in the future. Contact the agency in your community that will be helpful with your concerns.

Discipline versus Punishment The practice of corporal punishment, often a hotly debated issue in parenting, will illustrate the difficulty one encounters in determining what exactly it is that constitutes child abuse. Violence in our society is not only accepted but often revered. Some of the most popular movies of our time depict extreme violence. At the same time, the media bombard us with images of war and political unrest, institutional and parental child abuse, date rape, murders of young women, spousal abuse, and elder abuse. "Our society is so used to seeing and accepting violence that it is not uncommon to excuse the violence or blame the victim. We say, 'It was the alcohol,' or 'He had a bad day.' We may even ask, 'What did she do to provoke the violence?'" (Caring Communities Project 1994, Book 1, 12).

Federal and provincial/territorial governments have finally acknowledged the prevalence of child and spousal abuse, and have begun to take a stronger stand against violence in the home. Children are not their parents' property, nor is a wife owned by her husband. It may be hard to believe that only in the last 15 years was the Criminal Code amended to state that husbands have no legal right to force their wives to have sex.

Corporal punishment is the use of physical force to discipline children. It is *not* against the law in Canada, but it is illegal in a growing number of countries (e.g., Sweden, Austria, Denmark). The Criminal Code of Canada today defines assault as the use of physical force on an individual without consent. However, section 43 of the Code gives adults permission to use physical force on children. Children are the only people in Canada who can be legally "assaulted." Their assailants need not fear legal reprisal unless the force is deemed to be unreasonable.

The child welfare laws across Canada define the degree to which corporal punishment is legal, beyond which it is excessive and is considered child abuse. "Excessive" is sometimes difficult to distinguish from "not excessive," and the difficulty can lead to a vast range of interpretations. Excessive punishment results when the strikes leave marks, shapes, bruises, cuts, or scrapes; when the skin is burned; when bones are broken; when hair is pulled out in clumps; when retinas are detached; or when the brain hemorrhages.

Several national and regional groups concerned with children's rights are advocating for the repeal of section 43 of the Criminal Code, to make corporal punishment of any kind illegal, including spanking. To date section 43 has been successfully used by some parents as a defence for injuring their children. Repealing this law would send a strong message to the community that this method of "child-rearing" is no longer condoned.

Many parents who adhere more closely to authoritarian discipline believe that corporal punishment in the form of slapping, spanking, or even beating is an appropriate form of discipline. These parents may use the familiar refrain "spare the rod and spoil the child" or insist that their own parents had spanked them as children, and they've turned out fine. Miller (1987, 10) suggests that by playing down the consequences of their own experience, parents contribute to the continuation of cruelty. She points out that those concerned with raising children have always had trouble dealing with children's obstinacy, willfulness, defiance, and exuberance. Much of raising children has been subtly or overtly concerned with being master over them—controlling children or breaking their spirit. Even when parents or caregivers have a theoretical understanding of child development, authoritarian control over children can, in practice, take over as an overriding need. In some child care programs, we hear phrases such as "Can the teacher control the children?" or "Does she have control over the group?" This is not surprising, according to Miller, because many adults have been raised with these principles. No one is implying that children shouldn't learn respect for others, but we must be aware of methods and motivations in guiding children if our goals are to promote self-esteem and model self-control.

The primary objective of discipline is to help children learn—to help them develop the ability to use their own judgment and to cultivate self-control. With discipline, the adult has control, but the child's needs, wishes, and abilities are respected in light of her or his development and personality. Positive relationships between children and parents, as well as other caring adults, play a significant role in a child's self-esteem (Canadian Institute of Child Health 1997, 82).

Corporal punishment often results from an adult's failure at self-control—as a means to relieve their anger, stress, and frustration. Who benefits? What are children learning from being slapped, spanked, shaken, beaten, constantly yelled at, or told hurtful things? Anti-spanking advocates believe that children learn that

▶ it's OK to hurt and humiliate someone, especially someone smaller than you ("My parents do it to me, so it's acceptable.")
▶ the reason they need to obey rules is to avoid being hit
▶ when they get bigger, they will have power over others
▶ violence is an acceptable way of expressing anger and solving problems

Parents who believe that spanking is acceptable and appropriate may justify their actions in the following ways:

▶ "We are teaching them right from wrong." In reality, spanking teaches children only what is not acceptable. They will not learn right from wrong without being taught what they should be doing; spanking may also communicate to children that they are "bad" persons.
▶ "It is an act of love." This is a confusing message for children, who learn that people who love them also hurt them. It's not surprising, then, that so many women choose husbands and boyfriends who abuse them, since traditional gender socialization teaches girls to be submissive and boys to dominate.
▶ "It's a cultural practice." Hitting children is widespread practice throughout Canada. Many adults today, regardless of culture or race, were hit as children and believe that it is an acceptable parenting practice.
▶ "I don't want them to become spoiled." Children who are spoiled learn disrespectful behaviour from inconsistent parenting, insufficient provision of necessary structure, and neglect of children's needs, not from lack of spanking.

The debate over spanking becomes relevant when we discuss child abuse. Corporal punishment by parents is not, in itself, against the law, but child advocates agree that it is not a positive way to discipline children. Trocmé et al. (1994, 47) noted that many of the physical abuse cases in Ontario involved the child protection agency's difficulty in distinguishing between corporal punishment and physical abuse. The distinction must be made before charges of abuse can be laid. (See Caregivers' Role in Primary Prevention, page 418.) Built into the use of corporal punishment is a lack of societal respect for the child. This is evident in the legal ambiguity. Assault charges can be laid *whenever* an adult strikes, shakes, or kicks another adult. There is no ambiguity here. It is important to realize that children benefit when parents, rather than viewing corporal punishment as an option, learn to guide their children with positive discipline, not punishment.

Two essential components of effective parenting skills are responsiveness and discipline. Appropriate discipline is firm but not excessively restrictive, and does not involve bullying or shaming. There are clear limits and expectations on children's actions, children are encouraged to take responsibility for their actions, and learn from the consequences of their behaviour. When confrontation becomes necessary, parents should encourage children to find acceptable alternatives to actions which are not acceptable. The parenting style that combines a high level of caring and involvement with high but reasonable expectations is most likely to help children develop the confidence, and coping skills needed to maintain competence and the sense of perspective that shapes how they react to stress. The interaction of these factors contributes to the achievement of resiliency.

Data from the National Longitudinal Survey of Children and Youth showed that positive parenting practices, which included positive interactions and consistent supervision, help children get along with others. Positive parenting practices make a real difference, especially in families where there are challenges and difficulties for children. (Guy 1997, 75–76. Reprinted with permission.)

EMOTIONAL ABUSE

Emotional abuse is the most widespread type of abuse, yet it is also the most difficult to prove. Children can't escape emotional harm when they are physically or sexually abused or neglected. Although the physical injuries may heal, the scars of emotional abuse last forever. The Toronto Child Abuse Centre (1997–1998, Information Package Nos. 1, 2. Reprinted with permission) lists the following behaviours of a parent/caregiver who is emotionally abusive to a child:

▶ rejecting (e.g., saying "I wish you were never born")
▶ criticizing (e.g., saying "Why can't you do anything right?")
▶ insulting (e.g., saying "I can't believe you would be so stupid")
▶ humiliating (e.g., embarrassing a child in front of other people)
▶ isolating (e.g., not allowing a child to play with friends)
▶ terrorizing (e.g., scaring a child by saying "The police will come and take you away")
▶ corrupting (e.g., always swearing in front of the child, or getting the child to participate in things against the law)
▶ not responding emotionally
▶ punishing a child for exploring the environment

Emotional abuse can occur without children being abused in any other way. Parents who never use physical discipline may not realize that they are being abusive when they verbally ridicule children or constantly use sarcasm, harsh criticism, or make inappropriate demands. This ongoing rejection is harmful to children's self-esteem. "Emotional abuse derails the child's sense of mastery and competence. The push to conquer the environment is fueled by curiosity, autonomy, and a positive sense of self, all of which are often damaged in these children" (Ayoub et al. 1990, 235).

For some parents, particular times create situations that trigger feelings of anger, disapproval, frustration, etc. Perhaps it is at a time of a developmental milestone (e.g., learning to use the toilet) or the time of the day (e.g., bedtime). In some family situations, one child is singled out as the scapegoat—the target for parents' anger is inappropriately directed at this child.

A woman is emotionally abused by her husband. She feels powerless over her husband or to stop the abuse. Because she has no control over her situation, her need for power and control over someone—and her negative feelings—are directed at her daughter in the form of emotional abuse.

The witnessing of spousal abuse by children is now recognized as a form of emotional abuse. The vast majority are cases in which the child's mother is being abused emotionally and/or physically by her partner (e.g., the child's father or step-father, the mother's boyfriend). In these cases, the emotional damage to a child can be equal to, or even greater than, the damage suffered by a child who had been emotionally or physically abused directly (Jaffe et al. 1986, 144). They are deeply affected by the atmosphere of threat and fear even though they themselves are not assaulted (Canadian Institute of Child Health 1997, 55). Children who witness spousal abuse are in physical, emotional, and psychological danger. They are not having their needs met. They feel powerless. In addition, "[c]hildren who escape violence in the home by leaving with their mothers are almost sure to move from one form of violence, physical assault, into another form of violence, poverty" (Skelly 1993, 15).

The Ontario Women's Directorate (1989) summarized a study conducted in Toronto that indicated that children witnessed 50 percent of spousal abuse incidents and were physically abused in 12 percent of those incidents. Because so many incidents of spousal abuse are unreported, the estimate that one in 10 women is abused is conservative, and the number of children who witness violence in their home is substantial.

SEXUAL ABUSE

There is no one definition of child sexual abuse; however, it is generally defined as the involvement of children in sexual activity in which the offender uses power over the child. The children's sexual behaviour is designed by the offender for the gratification of the offender, who may or may not be of the same gender as the child.

Sexual abuse includes oral, anal, genital, buttock, and breast contact, or the use of the penis, fingers, or objects for vaginal or anal penetration, fondling, or sexual stimulation. Although vaginal and/or anal intercourse don't occur in most incidents of sexual abuse, they are a possibility.

Exploitation of the child for pornographic purposes and making a child available to others as a child prostitute are also sexual abuse. Inappropriate solicitation, exhibitionism, and exposure to erotic material for the purpose of sexually arousing a child, or for adults to use to stimulate themselves, are further forms of sexual abuse.

Sexual abuse is never the child's fault. Some offenders use the excuse that the child or adolescent had initiated ("She came onto me") or were willing participants in the sexual behaviour or activities, as though the child actually had the choice to refuse. The offender is in a position of power and must exercise self-control. Children are vulnerable not only because of their physical size but also because they are emotionally and economically dependent on adults and are easily manipulated due to their limited understanding of adult sexuality (Caring Communities Project 1994, Book 1, 12). "Seductive sexualized behaviour and/or sexual promiscuity in children should be understood to be the result of sexual abuse, not the cause of it" (Caring Communities Project 1994, Book 1, 8). Young children who are sexually abused become confused about how they are expected to relate to others (Tower 1993, 65).

Less than half of children who have been sexually abused have any physical changes noted during a medical examination (e.g., bruises on the breasts, tears in or bleeding from the vaginal wall or the anus and rectum). For some of the children who do show physical signs, the physician can't confirm that the changes are due to sexual abuse. However, any physical evidence of a sexually transmitted disease is clear evidence. Other common indicators of sexual abuse are complaints by the child that suggest that the genitals have been injured, irritated, traumatized, or infected, including genital discomfort, pain on passing urine, blood in the diaper or underwear, the presence of infection, and so on. Children may also complain about headaches and stomachaches, which are related to the stress of sexual abuse.

The report of the Committee on Sexual Offences against Children and Youths (Badgley 1994) summarized a national survey and made the Canadian public realize that sexual abuse is not rare and that young children are frequently victims. "Drawing on the information from the Badgley Report and on the other research, current estimates are that one in four girls and one in eight boys will be sexually abused before the age of eighteen" (Caring Communities Project 1994, Book 1, 8).

The vast majority of sexual abuse offenders are men. Yet women too can be offenders. A *small* unknown percentage of offenders are pedophiles who are sexually excited only by children. "*Most* sexual offenders are heterosexual males who often have sexual relationships with adult women as well as the children they molest" (Herringer and Rivkin 1989, 12). Finally, the commonly held assumption that most offenders are strangers is not true:

- ▶ 80–90% of offenders are known to the child; of these,
  - ▷ 35–40% are father, brother, common-in-law father, grandfather, mother's boyfriend, cousin, uncle, other relatives

    ▷ 45–50% are babysitter, neighbour, friend, friend of the family, etc.
- 10–15% of offenders are acquaintances or strangers (Metropolitan Toronto Special Committee on Child Abuse 1993a, 2)

Due to the nature of these relationships, the abuse can go on for years. Even in cases in which sexual abuse happened only once, children may experience an enormous degree of emotional turmoil, and the sooner children are able to seek professional help, the better.

Children often feel confused, especially since in many cases the sexual abuse is not painful and many even feel somewhat pleasurable. For some children, this contact may be the only physical affection they receive. When children realize that a trusted adult has betrayed them, children may feel guilt about "causing" the abuse, or shame that it felt good sometimes. Children with high self-esteem and strong communication skills may be less likely to be sexually abused, but it is clear that the abuse is *never* the child's fault. It is almost impossible for the child to resist the abuse; offenders put a great deal of thought into how they will manipulate children.

NEGLECT

Neglect occurs when parents do not meet their children's physical, emotional, and social needs. Neglect can be acute or chronic. In acute neglect, the care usually improves when the crisis has passed. Chronic neglect, though, usually results from the parents' incompetence to respond to children's needs. However, neglect is not based simply on monetary standards. Families that live in poverty and are doing the best with what they have must be acknowledged and not unjustly suspected of neglect. "Standards of neglect are culturally derived. Some situations have little ambiguity. Many others leave families vulnerable to standards that may speak more to an ideal than to essential components of child care" (Ayoub et al. 1990, 236).

The consequences of neglect can be extreme, especially for infants and young children. Inadequate emotional and physical stimulation and malnutrition cause a condition known as failure to thrive. Infants who suffer from this condition gain little weight with no medical explanation and experience delays in development, particularly in language, during the second year of life.

Trocmé et al. (1994) studied the Ontario Children's Aid Society's reported cases of neglect and identified eight forms. See Table 6.1. Note that in 87 percent of the cases, the parents either failed or refused to ensure that the children's basic physical needs (food, clothing, shelter), safety needs, and security needs were met.

Behavioural Indicators of Abuse

This section examines some of the behavioural and emotional indicators that caregivers may observe in children who suffer from any type of abuse or neglect. What are behavioural or emotional indicators? They are signs, symptoms, or clues seen in a child, or in the adult in the child's life, that lead caregivers to suspect that the

TABLE 6.1 EIGHT FORMS OF NEGLECT	
FORMS OF NEGLECT	**SUBSTANTIATED**
1. Parents fail to supervise children, which results in injuries or the risk of injury.	39%
2. Physical neglect: Parents provide inadequate levels of nutrition, clothing, and living conditions (e.g., clean laundry, warm, dry home, etc.).	34%
3. Parents abandon children or refuse to have children return to their custody.	14%
4. Educational neglect: Parents know that children are not attending school.	5%
5. Medical neglect: Parents either don't, refuse to, or are unable to seek necessary medical care.	4%
6. Parents' failure to supervise the children, which leads to sexual assault: parents knew there was the possibility of sexual abuse but failed to adequately protect the children.	4%
7. Psychological treatment neglect: Parents either don't, refuse to, or are unable to seek necessary psychological/emotional care.	4%
8. Permitting criminal activity: Parents have either encouraged the child to commit a crime or have failed to adequately supervise the child.	2%
Total: Because of overlap among multiple forms of maltreatment, the total is greater than 100%.	106%

Source: Developed from Trocmé et al. (1994), 50–51.

child is being abused. Except in situations in which we actually witness abuse, or a physician diagnoses physical injuries or symptoms consistent with abuse, we must remember that no single behaviour confirms child abuse. Nor should we make assumptions based on indicators alone until we have justification to be *suspicious*. A cluster of indicators would lead the caregiver to pursue her or his suspicions further.

 Lars, usually a cheerful, sociable child, now acts withdrawn. To suspect abuse in his case is making a big leap. We must know more about what is happening in Lars's life and family. Perhaps his whole family is anxious about his mother's losing her job. Maybe Lars is afraid of being bullied on the school playground.

Abuse or neglect leads to serious emotional distress in children and damages their self-esteem. Almost any behaviour indicating emotional distress can be a symptom of child abuse. Behavioural indicators differ depending on the child's personality and temperament.

The following list is abbreviated. It focuses on general behavioural indicators that children who are being abused *in any way* may exhibit. An abused child may

- ▶ either be overly compliant or overly aggressive
- ▶ either resist physical contact or not hesitate to go to strangers for affection
- ▶ either be overanxious to please or resist all limits and react with temper tantrums or rage
- ▶ be afraid to go home or fearful when a parent or a particular adult arrives at pickup
- ▶ experience delays in development, particularly in language and occasionally in gross and fine motor development or in the development of age-appropriate social relationships with peers
- ▶ be overwhelmed with sadness, anger, or apathy
- ▶ lack confidence in their abilities and have low self-esteem
- ▶ not be emotionally attached to anyone
- ▶ demonstrate regressive behaviour, as when a 5-year-old wets her pants or reverts to constant crying, rather than using words
- ▶ lack curiosity and interest in their surroundings (e.g., not interested in play)
- ▶ disclose to caregivers that someone has, for example, caused the present or past injury (physical abuse), constantly puts down the child (emotional abuse), had sexual activity with the child (sexual abuse), or left the young child without supervision or other basic needs for periods of time (neglect)

The preceding behavioural indicators can apply to any of the four types of abuse. However, because of the individual nature of the different types of abuse, some indicators tend to be more relevant to one type of abuse than another.

- ▶ In physical abuse, the child is often absent, and returns with signs of an injury that is healing (e.g., bruises that have changed from red-purple to greenish).
- ▶ In emotional abuse, the child sets unreasonably high expectations for self and refuses to try again if she doesn't succeed the first time.
- ▶ In sexual abuse, the child has an unusual level of sexual knowledge, sexual play, or excessive self-stimulation (masturbation) for his age and developmental level.
- ▶ In neglect, the child seems hungry, tired, or dirty all the time.

Caregivers observe not only children but the relationships they have with their parents. We will not provide a list of possible indicators for a suspected offending parent, since this can lead to stereotyping. A caregiver's role is to objectively and carefully document his or her observations (which aids the child protection agency in their investigation), not to identify the abuser. Remember that as a professional you have a legal and ethical obligation to report your suspicions of child abuse. If you are unsure of whether your observations are reportable, call your local child protection agency to consult.

Consequences of Abuse

Each individual child is unique in terms of development, personality, temperament, and so on. It is impossible to make generalizations about all children or children who are survivors of abuse. No one can predict the outcomes that children will experience as a result of their having been abused. We don't understand why one child who experienced one incident of abuse may suffer far more than another who had been abused for a number of years (Tower 1993, 66). However, we can draw some conclusions.

As you read the following summaries, remember this qualifier: These are the overall conclusions drawn by various researchers. *Don't assume that 100 percent of children who are abused behave in any one certain way, but be aware that a statistically significant number of children display similar characteristics.*

▶ Many children who are abused experience significant socioemotional and cognitive delays. Often, in addition to the abuse, these children are exposed to other negative family factors, such as parents' constant fighting or frequent moving (Wolfe et al. 1985).

▶ Developmental delays may be evident at a very young age in children who are being abused. Trocmé and Caunce (1995, 17) cite Erickson et al.'s longitudinal observational study of infant–mother interactions. This research demonstrated that infants as young as 12 months who were abused showed evidence of developmental delays when compared with a control group. By 24 months of age, the children who were abused were more easily frustrated and angry, and were generally less happy than those in the control group. In the consecutive years' observations, these children demonstrated similar patterns of delays and difficulties. By 6 years of age, these children were found to have significant delays in comparison to those in the control group. The earlier that intervention begins for a child who is abused, the better the chance to make a long-term difference to the child's confidence and competence.

▶ The emotional and psychological consequences of any type of abuse are broad-ranging and may relate to the age of the child when the abuse occurred. "Changes in brain chemistry caused by acute stress at key developmental periods may cause a child to react to stress with aggression or fear and withdrawal" (Guy 1997, 17). The stress that results when a child lives often in a state of neglect or trauma causes a chemical reaction that alters the brain (Perry 1995, 18). This can lead to an overdevelopment of anxiety and impulsive behaviour and underdevelopment of the ability to empathize and solve problems—conditions that increase the chance of violent behaviour.

▶ Poor infant–mother attachments are a notable result of early abuse and a risk factor for the continuation of abuse. There is increasing evidence to show that the quality of infants' attachments to their parents predicts later socioemotional competence (Sroufe 1988).

▶ Children had little confidence in their power to affect and shape their experiences, feeling that their achievements were determined by factors outside of themselves. This decreased their motivation when engaged in tasks and activities (Barahal et al. 1981).

▶ Physical aggression and antisocial behaviour are among the most common characteristics of children who have been physically abused (Amnerman 1989).

▶ Compared to their peers who were not abused, preschool children who were abused

▷ engage in less parallel and group play

▷ have shorter involvement with play materials, so they don't progress to using these materials in more complex, creative ways

▷ are less socially competent with peers

These behaviours were interpreted as developmental delays in the play behaviour of children who were abused (Alessandri 1991).

▶ Abused children showed significant delays in language abilities, both receptive (i.e., comprehension, memory) and expressive (i.e., naming, describing), compared to the language development of the control group (Allen and Oliver 1982). The results suggest that these delays may be related to a lack of stimulation at home (Allen and Oliver 1982).

▶ Children demonstrated significantly less willingness to learn, especially with new adults. This has implications for children's ability to balance establishing safe and secure relationships with adults and feeling free enough to venture out to explore the world in a way that promotes cognitive competence (Aber et al. 1989; Cicchetti 1989).

▶ Many of the children were not achieving cognitive developmental milestones. To a large degree, this may be due to their difficulties with social skills and their need for external cues (i.e., they rely on others to direct them rather than taking the initiative). These difficulties are not due to cognitive deficits (i.e., lack of intelligence) but rather to their low level of self-esteem (Goldson 1991). The ongoing National Longitudinal Survey of Children and Youth has found to date that children who live in environments with multiple risk factors are likely to have less ability in building relationships, helping behaviour, and vocabulary (Guy 1997, 101).

This summary highlights some of the short- and long-term effects experienced by children who have been abused. Emotional and social difficulties affect children in the areas of attachment, security, trust, confidence, motivation, social sensitivity, and play behaviour, and result in lower self-esteem. Frustrated by their limited social skills, by their lack of achievement, and by difficulties in their home environments, these children are frequently aggressive or withdrawn. Research has provided a strong rationale for focusing treatment on socioemotional problems to improve life chances, because an increased belief in oneself, trust in others, and positive social skills are springboards to developing other competencies. Research also reinforces the importance of ECE training for caregivers. Because much of what caregivers do on a daily basis is to promote each child's self-esteem, this is even more crucial for children who have been abused or have experienced other trauma. (See Providing a Secure Environment, page 440.)

Causes of Child Abuse

Child abuse occurs for a variety of complex reasons that cannot be explained by any one theoretical model. What does seem clear is that many factors are involved in causing and perpetuating child abuse. Society consists of a number of interacting components, including economic, social, educational, cultural, individual, familial, and religious ones. Inevitably, some interactions create stress.

Although there are many stress factors that can affect parents' lives, *it is important to remember that not all parents under stress abuse their children.* Just because parents are separating doesn't mean that you should look for signs of abuse. If you have developed a relationship with the family, you probably know how they coped with stress in the past. If a family is experiencing several life events at about the same time, the increased stress may be more than they are able to cope with, which can contribute to child abuse. Some families are under ongoing stress, such as those living in poverty or those in which one or more members has a chronic debilitating illness. Again, these families do not necessarily abuse their children Nor, on the other hand, does a family's financial stability mean that a child cannot possibly be suffering abuse within the family unit. When the child care program is a support system for families, it reduces the sense of isolation. Families are then more likely to seek help if they are at risk of abusing.

We live in a mobile society, and one consequence of this is that many adults live in places other than where their parents, siblings, or extended family live. As early as 1990, only 35 percent of Canadian adults had lived in their current residence for at least 10 years. Only 5 percent had never moved (Centre for International Studies, cited in the Vanier Institute of the Family 1994, 124). Our social environment can either contribute to or prevent incidents of child abuse. As a society, and as a community, and as individuals, we can help parents to raise children in abuse-free

environments by reducing stressors and helping them cope. Some parents are fortunate enough to have a network of friends or extended family members that provide emotional support or help (sometimes in the form of respite) when they need it. Those families who are isolated, with no one to turn to in times of extreme stress, can be at higher risk for abuse.

Preventing Child Abuse

 **OBJECTIVES** To describe the function of child protection agencies with regard to child abuse.

To define primary prevention and outline the caregivers' role in the child care environment and beyond.

To define secondary prevention and discuss the caregivers' role in identifying suspected child abuse, and in documenting and reporting it to the child protection agency.

To define tertiary prevention and discuss the caregivers' role in working with children, families, and agencies.

Everyone in the community has a role to play in preventing child abuse. Caregivers are professional advocates for children and they can make a significant contribution in preventing the abuse of children. Caregivers' roles can be divided into three levels of prevention: primary, secondary, and tertiary. We begin this section with a brief introduction to child protection agencies that are involved in prevention.

Child Protection Agencies

Child welfare legislation and services are under provincial/territorial jurisdiction, as are health, education, and child care. As a result, the delivery system varies not only across Canada but between regions within a province/territory. Because of these inconsistencies, and for the sake of clarity, we use the term "child protection agency" throughout this unit. Each agency office operates autonomously and may differ in the way documentation, reporting procedures, investigations, and treatments are carried out. Despite these variations, the primary goal remains the same: prevention and community support services. Child protection agencies are required by law to investigate all reports of suspected child abuse and to take steps to protect children from further abuse. This discussion touches on the broad responsibilities of the agencies.

The job titles of the personnel working in an agency's office vary. We use "child protection workers" to describe the people who take the calls from centre directors or caregivers, teachers, and other members of the public, and who are assigned to the child's case. They are usually social workers trained to assess situations in which children may be at risk. As it relates to centres, the child protection worker talks with the director or caregiver and advises her or him on how to proceed. The centre may be asked to continue to observe the child and document observations in the child's file or to make a formal report to the agency. Based on this report, a child protection worker is assigned to the child's case, and an investigation begins. In the section Secondary Child Abuse Prevention, you will read more about this process. There will be situations in which the worker and director believe that the child is at immediate risk and the worker, perhaps with the police, may apprehend the child.

The agency's priority is to maintain the family unit while preventing further abuse to the child. There is recognition that in Canada today, significant changes to child welfare legislation are required to ensure that children's health and safety are the first priority. With that in mind, the agency's investigation determines that child and offender are best served by

▶ appropriate community services that meet the needs of the child and the family, or by
▶ temporarily removing the child from the home while the offender seeks treatment.

Only in a small number of the cases in which the offender is identified are criminal charges laid and the individual found guilty of abuse.

Primary Child Abuse Prevention

Primary prevention refers to child care programs' policies and practices that support relationships in children and families so that child abuse doesn't happen. Caregivers are not immune to abusing children. For this reason, centres' policies address child abuse, child guidance, child-centred programming, nutrition, and health, and establish procedures that are implemented by staff. These policies and practices, combined with training, enhance caregivers' ability to provide and model quality care.

CAREGIVER'S ROLE IN PRIMARY PREVENTION

Caregivers have a unique opportunity to demonstrate that abuse can be prevented. Prevention begins within child care programs by

▶ supporting each child in developing positive self-esteem and confidence
▶ providing a positive role model for parents
▶ supporting parents in their parenting rights and responsibilities

Creating a Positive Child Care Environment   Quality child care environments are caring and nurturing and respect children and their families. Parents see how caregivers interact with their child and other children, and how they guide behaviour and

provide a safe, suitable physical environment for children. Knowing that their child is well cared for in their absence alleviates stress for parents.

In terms of the children, a high-quality child care program promotes children's health—and helps prevent child abuse. The most obvious example is the promotion of self-esteem as an essential part of all practices and curricula. Children who feel good about themselves may be better protected from child abuse than those who don't. They may be more aware of their rights and those of others. A high-quality program also helps prevent sexual abuse by integrating children's awareness of their bodies, healthy sexuality, and personal safety. (See Sexuality, page 473.)

Enrollment interviews are ideal opportunities for directors (or caregivers) and parents to begin getting to know one another. Over time, caregivers develop meaningful partnerships with families. Often these result in parents sharing more personal information, such as their views on discipline, their support systems, or their relationship with a spouse or partner. Caregivers combine this information with observations of parents and children interacting to help them understand the parent–child relationship. Some parents do not feel comfortable sharing personal details about their family. This is perfectly acceptable and they deserve the same respect as other parents. Caregivers need to be careful not to pry or make judgments based on the family's wish for privacy. They shouldn't assume that parents are trying to hide something. Providing parents with nonjudgmental support is a positive primary strategy.

e.g. A parent rushes into the centre at the end of each day. She seems to be in a never-ending battle with her 3-year-old. He doesn't want to go home and often has a tantrum. This is an upsetting way to begin the evening. As the caregiver, you have two options. You can either do nothing, which in some ways

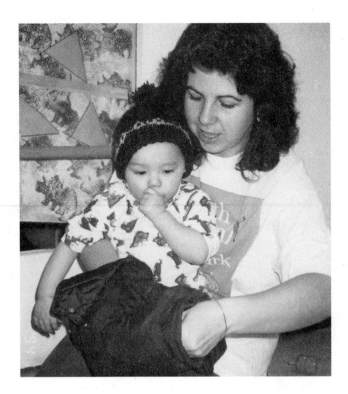

contributes to the tension—the tired, frustrated, rushed mother may yell at or slap her child—or you can recognize the stress she is under as she tries to leave work on time and travel across town to pick up her son. By acknowledging how difficult this is for her, by talking about how the two of you can work together, you can make the stress more manageable. Perhaps the mother could call the centre when she is leaving work or try to arrive at the same time each day so that you can have her son prepared for the transition. As well, spending 10 minutes together in the play area before getting ready to leave, or sitting down and relaxing together over a snack before the commute home, may be options that the parent and child like.

Caregivers often establish closer, more personal relationships with some children than with others. These quality relationships are essential for children if they are going to trust a caregiver enough to disclose abuse. There may be times when you have concerns about a child, though he or she hasn't said anything to you or any other caregiver. In this situation, the caregiver with the closest relationship with the child is probably best positioned to talk with the child. Discuss your observations of the child's behaviour. You might say, "Emily, I have noticed lately that you are getting angry with your friends and storming off a lot. Is something bothering you?" The child may actually have something to talk about that has nothing to do with child abuse. Opening the door in this way may help her or him to feel comfortable enough to talk. Children often want to protect offenders, especially if they are significant in their lives. Children may not want to talk at first but may approach you at another time when they know that a caregiver will listen and is concerned about them. However, if a child does not disclose abuse to you, though your observations lead you to suspect abuse, follow the steps in the centre's child abuse protocol. For a number of reasons, a child may not disclose abuse or may recant—say it didn't really happen after disclosing earlier. (See Secondary Child Abuse Prevention, page 427.)

Caregivers can contribute to reducing the incidence of parental spanking and other forms of punishment by

▶ modelling positive guidance with children
▶ being open to discussion with individual parents about discipline issues, avoiding being judgmental or prescriptive, which undermines a parent's authority
▶ providing access to resources on discipline and parenting such as articles, books, and videos for parents (e.g., the videotape *Shaking, Hitting and Spanking: What to Do Instead*)
▶ providing opportunities for group discussions such as parent meetings or workshops (e.g., *Nobody's Perfect*) and ensuring that the facilitators are flexible, able to suspend judgment, and trained to recognize suspected child abuse
▶ accessing community resources that may be of assistance to parents, including ethno-culturally relevant resources, if available
▶ becoming involved in organizations that are committed to reducing violence in society and, in particular, advocating for positive environments for children

Personal Safety Programs for Children Caring adults want children to be safe. Personal safety programs seem, on the surface, an obvious way to help protect children from

harm. However, ongoing research has shown that the issue is not as simple as it seems. Before deciding to evaluate a specific personal safety program for children, please consider the following concerns about such programs:

▶ The main challenge of primary prevention is that it is a socialization process as well as an educative one—child abuse, and particularly sexual abuse, occurs in a society that fosters the sexualization of children and the absolute power of adults. Protecting young children is the responsibility of adults who are in charge of creating the environment. This is a huge ongoing task, but it helps keep in perspective who has the major responsibility and the focus that must be maintained (Institute for the Prevention of Child Abuse 1995, 53). We want children to have tools that can help them in a potentially abusive situation, but we don't want them to feel responsible for protecting themselves, or to believe that they failed in any way if they were unable to protect themselves from an offender.

▶ Prevention programs may be presenting concepts that make sense to adults but are beyond the young child's cognitive capacities. All children relate to prevention strategies on different emotional and cognitive levels, and respond in accordance with their developmental stage. (See Table 7.1, page 489.) Evaluation of prevention programs has not as yet given us specific recommendations for program development.

▶ Young children can acquire skills and concepts, but the issue is whether they can retain the information over time (Institute for the Prevention of Child Abuse 1995, 54). Interactive and comprehensive programs in which children can role play and practise skills are likely helpful, although children won't necessarily be able to apply the skills in real-life situations. Programs that include relevant information and resource materials for parents and caregivers likely reinforce the learning as well as involve the adults in a meaningful way. This potentially reduces the burden of responsibility that children feel.

▶ The inclusion of self-defence strategies is controversial. They may help the child develop self-esteem and skills to escape, but their use could potentially place the child in greater danger. The program must stress that the goal of using self-defence is flight, not fight.

▶ Finkelhor and Strapko (1992) have found that disclosure by the child (of abuse that the child has already experienced) is the most tangible result of these programs (a secondary prevention function). It is important for caregivers to be both aware of and prepared for this possibility.

▶ Caregivers must be committed to critically examine the assumptions behind a particular personal safety program, as well as the specific content. Refer to Rimer and Prager (1998, 146) for assumptions implicit in child sexual abuse prevention programs and criteria for evaluating these programs.

Networking with Community Resources Every centre has access to professionals and printed resources on child abuse. Access to parenting consultants and parenting courses may be limited to larger urban communities. Centres must have the name and phone number of the child protection agency and a clear understanding of the centre's role in reporting and documenting suspected abuse. In-service training for staff on child abuse is always beneficial. Caregivers are also in a position to respond to parents' requests for information or consultation with a specific agency related to parenting, health, housing, or finances. Centres should make it a priority to ensure that their staff are aware of ethno-culturally and language-sensitive resources.

PROFILE

TORONTO CHILD ABUSE CENTRE

Toronto Child Abuse Centre believes that all children have the right to a safe, nurturing environment within which to grow to their full potential, free from violence, abuse, and neglect. Working collaboratively with the community, the agency helps coordinate efforts to improve prevention, detection, reporting, investigation, and treatment of child abuse.

THE CHILD CARE COMMUNITY RESPONSE TO CHILD ABUSE

Making a Difference: A Child Care Community Response to Child Abuse and *Making a Difference: The Community Response to Child Abuse* are programs designed to train individuals who provide frontline services to children and families in early identification of child abuse and effective intervention in situations where children are at risk of being abused. More than 4000 people have participated in the training program, and hundreds more are using the manual in the workplace to support staff who work with children every day.

The centre offers crisis support programs for children and their families, child abuse offender treatment programs, and court preparation for children who have experienced or witnessed violence and who will be testifying in court. In addition to these direct services, the agency is developing an innovative *Primary Prevention* program for children between the ages of 4 and 16. The *I'm a Great Kid!* program will be a series of three videos and activity manuals. The first video and manual is now complete.

For information about these programs and other services of Toronto Child Abuse Centre, call (416) 515-1100 or reach them through their Web site: www.tcac.on.ca.

Source: Adapted with permission from the Toronto Child Abuse Centre.

Preventing Child Abuse by Caregivers

The primary focus of this unit is the prevention of child abuse within families. Abuse can happen anywhere and by any persons of authority, including caregivers in child care programs. Factors that contribute to abuse in families are not unlike those that may lead to abuse within centres. *Abuse is always a violation of power.* Feelings of frustration or of being trapped lead to short tempers and striking out physically or emotionally as a way of regaining a sense of control and power. Although it is rare that caregivers hit or spank a child, they may be likely to shake or excessively restrain, threaten, use sarcasm, or yell at a child. Work environments that contribute to caregivers' physical, emotional, and social health are vital in providing caregivers with a true sense of autonomy, job satisfaction, and improved overall well-being.

Sexual abuse in centres is rare, yet it is understandably alarming for parents to realize that this, and other forms of abuse, can happen when they entrust their child's care to others (Finkelhor et al. 1988). This realization has had both positive and negative effects on child care programs. On the positive side, parents demand that programs have an open-door policy for parents. Parents may want to be more closely involved in the program to understand what the children are doing all day, and to ensure that all policies and procedures are respectful of children. On the negative side, some parents may become suspicious of caregivers, leading to allegations of child abuse that, in many cases, are retracted or prove to be unfounded. However, the process is a difficult emotional experience for caregivers. Caregivers may be overly cautious about the physical affection they give to children. They may feel inhibited because of the possibility that parents will misconstrue appropriate behaviour as inappropriate. This is particularly the case for male caregivers, who fear that they are suspect because of their gender. (See Men Working in Child Care, page 89.) Although it is not common practice, there are centres where staff are,

CHART 6.1 STRATEGIES TO ENHANCE POSITIVE RELATIONSHIPS

The following are strategies that, when in place, create a child care environment supporting high-quality relationships between caregivers, children, and their families. The intent is to reduce situations that may either place children at risk of being abused by caregivers, or make caregivers vulnerable to false allegations.

Hiring and Employment Probation policies

- Each successful candidate must sign a consent form that permits the employer to have the police check for criminal convictions. Depending on your child care regulations, this may be voluntary or a hiring requirement, and a standard consent form may be provided by the licensing office.
- Check employment and personal references thoroughly and regard them as important information when evaluating job candidates.
- Hire ECE-trained staff.
- Familiarize new staff and volunteers with the centre's policies and procedures, particularly those that involve child guidance and child abuse. Review these policies regularly with all staff.

Staff Supervision

- Work toward exceeding the minimum caregiver–child ratio required in the child care regulations. This demonstrates the centre's commitment to provide the best environment for children and counters any charge of inadequate supervision resulting in negligence, in the event of an investigation of suspected abuse by a caregiver.
- Provide staff on employment probationary period with supervision throughout their shift, and do not give them full responsibility for opening and closing duties.
- Maintain adequate caregiver–child ratios throughout the day.
- Provide regular, consistent supervision for all staff.
- At all times, keep co-workers informed of what each is doing with children and where.
- Never leave volunteers, visitors, or students alone with children.
- Minimize hard-to-supervise areas wherever possible. Place equipment in a way that ensures easy supervision and install windows or doors in secluded spaces.
- Minimize, as much as possible, staff working in isolation from other adults in private areas such as in the nap room, or diapering or toileting areas.
- Provide staff with effective guidelines for field trips.

Observation and Child Guidance

- Observe children as they arrive at the centre, and follow the centre's procedure for documentation and reporting to the child protection agency.
- Staff must follow the child guidance policy. If an interaction between a child and caregiver goes out of control, call a co-worker for assistance.
- Provide and make available personal care and safety kits and training opportunities on child abuse for staff and parents.
- Provide guidelines for staff on how and when to intervene appropriately in child sexual play.
- Provide developmentally appropriate personal safety teaching for children in the centre.
- Use the correct terminology for body parts with children.
- Exercise good judgment in the choice of language used with children. Adjectives such as "sexy," "babe," "little bugger," and "brat" are unacceptable and disrespectful.

(chart continues on next page)

CHART 6.1   STRATEGIES TO ENHANCE POSITIVE RELATIONSHIPS (continued)

Involvement of Parents

• Inform parents of all parent policies at registration. It is recommended that parents be provided with a copy of the policies. At the very least, child guidance policies must, according to child care regulation, be posted.
• Invite and welcome parents to observe in the centre at any time of the day.
• Inform parents how to report concerns they have, with respect to the centre, to the child care office.
• Provide opportunities for parents to network with one another.
• Inform parents of any change in centre practices and procedures and the rationale for changes.

Source: Adapted with permission from *Child Abuse: How to Handle Allegations against the Child Care Provider/Prevention Strategies* (Manitoba Child Care Association, 1993).

unfortunately, discouraged from reciprocating children's hugs or having children sit on caregivers' laps. Policies and practices must provide checks and balances: warm, sensitive caregiving with ways to ensure that caregivers' behaviour is verifiable.

Assessing the situation:
How could you manage this situation to reduce the stress of the caregiver and child and reduce the risk of abuse?
Scenario: After half an hour, a caregiver is still unable to comfort a toddler. She is becoming increasingly frustrated and has said, "I just want to leave him in the crib until he stops crying." You can see that she is handling the child less and less gently.

Training in early childhood education is extremely important in all areas of working with groups of children. Working with groups of children is hard work, both physically and emotionally, and the difficulty can be compounded by caregivers' low status and wages. Trained staff should have the knowledge and confidence to create programs that are caring, interesting, varied, stimulating, and rewarding for both children and themselves. Those with little or no formal child care training often lack the knowledge and skills necessary to manage the everyday stresses of the work.

Teamwork is a crucial component of working effectively in child care. Of course, new graduates want to focus their efforts on a high-quality team approach to their work and learn from their more experienced caregivers. This is ideal when caregivers are positive models, but not if a co-worker is abusive in any way to children. In worst-case scenarios, new graduates begin to take on some of the negative behaviour, such as belittling children; using sarcasm; or grabbing, shaking, or restraining children. As trained caregivers, they should recognize that this behaviour is unacceptable and ask the director for assistance.

Secondary Child Abuse Prevention

Secondary prevention encompasses

► identifying children who may be victims of abuse
► documenting observations and possible indicators
► reporting to the child protection agency

This is a balancing act indeed for caregivers whose role in secondary prevention is complex. First, caregivers are not "child abuse police." They must not be suspicious every time a child comes in with a bruise or in dirty clothes or yells at a doll in dramatic play. Second, caregivers make numerous observations about dramatic changes in a child's behaviour, emotional state, and/or physical appearance. Using these indicators, the caregiver attempts to find out why the child's behaviour has changed. Third, caregivers must understand that it is the child protection agency's responsibility to respond to suspicions, investigate the abuse, and identify the offender. It is *not* your job to prove that abuse has occurred.

IDENTIFYING SUSPECTED CHILD ABUSE

The identification of suspected child abuse and the subsequent intervention with children and families are complex and difficult issues. Because caregivers spend so much time with children and because of their observation skills, they are often the first people in children's lives to suspect the possibility of abuse. They are also in a position to provide support to the family. This can often create a conflict for the caregiver. *Stopping abuse now can have long-term positive effects for children and often for their whole family.*

As a result of their suspicions that a child in their care is being abused, caregivers may have the following reactions:

► They may refuse to believe that this parent would do this to his or her child. This may be especially difficult if you've known the parent for a while and have established a relationship.
► They may be afraid
  ▷ of the parent's anger, and as a result fear for the child's safety or their own safety
  ▷ of having falsely suspected the parent
  ▷ that the child will be removed from the home and/or withdrawn from the program.

Ultimately the child's welfare is your overriding concern. Most parents love their children and don't want to continue to hurt them once they understand the negative effects of abuse on children. Even after parents have been made aware of the caregivers' suspicions of abuse, caregivers need to ensure that the parents still feel welcome in the centre—otherwise staff are not fulfilling their role as child advocates. It's important for caregivers to support positive change within the family and not to expect miracles to happen overnight. Caregivers are a part of the child's life for only a few years, whereas the parent is involved for a lifetime.

Caregivers know each child's temperament, personality, and family. They observe children achieving developmental milestones and the normal range of behaviour. Caregivers draw on this experience in making judgments about children's behaviour and observing physical injuries. By asking themselves questions, caregivers rule out other possible explanations such as an illness, usual locations of bruises, vision or hearing problems, anxiety about specific stressors (e.g., a grandmother's recent death), developmentally appropriate fears, or developmental delays unrelated to abuse. Caregivers discuss concerns among themselves as well as ask parents questions (e.g., "How did Sam get the bruise on his back?"). However, it is important not to talk to the parent about your suspicion of child abuse. It can be useful to call the child protection agency and discuss concerns before formally reporting. Such consultation may lead to a resolution that works in the child's best interests (e.g., feedback to the family, referral for counselling, a change in your program that may help the child during a crisis period). For school-agers, it may also be appropriate to speak with the child's school teacher to verify whether she or he has made similar observations.

Suspecting Child Abuse   Caregivers' suspicions of physical abuse are based on

▶ the severity of the marks or injuries that can't be explained by a mishap during play
▶ the type, number, size, and/or shape of the trauma to the skin

Whenever a child is hurt, you must ask yourself, "How did this happen?" and "Did adults fail to protect the child?" Just as in centres, injuries that occur at home are understandable; bumps and bruises are a normal part of every child's life. Figure 6.1 (see page 404) illustrates the parts of the body on which caregivers are most likely to see bruises due to everyday activities as well as the locations where bruises may be cause for concern. Even though it is not your role to determine which bruises are suspicious or to interpret their origins, some markings do have identifiable shapes. Ask the child for explanations for burns, scalds, and fractures. Suspicious physical marks should be seen as soon as possible by your director. This should be done respectfully and with as little commotion as possible. If it is appropriate, you and the director may gently question the child about the nature and circumstances of the injury. Use non-leading questions such as "What happened to your arm?" followed by "What happened next?" Leading questions such as "Who did this to you?" or "Why did your mother hurt you like that?" not only put ideas or answers into the child's mouth but may also result in an unwarranted accusation. It is important to stay within your role boundaries and to remember that you could potentially jeopardize the investigation if you seem to ask leading questions. Confirmation of trauma is made by child protection workers, often in consultation with physicians. One of the strongest indicators of suspected physical abuse is a delay in seeking medical treatment for extensive and serious injuries. Although some children are more injury prone, children who repeatedly injure themselves raise serious concerns about the possibility of physical abuse or the level of supervision and guidance at home.

Purposeful Disclosures of Abuse or Witnessing Domestic Violence When children decide to disclose, it is a call for help. When they approach caregivers, caregivers must not only listen to their story but also support them. It is difficult for children to disclose abuse for a host of reasons. Here are a few:

▶ The child has only started to realize that something "not right" is happening to him or her.

▶ The child has been threatened with physical or emotional consequences if she or he tells.

▶ The child feels it is his or her fault and will be blamed.

▶ The child feels vulnerable or powerless, and does not think she or he will be believed.

Do's and Don'ts When There Is a Disclosure

If you have seen or heard something that leads you to suspect child abuse, remember to:

1. Control your emotions.
   ▷ Try to be calm and relaxed.
   ▷ Do not look shocked, disgusted, or say mean things about who you think may have abused the child.
   ▷ If you feel that you cannot control your feelings, call your director or a trusted friend to talk.
2. Offer comfort.
   ▷ Support children by letting them know that:
     • they were very brave to tell
     • you are glad they are telling you about this
     • you are sorry that this has happened to them
     • they are not alone—this happens to other children too
     • you will do everything you can to help
     • you are there to love and support them
   ▷ Do not say things like:
     • "How can you say those things about . . . ?"
     • "Liar."
     • "That horrible man has ruined you forever!"
     • "How could you let him do those things to you?"
     • "Why didn't you tell me this before?"

Children may "take back" (recant) what they have said. These children continue to need your love and support.

3. Be aware of the child's age and skills.
   ▷ Accept the words a child uses (including "slang" words) to describe what happened. Some children do not know the right words for body parts or sexual behaviours. Do not correct or change the words the child uses—it is extremely important for the investigation that the child's words are used when telling what happened.
   ▷ Do not use words that may frighten the child—for example, rape, incest, child abuse, wife assault, or jail.
4. Ask questions that let the person tell the story in his/her own words.
   • "Can you tell me what happened?"
   • "What happened next?"
   • "How did you get that bruise?"
   ▷ Avoid asking questions that might lead a child to provide a story different from the one he or she actually wanted to tell.
   • Do not ask leading questions—questions that suggest what happened or who did what—for example, "Did you get that bruise because mommy hit you with a brush?"
   • Do not question what the child tells you by asking, for example, "Are you sure it was Uncle Ted?"
   • Do not interrupt or add your own words when the child or adult stops talking.
   • Do not ask children why something may have happened. Children may think you are blaming them for what happened.
   • Do not try to change the mind of a child who has recanted or changed his/her story.
   • Do not keep on asking questions because you want to prove child abuse.
5. Respect the person who discloses.
   ▷ If a child or adult is telling, listen.
   ▷ If a child or adult is quiet, do not try to make him/her talk.
   ▷ Do not use force to undress a child to see injuries.
   ▷ Do not show off the child's injuries to others.
6. Tell the child what will happen next.
   ▷ Do not make promises you cannot keep. For example, do not agree to keep what the child called a "secret." It is important to explain to the child that some secrets must be shared in order to get help, or to keep people from being hurt. Tell the child the information will be shared only with people who will try to help.
   ▷ Answer the child's questions as simply and honestly as possible. Do not make up answers. For example, if a child asks, "Will Daddy have to go to jail now?" you can only say "I don't know. Other people decide that."
   ▷ Do not tell the child to keep any of your discussions with him or her secret.

Source: Adapted with permission from P. Rimer and B. Prager, *Reaching Out: Working Together to Identify and Respond to Child Victims of Abuse* (ITP Nelson, 1998), 75–79.

Clarifying Your Concerns with Parents   Even when there are concerns about suspected child abuse, ongoing communication with parents is of utmost importance in promoting children's well-being. When approaching parents, your goal is to clarify a situation, not to suggest that they are the offenders.

Start with your observation and follow with a question:
▷ "Jacob has a black eye. Do you know how it happened?"
▷ "Josie has seemed very sad for the past week and hasn't been interested in playing. Have you found that Josie is behaving this way at home too?"

Additional observations or questions depend on the parents' responses to your initial observation and question.

▷ You may ask Jacob's mother, "Did he see the doctor and were there any special instructions to care for him or concerns about his eyesight?"
▷ Josie's dad has noticed her lack of interest too. And you respond by saying, "Do you have any idea why Josie seems so sad?"

Take the parents' lead while being careful not to put them on the defensive. Questions starting with "Why did you …?" or "Why weren't you …?" are inappropriate and most parents, whether or not they are guilty of the abuse, will feel they are being judged. In most instances, the parents' explanation is sufficient and your questions and concerns are resolved. The parents appreciate your concern, and your positive relationship with them is maintained. Even in cases in which you are no longer concerned, it is important to document, in the child's file, your initial concerns and the conversation. Jacob may have recurring black eyes or other injuries that may begin to form a pattern that is of concern later on.

There are times when the parents' response reinforces your suspicion of child abuse. If the explanation for the black eye seems unusual, the parent seems nervous in her or his response, and perhaps the child looks fearful, you will likely question the validity of the explanation. After the parent leaves, express your concern to the director.

Caregivers are strongly discouraged from approaching parents in the following situations:

▶ Whenever *sexual abuse* is suspected. There are a number of reasons for this. If the offender is the mother's husband or boyfriend and he talks with the child's mother before the child protection worker or police do, he may convince her that he could never have done such a thing. After all, who would want to believe that her partner is capable of sexually abusing her own child? It is even more devastating for children if their mother does not believe them.

▶ When you are concerned that the child may be abused again as a result of your conversation with the parents.

▶ When you fear the family would disappear, making follow-up impossible. You may base this decision on the family's history of moving frequently.

In fact, child protection agencies prefer that any action beyond clarifying a situation be checked with them first. In other words, contact the child protection agency for direction. The child protection worker may indicate that they and/or the police will contact the parents. Or the child protection agency may advise the director to call the parents and ask them to come in for a meeting. A director with at least one other person present (e.g., a caregiver or staff person from the child care office) would then talk to the parents about the report. It is important to follow the direction of the child protection agency.

Documenting Suspicions

Caregivers may hesitate to document their suspicions in children's files for the following reasons:

▶ They don't fully understand the importance of documentation in proving a case of child abuse.
▶ They believe that they don't have time to document suspicions.
▶ They are concerned that their report may be made public.

Documentation is an important part of the administrative responsibilities of caregivers for a range of health care concerns. Every centre's work schedule needs to provide staff with the time to write relevant notations in children's files concerning illness, observations on their development, or suspected child abuse. Because of the serious legal implications of child abuse, documenting your observations, concerns, and questions is critical in that it provides evidence for the child protection agency. Although the child's file and the caregivers involved may be called to testify in court, this is the exception rather than the rule. This is why the quality of your documentation is so important.

Documentation serves two main purposes:

1. *It provides a guide for caregivers and the director in determining their next step*. If, after talking with the parents, your concerns are resolved, your documentation supports your decision not to proceed further. If you are still concerned after your discussion with the parent, documentation is critical. Remember that you must report your suspicions rather than waiting until you believe there is "proof."
2. *All the documentation on the child is used by the child protection agency, and possibly the police, in their investigation of the alleged abuse*. The more complete and comprehensive the information is, the more able the agency is to fulfill its important role in protecting children. Verbal accounts based on your memory are not as reliable as documentation written at the time. Child protection agency staff view caregivers who document well as conducting themselves as professionals, and will respond to you and your report accordingly.

Documentation: What Is Involved?   What makes a document objective, clear, concise, and complete? Every time you document, observe the following guidelines:

► Include the full name of the child, the date and time of recording, and the date and time of your observations.

► Describe clearly whatever you observed—both the child's physical injury and/or behaviour—that is of concern. Note the type of injury (i.e., burn, bruise, cut, fracture), the shape, size, colour, and number. A form that has a line diagram of a child's body makes it easier for caregivers to indicate where the mark(s) appeared on the body than to write, "It was 3 inches to the left of the belly button and maybe 2 inches above." In terms of behaviour, document any patterns that contribute to your suspicions (e.g., aggressive behaviour toward others, unexplainable fears) and *direct quotations* (if possible) of comments the child made during play (e.g., dramatic play).

► In chronological order and using direct quotations, write down anything that was said by the child, by the parents, and by you. This will assure the agency staff that you did not ask the child leading questions, such as "When did your dad hit you so hard?"

► List the names, time, and date when you told others about your suspicions.

► Sign and date your form in ink and have the director do the same.

► Remember to record everything in your own handwriting.

► Use a new form if you have concerns on another day.

► Document objectively. Do *not* include how you are feeling about the incident or ideas about what you think might have happened.

Put one copy in the child's file and give a second copy to the director. Your child care office may require a call and/or a copy whenever child abuse is *suspected*. Documentation should be completed as soon as possible after you become aware of the physical or behavioural indicators or after a child's disclosure.

Remember, frequently you'll find that once you've talked with the parents about the child's injury or change in behaviour, your concerns will be resolved. After you've documented and talked with your director, no further steps need to be taken. In the remainder of cases, you will call the child protection agency, with the director's support.

Reporting to the Child Protection Agency

Centre staff are included in provincial/territorial child welfare legislation's list of professionals working with children who are legally obliged to report to the local child protection agency when they have reasonable grounds to suspect child abuse. You are expected to become familiar with the child welfare legislation in your province or territory and to read the section that covers children in need of protection.

The staff member who initially suspects abuse is expected to call the child protection agency, with the support and direction of the centre director, if possible. When telephone contact is made with a child protection worker:

► the person reporting is asked a number of questions, many of which are answered by the documentation in the child's file

▶ the agency may recommend that the director refer the family to resources that are appropriate for the situation in order to prevent further abuse

▶ the child protection worker advises the caller on whether further evidence is required. If it is, the caregivers are required to continue monitoring the child before a formal report is submitted. Otherwise, the child protection worker proceeds with the case and instructs the caller about who should contact the parents: child protection staff or child care program staff.

When the child protection agency decides that a formal report is required, it usually follows a set of guidelines, which it shares with the centre staff. The style of these guidelines varies from agency to agency within a region.

As you are probably aware, reports can be made anonymously, and by caregivers. However, Trocmé et al. (1994) suggest that anonymous reports are taken less seriously than reports by someone who identifies herself or himself. Centre staff are professionals, have specialized skills and knowledge, and have a relationship with the child in question. They are able to work effectively with another group of professionals. The agency's staff often incorporate caregivers into the child's treatment plan, but if they don't know who is calling, this obviously can't be done. The agency is not obligated to reveal who made the report; however, the parent will likely suspect that it came from the centre. If a parent approaches you angrily after a report is made, it is important that you explain that you are legally obligated to report any suspicion of child abuse, so that the concern can be investigated by the proper authority. You are fulfilling your responsibilities under the law and are not making any accusations.

Even if the abuse cannot be proved, someone who reports suspected abuse is not vulnerable to any consequences unless the report was made maliciously or without reasonable grounds. For caregivers, it is evident that they have opportunities to get to know children, to know what is "normal" for individuals, and to have a positive impact on the child's life when abuse is stopped early on. It is extremely rare for caregivers' reports to be considered malicious. Malicious reporting comes into question at times during a custody battle, when one parent has wrongly accused the other of child abuse to prevent him or her from having access to the children.

Hesitations in Reporting Caregivers and directors may be hesitant to take the final step and make the formal report even when they have reasonable grounds to suspect child abuse. Here are some reasons why:

▶ Reporting is a difficult emotional experience for anyone. Centre staff benefit from discussing their reactions and feelings with appropriate professionals, such as someone from the child protection agency, the child care office, or their regional public health unit or social service office.

▶ The child or parent requests that the staff keep the abuse a secret. No one benefits from keeping it secret, and it is against the law. Not reporting may bring further harm to the child.

▶ Staff may be uncertain about what information is required, so they are discouraged from reporting. If they are uncertain about what to report, consult with:
  ▷ the child protection agency to discuss the general situation and ask for their advice
  ▷ the consultant from the child care office

▶ Individual caregivers may not be aware that it is their professional and legal obligation to report suspected abuse, if for some reason the centre's child abuse protocol is not comprehensive or the caregiver did not learn about reporting responsibilities while in training.

You and a co-worker have documented a number of observations and are confident that the suspicion of child abuse is valid. However, your director repeatedly refuses to support your decision to call the child protection agency and will not provide you with an adequate explanation for her refusal. Your attempts to adhere to the centre's protocol have been unsuccessful, and now the legal responsibility falls directly on your shoulders: you make the report without the director's approval. Admittedly, this is a stressful situation. Caregivers must seek help in dealing with the situation. Your legal responsibility to report is a serious matter.

▶ Staff don't believe that the child protection agency will act on their report. Remember that it is the child protection agency's responsibility to investigate. The child protection agency acts according to its assessed risk of the case.

What Happens during Investigations   The child protection worker decides whether the reported concerns require an investigative response based on the conditions set out in the provincial/territorial child protection legislation. If the case doesn't meet at least one of the conditions, the agency does not have legal grounds to intervene. If a decision is made by the child protection agency not to intervene, your report and the information obtained in the investigation is retained and filed for future reference. Unfortunately, the agency may not always call the director back and tell her or him of this decision. This often leads caregivers to feel that making the report was a waste of time. Every situation is unique, so the response depends on the circumstances.

▶ Where there are visible injuries, someone from the agency will probably see the child on the day the report is made. When there are concerns of physical abuse but no visible trauma, the child protection worker may not proceed any further that day. Remember that the agency must assess each case and decide which cases require their immediate attention.

▶ Investigations of sexual abuse usually start immediately, and almost always immediately when the alleged offender lives with the child. Occasionally the child protection worker waits a day or two, if the wait improves the quality of the investigation and the agency's ultimate ability to protect the child.

▶ Investigating neglect requires the collection of documentation from all agencies and professionals involved with the family, including the family physician or pediatrician, the public health nurse, caregivers, teachers, and any social agencies involved with the family. Because of this consultation, the investigation takes time.

▶ For reports that children are left unsupervised, or refuse to go home, or when parents call the agency and demand that they remove their children from the home, child protection workers respond immediately (Institute for the Prevention of Child Abuse 1991b). If reasonable time has lapsed with no response from the child protection agency, it is appropriate for the staff who reported or for the director to phone again. Once a decision is reached by the child protection worker, and if the staff or director believe that their concerns have not been adequately addressed, a follow-up call may be placed to the worker's supervisor.

Child protection workers may not conduct the investigation on their own but may include others on the team. Some communities have put protocols in place that determine how investigations are responded to and conducted, and by whom. As mentioned above, cases of sexual abuse are usually investigated jointly with the police department. For other types of abuse, police may be consulted. If there is concern for the child protection worker's safety, a police officer may accompany her or him when going to the child and/or alleged offender's home. The agency staff often consult with other social service and health professionals during the investigation, calling on them to assess the child and/or the alleged offender. Investigative interviews are analyzed according to specific clinical criteria, findings of medical exams are gathered, and a thorough assessment of the circumstances surrounding the allegations is conducted. Family dynamics and the presence or absence of indicators of abuse are taken into account.

There are four possible outcomes of an investigation:

▶ unfounded, because the evidence leads authorities to conclude that the child has not been abused

▶ unsubstantiated, because adequate evidence is lacking to establish proof of abuse.

▶ suspected, because there is enough evidence to suspect but not to prove abuse

▶ verified, because there is adequate evidence to establish proof of abuse

When we report suspected child abuse, children who are being abused learn that someone significant in their life is telling them that this should not be happening to them. This information can be instrumental for children in the long term. The important messages that we send to children are that they are not to blame for the abuse, that it should stop, and that someone cares enough to try to stop it. Even in situations in which the abuse doesn't stop after authorities are involved, the offenders get the message that someone in authority is aware of their suspected abusive behaviour and is watching for opportunities to prove abuse and stop it.

Role in Assisting Investigations   As stated repeatedly in this unit, staff in child care centres are not responsible for investigating suspected child abuse. However, their *assistance* to the authorities in the investigation can be summarized as follows (Rimer and Prager 1998, 94–95):

1. Be attentive to physical and behavioural indicators of child abuse and your role if a child discloses. (See Purposeful Disclosures of Abuse or Witnessing Domestic Violence, page 429.)
2. Document effectively. (See Documentation: What Is Involved?, page 432)
3. Know your legal responsibilities and the internal policies and procedures of the organization regarding suspected abuse.
4. Be aware of your emotional responses to the situation and deal with them effectively.
5. Provide clear and complete information to the authorities, and document any advice or direction provided by the child protection agency, police, or other involved agency.
6. Consult with the child protection agency or police to determine whether the child would benefit from your presence during an interview.
7. Find out whom to contact at the child protection agency to follow up or ask further questions.
8. Continue to monitor the child, document, and report further, if warranted.
9. Respect the confidentiality of the information related to the case.

Refer to Rimer and Prager (1998) for an in-depth look into all aspects of the child abuse response process.

Dealing with Your Emotions   It is a very emotional experience to deal with a case of suspected child abuse. Most caregivers experience a range of conflicting emotions, such as anger, frustration, concern, sadness, denial, and disbelief. It is important, for your own well-being, to acknowledge your feelings and try to find ways to cope constructively with them. If you are fortunate, you will be working in a supportive environment where you can speak with your co-workers or the director about your feelings. Perhaps a counsellor would be helpful. You may find that your usual ways to relieve stress (e.g., physical activity, deep breathing, tai chi) are good coping mechanisms too. In any case, you need to find ways to care for yourself and your own health as well as to ensure that you are in control of your emotions. This is important so that you have an effective response to the entire situation (e.g., the anger must not come through to the child or the frustration to the parent).

PREVENTING ABUSE BY CAREGIVERS

The line between child abuse and excessive discipline may be blurred at times—when observing both parents' and caregivers' behaviour. Corporal punishment and emotional putdowns are never to be tolerated in child care programs. Suspicions that a co-worker is maltreating children physically, emotionally, or sexually, or is neglecting their needs, are stressful, to say the least.

Any allegation must be responded to immediately. Not responding quickly creates the feeling that the centre is not prepared to deal with the situation, and that there must be something to hide. Document any concerns, questions, or suspicions about caregivers abusing children. If you witness physical or sexual abuse, your actions are much more clear-cut. Because emotional abuse is more subjective than other types of abuse, you must carefully document what was said and by whom, what was going on at the time (e.g., the activity), and the child's behaviour in response to the caregiver. Commonly, a caregiver is emotionally abusive to certain children, perhaps only one or two from the group. Often, when talking with this caregiver about the group, you will find that she or he shows hostility toward those children. Comments like the child "never listens" or "does things just to annoy me" or "is basically a bad kid" are objective clues that may support your suspicion.

If a caregiver has suspicions, she or he should talk with the immediate supervisor about the observations. The individual who suspects the abuse, whether it is a caregiver, a parent, or someone else, should call the child protection agency for advice and be assured that the matter will be kept confidential until the initial investigation is complete. The children's parents or other people involved will be notified according to the child protection agency's recommendations.

An equally difficult situation arises when staff suspect the centre director of child abuse. The caregiver documents the concerns and contacts the president or chairperson of the board of directors (or owner, if applicable). The staff who suspects abuse must also call the child protection agency to report. As with any suspicions of abuse, remember that you are legally bound to report, even if another party (e.g., board member or owner) tries to dissuade you from calling against your better judgment. The board member or owner must call the child care office and speak with the consultant responsible for their centre and inform that person of the situation. This individual advises them about sending the letter to their office.

Incidents of Sexual Abuse   Staff may suspect the child is being abused but not realize that it is happening in the centre, or staff may suspect a caregiver. Sexual abuse by caregivers may be identified through the child's disclosure or by parents who approach the director with their concerns and perhaps their suspicion of a particular caregiver. Regardless of how the director is made aware of the alleged abuse, the director notifies the child protection agency and proceeds accordingly. As in the case of suspected sexual abuse of children in the home, the caregiver is not confronted. In the interim, if the alleged offender is known, the director takes the following action:

▶ removes the caregiver from any possibility of being alone with children
▶ notifies the child care office
▶ informs the centre's board of directors immediately. It may be appropriate to remove the accused staff from the centre until the investigation has been completed or to assign him or her to administrative duties.

Tertiary Child Abuse Prevention

Investigations into child abuse may confirm that a child has suffered abuse. The offender may be identified and criminal charges may be laid. In tertiary prevention, there are a number of objectives. For the child it means preventing further abuse and developing a care plan for the individual child's recovery. For the family the objective is to work toward short- and long-term change. Beyond any criminal charges for the offenders, treatment must be explored to prevent abuse from recurring.

CAREGIVER'S ROLE IN TERTIARY PREVENTION

The role of caregivers in tertiary prevention is threefold:

▶ They maintain ongoing communication with the child protection and other agencies' staff involved with the child and family, and work as part of the team.
▶ They provide a secure and developmentally stimulating environment for the child.
▶ They support change in parents who have been abusive by providing good role-modelling and resources.

Communicating with Child Protection Agencies   Quality child care programs recognize that staff can't be all things to all people. This is why directors establish connections with relevant professionals in their community and collect materials for the centre's resource library and for distribution among parents. Depending on the issue, caregivers are called on to work collaboratively with other professionals—for example, the public health nurse during an outbreak of diarrhea. In the case of child abuse, caregivers are team members with a child protection worker and possibly other specialists assigned to an individual child.

 The director has already established a working relationship with someone at the child protection agency during the reporting and investigation process. Now the director and caregivers are requested to participate in the child's recovery process along with the child protection worker. Following her assessment of the child, she may determine that play therapy is a valuable tool. However, this aspect of the child's therapy must be conducted and supervised by trained play therapists. The child's play therapist and behavioural therapist may have particular recommendations for the caregivers to incorporate into the child's everyday program. Whether these are specific guidelines for play or for all the caregivers to consistently manage a child's inappropriate behaviour (i.e., the 6-year-old's temper tantrums), the recommendations are an important aspect of the child's care.

Because children's situations and types of abuse vary so greatly, it is impossible to discuss fully the range of professionals and therapies that may be part of an individual child's recovery.

As part of the child's care plan, caregivers may be asked to observe, document, or complete developmental checklists to aid these professionals in assessing the child's progress. Caregivers are encouraged to call on the child protection worker when they are uncertain about a particular behaviour (e.g., self-mutilation), and for guidance in supporting children and families that are going through the court process.

There are times when a child who has been abused is enrolled in a centre for the first time by the child protection agency or another agency as part of her or his care strategy. Social workers recognize that trained professionals in quality child care programs enhance the child's well-being. Usually, the goals for enrolling a child who has been abused into a program include building positive relationships, overcoming developmental delays, and increasing self-esteem, and providing modelling and support for parents. The decision to accept this added responsibility should not be taken lightly. It will not be in anyone's best interest, including the child's, if the caregivers can't cope with the challenges and stresses of the situation. Caregivers will not yet have an ongoing relationship with the new child and may therefore need increased support.

Reaching Out: Working Together to Identify and Respond to Child Victims of Abuse (Rimer and Prager 1998, 120–25) lists the following strategies in working with children identified as victims of abuse. Professionals, which includes caregivers, help the child to

▶ develop a positive self-image and self-esteem
▶ trust
▶ identify and express emotions
▶ learn to communicate
▶ identify and solve problem situations
▶ get through the mourning process
▶ overcome developmental lags
▶ develop a personal safety plan

Quality child care programs strive to provide most of these things for all children in their program. You are already participating in the child's recovery regardless of the specific therapies carried out by other professionals. If you refer back to the discussion on the consequences of being abused, you will see just how they interconnect with these strategies.

Providing a Secure Environment   Beyond the essentials included in the preceding list, certain aspects of your everyday work come into play when caring for children who have been abused:

▶ Provide predictability and security in the day's routine (e.g., bringing a transition object such as a toy back and forth between home and the centre). Routines and rituals are important coping mechanisms for children, especially if their lives have been stressful or disorganized.

▶ Help children learn appropriate ways to have their needs met, even when that means learning to delay gratification (e.g., a caregiver explains to the preschooler that he will be able to use the swing as soon as the next swing is free).

▶ Provide clear, and firm but kind and reasonable limits as an important part of the child care environment. Since they suffer from injuries and pain, or fear that someone will hurt them again, children who have been abused often feel unsafe. As a result, they may take risks even though they may know, or have been told, that an action can result in an injury. Or they may intentionally hurt others, since they have learned that others have hurt them.

▶ Model and guide children to help them learn age-appropriate behaviour. Abuse may result in children having developmentally inappropriate behaviour.

▶ Be an active listener. Children can sense when they can trust a caregiver and express worries, fears, and concerns related to their family. This is not a counselling relationship but one in which a caregiver can help the child deal with stress.

A family's situation rarely changes from inadequate to wonderful overnight. The child probably feels frustrated and worried about the family, or has fears and concerns about social services or a legal proceeding that he or she is involved in.

Recognize that children's behaviour can have many different meanings. Consider a child with a short attention span. Although it may be a developmental stage, perhaps it is a learned behaviour that is used as a survival tool (e.g., he expects that his activity will be interrupted with yelling or a smack, and so is overly attuned to every movement or conversation in the room, always ready to move quickly).

SUPPORTING CHANGE IN PARENTS

Communicate respect for the parent and the parent's own ways of coping and adapting to his or her unique realities. When supported and respected as a person, a parent is more likely to use the day care setting as a resource to develop the confidence and skills needed to interact successfully with other persons and institutions in his or her life. (Ayoub et al. 1990, 244)

All parents bring strengths and weaknesses, past experiences, and expectations to parenting. Most parents who abuse their children love them and want to stop. One of the child protection agency's roles is to identify the offender, whenever possible, and assess what form of treatment would be most appropriate. A range of treatments have been developed for parents/adults who abuse children, many based on the various theories on what has caused the abuse. The success of the treatment depends in part on two variables:

▶ the offender's willingness to accept the fact that he or she has abused children
▶ the offender's potential and desire for change

As was the case for children who are abused, caregivers' communication with the child protection worker is important in providing consistency and support to parents who are abusive. Here are just three ways caregivers can play a role in the treatment of these parents:

1. Provide respite for parents. Parents may need to work on managing or eliminating stress factors or problems that directly or indirectly relate to their parenting (e.g., counselling or treatment sessions, resolution of marital, housing, education, or employment issues). Centres can provide quality care for the child during this time. The child protection worker may request that these parents enroll their children in a centre for the first time. This may not only benefit the parents but also encourage the development and recovery of the children.
2. Provide modelling of positive ways to interact with children (e.g., talking, playing) and guide their behaviour. As part of their treatment, parents may be expected to spend a certain period each week in the child care program.
3. Supervise the non-custodial parent during supervised access visits with his or her child as part of the treatment. Some centres and parent/child drop-in programs have established agreements with the child protection agency.

Ultimately, the child's rights must be at the forefront of our concerns. In recent years, tragic stories of children who have suffered further abuse or who have been killed while in the care of known offenders have been terrible reminders that not all parents have the support or possibly the will to change their abusive behaviour. Caregivers who continue to have concerns about the well-being of a child whose report has already been filed must report any new information. In the big picture, re-evaluating existing child welfare legislation, policies, and protocols is part of the solution to this important social problem.

Revisiting the Health Promotion Action Plan

Child abuse is a major social problem that requires a multidimensional approach by all members and levels of society. With reference to the Action Blueprint for Health Promotion introduced in Unit 1, the following example demonstrates how the plan incorporates child abuse prevention.

Individual Problem-Solving and Self-Reliance Increase our awareness of the factors that contribute to child abuse and try to eliminate them or at least lessen their effect. Organize staff training on child abuse and invite a child protection worker to speak at a parent night. (See Profile, page 423.) Or, offer the *Nobody's Perfect* program to all interested parents with a trained facilitator. Of course, you as caregivers can play a significant role in primary, secondary, and tertiary child abuse prevention, as this unit has shown.

Collective Self-Help After talking with single parents from the centre, a caregiver who is a single parent herself organized a support group. The group set up a baby-sitting exchange that allowed a parent to go to the laundromat without the children. Besides making these errands less stressful, this arrangement provides the parent with respite time. They also exchange clothing and toys. This group provides valuable and enjoyable opportunities for the parents to establish friendships and also reduce feelings of isolation. Time is allotted in staff meetings to discuss program issues and problem-solve as a group. Policies and procedures are regularly evaluated to maintain focus on supporting children and families.

Community Action Within some communities, professionals who work in the area or have an interest in child abuse form a child protection team (e.g., professionals working in the fields of education, medicine, public health, mental health, social work, law enforcement, law). These teams improve communication among professionals, and they coordinate more effective prevention programs, training, and child abuse response in the community. Caregivers and parents should be encouraged to become involved as participants. Caregivers contribute valuable knowledge and skills.

From the grass roots, community action can include the establishment of parent resource centres; books, toys, and clothing exchanges; and telephone helplines (e.g., Kids Help Line). Recognition of the importance of parent–child attachment is resulting in community attention on home visiting programs for the first three years (some with public health nurses based on Olds' Prenatal and Early Infancy Project; others with paraprofessionals based on the Hawaii Healthy Start Project). These are all examples of services developed by concerned people at the community level, and often by those who actually use the services. Through their network of community resources, caregivers can explore potential sources of funding, start-up grants, and so on, which are essential in the development and maintenance of these services.

Societal Change As child advocates, caregivers can be involved in organizations that work to reduce the acceptance of violence in our society, which is a root cause of abuse. Child advocacy associations, for example, are working toward laws against any type of corporal punishment of children. Changes in legislation would lead to tighter restrictions on, and greater penalties for, persons responsible for child abuse, spousal abuse, elder abuse, rape, child prostitution, violence portrayed in the media, children being portrayed as sexual objects in the media, and pornography. An important focus is to help support parents in raising their children. Social policy that reduces poverty would lower stress for families. To address the many other stressors for families, governments should have adequate child welfare budgets for prevention and quality services (Canadian Institute of Child Health 1997, 135).

Understanding why individuals abuse children is only part of prevention. As a society, we must move from focusing on individuals to addressing the root causes of abuse, which will take a multifaceted approach.

Conclusion

Whether we are referring to primary, secondary, or tertiary prevention, the prevention of child abuse has a lot to do with working collaboratively. This issue, more than any other in the child care program, illustrates that promoting children's health is not done in isolation.

The safety and well-being of every child in Canada should be a priority for each adult and level of government. Regrettably, it is not a priority. As part of a process of public education, we need to persuade the community to begin to look at children as the Europeans do—as a shared natural resource that represents society's future—rather than as most North Americans do—as solely the responsibility of their parents (Steinhauer 1998, 91).

WHAT'S YOUR OPINION?
TO REPORT OR NOT TO REPORT?

You have a good relationship with one child's mother and have become friends over the last two years. You know that she is in the midst of a nasty separation and has been taking work home at night to do after her three children go to bed. Through all of this, she seems to have been handling the situation fairly well. This morning, though, she comes to you in tears and tells you that she slapped her toddler across the face and left a bruise on his cheek. Would you document this parent's disclosure in the child's file, tell the director, and have her call the child protection agency?

ASSESS YOUR LEARNING

Define terms or describe concepts used in this unit.
- child abuse
- physical abuse
- emotional abuse
- sexual abuse
- neglect
- behavioural indicators
- parenting approaches
- corporal punishment
- child protection agencies
- documentation
- reporting
- primary child abuse prevention
- secondary child abuse prevention
- teriary child abuse prevention

Evaluate your options in each situation.

1. Over time, you and a co-worker strongly suspect that a 2-year-old is being neglected. You have documented your observations and spoken with the director more than once. She refuses to consult with the child protection agency and tells you not to anger the child's parents, because the program can't afford to lose any enrolled children.

2. A co-worker remarks that there are probably a lot of children in your centre who are abused, because most are part of single-parent families.

3. A month after a director reported a case of suspected abuse to the child protection agency, there has been no news. The child continues to come to the centre each day, and is demonstrating the same behaviour that led you to make the report in the first place. You are angry and confused by the lack of response from the agency.

4. A co-worker who spanks her children starts a conversation at lunchtime about repealing section 43 of the Criminal Code. She suggests that doing so would mean parents would be charged for "a little slap."

5. The director meets with the caregivers to inform everyone that the child protection agency has requested that a child who has been abused be enrolled in your program as part of his treatment. He requires a caring, consistent environment to help reduce developmental delays and build self-confidence. While you are flattered, and the director obviously wants to say yes, you are concerned because you and the other care-givers are already feeling stretched meeting the needs of the present children.

► RESOURCE MATERIALS

Organizations

Canadian Council on Social Development (CCSD), 441 McLaren Street, 4th floor, Ottawa ON K2P 3H3. Tel. (613) 236-8977, fax (613) 236-2750.

Canadian Institute of Child Health (CICH), 885 Meadowlands Dr. E., Suite 512, Ottawa ON K2C 3N2. Tel. (613) 224-4144, fax (613) 224-4145.

Canadian Society for the Prevention of Cruelty to Children, 356 First Street, Box 700, Midland ON L4R 4P4. Tel. (705) 526-5647, fax (705) 526-0214.

Child Welfare League of Canada, 180 Argyle Avenue, Suite 312, Ottawa, ON K2P 1B7. Tel. (613) 235-4412, fax (613) 788-5075.

Kids Help Phone, 439 University Avenue, Suite 300, Toronto ON M5G 1Y8. Tel. (416) 921-7827, fax (416) 921-9656, national toll-free for children (800) 668-6868.

The National Clearinghouse on Family Violence, Family Violence Prevention Division, Social Service Programs Branch, Health Canada, Ottawa, ON K1A 1B5. Tel. (613) 957-2938, fax (613) 957-4247, national toll-free (800) 267-1291.

National Victims Resource Centre, Department of Justice Canada, Access to Justice and Law Information Programs, 239 Wellington Street, Ottawa, ON K1A 0H8. Tel. (613) 957-9608, fax (613) 941-2269, national toll-free (800) 267-0454.

Toronto Child Abuse Centre. 890 Yonge Street, Toronto, ON M4W 3P4. Tel. (416) 515-1100, Web site: www.tcac.on.ca.

Vanier Institute of the Family, 94 Centrepointe Drive, Nepean, ON K2G 6B1. Tel. (613) 228-8007, fax (613) 228-8500.

Printed Matter

The Courage to Heal: A Guide for Women Survivors of Child Sexual Abuse (1988), by E. Bass and L. Davis (Harper & Row).

"Discouraging the Punishment of Children" (1994), by T. Hay, *Interaction* (Fall) 8(3):3–5.

Family Violence Audio-Visual Source Guide, by the National Film Board of Canada (NFB Sales and Customer Services, D-10, P.O. Box 6100, Station A, Montreal, PQ H3C 3H5). Fax (514) 283-7564, national toll-free (800) 267-7710 (list of materials available throughout North America).

My Father's House: A Memoir of Incest and Healing (1987), by S. Fraser (Doubleday).

Nobody's Perfect, by the Family & Child Health Unit (Health Canada, 467 Jeanne Mance Building, Ottawa ON K1A 1B4). Tel. (613) 957-7804, fax (613) 990-7097.

Nursery Crimes: Sexual Abuse in Day Care (1988), by D. Finkelhor et al. (Sage Publications).

Reaching Out: Working Together to Identify and Respond to Child Victims of Abuse (1998) by P. Rimer and B. Prager (ITP Nelson).

Shaking, Hitting and Spanking: What to Do Instead (1990) (distributor: Family Nurturing Center, 3160 Pinebrook Road, Park City, UT 84060). (video and handbook)

"Spanking: Do We Need Alternatives?" (1994), by N. Burns, *Interaction* (Fall) 8(3):6–7.

Spanking: Should I or Shouldn't I? (1995), by J. Durant and L. Rose-Krasnor. To obtain copy of brochure: fax Dr. Joan E. Durant (204) 275-5299.

S.T.E.P.: Systematic Training for Effective Parenting Kit. Parent Books, 201 Harbord Street, Toronto, ON M5S 1H6. Tel. (416) 537-8334, fax (416) 537-9499.

Victims No Longer: Men Recovering from Incest and Other Sexual Child Abuse (1988), by M. Lew (Nevraumont Publishing).

Vis-à-Vis. A national newsletter on family violence published by Canada Council on Social Development; Newsletter Subscriptions, 441 MacLaren, 4th floor, Ottawa, ON K2P 2H3. Tel. (613) 236-8977, fax (613) 236-2750 (available at no charge).

▶ BIBLIOGRAPHY

Aber, J.L., et al. (1989) "The Effects of Maltreatment on Development during Early Childhood: Recent Studies and Their Theoretical, Clinical, and Policy Implications," in *Child Maltreatment: Theory and Research on the Causes and Consequences of Child Abuse and Neglect*, D. Cicchetti and V. Carlson (eds.). Cambridge: Cambridge University Press.

Alessandri, S.M. (1991) "Play and Social Behavior in Maltreated Preschoolers." *Developmental Psychopathology* 3:191–205.

Allen, R.E., and J.M. Oliver (1982) "The Effects of Child Maltreatment on Language Development." *Child Abuse & Neglect* 6:299–305.

Amnerman, R.T. (1989) "Child Abuse & Neglect," in *Innovations in Child Behavior Therapy*, M. Herson (ed.). New York: Springer.

Ayoub, C., et al. (1990) "Working with Maltreated Children and Families in Day Care Settings," in *Psychosocial Issues in Day Care*, S.S. Chehrazi (ed.). Washington, DC: American Psychiatric Press.

Badgley, R. (1994) *Report of the Committee on Sexual Offenses against Children and Youths*, Vol. 1. Ottawa: Minister of Supply and Services.

Barahal, R.M., et al. (1981) "The Social Cognitive Development of Abused Children." *Journal of Consulting & Clinical Psychology* 49(4):508–16.

Bennett, H., and T. Pitman (1995) *Yes You Can! Positive Discipline Ideas for You and Your Child*. Toronto: Today's Parent Group and the Psychology Foundation of Canada.

Camaras, L.A., et al. (1983) "Recognition of Emotional Expression by Abused Children." *Journal of Clinical Child Psychology* 12(3):325–28.

Canadian Institute of Child Health, (1997) *Our Promise to Children*, Ottawa: Health Canada.

Caring Communities Project (1994) *Child Sexual Abuse Prevention: A Resource Kit*. Ottawa: Canadian Institute of Child Health.

Chehrazi, S.S. (ed.) (1990) *Psychosocial Issues in Day Care*. Washington, DC: American Psychiatric Press.

Cicchetti, D. (1989) "How Research on Child Maltreatment Has Informed the Study of Child Development: Perspectives from Developmental Psychopathology," in *Child Maltreatment: Theory and Research on the Causes and Consequences of Child Abuse and Neglect*, D. Cicchetti and V. Carlson (eds.). Cambridge: Cambridge University Press.

Cicchetti, D., et al. (1988) "Developmental Psychopathology and Incompetence in Childhood: Suggestions for Intervention," in *Advances in Clinical Child Psychology*, B. Lahey and A. Kazdin (eds.). New York: Plenum.

Clement, M. (1994) "Mutilation in Canada?" *Toronto Sun*, 10 October:22.

Dinh, D.-K., et al. (1990) "The Vietnamese," in *Cross-Cultural Caring: A Handbook for Health Professionals in Western Canada*, N. Waxler-Morrison et al. (eds.). Vancouver: University of British Columbia Press.

Erickson, M.F., et al. (1989) "The Effects of Maltreatment on the Development of Young Children," in *Child Maltreatment: Theory and Research on the Causes and Consequences of Child Abuse and Neglect*, D. Cicchetti and V. Carlson (eds.). Cambridge: Cambridge University Press.

Finkelhor, D., and N. Strapko (1992) "Sexual Abuse Prevention Education: A Review of Evaluation Studies," in *Prevention of Child Maltreatment: Developmental Ecological Perspectives*, D.J. Willis et al. (eds.). New York: John Wiley.

Finkelhor, D., et al. (1988) *Nursery Crimes: Sexual Abuse in Day Care*. Beverly Hills, CA: Sage Publications.

Fox, L., et al. (1988) "Patterns of Language Comprehension Deficit in Abused and Neglected Children." *Journal of Speech & Hearing Disorders* 53:239–44.

Garbarino, J., et al. (1992) *Children in Danger: Coping with the Consequences of Community Violence*. San Francisco: Jossey-Bass Publishers.

Glasser, M. (1990) "Toward the Prevention of Child Abuse in Day Care," in *Psychosocial Issues in Day Care*, S.S. Chehrazi (ed.). Washington, DC: American Psychiatric Press.

Goldson, E. (1991) "The Affective and Cognitive Sequelae of Child Maltreatment." *Pediatric Clinics of North America* 38(6):1481–96.

Gonzalez-Mena, J. (1993) *Multicultural Issues in Child Care*. Toronto: Mayfield Publishing.

Gullen, J. (1992) *Report on the First International Study Conference on Genital Mutilation of Girls in Europe*. Ottawa: Family Service Centre (unpublished).

Guy, K. (ed.) (1997) *Our Promise to Children*. Ottawa: Health Canada.

Herringer, B.M., and S. Rivkin (1989) *Child Sexual Abuse Victim Support Worker Handbook*. Vancouver: Justice Institute of B.C.

Institute for the Prevention of Child Abuse (1995) *Getting It Right: Responding to the Sexual Abuse of Young Children*. Toronto: IPCA Conference Services.

———— *TRUST II: Instructor's Manual*. Toronto: Institute for the Prevention of Child Abuse.

———— (1991a) "Factors That Inhibit Reporting of Child Abuse," in *Child Protection: Current Issues & Practices, Vol. 2: For Educators*. Toronto: Institute for the Prevention of Child Abuse (audio tape).

———— (1991b) "What Happens When a Report Is Made to the Children's Aid Society," in *Child Protection: Current Issues & Practices, Vol. 2: For Educators*. Toronto: Institute for the Prevention of Child Abuse (audio tape).

Jaffe, P., et al. (1988) "Specific Assessment and Intervention Strategies for Children Exposed to Wife Battering: Preliminary Empirical Investigations." *Canadian Journal of Community Mental Health* 7(2):156–63.

———— (1986) "Similarities in Behavioral and Social Maladjustment among Child Victims and Witnesses to Family Violence." *American Journal of Orthopsychiatry* 56:142–46.

Kolko, D.J. (1992) "Characteristics of Child Victims of Physical Violence, Research Findings and Clinical Interpretations." *Journal of Interpersonal Violence* (June) 7(2):244–76.

Lero, D., et al. (1988) *Child Abuse: An Instructor's Manual and Resource Guide*. Toronto: Ontario Centre for the Prevention of Child Abuse and Ontario Ministry of Community and Social Services.

Manitoba Child Care Association (1993) *Child Abuse: How to Handle Allegations Against the Child Care Provider/Prevention Strategies*. Winnipeg: Manitoba Child Care Association.

Metropolitan Toronto Special Committee on Child Abuse (1993a) *Educator In-Service Training Booklet*. Toronto: Metropolitan Toronto Special Committee on Child Abuse.

———— (1993b) *Why Children Do Not Tell & How to Respond if a Child Discloses.* Toronto: Metropolitan Toronto Special Committee on Child Abuse.

Miller, A. (1987) *For Your Own Good: Hidden Cruelty in Child-Rearing and the Roots of Violence.* Toronto: Collins.

Monahon, C. (1993) *Children and Trauma: A Parent's Guide to Helping Children Heal.* Toronto: Maxwell Macmillan Canada.

Monsebraaten, L. (1994) "Woman Given Refugee Status to Save Daughter from Sexual Mutilation." *Toronto Star,* 14 July:A1.

Ontario Women's Directorate (1989) *Wife Assault: The Impact on Children.* Toronto: Ontario Women's Directorate.

Perry, B. (1995) "Incubated in Terror: Neurodevelopmental Factors in the Cycle of Violence," in *Children, Youth and Violence: Searching for Solutions,* J. Osofsky (ed.). New York: Guilford Press.

Priest, L. (1994) "Our MDs 'Involved' in Genital Mutilation." *Toronto Star,* 3 Oct.:A9.

Rimer, P., and B. Prager (1998) *Reaching Out: Working Together to Identify and Respond to Child Victims of Abuse.* Toronto: ITP Nelson.

Skelly, C. (1993) *Prevention Initiative: Violence against Women Partners—Module 3: Children Who Witness Violence against Their Mothers.* Toronto: Ontario Ministry of Education and Training.

Sroufe, L.A. (1988) "The Role of Infant Caregiver Attachment in Development," in *Clinical Implications of Attachment,* J. Belsky and T. Nezworski (eds.). Hillsdale: Erlbaum.

Steinhauer, P. (1998) *Developing Resiliency in Children from Disadvantaged Populations: Canada's Health Actions, Building on the Legacy,* Vol. 1 (Children and Youth). Ste-Foy, PQ.

Thompson, A. (1994) "Genital Mutilation Illegal, Copps Says." *Toronto Star,* 4 Oct.:A10.

Toronto Child Abuse Centre (1997–98) *Information Packages and Sheets.* Toronto: Toronto Child Abuse Centre.

Tower, C.C. (1993) *Understanding Child Abuse and Neglect.* Toronto: Allyn and Bacon.

Trocmé, N., and C. Caunce (1995) "The Educational Needs of Abused and Neglected Children: A Review of the Literature." *Early Child Development and Care* (in press).

Trocmé, N., et al. (1994) *Ontario Incidence Study of Reported Child Abuse and Neglect: Final Report.* Toronto: Institute for the Prevention of Child Abuse.

Vanier Institute of the Family (1994) *Profiling Canada's Families*. Ottawa: Vanier Institute of the Family.

Wolfe, D., et al. (1985) "Children of Battered Women: The Relation of Child Behavior to Family Violence and Maternal Stress." *Journal of Consulting and Clinical Psychology* 53:657–65.

Unit 7

Supporting Children's Development

Unit 7: Supporting Children's Development

Quality child care programs strive to support children's growth and development. Caregivers think about each child in a holistic sense to achieve a balance in their physical, emotional, and social health. In other words, students and ultimately, graduates integrate their knowledge of health, illness, safety, and nutrition with what they learn about child development, curriculum, families, diversity, and inclusion to create child care programs that meet the needs of both the individual children and the group. Although many elements influence development, there is general agreement that human development follows predictable sequences in all areas—cognitive, emotional, social, physical—but that individuals have unique "timing." Children learn through interacting with people, objects, and the environment.

Children's growth and development is an ECE course in itself, and you will have taken it before you graduate. However, for the purpose of this textbook, Chart 7.1 provides you with a quick reference when discussing children's emotional well-being, the rhythm of the program, and health curriculum. The chart includes developmental highlights and stages of growth. This textbook examines certain issues relating to children's well-being that readers can integrate with their knowledge of child development, psychology, and sociology. The topics covered here will add to your understanding and ability to support children's well-being. Caregivers are in an ideal position to support children in their learning of lifelong healthy habits and positive attitudes toward their overall well-being. The latter portion of this unit is devoted to health curriculum for children in child care programs.

Children's Emotional Well-Being

 OBJECTIVE   To outline caregivers' roles in supporting each child's emotional well-being in terms of the child's self-regulation and relationship development, stress levels, and sexuality.

The importance of our emotional and social well-being and how these relate to physical well-being cannot be overstated. How you feel about yourself and the effectiveness of your relationships with others profoundly affect your health. Your self-concept is shaped by how others treat you—especially by significant others and your community. Racism within a community, for example, can have only negative effects on the self-esteem of those targeted. Labonté (1993, 5) illustrates how powerful emotional and social well-being are to our overall health.

People's experience of health usually relates to such phenomena as:

1. feeling vital, full of energy
2. having good social relationships
3. experiencing a sense of control over one's life and one's living conditions
4. being able to do things one enjoys
5. having a sense of purpose in life

CHART 7.1   QUICK REFERENCE: CHILD DEVELOPMENT

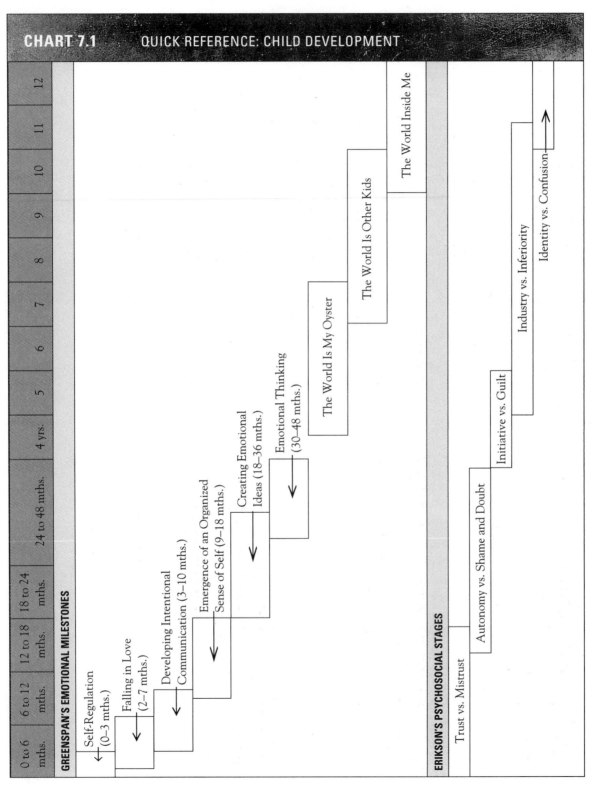

0 to 6 mths.	6 to 12 mths.	12 to 18 mths.	18 to 24 mths.	24 to 48 mths.	4 yrs.	5	6	7	8	9	10	11	12

GREENSPAN'S EMOTIONAL MILESTONES

Self-Regulation (0–3 mths.)

Falling in Love (2–7 mths.)

Developing Intentional Communication (3–10 mths.)

Emergence of an Organized Sense of Self (9–18 mths.)

Creating Emotional Ideas (18–36 mths.)

Emotional Thinking (30–48 mths.)

The World Is My Oyster

The World Is Other Kids

The World Inside Me

ERIKSON'S PSYCHOSOCIAL STAGES

Trust vs. Mistrust

Autonomy vs. Shame and Doubt

Initiative vs. Guilt

Industry vs. Inferiority

Identity vs. Confusion

(chart continues on next page)

CHART 7.1 — QUICK REFERENCE: CHILD DEVELOPMENT (continued)

	0 to 6 mths.	6 to 12 mths.	12 to 18 mths.	18 to 24 mths.	24 to 48 mths.	4 yrs.	5	6	7	8	9	10	11	12

PIAGET'S COGNITIVE STAGES

Sensorimotor

Preoperational

Concrete Operational

Formal Operational →

STAGES OF MORAL DEVELOPMENT: KOHLBERG (JUSTICE PERSPECTIVE) AND GILLIGAN (CARE PERSPECTIVE)

Preconventional Morality:
Kohlberg—Stage 1: Avoid Punishments and Stage 2: Seek Rewards
Gilligan—Concern for Self and Survival

Conventional Morality:
(K.) Stage 3: Gain Approval, and
Stage 4: Conformity to Society's Rules
(G.) Concern for Being Responsible and Caring for Others

PHYSICAL GROWTH AND DEVELOPMENT

By 6 Months: rolls over, sits with support, begins finger-feeding

By 12 Months: pulls to stand, cruises, crawls, walks, crawls on stairs, pincer grasp, drinks from cup

By 18 Months: teeth coming in, tries to run, falls often, walks up stairs, pulls off clothes, uses spoon and cup

(chart continues on next page)

CHART 7.1   QUICK REFERENCE: CHILD DEVELOPMENT (continued)

0 to 6 mths.	6 to 12 mths.	12 to 18 mths.	18 to 24 mths.	24 to 48 mths.	4 yrs.	5	6	7	8	9	10	11	12

PHYSICAL GROWTH AND DEVELOPMENT (continued)

By 24 Months: walks and runs well, goes up and down stairs, scribbles, pours, fills, dumps, enjoys self-feeding, likes riding toys

By 3 Years: balances on 1 foot, hops, kicks large ball, jumps in place, uses tripod grasp, builds structures, may ride a tricycle, self-feeds well

4 to 6 Years: walks straight line, climbs well, throws overhand, uses scissors, threads small beads, uses fork, alternates feet on stairs, balances on either foot, walks backward, heel to toe, starts to lose primary teeth, ties shoes laces

6 to 9 Years: learning sports and games, improving coordination, gets more tired from sitting than playing, rides bicycle, climbs trees

9 to 12 Years: good fine motor coordination, can use hands independently with more precision (e.g., crafts, woodworking)

Note: This chart's design may give readers the impression that the stages have fixed time periods. In fact individuals fluctuate through the stages of their lives. In each stage is a specific task that we are to accomplish. Our success or failure at achieving one stage affects the outcome in the next stage. Each child moves through the sequences at a unique pace, influenced by personality, relationships, learning styles, experiences, and so on.

(chart continues on next page)

CHART 7.1 QUICK REFERENCE: CHILD DEVELOPMENT (continued)

Greenspan's Emotional Milestones S. Greenspan's nine emotional milestones focus on children's development of emotions: each child's unique sense of self and of the world. Adults can recognize and support each child's age-appropriate emotional experiences as well as her or his uniqueness in the quest for emotional engagement, mastery, and control. During the first three months of life, the challenges for babies are to organize and adjust to all the stimulation surrounding them and to then become interested in reaching out for it. During the second phase, the more relaxed and interested baby falls in love with the primary caregiver(s). Babies' third phase is characterized by the development of intentional communication. Emergence of an organized sense of self, linking feelings and actions, happens between 9 and 18 months of age; children are connecting feelings and social behaviour into complex patterns. In beginning to achieve the fifth milestone, creating emotional ideas, toddlers are developing the ability to create images in their own mind, picturing parents when they are not there and remembering interactions. This results in dreams that seem real and vivid. Emotional thinking, the sixth phase, enables children to organize and manipulate ideas to reason about feelings instead of only acting them out in pretend play. Around 4 1/2 years of age, children build on the ability to relate, communicate, imagine, and think. During the seventh phase children experience a wider range of emotions and, with support, explore more complicated relationships. These abilities prepare them to move relationships out into the wider world. In the eighth phase, children's horizons expand to their peers. They experience the pain and benefits of moving into a group and defining themselves as members. Around 10 to 12 years old, approaching milestone nine, children develop a clearer inner picture of themselves, less influenced by the issue of the moment. As their cognitive abilities mature, they are better able to take their moral and emotional strength from within, rather than from friends and family (Lally 1990).

Erikson's Psychosocial Stages E. Erikson's theory of psychosocial development consists of a continuum of eight stages that unfold through the life cycle. Our start in infancy provides us with a foundation to progress through the other stages. Infants begin to develop trust first with their parents and then with the world around them. A sense of trust gives them the confidence to gradually achieve autonomy (a sense of being separate from their parents and having inner control over their lives), to control elimination (i.e., bladder and bowel control) and motor functions, and to show a strong interest in exploring their environment. During the preschool years, children burst with initiative (e.g., "I want to do it myself," or "Look what I can do"), imagination, and fantasy play. School-agers are faced with the task of industry, the need to accomplish skills, and that success is recognized by self and others. Around the time of puberty, children are faced with the "Who am I?" identity crisis. With success at each stage, we build on how we feel about ourselves, beginning with a sense of hope, then willpower, purpose, competence, and, finally, fidelity.

Piaget's Cognitive Stages J. Piaget's cognitive (or intellectual) theory is composed of four stages. In each stage we think quite differently. All learning is based on the premise that individuals are able to adapt to their world through assimilation and accommodation. Piaget believed that children must be active participants in their cognitive development. Assimilation occurs when we add new information to what we already know. Accommodation occurs when we can make adjustments in how we think about something (e.g., a child saw her mother holding a hammer with one hand, but when she tried to use it, she found it too heavy, so she used two hands). In the first stage, sensorimotor, infants construct an understanding of the world by coordinating sensory stimuli with motor actions (i.e., infants and toddlers learn by exploring space by moving their body and using their senses). For example, an infant learns about a chair by touching it, climbing on it, etc. During the preoperational stage, children see their world in "the here and now,"

(chart continues on next page)

CHART 7.1   QUICK REFERENCE: CHILD DEVELOPMENT (continued)

Physical Growth and Development Newborns' heartbeat, at 120 times per minute, and breathing, at 33 times per minute, are twice as fast as adults'. The first 12 months is a time of tremendous physical growth and development; infants triple their birth weight and half again their birth length. Motor skill development is astonishing. Changes in growth follow the head down (cephalocaudal) and from the trunk out to the tips of the fingers and toes (proximodistal). This is why infants' gross motor skills develop before their fine motor ones (e.g., they can roll over and crawl before they are able to finger-feed). Between 12 and 24 months, the growth rate decelerates, but gross and fine motor skills continue to increase rapidly. During the preschool years the growth rate continues to slow, with most children growing about 6.25 cm (2 1/2 ins.) and gaining about 2.3 to 3.2 kg (5 to 7 lbs.) per year. The trunk of the body lengthens, so that by the time they are 6 years old, the head isn't as predominant and they approach more adult-like proportions. Heart rate slows to 90 to 110 beats per minute. This consistent physical growth continues into the school-age years with much of the increase in weight due to the increase in size of the skeleton and body organs. Then around puberty, usually at 10 years of age for girls and a year or two later for boys, there is another growth spurt. This is why girls are often taller than the boys for a time. Girls' hips and thighs become fuller and their body stores at least 17 percent body fat needed for menstruation to begin and continue (Santrock 1997, 460). Physical activity is essential in order for all children to refine developing skills and, of course, build self-esteem.

and view their surroundings in terms of themselves (the egocentric "me, me, me"). They are not yet able to perform mental operations that are reversible (or able to imagine doing the steps backward). In the concrete operational stage, children reason logically about things and ideas, and can consider another's point of view. As well, they have reversibility and conservation. Our ability to think in the abstract, manipulate ideas, and make hypotheses develops in the formal operational stage.

Stages of Moral Development: Kohlberg and Gilligan Based on Piaget's cognitive theory, Kohlberg's stage theory explains how our ability to reason morally unfolds and links moral development with cognitive development—our ability to reason. In the first level, preconventional morality, children decide what's right and wrong based on whether they have been rewarded or punished. At the conventional morality level, children's moral decisions are based on the belief in law and order established by parents and society. At the highest level of moral reasoning, postconventional morality (stages 5 and 6), adults' moral decisions are based on a commitment to abstract principles (e.g., human rights), which may at times differ from existing laws. Kohlberg believed that regardless of where one lives in the world, the pace of the development of moral reasoning is the same among all cultures. Others, such as Garbarino and Bronfenbrenner, argue that in communities in which children are exposed to a variety of ethno-cultures, religions, political views (e.g., democracy), etc., the pace of the child's moral development is faster, and that the opposite is also true (Santrock 1997, 443). Another criticism of Kohlberg's theory was that his research was conducted on males. Gilligan felt that Kohlberg's theory underplayed the importance of care (or the connectedness with others, particularly in girls). This omission has been widely recognized by others, and has resulted in identifying both Kohlberg's and Gilligan's theories of moral development. Gilligan uses the same three levels, but acknowledges the caring aspect of moral reasoning.

Self-Regulation

Self-regulation and our ability to relate to others are two complex and *recurring* emotional and social tasks that are themes in our lives from birth. Self-regulation refers to the ability to focus attention, control emotional energy, and initiate and recover from anger, disappointment, joy, or other emotions, as well as manage facial and body movement. How well a child (or adult) can self-regulate has a dramatic effect on his or her day-to-day quality of life. To adapt, the child must be capable of flexible regulation because life requires action and reflection, intensity and calm, concentration and split attention.

Responsive relationships are the cornerstone of emotional development and self-regulation. A newborn needs the caregiver to regulate her state. As the child grows regulation becomes dyadic—child and caregiver work together. During the preschool years the child begins to *self-regulate*. The child learns to tolerate strong emotions and recover from arousal in secure, responsive relationships that support regulation. Self-regulation develops when children are exposed to manageable levels of stimulation and are protected from over-arousal. Differences exist among children in their ability to regulate and tolerate stress. Children use a variety of sensory and motor skills to regulate. Temperament also accounts for individual differences in a child's emotional arousal and reactivity. But it is through the relationship that the child learns to recover from arousal and stress. When caregivers remain emotionally available, and are sensitive to individual differences and responsive, children learn to regulate. When children anticipate the empathy and understanding of their caregiver, they are more likely to cope with distress.

Children need to experience a full range of emotions and feel that it is safe to express them. When they do, they learn to regulate emotions and practise the culturally determined display rules for expressing emotions. For example, they learn when to make eye contact and how to show gratitude. They must know how to regulate emotions and behaviour in order to choose actions that will achieve their goals when exploring and relating to others. If a child wants to play with peers, he needs to regulate his impulses to take all the toys. Self-regulation is therefore central to the child's social, cognitive, and emotional development. Focusing on self-regulation means understanding individual capacities for stimulation and patterns of recovery from arousal. Caregivers need to use this information to create a safe environment and relationship for exploration and the development of self-regulation. As the child develops new language and cognitive and social skills, they are used for regulation. These new skills are practised and sorted out in the context of secure caregiver–child relationships.

Relating to Others

Relating to others refers to children's ability to build relationships, which begins at birth with their parents and develops with other significant people. In addition to relationships with adults, peer relationships are very important. The three major tasks of early

Caregivers support self-regulation when they

- initiate and maintain communication with parents and staff that increases sensitivity to the individual child's security and exploration
- create an environment that is safe for exploration and the expression of impulses
- observe and record individual sensory and motor skills that are used to regulate
- are responsive to the child's signals and intentions
- remain emotionally available
- pair novel stimulation with familiar experience
- maintain sensitivity to individual differences in coping and relating
- expose the child to stimulation that matches her ability to cope and when she is over-stimulated, the child's recovery within the relationship
- avoid the following measures that violate the relationship: emotional withdrawal, punishment, imposition of caregiver control, intense expression of the caregiver's negative emotion
- create optimal individual stimulation, taking into consideration the type of stimulation, its form, intensity, and variations in presentation
- increase stimulation over time in small increments that are responsive to the individual's ability to cope
- respond to the child's signals and intentions (signals can be bids for regulation, requests for assistance to deal with feelings; signals are not only an expression of an internal state but an outward show of feelings)
- observe the child's behaviour and figure out the meaning that her experience has for her
- create spaces in the playroom with reduced stimulation
- create stimulus shelters and comfort zones in the playroom
- create spaces for one-to-one interaction in the playroom

Source: Goulet and Schroeder 1998, 37–45.

childhood are peer group entry, conflict resolution, and maintaining play (Guralnick and Littmann 1992). Children need to regulate their emotional energy in order to accomplish all three tasks. Individual differences exist in the speed, intensity, and duration of emotional responses. Caregivers must know each child's emotional reactions to promote regulation and recovery before the child can achieve the three major tasks.

To support the achievement, the caregiver must understand all developmental areas. She must observe the child to determine how he regulates emotional energy, his preferences for other children, the familiar play situations he chooses, the types of toys, and the pretend themes in which he engages. When these things are known,

caregivers can design environments that maximize the child's interactions with other children.

Making friends during the early years forms the basis for children's future relationships (Guralnick and Littmann 1992). Caregivers can enhance children's opportunities to make friends through social play by

▶ providing equipment and activities that help children learn social rules and roles, and practise taking turns and ownership as they are developmentally ready

▶ observing children's individual strengths and interests, and using these to involve the child with others

▶ actively guiding children to initiate play with one another when a caregiver observes an opportunity to foster a friendship. Insisting, however, that children play together, or that "we are all friends," is artificial and does not help children make friends. The reality is that although we all need to show respect for one another, children choose friends.

▶ choosing and arranging furniture to promote social interaction

▶ providing equipment that provides the child with the opportunity to release emotional energy

▶ recognizing those school-agers who are having difficulty making friends and using observation to determine how caregivers can foster these skills. This may also mean making changes in the program (Musson 1994).

Helping Children Cope with Stress

We are never too young to react to stress, but reasons for stress change with age. In addition, stress factors are unique to individuals: adults should be sensitive to each child's stress factors, realizing that they have meaning for the child. Urging a child to stop worrying, or suggesting that he or she shouldn't be upset, trivializes a child's concerns, causing more stress. Almost anything can cause stress. Regardless of the cause, however, stress management is crucial for a child. In some ways, children can be very resilient, but emotional vulnerability that begins in childhood can affect someone for a lifetime.

Sterling Honig (1986, 145) points out that although infants, toddlers, and younger preschoolers have personality strengths, they don't yet have the cognitive skills to develop optimal coping on their own. They need adults to create environments that are low in stress and to help them find ways to cope with stress. Young children hear about things that relate to the outside of their bodies (e.g., changing a diaper, putting a coat on because it's cold outside, tying shoes); but beginning in the preschool years, their awareness of how they are affected by stress involves the inside as much as the outside of their body (e.g., Priya's heart beats faster, her mouth becomes dry, and she has butterflies in her tummy). When children become aware of their internal body cues, they can better recognize when they are experiencing stress. This leads to adults helping children to learn to regulate their internal responses and acquire coping strategies, such as relaxation techniques (e.g., taking slow, deep breaths) or moving away from the situation that is causing the stress. Coping skills are usually more developed in older children, because they have developed the sequential and logical thinking skills to be able to think about their problems and anticipate consequences.

Most children can cope with the usual stress factors arising from growth and development and everyday living, especially with the support of adults. "Separation protest is a healthy and normal reaction in young children, because these children lack a sense of control or ability to have an effect on their environment; despite the child's protest, the parent can leave anyway" (Kalmanson 1990, 163). During stress the brain produces cortisol, a brain hormone that prepares the body for action. Sustained levels of cortisol are associated with brain cell destruction. An individual's control or perceived control reduces elevations in cortisol. Children who are more certain about their ability to control their distress and who generate a number of strategies to do so, exhibit less stress and have lower levels of cortisol. Caregivers must support the development of children's personal control over the environment and over their own internal body state to reduce stress and regulate the production of cortisol (Stansbury and Gunnar 1994).

CHILDREN'S STRESS FACTORS

It is difficult to categorize stress factors into those that are less serious and usually of short duration and those that are not. We will, however, attempt to do just that. The following stress factors are often less serious or short-term:

▶ those related to developmental milestones with no other mediating forces (e.g., toilet learning, separation anxiety, new baby in the house, making friends, learning to read, most fears)
▶ those related to everyday frustrations, such as too many choices, no choices, or no or little control over decisions that affect their life
▶ common but often anxiety-inducing experiences, such as visits to the doctor (e.g., for immunization shots or blood tests), dentists, hospital emergency rooms; short stays in the hospital for minor ailments; short separations from family; moving; transition to centre; leaving child care to attend school; transitions within a centre or school (e.g., from infant to toddler room); rejection from a peer

The following stress factors are often more traumatic or long-term:

▶ parents' separation or divorce; death of a family member
▶ everyday life in poverty; homelessness
▶ living with violence in the family

- ▶ bias (e.g., racism or a home culture that is incongruent with that of the centre or school)
- ▶ extreme fears or phobias
- ▶ repeated hospitalizations or a long stay in a hospital, particularly between the ages of 6 months and 4 years, especially when separated from parents
- ▶ refugee experiences (e.g., war, the witnessing of torture or death, the separation or loss of family members, different climate or weather, different language)
- ▶ the witnessing of a catastrophe or disaster (e.g., hurricane, tornado, fire, kidnapping)

Although the preceding lists are incomplete, they convey the idea that children can have a range of stress factors, some of which they resolve or cope with competently with time or experience. Others are overwhelming, or begin as something relatively minor and then escalate, resulting in a major negative effect on how the child functions every day.

IDENTIFYING CHILDREN WHO ARE EXPERIENCING STRESS

Many people assume that signs of stress are easy to pinpoint in children. However, with the exception of some very obvious signs, identification relies on caregivers' observation skills and sensitivity to individual children. Identifying that the child is experiencing stress is only the beginning. Effective communication with parents is critical in determining the stress factors and deciding how you can work together to support the child. Possible signs are endless, but these are some common ones:

- ▶ seems sad, has a vacant expression, whines a lot, has frequent temper tantrums
- ▶ clings to caregivers, although he or she has been in child care for an extended period, or hasn't connected with at least one caregiver
- ▶ is constantly worried
- ▶ complains about physical symptoms (e.g., headaches or tummy aches, especially for school-agers)
- ▶ seems to be tired and run-down, and gets sick a lot (e.g., has frequent colds)
- ▶ has nightmares
- ▶ bodily functions are not working properly—the child may have trouble with feeding, be constipated, have diarrhea, or is able to sleep or wants to sleep all the time
- ▶ self-stimulates constantly (e.g., rocking back and forth, thumb-sucking, self-pleasuring)
- ▶ child's overall behaviour suddenly changes drastically (e.g., becomes very aggressive or withdrawn)
- ▶ child's development regresses
- ▶ child is hyper-vigilant; lives in a state of anxious readiness

Suggestions for Reducing Children's Stress

Supporting children in their coping with their stress—helping them integrate healthy ways to cope with what is usually normal stress—is one of the caregivers' roles in promoting the child's emotional well-being. Developing coping skills contributes to children's self-control and self-esteem. Although we tend to think of stress as primarily affecting emotional health, caregivers should help children become aware of the mind/body/emotions interconnection whenever possible.

 Asking a school-ager who has started biting her nails lately what she is thinking and feeling at that moment can help her with this connection.

In order to reduce overall stress for the children in their centre, caregivers can implement a number of strategies to create a "stress-aware" environment. Here are some of those strategies:

▶ Provide a secure, calm environment where schedules, routines, and transitions contribute to stability, not to heightened stress. Do what you can behind the scenes to reduce stress.

▶ Maintain an emotional climate of trust. Children will feel that they can express a range of emotions and be supported.

▶ Be calm and provide security for children.

▶ Recognize and respond to children's feelings, taking your cues from the child.

▶ Create a curriculum that supports the development of children's learning about self—feelings, rights, responsibilities.

▶ Help children develop coping skills by responding to needs and cues (e.g., comfort a distressed infant as promptly as possible, respect a toddler's need to try it himself, offer a preschooler a choice whenever possible, provide a school-ager with opportunities for decision-making without adult interference).

▶ Create developmentally appropriate stimulus shelters where a child can choose to be away from the group (e.g., pillows in a cozy corner for infants and toddlers, lofts or tents for preschoolers and school-agers).

▶ Evaluate the level of stimulation.

Caregivers play a role in helping children broaden their repertoire of coping strategies, so that children feel that they can have an effect on reducing their stress level. With infants and toddlers, this usually means comforting them, but it also means helping them find ways to comfort themselves, identifying for them what they are experiencing, and guiding them to activities that help them work out some of their anger or frustration (e.g., large motor activities, water and sand play). With preschool and school-age children, caregivers can help them to identify the "inside and outside" body cues for their stressful feelings, and suggest ways they can alleviate those feelings now and in the future. As children learn about what makes them feel stressed and how they react, they learn a lot about themselves that will be beneficial in the long term.

Here are some examples of coping strategies that caregivers can help children to develop:

▶ deep, slow breathing to help slow down the body
▶ stretching exercises (e.g., tensing and relaxing muscles), which can be incorporated into a creative movement activity for preschoolers (e.g., jungle animals), or relaxation exercises, which use imagery (e.g., the children lie down with eyes closed and a caregiver takes them on an imaginary journey)
▶ discussions in small groups, in which the children are asked what they would do if a big dog came up to them, if they got lost, if they smelled smoke in their bedroom. Helping children think of options encourages them to participate in overcoming fears. Note that such discussions would be inappropriate if any child in the group had an intense fear of dogs or fire; in that case a one-to-one conversation with that child would help gauge her or his reactions.
▶ helping individual children identify what is a stress release for them. Some need vigorous physical activity, others prefer time alone looking at books or listening to music, others may need to pound clay.
▶ asking children to identify what causes their stress and what they can do to prevent a reaction (e.g., remove themselves from a stressful situation if possible, think about something else)

▶ resolving conflict—much of school-agers' stress, in particular, is related to inter-action with peers

HELPING SPECIFIC CHILDREN

Caregivers create a stress-aware environment for all the children, but there are times when an individual child needs extra support because stress is affecting her or him significantly. Caregivers use their observation skills to identify signs and possibly stress factors. The director may also be involved, and certainly parents are fully involved unless there is a strong suspicion of child abuse.

When children's stress reactions are developmentally based, caregivers and parents are often able to support children through this process in a positive way. In the example that follows, of a preschool child's fear of doctors and hospitals, we'll examine how caregivers offered support along with his family.

Desmond is 4 years old. He has always been afraid of the doctor's office, mainly because of the immunization shots that he hates so much. Next month, he is to be hospitalized for two days to have his tonsils removed. His mother, Lorna, tells you that he is terrified. His stress is evident in the centre as well as at home. He is not sleeping well and is having recurring nightmares. At the centre, he can't lie still to rest, although he is obviously tired and irritable. Desmond is usually quite involved in play—able to concentrate for periods of time at the blocks and in dramatic play. Lately he flits around aimlessly, unless a caregiver spends one-to-one time with him.

The mother and caregivers have decided to try and help Desmond in the weeks leading up to the surgery, in a number of ways:

▶ Desmond and Lorna are scheduled to take the guided tour of the hospital, which is designed for children about to have surgery. The goal of these tours is to decrease children's anxiety about the unknown, including the operating room, the playroom, and their own room.
▶ Caregivers will be particularly sensitive to providing Desmond with one-to-one time whenever possible, reading books and encouraging him to discuss his feelings when he is comfortable.
▶ Because Desmond enjoys dramatic play, the caregivers have set up this area as a hospital. The setting encourages him to act out his feelings and experiences. Since children tend to play about what they already know, the caregivers realize that his most meaningful play will be after the surgery. However, it is helpful for Desmond to handle the medical instruments and for caregivers to listen to his fears. He hasn't been able to articulate those when asked, but he does in the context of play with dolls.

Desmond is worried that when he is in the hospital the doctor will remove a leg or arm rather than just his tonsils. He's afraid that the doctor is mad at him because he always cries when he gets his shots. He's afraid he is going to be punished. This is helpful information to share with Lorna, because until now she thought his only fear was that she was going to leave him in the hospital. During the hospital tour, Lorna focuses her questions on issues that help reduce Desmond's fears.

▶ She finds out that she can stay in the hospital room with him.
▶ In the children's playroom, Desmond talks with two children who had their tonsils out and sees that they have both arms and legs.

After the visit, Desmond is more focused at the centre. Although he is still stressed, he's playing with other children again and isn't as hesitant to voice his fears. He isn't crying as much or talking about cutting off arms during play in the hospital play area. Lorna says that Desmond is sleeping better and has had only two nightmares.

The day of surgery arrives. When the doctor comes in to see Desmond, she assures him that she will take out only his tonsils and that he has done nothing wrong; his tonsils had become sick. When Clarisa, a caregiver, comes to visit with two of Desmond's child care friends the day after surgery, he is happy to see them and shows them his room and the playroom. Within a week of his return to the centre, Desmond seems to be back to his old self, proudly showing the pictures that his mother took at the hospital. Lorna isn't anticipating that he will love the doctor from now on, but she believes that the preparation and positive hospital experience alleviated Desmond's stress and fear. Caregivers observe a change in his dramatic play, which reflects Desmond's positive experience and ability to cope with this fear.

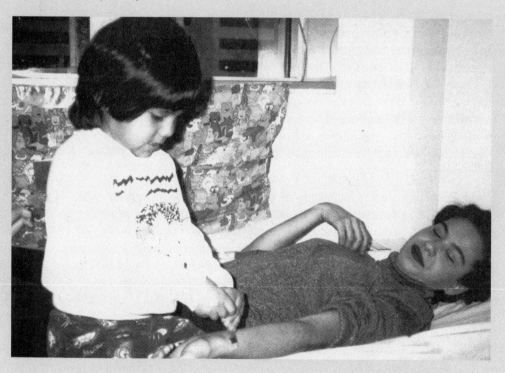

This example highlights the benefits of centre involvement with parents in managing children's stress factors that may be developmentally based and, it is hoped, short-term. In studies conducted with children who were to be hospitalized, those who were prepared recovered faster both physically and emotionally (Thompson, cited in Mather 1988, 94).

When children's stress is due to a very serious or long-term factor such as child abuse, the death of a parent, or an experience as a refugee, caregivers will likely need to collaborate with others in ensuring that the child receives consistent support.

Other agencies may be involved, and caregivers may be given recommendations from play therapists or other developmental specialists and counselling services.

Sexuality

Sexuality is part of us all, regardless of our age. Yet this topic often makes adults feel uncomfortable because they may be hesitant to acknowledge young children's sexuality. Young children's sexual feelings provide sensory pleasure, but without the erotic overtones that develop during and after puberty. Children's sexuality is an integral part of growth and development.

Stimulating our genitals in some way is called masturbating or self-pleasuring. Masturbation is an act of stimulating oneself to reach orgasm. Touching oneself for pleasure is normal and a natural behaviour, and in keeping with this positive view, we use the term "self-pleasuring" in this textbook. In fact, self-pleasuring more closely describes the child's intent. The word masturbation may evoke negative feelings for some adults, due to taboos or messages learned as they were growing up. Self-pleasuring is a healthy behaviour for children unless it becomes the focus and interferes with the child's involvement in activities. When you observe children self-pleasuring, your reaction should be to help children to learn social parameters, as with all behaviour. Acknowledge the child's pleasure, and help him or her to regard it as private, to be performed when alone. If children feel shame or embarrassment for normal, curious, or stimulating behaviour, this negativity about sexual matters may stay with them.

DEVELOPING HUMAN SEXUALITY

With an understanding of development, caregivers are able to predict the normal patterns of sexual behaviour and are prepared for and respond calmly to them.

Infants:

▶ Early experiences with sucking, being held, rocked, and cradled provide a foundation that fosters positive feelings toward self and relationships.
▶ Touching or fondling the genitals when the diaper is off is normal, as infants explore all parts of their body.
▶ Activities such as bouncing, swinging, and jumping may produce sexual pleasure; boys may have an erection and girls, although it is less noticeable, may have vaginal secretions (Maguire 1993, 33).

Toddlers:

In addition to the experiences and activities listed above for infants:

▶ They learn words for private body parts and toileting.
▶ They have increased interest in others' genitals, an interest heightened by learning to use the toilet.

Preschoolers:

▶ They have concerns about their genitals. Boys might worry about their penis falling off, or girls wonder why they don't have a penis. If they tell a caregiver of their concern, children must be reassured and not teased. Boys need to know that their penis won't fall off, and girls need to know that they have all their sexual parts, some of which are inside their body and not as obvious as boys' genitals.

▶ They self-pleasure or explore genitals.

▶ They observe each other during washroom routines.

▶ They sex-play, including Show and Show, Doctor, and so on.

▶ They question caregivers about how their body works, where babies come from, why those two dogs in the park are stuck together (i.e., mating), why girls and boys are different, and so on.

School-Agers:

▶ They sex-play.

▶ They possibly self-pleasure in public, though most school-agers understand privacy rules.

▶ They use slang or swearwords for private parts, sexual acts, or sexual orientation.

▶ They ask caregivers questions similar to those that preschoolers ask, but are somewhat more sophisticated (e.g., "How do babies get into a uterus?" or "What are those animals doing?"). Questions such as "What does homosexual mean?" and "How do people get AIDS?" or those related to puberty (e.g., "When will I get hair down there?") are common. ECE students and caregivers should also be prepared for personal questions from school-age children, such as "Do you have sex with your boyfriend?" These questions are personal. You should feel confident in responding respectfully by saying that this is a personal question, and that you will not answer a question that is private. By asking questions, children learn which questions are private and which we will answer. Here again, caregivers help children to learn social skills.

KNOWLEDGE PROMOTES HEALTHY ATTITUDES

Knowing about sex does not encourage children to become sexually active too early. The World Health Organization (1983) states that it is a *lack* of knowledge that leads to early sexual adventures. Of course, this doesn't mean that 4- or 5-year-olds are interested in, or should be taught about, sexual intercourse. A 5-year-old may have an idea that a man and a woman are on top of each other and rub bodies (and may even play this out with a partner in dramatic play with clothes on). However, the child probably does not understand the specifics of intercourse, and if he or she does, the caregivers should explore the possibility of sexual abuse. Caregivers should be prepared to discuss anatomical facts related to gender identity and sexual differences. Adults' comfort level concerning sexuality may reduce children's anxiety about this topic. However, developing a common approach to this topic is difficult because of differences in opinion (American Public Health Association and American Academy of Pediatrics 1992, 61).

 Caregivers should not offer their opinion on sexual intercourse outside of marriage. It is the family's right to convey their moral beliefs. Caregivers must try not to be judgmental about family beliefs and teachings. However, if there is concern that the child is being physically, emotionally, or sexually abused as a result of the family's sexual mores, caregivers cannot ignore this possibility and must explore it further.

Around 2 years of age, children begin to be interested in parts of the body—both theirs and those of the opposite sex. Giving nicknames to genitals rather than the anatomically correct term, or discouraging children from mentioning these body parts, leads to confusion later when they hear another child or adult call a penis a "wee-wee." They begin to assume that there is something wrong with using the word "penis," though it's acceptable to use the correct names for other body parts. The same confusing message is learned by infants. Adults smile at them when they play with their toes but slap them or say no when they touch their genitals. If these messages are reinforced as children grow, they will view self-pleasuring and their genitals as bad or dirty.

Preschoolers and young school-agers between the ages 3 and 8 may be eager to explore similarities and differences in their bodies with peers. Sexual games like Doctor or You Show Me and I'll Show You, often while playing House, are motivated by natural curiosity, not by erotic drive. Although these games are predictable and part of development, adults often overreact to them.

For preschoolers, one of the important aspects of their emerging sense of self is awareness of their gender. Around age 4 or 5, many become focused on gender stereotypes, much to the chagrin of parents and caregivers who foster less rigid roles for males and females. When children reach the school-age years, many are naturally drawn to stereotypes in clothing, hairstyles, toys, and play behaviour. They also observe and experience gender stereotypes around them. Without devaluing individual children's interests and inclinations, caregivers must give the same kind of care and attention to girls as to boys, and continue to offer them the same range of choices. Ongoing commitment to a nonsexist approach in the program helps to counteract the gender stereotypes that children face in society. Adapting to a stereotype is harmful because it replaces behaving in accordance with your own personal identity with behaving in accordance with expectations of how you should behave.

A relatively common stereotype is that boys should not cry. This may result in a boy's reluctance to talk to anyone about what is worrying him for fear that he will cry. This can negatively affect his long-term emotional health.

Parents' Perspectives on Children's Sexuality

We have made some clear-cut comments in this textbook on the advantages of direct communication about children's sexuality. Just as it is important to acknowledge parents' views on issues such as guidance, illness, and safety, the same principle applies to sexuality. Some parents may not agree with this open approach, and caregivers must respect their position. So how do caregivers handle situations in which a child's sexual question or behaviour is one that you know the parent discourages or forbids?

First, caregivers need to come to an agreement among themselves on how they approach sexual questions and behaviour. This type of discussion provides opportunities for staff to talk about differences of opinion. Centre staff may benefit from additional post-diploma training (in-service) or consultation with a sexual health educator, often affiliated with the local public health agency. Libraries too provide educational materials. Some adults grew up with negative feelings or attitudes about bodies and sexuality. Or their values are based on religious or ethno-cultural beliefs about sexuality or sex roles. Although you must respect these views, it is inappropriate for a professional working with children to impart them to children.

- John believes that children should not explore or stimulate their genitals under any circumstances. He recognizes that he needs to explore why he feels this way. Meanwhile, he knows that he must avoid reacting negatively to children's self-pleasuring.
- A child asks how babies are born. Madeline is tempted to answer, "They are found in a cabbage patch." Madeline must recognize that giving children false information is not helpful. The child will eventually find out that she wasn't telling the truth. Older children already have some idea, and may be testing their caregiver's honesty.

Second, centres' policies on child guidance and curriculum should clarify staffs' commitment to answering children's questions, including ones of a sexual nature. Written information that caregivers develop for parents should mention that children's awareness of self, others, and the world is part of the ongoing curriculum. To avoid misunderstanding, include examples such as "We use anatomically correct names for all parts of the body," and "A preschooler who is exploring his or her genitals is redirected if this occurs in a social situation. He or she is reminded that this is a private activity, which is acceptable at nap time."

Third, meeting with the parents at the time of enrollment allows the director to raise this issue and discuss the parents' views, and how they wish to handle their child's questions. Differences of opinion may arise, and in those cases a workable and practical compromise can be reached. In the future, if a sexuality issue arises that is relevant to all parents, it would be beneficial to have a parent meeting facilitated by a sexual health educator (or other expert in the area).

Some children have shown a keen interest in playing Doctor, and parents have concerns that individual children may be hurt either physically or emotionally.

At a parent meeting, a staff person outlines how caregivers manage these situations in the program:

▷ The children are clearly told that their individual rights are to be respected and that no one has a right to touch them in a way that makes them feel uncomfortable. They are also not permitted to touch another person against his or her wishes. This rule applies at all times, whether it concerns aggressive behaviour (e.g., hitting, pushing) or sexual behaviour (e.g., kissing, touching private body parts).

▷ No child is permitted under any circumstances to insert parts of the body (e.g., fingers) or other objects into another child's body.

▷ If one child is being forced to play Doctor against her or his wishes, the children are reminded of individual rights and the importance of respecting those rights. If children are discovered playing Doctor (e.g., with clothes off), the caregiver responds by calmly instructing children to put their clothes on and redirecting their play to another area (i.e., the rule is that children keep their clothes on at the centre).

The sexual health educator facilitates a discussion to identify concerns and issues that need to be addressed. Changes in a centre's policy or practices may be required.

Assessing the situation:
How would a conversation between you and the parent proceed?
Scenario: A parent asks you to tell her 4-year-old son that it is "bad" whenever you see him touch his penis. She tells you that the behaviour is morally wrong.

ROLE OF CAREGIVERS AS SEX EDUCATORS

Parents are the primary sexual health educators in children's lives. But caregivers too have a significant role to play as sex educators, whether they are aware of it or not. How? Children are constantly learning about their sexuality by

► listening to adults and other children
► observing the way adults interact with each other, and react to events and comments, and so on.
► absorbing attitudes that are communicated in adult conversation and action
► interacting with adults and other children

In other words, caregivers are teaching about sexuality simply by the way they act, what they say, and what they don't say.

A school-age girl is looking at a magazine that has a picture of a girl about the same age as she posed in a way that looks seductive. The caregiver who remarks "Isn't she gorgeous?" is teaching something different from the caregiver who asks, "What do you think of this advertisement?" The question may initiate a conversation between the girl and the caregiver about how advertisers use children in inappropriate ways and how they affect the way that girls and boys view females.

Caregivers contribute to children's sexual learning in a number of ways:

▶ They contribute to children's self-esteem and positive body image, by helping them to feel proud and in control of their body.

▶ They help children to value themselves as female or male, by using implicit and explicit messages about real similarities and differences, and celebrating these similarities and differences.

▶ They encourage knowledgeable and responsible behaviour, by being informed about sexuality, answering questions simply and honestly, and responding gently to normal, curious sexual behaviour—while at the same time setting clear limits that help children to learn about boundaries.

▶ They serve as role models, by helping children understand acceptable and unacceptable private and public behaviour.

▶ They help to protect children from exploitation or sexual abuse, by teaching preschool and school-age children about the idea of privacy, about private body parts, and that sexual touching between children and adults is inappropriate (Brick et al. 1989, 2).

CHILDREN'S QUESTIONS ABOUT SEX

Questions about sexuality emerge from children as they become interested. Sexuality, like any other aspect of what is going on inside and around them, is something that children naturally want to know about—their body, how it works, and sex. Be sensitive and follow the child's lead. Remember, the story unfolds for children over many years along with their cognitive development. It is inappropriate to provide a long, detailed explanation that holds more information than the child wants or needs. Even for many older school-agers, the whole idea of sex can sound disgusting (Greenspan 1993, 240). Many children ask questions when you least expect them. Don't be surprised when at times you feel uncomfortable with a question or panicky at the prospect of answering it. Many caregivers feel this way. Part of this reaction stems from the fact that you aren't the child's parent and want to avoid saying anything that contradicts what the parents have told, or will tell, their child.

Often a simple answer is all the younger child wants or needs. If he asks, "What are those two dogs doing?" you could answer, "The dogs are making puppies." Remember three key points when answering children's questions at any age:

1. Be sure you understand what it is the child wants to know. For example, when Chantal asks, "Where did I come from?" she might not be interested in the sexual act but rather what city or country she originated from, or that she came from her mother's uterus.

2. Find out what the child already knows. For example, ask Chantal, "Where do you think you came from?" This will help you clarify what she is actually asking and what she already knows.
3. If you can't answer immediately, be sure to get back to the child soon (City of Toronto Department of Public Health n.d., 10–11).

Assessing the situation:
How would you have responded to this 8-year-old's question?
Scenario: An ECE student who is pregnant is approached by a boy who asks: "How did you get pregnant? Were you raped?" The student responds angrily, "That's not a very nice question. Do you know you could hurt someone's feelings by asking that?"

Sexual orientation, like race, gender, class, and religion, is part of an individual's identity and must be respected as such. When children ask what the words "gay," "homosexual," or "lesbian" mean, or when they use derogatory names for sexual orientation to name-call, this is a very important learning moment. Some children may be part of a family with gay parents or be friends with someone who has gay parents. However, even these children may use negative remarks or stereotypes based on lack of knowledge or misconceptions due to overwhelming stereotypes.

A 7-year-old is angry at his friend on the playground and shouts "You fag!" When the caregiver asks him whether he knows what the word means, he replies, "It means stupid." After reminding the child that name-calling is unacceptable, she must clarify this child's confusion.

For most children, it is not the homosexual or heterosexual sex act that they generally want to know about but the importance of different kinds of families and relationships. What is important for adults to focus on is the caring part of the relationship (Gambini, cited in Brown 1994, C1, C3).

Gay families are the same as any other family! It is commonly believed, although it is not possible to substantiate, that approximately 10 percent of the adult population is lesbian or gay (Corbett 1993, 30). Consequently, there will be parents or co-workers who are lesbian or gay. There will also be children that we are caring for now in centres who will become aware of their lesbian or gay sexual orientation as they get older. Most individuals who are homosexual were raised by heterosexual parents, and the children of most lesbian and gay parents grow up to have heterosexual orientation (Corbett 1993, 30). Perhaps this reality helps to highlight the importance of caregivers' attitudes in acknowledging families with same-sex parents as we do single parents, stepparents, and so on. This is as integral a part of a child's identity as his or her race, religion, and socioeconomic level.

Older children are bombarded by stereotypes from the media and possibly from adults in their lives. They may repeat some of what they've heard. They may ask more direct questions such as "How do you get to be gay?" To respond appropriately to children's questions, comments, and behaviour, caregivers need to explore their attitudes and knowledge about homosexuality. People who hold negative attitudes about a sexual orientation that is different from their own must recognize that this bias is discriminatory. Discrimination perpetuates unjust treatment of individuals based on their identity. Though caregivers may not agree with someone's sexual practice (just as they may disagree with some religious beliefs), they must tolerate diversity. Children and parents need to be accepted and supported as families, and if caregivers are either subtly or overtly disapproving they are not contributing to emotional health. Caregivers can seek out community resources to help them understand more about homosexuality and gay families.

Rhythm of the Program

 OBJECTIVE To describe essential principles in planning and carrying through with a program that recognizes children's needs for rest and physical activity.

The rhythm of a program refers to the pace of daily routines and activities. Establishing a rhythm that is respectful of and responsive to the children is a caregiver's daily role, beginning with greeting and talking with parents and children at drop-off. The rhythm is influenced by the ages of the children and other factors such as group size, ratios, interests of the children, time of day, weather, space available, mood of the group, and individual children. Adequate opportunities for physical activity, cognitive stimulation, and nutrition must be balanced with opportunities for rest and relaxation. Respect for individual children is paramount in planning and carrying out the day's activities.

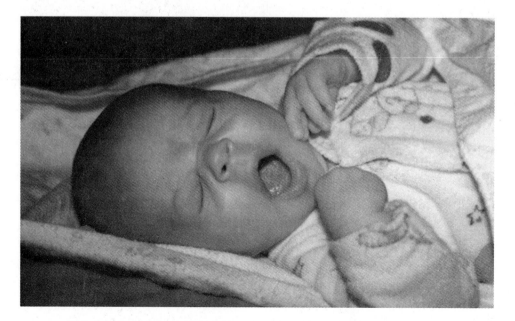

The Need for Rest and Relaxation

Napping or resting is an issue that arises in every centre and with every age group. Caregivers balance the needs of the group with those of the individual. This requires acknowledging the limitations of group care while recognizing and carrying through with practices and routines that endorse the child's uniqueness. When this is not done, children may be negatively affected:

▶ They may not get the rest they need.

▶ They may be forced to comply with rigid rules, such as lying on a cot for over an hour even if they don't need to nap.

▶ They may be involved in a lose–lose situation, with child and caregiver developing unhappy relationships around routines such as napping or resting.

It is evident, then, that even with a physical need like rest, emotional and social needs are interrelated.

Opportunities for rest and relaxation take into account the developmental and individual needs of children in the group:

▷ Infants follow their own individual nap schedules, which should be somewhat consistent with nap times at home.

▷ Some toddlers may need only one nap while others need two. While these latter nap, the others will need physical areas and opportunities to do quiet, relaxing, less stimulating things (e.g., being read to, working at puzzles).

▷ Preschoolers, especially older ones, don't require a nap any longer but still need to slow down and rest. They are only expected to lie on cots for a half-

hour and then they can get up and do quiet activities. However, even some older preschoolers need nap time, and provisions should be made for this.

▷ School-agers are provided with comfortable furniture or spaces to wind down or do quiet activities, if they need to, after school.

Massage is gaining recognition as an effective relaxation technique. But there are differing opinions on the appropriateness of infant massage in centres. Some people believe that massage can be soothing or stimulating for infants, and involves caring touch. Others believe that infant massage is an intimate practice that should be done only by parents (if they choose). Some infants enjoy being massaged. Others are not comfortable with a tactile approach and show signs of distress. When an infant is obviously not relaxing or enjoying it, the caregiver must stop the massage. Not stopping indicates a lack of respect for the infant's physical and emotional needs. Caregivers who practise infant massage recognize the importance of following infants' cues, and should seek training from appropriate resources in the community and obtain the parents' permission.

The Need for Physical Activity

The need for rest and relaxation must be balanced with the need for physical activity. Prudden (1988, 7) states that fitness is the foundation for healthy living: fit persons have prepared their body to respond to most of the demands they make on the body. The four components of fitness are endurance, strength, coordination, and flexibility. Physical activity enables children and adults to release tension, have fun, learn social skills, and feel good about themselves as they develop skills. A body that is physically fit works better. Physical activity should be part of everyday life for everyone. It is common knowledge that exercise builds a healthy heart and contributes to increased energy and better eating and sleeping habits. A six-year study in Quebec found that children who exercised regularly had "better concentration, memory, creativity, problem-solving ability and overall mood for up to two hours following exercise" (Barker 1994, 25).

The Canadian Association for Health, Physical Education and Recreation (1992b) has outlined the physical, emotional, and intellectual benefits of daily physical activity for children and adults:

► increases the peak bone mass of early adulthood, and delays the onset of bone loss, which results in osteoporosis
► alleviates stress and teaches children how to recognize and prevent stress
► alleviates at least one risk factor for heart disease
► lowers or eliminates smoking and alcohol consumption, supports healthier eating habits, and increases self-esteem
► enhances intellectual skills

Depending on life circumstances, children of all ages may have a lot of or little opportunity outside the centre to be physically active. Children may live in urban dwellings (e.g., high-rise buildings) where there is no back yard or safe area in which to run and play either indoors or outdoors. Parents may have neither the time nor place available to take their children for regular physical activity. In towns and cities where the population is growing, trees and grass are often replaced with malls and subdivisions. In most communities, parents are concerned about their children's safety outdoors when they are not actively supervised. In addition, parents' lives are so busy that preparing dinner, doing laundry, or finishing work from the office seems easier if their child is safely indoors, watching television, reading, or doing other passive activities. Studies have found that the body's metabolism slows significantly during television watching (Barker 1994, 25).

The number of hours that most school-agers sit in class each day emphasizes the importance of providing physically active school-age programs. With the growing number of children who are overweight or unfit, the need to encourage children to be physically active is essential. Some school-agers are involved in after-school physical activities such as basketball, soccer, hockey, gymnastics, dance, or karate. Yet other extracurricular activities are sedentary: music lessons, choir, chess, computer clubs. All these activities are valuable to the child, but daily physical activity needs to be fitted into the schedule.

It is important to recognize the benefits of physical activity for all children in your program, regardless of body type, size, or physical agility. Caregivers should plan a program that integrates physical activity in ways that invite children to become involved. The goal is not to produce Olympic athletes but to contribute to lifelong attitudes that value regular physical activity. Most children want to be active, especially when offered a range of possibilities. The child who is reluctant to join active games or activities may need more encouragement. However, children should never be centred out or embarrassed into physical activity. Instead, caregivers can use their observation skills to identify clues to explain the reluctance and then find ways to encourage that child's involvement.

The 8-year-old whose peers are more physically skilled and better coordinated than he is is embarrassed to play ball games with the group. Roberto always strikes out, highlighting his lack of batting skills, and his peers are impatient because he runs slower than they do.

You can find a range of issues in this example:

► Roberto's lack of confidence
► his reluctance to join group games and sports
► his lack of interest in physical activity (which increases neither his skill nor his fitness level)
► his peers' intolerance and focus on competition

The last issue is a difficult one to counterbalance when we consider the school-ager's developmental level and interest in rules, and the constant messages about winning that he or she is bombarded with in our society (see Erikson's Industry versus Inferiority and Greenspan's The World Is Other Kids, Chart 7.1, page 458). A focus on skill competence is a developmental task. Most children of this age have been playing cooperative games since early preschool age. Caregivers can do their best to adapt competitive games to be more cooperative (i.e., by moving the focus away from winning and losing and toward participation, playing together, and having fun). Caregivers recognize in Roberto his need for long-term physical fitness and to be part of a social group. First, he is eager to practise ball skills with a trusted caregiver. As he progresses, one of his peers becomes interested in playing ball with him. Eventually, the group plays their ball game cooperatively (any game can be adjusted with minimal changes) part of the time, so that all children can be involved.

Caregivers' sensitivity, creativity, and determination to support children's physical involvement encourage children like Roberto to build the interest, skill, and confidence they need to join in. This example is not meant to provide a "recipe for success," because obviously every child is unique and every group has its own social dynamics. However, caregivers can be confident that the effort they put into children's physical involvement is worth the long-term benefits.

For all age groups, caregivers who model a physically active lifestyle contribute to the children's interest in activity. When caregivers participate with children and observe them in active play, they use their observations to design the environment and to facilitate so that children can challenge themselves in play.

ACTIVE INFANTS AND TODDLERS

Caregivers set up the environment to enhance each child's physical development. Taking cues from the child, caregivers engage in one-to-one interaction when the child is alert and interested. This provides an opportunity to focus on the child's needs and interests (e.g., action songs).

Infants' need for physical activity changes dramatically in the first year—from rolling over, to pulling themselves up, to creeping, crawling, and walking. Caregivers are continually responding to these needs by providing an environment that is developmentally appropriate, challenging, and safe.

Toddlers are at a stage of motor development where they often need to run more than walk. They need an adequate amount of open space, small climbing equipment, and slides to go up, down, around, in, and out. Ramps and steps need to be the right size to encourage toddlers' exploration, not to frustrate them or make them prone to falls. Creative movement can be enhanced when the toddlers are in smaller groups. Opportunities to dance to music or move like animals minimize caregivers' expectations for sit-down time and maximize opportunities to move. Passive activities such as reading a book and singing quiet songs are more appropriate with one or two toddlers, who join and leave the activity as they wish. Of course, toddlers should always be allowed to come and go with group activities, unless supervision and safety is an issue (e.g., walking to the park).

Most infants and toddlers go for daily walks in strollers or wagons, which provide them with fresh air and stimulation and sometimes rest. They also need plenty of opportunity to move around freely, out of strollers and wagons, with a minimum of restrictions.

ACTIVE PRESCHOOLERS AND SCHOOL-AGERS

Preschool and school-age children need plenty of indoor and outdoor space in which to play in order to practise their locomotor skills, such as running, jumping, galloping, balancing, riding bikes, and ball skills. Though centres must meet the space requirements in the child care regulations, remember that those are minimum requirements. Centre staff are often called on to be creative in finding additional space to use. Community facilities such as schools, recreation agencies with gyms, pools, skating rinks, and neighbourhood parks, often cooperate by offering space at times when a facility isn't in use.

Children need a variety of play equipment and activities to develop the four areas of fitness that we have already named. They don't need large, expensive pieces of equipment. Car tires can be used for many activities, and scarves, ribbons, hoops, beanbags, and balls can be used for creative movement. Child care programs can offer a range in physical activity curriculum, including

▶ total child-directed outdoor use of playground equipment and free space to run around in
▶ outdoor organized games such as ball games, obstacle courses, cooperative games, and games that children, parents, and staff teach each other (e.g., a game that originates from their ethno-cultural background)
▶ indoor or outdoor creative movement or dance, with as many open-ended challenges as possible. This encourages children to use and move their bodies in different ways.

Ask children to crawl with their beanbag balancing on one body part or move across the room with one body part leading the way. Children will use their

imagination, physical skills, interests, and problem-solving skills to rise to the challenge—resulting in all sorts of possibilities.

▶ organized activities run by local agencies, such as the YMCA/YWCA, Kindergym, Boys' and Girls' Club, karate club, that teach lessons. Or centres can invite a qualified instructor (e.g., in creative movement, movement and music, yoga for children) into the child care program. This service depends on availability and the centre's or parents' ability to pay for the service. Programs may be able to use parent or volunteer talents or skills.

PHYSICAL ACTIVITY CHECKLIST

An integral part of the child care curriculum is physical activity. By evaluating the variety of physical activities in the centre, caregivers can determine to what degree the children are provided with opportunities to be active and the essential components of activities. Developed from the Canadian Association for Health, Physical Education and Recreation's *Physical Education Report Card* (1992a), the following are indicators of a quality physical activity program:

▶ Caregivers demonstrate attitudes and behaviour that show their commitment to physical fitness.
▶ Children's development is the basis for planning the curriculum.
▶ Activities are child-directed to provide children with problem-solving opportunities. This does not eliminate the need for children to learn when to stop and listen to the person leading the activity.
▶ Caregivers promote equal opportunities for all children, respecting individual skill, energy, and interest level, and encouraging and celebrating each child's attempts and successes.

► Caregivers downplay competition, focusing instead on individual competence and cooperating together with group activities.

► Caregivers emphasize fun, socialization, and active living.

► Caregivers offer a wide variety of physical activities.

► Caregivers provide various types of equipment in quantities that do not overwhelm children with choices or result in children being left out or fighting over the few pieces of equipment.

► Caregivers offer planning that includes active alternatives when the weather doesn't permit outdoor play.

► Activities incorporate music when possible, fitting the tempo of the activity-promoting rhythm.

► Caregivers provide music and activities that reflect a range in musical styles (e.g., jazz, R & B, folk, classic, reggae) and ethno-cultural diversity.

► Caregivers use clear, simple, and minimal directions to promote maximum child-directed involvement in the activity, encouraging children to challenge themselves.

► Caregivers maintain safety in all aspects of the physical activity program (i.e., supervision, equipment, children's level of involvement). The child isn't expected to go beyond his or her skill level or energy level.

► Caregivers invite parents, older siblings, and extended family members, and encourage them to provide input and be involved whenever possible (e.g., share active games from their childhood).

Refer to Health Canada's *Physical Activity Guide*, Appendix 2.2.

Health Curriculum

► **OBJECTIVES** To identify and describe four factors that influence children's understanding of health.

To discuss the guidelines in developing appropriate health curriculum and identifying inappropriate practices.

To identify developmental health needs and interests for each age group.

To offer suggestions for integrating health curriculum in each age group on topics such as environmental education, dental health education, and handwashing and germs.

To identify the who, what, when, where, and why of cooking with children.

To discuss how caregivers promote dental health with each age group.

As with all aspects of the curriculum, health curriculum should be designed using this principle: Curriculum design requires that teachers identify the play and learning priorities for the young children in the program. This step relies on information about individual children based on observation and assessment of children's developmental levels and needs. (Shipley 1993, 355)

In other words, children's health education should be integrated into the program in ways that relate to their developmental needs and interests.

Children's Understanding of Health

Children's understanding of health is influenced by the interaction of a number of factors:

▶ stage of cognitive development
▶ personality characteristics
▶ family connection: cultural identity, socioeconomic circumstances, parenting styles
▶ peers, their community, and the media

COGNITIVE DEVELOPMENT

Young children's growing cognitive abilities affect what and how they think about health, prevention, and health promotion. Combining Piaget's theory of cognitive development and Natapoff's research on children's understanding of health, Table 7.1 provides examples of how children perceive concepts of health and prevention at each level. The term "prevention," for example, assumes an understanding of future and causality—actions that you take today can affect your health in 20 years. Do you think that a 3-, 5-, or 7-year-old understands this concept? No. To fully understand and talk about these and other concepts, we have to reach Piaget's formal operational level in our cognitive development (at about age 12).

Does that mean that teaching young children about health is pointless? No. It means that health curriculum, in order to be relevant, should be based on children's cognitive abilities. Content that fits their ability to process information is more likely to have a positive effect on long-term health behaviour (Natapoff 1982).

Appropriate health education focuses on what children want and need now, not on what they'll need in future.

Explaining to Emily, a preschooler, that if she brushes her teeth every day her teeth will be healthy in 20 years is too abstract.

Memorizing rules is fairly easy for children. Yet we can't assume that when Emily repeats "Brushing my teeth every day will keep them healthy in 20 years" she fully understands what she has said. For Emily, 20 years from now holds no meaning. It makes more sense to Emily if we relate health education to her everyday life.

Brushing your teeth takes all the sticky food off your teeth so you won't get cavities (or a hole in the tooth). Brushing makes your mouth clean and makes it smell good too.

	TABLE 7.1	COGNITIVE UNDERSTANDING OF HEALTH	
CONCEPT	**SENSORIMOTOR: BIRTH TO 2 YEARS**	**PREOPERATIONAL: 2 TO 7 YEARS**	**CONCRETE OPERATIONAL: 7 TO 11 YEARS**
Health	• Concept too abstract for a pre-symbolic child. Groundwork is laid for later cognitive stages through child's experiences of healthy environments.	• Only the physical dimension of health Egocentric (e.g., if candy makes me feel good, it must be good for me) • Can't focus on the whole and the part at the same time. E.g., child believes that if you have a Band-Aid on your knee, you are not healthy (the physical signs of injury or illness are less of an abstract concept)	• Beginning awareness of health as more than a physical dimension (e.g., understanding that emotional stress can cause physical symptoms) • Has conservation—believes that it is possible to be partly healthy and partly not healthy (e.g., realizes that he is still healthy even though he has a sprained ankle)
Causality	• Too abstract—repeated experiences with cause and effect will contribute to development in this realm	• Has "magical thinking" and is intuitive rather than logical—sometimes unrelated practices are thought to affect health or illness (e.g., child believes that getting sick must have been a result of misbehaviour. That is, "Why did Rena give me chicken-pox? I wasn't mean to her")	• Has cause-and-effect reasoning—understands that certain actions or inactions can affect health (e.g., eating breakfast helps you concentrate at school)
Time	• Too abstract—consistent daily routines provide some predictability in their day (e.g., toddlers know that after lunch they will have a nap; they understand sequence)	• Present-oriented—here-and-now orientation; does not have an understanding of the future	• Still present-oriented • Has reversibility, enabling them to think through a chain of events and back—important in beginning to see more long-term orientation to health
Body	• Beginning awareness of body parts will contribute to later stages	• Has some body awareness but not a holistic view of how systems interrelate • Perceptually bound • Developing an awareness of body cues	• More aware of the body and mind and how they work together • Beginning awareness of body cues (e.g., child who has asthma recognizes early symptoms of an episode and by acting on these cues takes her medication)

Cognitive development is a natural process. We can no more speed up its progress than we can speed up physical development and get a 2-month-old to sit up. Learning is an interactive process and children's exploration and interaction enhance their development. Using the concept of the body as an example, caregivers can provide experiences, materials, and questions that promote children's learning. Children build on what they know. During diaper changes, caregivers can talk to infants about their tummy, knees, and toes, and ask them to help lift their bottom to take the diaper off. Toddlers are learning names and locations of body parts and beginning to identify feelings. Caregivers help preschoolers progress in their understanding of the body by asking them questions such as "How do you know when you are tired (or hungry, afraid, sick, happy)?" Caregivers can thus encourage children to become more aware of concrete body cues. School-agers begin to understand how the internal circulatory, digestive, and other systems work.

Personality Characteristics

The sequence of development is similar for children, though personalities are unique. Each child's personality has an effect on his or her understanding and view of health. One personality trait researched is "perceived vulnerability," which is a feeling of insecurity, a belief that one is at risk. Gochman and Saucier (1982) found that approximately 10 percent of children feel vulnerable to most everything (i.e., are born worriers). Perceived vulnerability seems to be a personality trait that may affect how the child perceives her or his own well-being.

Irena's parents let her walk to the corner store by herself. She feels proud, excited, and independent. On the other hand, her older sister Thea is relieved now that Irena can go to the store when the family needs milk or bread. She has always felt nervous about going because she worries about all the things that could go wrong (e.g., she could trip and fall, not have enough money, be hit by a car, be approached by a stranger).

Thea sees herself as a passive rather than an active participant in her well-being. Every personality trait is on a continuum with extremes at each end—born worriers at one end, and people who believe that they are invincible at the other. Of course, feeling invincible can also be developmental. When developing and implementing health curriculum, caregivers should consider the range of perceived vulnerability. However, the goal of increasing children's perceived vulnerability to encourage them to take positive health action has serious ethical questions. We must be careful not to raise anxiety levels in children, because increased stress for children does not mean increased health. (See Environmental Health Education, p. 500.)

Caregivers are planning to teach children to be cautious about crossing streets, ingesting poisons, or approaching animals by focusing on all the dangers. Caregivers are concerned about some of the children who feel invincible. While their approach may have a positive effect on the safety behaviour of some children, it may have a negative effect on those who worry. Their fears about crossing streets, exploring new things, or approaching animals are intensified. This negates children's confidence in striving toward self-care.

The Family Connection

Family is an essential connection to children's identity. The connection between children and their families is a powerful one that has a significant effect on their understanding of health. Members of various ethno-cultural groups connect the cause of disease, to varying degrees, with certain theories such as the imbalance of hot and cold in the body, spiritual or supernatural powers, or magic (e.g., the evil eye causing fever, vomiting, or diarrhea). Illness may be viewed as an invasion of body, mind, soul, and spirit (Waxler-Morrison et al. 1990). A family's health beliefs and practices may be effective in maintaining the health of an individual and his or her family even if these practices are not based on contemporary medical theories. In fact, traditional remedies may at times help someone feel better when conventional medicine has failed or has no recommendation.

It is critical that the child care program "respect the dignity and worth of each family's cultural beliefs and practices" (La Grange et al. 1994, 31). Of course, this statement must be qualified with regard to concerns that children are being mistreated, malnourished, or neglected in any way by a particular family practice. Other influences that may stem from ethno-culture are beliefs about health care professionals (e.g., conventional versus complementary practitioners) and types of treatment (e.g., prescription medicine versus herbs). Clearly, a practice that is unfamiliar to a caregiver is just that—unfamiliar. In their work with families, caregivers learn about health beliefs and practices other than those learned in their own families or at school, and use this knowledge and experience in health curriculum development. The differences in cultural practices can be overshadowed by socioeconomic factors.

> There may be more similarities between the health beliefs or practices of different ethnocultural groups at the same socio-economic level than there are among the people within the same ethnocultural groups who are from different socio-economic levels. (Masi 1993, 8)

In other words, if you are wealthy you probably have more in common with others who are wealthy than you do with people who are poor and from your ethno-cultural background. The reverse is true also.

Socioeconomic Factors Affecting Well-Being More than one in five children in Canada lives in poverty (21.1 percent in 1998). Compare this with one in seven in 1989 (14.5 percent). It is an alarming trend that in every province and territory in Canada the rate of child poverty has increased (Campaign 2000 1998, 4). Children who are poor are likely to be living in unhealthy environments that are beyond their ability to change. Poverty usually means food insecurity, substandard housing (e.g., cold, damp, drafty, crowded) in unsafe areas, inadequate clothing, and no access to safe play and recreation opportunities. These living conditions result in a higher incidence of disease, hospitalization, and deaths due to injuries (Canadian Institute of Child Health 1994, 113). Families in poverty rarely see reason to hope for improvement in their situation.

It is difficult for children to develop a future-oriented attitude toward health (e.g., health prevention) when the world they live in is filled with daily crises (e.g., uncertainty over when they will have food). Children who live in families that are comfortable financially have more reason to believe that they have control over and can affect their health.

Parenting Styles and Health   Parenting styles affect children's understanding of health and health promotion. An assertive parenting style fits closer with the definition of health promotion, because this approach fosters children's coping skills, demonstrating a problem-solving approach to life rather than a fatalistic acceptance. As well, children will probably be encouraged to interact with people in the community, enhancing social well-being and preventing isolation. Ethno-cultural backgrounds in which interdependence with the family, rather than individual autonomy, is fostered promote learning to care for others. Being aware and taking care of others' needs can of course be positive, as long as individual health needs are also met.

Extreme authoritarian parenting may result in children lacking trust in their own abilities and rarely feeling that they have autonomy. It would not be surprising then that children would not feel they had control over their health—or anything else, for that matter. The permissive parenting style may result in children having problems developing self-control, due to the lack of expectations on the child to give due regard to the rights of self, others, and property. A child's difficulty in learning to follow basic health and safety rules such as crossing roads at lights and washing hands before eating can affect his or her short- and long-term health and safety. Others' health and safety is put at risk too if the child doesn't follow socially acceptable behaviour such as covering the mouth while sneezing and waiting for a child to get off the slide before proceeding.

The ways that parents, caregivers, and teachers interact with children, their style of guiding children, and their expectations for children have an impact on children's view of health. If children's rights and needs are respected, they are more likely to develop autonomy, responsibility, active coping skills, and links with others. All of these are prerequisites for children's understanding and active involvement in health.

PEERS, THEIR COMMUNITY, AND THE MEDIA

As children grow older, the influence of their peers, community, and the media can have either a positive or negative effect on their health. Sam was eating a variety of nutritious foods until he was 6 years old; then he told his mom that he could bring in only those foods that his friends approved. Similarly, Olivia stopped washing her hands because it wasn't "cool" with her friends. On the other hand, if peers are excited about healthy habits or have positive views of health, they tend to influence one another positively. Children's willingness to try new foods that peers, possibly from different ethno-cultural backgrounds, bring in fosters an openness that promotes health. Friends who are willing to wait while their peer washes his hands are making a statement about health.

The community—neighbourhood, centre, school, recreation centre—in which children live also has an impact on their overall well-being and influences their view of health.

e.g.   Every morning the centre's playground is strewn with broken glass and discarded needles, syringes, and condoms from the night before. To date, nothing proactive has been done to change this and the children are getting the impression that we have to accept the situation. Using *Kids in Action: A Community Development Approach to Children's Health* (Pollack et al, 1991), the caregivers facilitated the school-agers in identifying and doing something about their concerns. Children, caregivers, parents, and the police collectively developed a plan of action that resulted in changing the situation. Children saw first-hand that it is possible to have an impact on our health.

The media influence children's understanding of health and perceptions of what is healthy. This varies with the age of children and how much television they watch. Children who watch a lot of television are inundated with themes and messages, some of which have negative influences on their understanding of physical, emotional, and social well-being (Levin and Carlsson-Paige 1994). Parents must take an active role in selecting the types of TV programs and videos that their children watch. Whenever possible, parents should watch with them to answer questions, clarify, and ensure that they are getting positive, health-promoting messages. The same applies to other media—radio, videos, music videos, music, print material, and advertising.

Developing and Implementing Health Curriculum

Many of the centres' healthy practices are important for all of us in our everyday lives—hand-washing, toothbrushing, healthy eating, physical activity, stress management. The hygiene practices described in Unit 3 are not of particular educational interest to children, even though they have a direct impact on their health (e.g., food storage, sanitizing mouthing toys). Providing health curriculum in a centre is more than occasionally reading a children's book about a health-related issue. Table 7.2 consists of guidelines for appropriate and inappropriate health curriculum for children that caregivers can refer to in evaluating their curriculum.

TABLE 7.2	DEVELOPING HEALTH CURRICULUM: GUIDELINES

APPROPRIATE HEALTH CURRICULUM Guidelines	Examples
focuses on the children's developmental needs, interests, and level of understanding (see Chart 7.1, page 458)	Preschooler's interest and readiness to learn simple safety rules that can be practised such as "stay away from matches" or "stop, drop, and roll" if clothes catch fire.
is interactive—children learn best when they interact with people and materials in their environment (play-based or fit into their daily lives)	Toddlers are encouraged, but not forced, to try new foods (e.g., pineapple). They can see peers and caregivers eating the food, hear its name, observe it with their other senses, and have opportunities in the home living centre to play with lifelike fruits and vegetables. They are learning about the food and are therefore more likely to try it.
has clear and reasonable objectives for children's learning based on developmental areas (cognitive, physical, emotional, social)	The primary objective for the preschool cooking experience is to encourage the child to follow a sequence. Secondary objectives include sensory exploration, cause and effect, promoting turn-taking, and small motor skills.
much of the health curriculum happens as part of the centre's routines—hand-washing, rest and relaxation, physical activity, healthy eating, and so on	Infants' hands are washed by the caregiver after diapering and before eating; school-agers are encouraged to respond to their body cues, such as needing to rest or drink water after vigorous physical activity.
practice is modelled by caregivers	Children see caregivers washing their hands after helping a child in the washroom and before eating with the children.
fits into the natural daily, weekly, monthly, and seasonal rhythm of the program	From the spring to the fall harvest is an ideal time to learn about growing vegetables and flowers from seeds.
is integrated into all curriculum areas—music, movement, science, literature, and so on	Preschooler body awareness: • art—body tracing on paper and children paint in body parts • music—songs about bodies • creative movement—body games, challenging children to explore their bodies with questions such as How tall/small can you be? How high/low can you jump? How angry/happy can you look? • science—use a magnifying glass to look at skin, • literature—many children's books (e.g., *The Bare Naked Book*) • numeracy—graph particular body characteristics (e.g., skin, hair and eye colour, "inny" or "outy" bellybuttons) by printing names or placing photos of children on paper • dramatic play—a full-length mirror
is flexible so that caregivers can take advantage of teachable moments or one-to-one interactions	Answering a preschooler's question during a food experience such as, "Why are vegetables good for me?"; showing a toddler how to sneeze into his sleeve after he has sneezed without covering his mouth

(table continues on next page)

TABLE 7.2	DEVELOPING HEALTH CURRICULUM: GUIDELINES (continued)

APPROPRIATE HEALTH CURRICULUM Guidelines	**Examples**
builds self-esteem and competence, moving from simple to complex	Using simple three-step recipe cards for "ants on a log" (celery, cream cheese, raisins) allows children to feel accomplishment in completing a task independently.
is respectful and inclusive of family beliefs, practices, and situations	A parent regularly comes in and teaches tai chi to the school-age children and caregivers and discusses its advantages to reduce stress in mind and body.
focuses on the concrete rather than the abstract, and present rather than future health	"Physical activity helps your body work better" rather than "Physical activity now lowers your risk of heart disease when you are an adult"
emphasizes all aspects of health, so that children begin to develop an awareness of holistic health involving physical, emotional, and social well-being	Healthy eating is viewed not only in terms of its effect on growth and physical well-being but also on mental alertness: if you eat well you learn better and you have opportunities to spend enjoyable, relaxed social time with your friends while eating.
moves toward increased understanding and responsibility for their own health with knowledge about what aspects of their health are in their control	Emphasizing to preschoolers that making hand-washing a habit before eating and after toileting is something they can take responsibility for, something that helps them take control over how often they get sick; letting preschoolers know that they have no control over how safely an adult drives a car, but they do have control over putting on their seat belts to protect themselves

INAPPROPRIATE HEALTH CURRICULUM Practices	**Examples**
a series of lessons are formally taught to children	Talking (or lecturing) to children about do's and don'ts of hygiene without hands-on practice, without interaction with children; reading a book about sexuality in group time
is based on themes, so that a health area is highlighted for a week but is not a priority for the rest of the year	Peacemaking is introduced as a week's theme in the school-aged room, when a conflict is in the news. For the remainder of the year, the principles of peacemaking are ignored by caregivers, and children are not developing the skills to put peacemaking into practice.
is based on the adults' health interests rather than the children's interests	A caregiver does aerobics every day. She conducts daily instructional exercises with the toddlers in her care and loses patience with them when they don't seem interested in following her lead.
is designed or implemented in a way that instills fear, an inappropriate sense of responsibility, or groundless vulnerability in the child	A caregiver uses pressure with her group of preschoolers at mealtimes, insisting that they eat everything on their plate because children elsewhere are starving; cautioning children to *never* talk to strangers because they may hurt you.

Health Needs and Interests of Children

Certain health education topics or behaviour are more appropriate to introduce at particular ages and developmental stages. Beginning to learn about germs, for example, makes much more sense to preschoolers than it does to infants! The following discussion is by no means exhaustive, but it indicates typical health areas of need and/or interest for each age group. Of course, each group of young children in child care is unique, and these general ideas must be tailored to the group.

INFANTS AND TODDLERS

The focus in health curriculum for infants and toddlers is on adults caring for children's health needs and modelling healthy attitudes and behaviour. Environments that support infants' and toddlers' emotional health and development are ones in which children feel safe and secure and trust that adults will meet their physical,

emotional, and social needs and respond to their cues. In order to achieve such environments, child care programs need to

▶ establish effective ongoing communication with parents (e.g., practices around separation for child and parent that promote trust)
▶ implement good hygiene practice, ensure safety, and actively involve children in routines. This would include as many one-to-one or small group experiences as possible. The very young child learns about health by experiencing healthy environments and by caregivers' actions. For example:
   ▷ responding to infants' and toddlers' verbalization, and talking about the activity's process, including naming parts of the body while diapering, while toileting, and during other routines
   ▷ encouraging the child's involvement in undressing (e.g., diapering, getting into sleeper for nap after outdoor play) and older toddlers' involvement with dressing
   ▷ hand-washing with children, who become increasingly involved as time goes on
▶ provide opportunities for children's bodies moving in space, minimizing restriction except for safety reasons
▶ relate physical activities to growth and development, such as short flexible tunnels for budding crawlers and large foam blocks for climbers
▶ ensure that infants are given a spoon and are encouraged to be as involved as they would like to be in self-feeding. Continue to be patient with toddlers' learning table behaviour and be respectful of cultural practices in eating that differ from yours (e.g., using hands to eat, or an adult feeding a child). Establish basic limits: Food is not to be thrown, for example.
▶ offer opportunities for various sensory experiences, including foods with interesting natural colours and textures, as appropriate
▶ serve nutritious food, encouraging preference for whole foods without a lot of processing and added sugar, salt, and additives
▶ monitor and control sudden loud noises in the centre because of young children's fears. When adults who are unfamiliar to the children visit the centre, or when the children are outside, be sensitive to the children's responses; and support children in daily separation from parents.

Toilet learning often begins somewhere between 18 and 36 months. The term "learning" highlights children's active role in this process. As with most aspects of working with children, caregivers should follow the child's lead. Readiness for using the toilet is demonstrated when *all three* of the following are observed in a child:

▶ physical maturity—stays dry for several hours, can get to the toilet, pulls down loose-fitting pants.
▶ awareness—of a full bladder or bowel. The child understands that she or he has wet or soiled diapers.
▶ desire—to use the toilet (or potty) and to have a dry diaper.

When all three aspects of readiness are in place, toilet learning is usually a positive process. Caregivers in toddler (or preschool) rooms often find that children's desire is high when peers are using the toilet. Children's feelings of self-esteem are paramount in the approach to toilet learning. In the best interests of the child, parents, and caregivers work together in supporting him or her through this period. When there is a difference of opinion on timing or approach to toilet learning, caregivers and parents work together to reach a compromise.

PRESCHOOLERS

This group of children is particularly interested in learning about

- cleanliness, toilet learning and toileting, good grooming, dressing themselves
- germs and sickness
- health and safety rules (e.g., cover your mouth when you cough and sneeze, look both ways before crossing street)
- safety and injury prevention, at least on an early-awareness level, and especially in simple rules
- personal safety, again on an early-awareness level, and especially with regard to strangers
- community helpers (e.g., role of firefighters, police officers, doctors, nurses, dentists), and especially what happens in a hospital if the child or a friend has been a patient
- some common fears: fear of the dark, monsters, loud noises (e.g., thunder, truck backfiring), abandonment (especially if divorce, death, hospitalization, or other trauma has occurred)
- food and good nutrition, how and where foods are grown or are eaten, different foods eaten by people and animals
- the role of sleep and relaxation
- the role of physical activity and movement

The following are usually of more interest and more appropriate developmentally for older preschoolers:

- body awareness, interest in more complex body parts and systems (e.g., internal organs, respiratory system)
- brushing, primary teeth coming out, new teeth coming in
- emotions, own feelings, awareness of similarities and differences (e.g., gender, race), manners, own family and others' families, having babies
- beginning awareness of conflict resolution and peacemaking
- basic understanding of importance of caring for the environment

SCHOOL-AGERS

School-agers are interested in more complex issues and want more details, but they still haven't developed abstract reasoning. The following are some examples that particularly interest them:

- ▶ illnesses
- ▶ loss of primary teeth, emergence of permanent teeth
- ▶ body awareness that is more complex than when younger (e.g., interest in body secretions and body noises, changes with puberty)
- ▶ consumer health, especially as reflected in advertisements in television commercials, magazines, product labels, prices
- ▶ environmental health issues, particularly issues around landfill sites, over-packaging, air quality, depletion of the ozone layer, animal extinction, and actions we take such as observing the three R's (reduce, reuse, recycle), composting, returning bottles and can, and renewing and refinishing
- ▶ personal feelings, making friends, family dynamics, getting along with others (e.g., bullies, peacemaking)
- ▶ human rights: racism, sexism, classism, homophobia, and concern for those whose rights have not been respected
- ▶ safety and injury prevention (e.g., bicycle, pedestrian, playground, home safety, first-aid treatments)
- ▶ dealing with stress
- ▶ how the body works (e.g., how nutrition, rest, and physical activity interrelate)
- ▶ physical fitness

- ▶ foods friends eat that may be different from theirs, and nutrients in foods
- ▶ self-care, as in learning to make snacks and meals independently, knowing what to do in an emergency, finding out about personal safety and streetproofing
- ▶ community awareness, and with support from adults work with others to affect health in the community (e.g., neighbourhood, school, centre)
- ▶ younger school-agers' fears: ghosts and other supernatural beings, and as children get older, more concrete fears such as being lost or kidnapped, being disliked, real-life catastrophes (e.g., floods, fires, nuclear war)
- ▶ older school-agers' fears: being humiliated in front of friends, being the victim of physical violence, family breakup or changes, looking or acting strange, news reports of war on television (some children arriving in Canada have firsthand experience)

Getting Down to Health Curriculum

When health is viewed holistically, countless topics and issues can be included in centres' health curriculum. Although this section does not include a multitude of ready-to-use activities for different age groups, it does offer suggestions for implementing health curriculum in a selected number of health-related topics. (See Resource Materials, page 520.) From here, students will be able to take what they learn from the entire discussion on health curriculum and develop curriculum on topics of their choice. Of course, specific curriculum must always be based on the needs and interests of the particular group of children. The following topics are discussed in more detail in connection with the guidelines for the various age groups of children:

- ▶ environmental health
- ▶ nutrition education
- ▶ dental health
- ▶ hand-washing and germs

ENVIRONMENTAL HEALTH EDUCATION

Over the past decade, concern about the health of our planet, which ultimately affects all life, has been a major educational focus for everyone. A multitude of available resources are available that encourage public involvement in environmental health. Of course, increased knowledge is essential for changes in public and personal attitudes and behaviour that will positively affect the earth.

Children can learn good helping habits and may even be involved in community action to improve the environment. However, we must never imply or state that children are solely responsible for the future of the planet. Because children have reached only the early stages of cognitive and moral development, they are liable to take this message seriously. Feelings of guilt (e.g., whenever a child uses a paper product), fear or hopelessness for the future, and other feelings will contribute to children's stress levels. They may begin to view the onerous task of saving the planet as theirs alone and become consumed by it.

Environmental health education can be a part of the everyday life at home and in centres. Adults who "live gently"—a term used to refer to a way of living that respects life, uses resources without wasting, and causes minimal harm to the planet—are helping children to learn about environmental health. Centres model these practices by

▶ participating in recycling programs, where available. The most common recycling programs are community-wide and accept glass, plastics, cardboard, and newspapers. Recycling can also include clothing, winter boots and coats, skates, and toy swaps in centres and between centres.
▶ composting
▶ choosing products that are safer for the environment (e.g., cloth diapers, biodegradable products)
▶ using dishes, cups, and utensils that are reused rather than paper plates, plastic cups, and utensils that are discarded after snacks and meals
▶ having litterless lunches on field trips
▶ using energy efficiently
▶ repairing, remodelling, and reusing, when possible
▶ respecting ecosystems

Within centres, caregivers need to be aware of the messages they are sending to children about their role in saving the earth. Our goal is for children to develop a positive attitude and belief that they can effect change, and to incorporate actions that contribute to that change, but not to be overwhelmed with a sense of personal responsibility.

Infants and Toddlers Environmental education for infants and toddlers should focus on role-modelling. Children observing caregivers who respect plants, trees, animals, and insects on walks, and children guided by gentle reminders when handling nature inappropriately (e.g., plucking flower petals, stomping on earthworms), are on their way to becoming environmental advocates. However, it is important to remember that, developmentally, these very young children are egocentric and that going beyond this level of environmental education would not be good practice.

Preschoolers As with all learning, preschoolers build on what they have already experienced with the environment. For preschoolers to develop respect for the environment, they first need to learn about it. However, environmental concepts and issues are complex. Since children learn from the simple to the complex, caregivers begin with simpler versions of relevant concepts for preschoolers. They learn best when they interact with people and objects.

Life cycles is an environmental concept that can be introduced at the preschool level in a number of ways. Planting and harvesting, composting, and observing trees change with the seasons are ways that preschool children begin to understand nature. Ideally, a respect for nature is a part of everyone's value system. "The world

needs people who may not necessarily love earthworms or spiders, but who respect the role they play in the environment" (Lewis-Webber 1993, 3). Sedgwick Galvin suggests that caregivers should let nature lead you and your group of children into learning (1994, 8). This means providing experiences through the seasons that serve as springboards for observing, investigating, discovering, and learning about the environment through nature. Adults, including ECE students and caregivers, sometimes feel that they do not know enough about nature, but they can learn along with children. Adults who demonstrate a quest for learning, rather than pretending to know everything, actually provide very good role-modelling!

Children can express their interests in the environment in all areas of the centre's curriculum:

▶ *Art.* Use easels outdoors to inspire children to paint their representation of trees or their feelings about trees; make leaf rubbings.
▶ *Music.* Sing songs about nature or create chants; identify sounds of nature.
▶ *Creative movement.* Express the rhythms of the earth or move like wind, water, and so on.
▶ *Science.* Care for a living thing through planting and gardening; adopt a tree in the park and see how it changes with the seasons.

▶ *Literature*. Read and discuss books about nature or about legends that involve nature, possibly stories from the children's backgrounds (e.g., Native Canadian legends embody nature).

▶ *Numeracy*. Compare sizes and shapes of plants, seriate, classify.

▶ *Dramatic play*. Add a small recycling box in the home living centre; play jungle animals; transform the play area into a forest with trees and animals.

▶ *Field trips*. Walk in your neighbourhood in the different seasons; visit a botanical garden, recycling plant, garden centre, farm, orchard, bird sanctuary, pond.

Though they are still young, preschoolers could become involved at a simple level with community action, along with their parents or caregivers.

e.g. City developers were planning to cut down trees in the centre's neighbourhood to build a parking lot. Caregivers and concerned parents involved the children in a walk of support for the park, the trees, and the play area. The event got media attention. As well, pictures the children drew of the park and trees were enclosed in a letter to the mayor.

Caregivers must be careful to ensure that participation of this kind does not instill fear, that children understand the purpose of what they are doing, and that they are not being exploited to gain public support for adults' issues. Many complex environmental issues are beyond a preschooler's cognitive level of understanding (e.g., animal extinctions).

Today's preschoolers will become the adults who make major environmental decisions in the future. The interest, knowledge, and concern for the environment that begin in their preschool years will eventually benefit everyone.

School-Agers   In our community, this age group is already targeted more than any other with regard to environmental education resources. School-agers, especially those who have reached a concrete-operational level of thinking, can have a fuller understanding of environmental issues, particularly if they have had environmental experiences earlier in life. Children are becoming interested in the democratic process. Those who have been developing decision-making and coping skills may have been involved in some social action. Any number of approaches and activities can be part of school-age child care programs.

One approach is a comprehensive action plan entitled the Green Team (Degler and Pollution Probe 1990, 6–7). School-agers are encouraged to think green and become the following Green Team characters:
  ▷ the Scientist, who carries out experiments to learn about environmental problems and possible solutions
  ▷ the Detective, who explores nature and uses detective skills to discover the effects of pollution
  ▷ the Crusader, who takes action, writes letters to decision-makers, and forms groups to fight for change
  ▷ the Shopper, who uses buying power to make even the largest companies think about the environment

Each environmental issue (including air and water pollution, animal welfare, pesticide use, waste disposal) can be explored using the Green Team approach. When children put their energy into contributing to change, a health promotion philosophy is put into practice.

By planning and networking with teachers in the children's school, ideally the caregivers and teachers can coordinate their environmental health policies and practices. As well, they can find out how much time is spent on the environment in the classroom. Your efforts will be in vain if children become turned off environmental education rather than motivated and excited by it.

Nutrition Education

Nutrition is the easiest health area to integrate throughout the curriculum and from infancy to school-age. The possibilities for learning are endless but usually centre on some general concepts. The following nutrition concepts can be appropriately incorporated into children's nutrition experiences:

▶ Everyone needs food in order to grow, feel good, and have energy to do things.
▶ A wide variety of foods are available and it is best for our body if we have variety every day.

▶ Foods have unique colours, flavours, textures, smells, sizes, shapes, and sounds.

▶ Foods that are unfamiliar to you are enjoyed by other people. Trying new foods helps you to learn about yourself and the world, and to gain respect and insight into other ethno-cultural backgrounds.

▶ Everyone has individual food likes and dislikes.

▶ Food should be respected for its role in fulfilling needs—and should *not* be used for art activities.

▶ Foods have different sources (e.g., some grow on trees or in the ground, some come from animals).

▶ Foods are made up of nutrients, and the foods that have more nutrients are better for our body.

▶ The way that food is handled and cooked affects the amount of nutrients in it, its safety, and its taste.

▶ Food provides the opportunity for social time, and the rights of self and others are considered through the sharing of food.

Nutrition experiences help children to develop cognitively, physically, emotionally, and socially. Here are some examples of how food can be incorporated into all areas of the centre's curriculum:

▶ *Art.* Use magazines and grocery store fliers to create collages of various foods; food cartons to be recycled after use can be painted or used in box sculpture; draw pictures of how you feel eating different foods (e.g., puckered face after drinking lemonade). *It is important to note that during art and craft activities the use of food that will not be eaten is unacceptable and is disrespectful of food and of those who do not have enough to eat.*

▶ *Music.* Sing songs about foods; the words to familiar children's songs can be modified to include nutrition messages.

▶ *Creative movement.* Pretend to be fruits or vegetables planted, picked, harvested, falling to the ground.

▶ *Science.* Design activities using one or more senses (e.g., discovery box with foods inside to touch and describe before eating). Grow foods (e.g., gardening in plots or boxes), comparing fruits and vegetables (e.g., fresh, frozen, canned, dried)

▶ *Literature.* Read books about food, cooking, gardening (e.g., *The Sandwich* or *Everyone Eats Rice* to support issues of diversity).

▶ *Numeracy.* Use scales and measures to compare weights of foods.

▶ *Social studies.* Share foods and eating customs with others—activities particularly relevant for older preschool and school-age children. Examples are foods eaten for Dwali, harvest foods, haggis, foods for Kwanza celebration, origins or inventions of foods and eating implements, cooking equipment, utensils).

▶ *Dramatic play.* Set up a grocery store (e.g., empty cracker and cereal boxes), restaurant, or pizzeria, and provide lifelike food. Use cooking and eating utensils to reflect ethno-cultural diversity.

▶ *Field trips*. Visit grocery stores, markets, bakeries, farms, local gardens, or a health food store, or invite a child's family member to come and cook a traditional dish.

Cooking with Children   Cooking with children is an ideal way to begin their nutrition education. Snacks provide an opportunity each day for children to have food experiences. Food preparation calls on children to use their five senses, to learn about colours, shapes, and textures, and to use simple kitchen utensils. Children can begin to learn the basic principles of hygiene and food safety, and of course take pride in their accomplishments and eat the "fruits" of their labour. Even older infants love to squeeze bananas or help mash potatoes. Children build their cooking skills—life skills that will serve them well.

The Five W's of Cooking with Children:
Who?

The ideal caregiver–child ratios:

- infants 1:1
- toddlers 1:2
- preschoolers 1:3
- school-agers 1:4 maximum

The worst situation:
A large group of children with one caregiver.

These ratios promote safe cooking practices and allow for individual participation.

TABLE 7.3	SNACKS CHILDREN CAN MAKE
AGE GROUP	**SNACK IDEAS**
Infants	simple fruit salad, mashed banana, applesauce, blended mango pudding, cottage cheese with a face made with Cheerios, frozen fruit juice on sticks, finger gelatin made with fruit juice and plain gelatin, well-cooked carrot sticks with yogurt dip,◇ smoothed avocado on crackers, fruit and yogurt blender drinks
Toddlers	devilled eggs using yogurt instead of mayonnaise, cottage cheese salad with crushed pineapple, porridge for a teddy bear picnic, ants on a log (i.e., bread sticks with apple butter and Rice Crispies), fruit or vegetable and cheese kabobs using Popsicle sticks, frozen bananas on sticks served with thinned peanut butter or applesauce dips,◇ banana coins in orange juice, nutritious milk shakes
Preschoolers	English muffin pizzas, dippidy-doo and vegetables too, guacamole and corn tortilla chips, pita sandwiches, unidentified frying objects (i.e., cut circle out of slice of bread and fry with an egg in the hole), homemade butter (shake cream) for sandwiches or crackers, vegetable (stone) soup, yogurt and fruit sundaes, "people" sandwiches (e.g., hummus on circles of bread with grated carrots, alfalfa sprouts, apple smiles, sunflower seeds, banana coins, etc., to make faces)
School-Agers	tacos, three-bean salad, muffins, baked apples, rice pudding, Waldorf salad, banana-egg pancakes, chop suey, stir-fried vegetables, pretzels, fondue, stuffed pita, hummus with crackers, sticky rice

◇ Provide children with individual dishes of dip. Double dipping in a communal dish spreads germs.

What?

Two ways of cooking with children:

▶ small group with a caregiver, usually using a recipe that makes enough food for a number of children (e.g., baking)

▶ individual children following the recipe, often called "production-line cooking," usually using a recipe that makes individual portions

Select nutritious foods that are developmentally appropriate and do not pose a risk for choking. Ensure that allergies and food restrictions (religious, ethno-cultural) are considered in planning any food experience.

Children learn from following recipes:

1. the names of food and food mixtures
2. sequential learning: recipes that are based on developmental appropriateness, for example:
   • 2 steps for infants
   • 3 to 4 steps for toddlers
   • 4 to 6 steps for preschoolers
   • 8 steps maximum for school-agers
3. measuring ingredients

Pictorial and written *recipe cards* are particularly useful for preschoolers and school-agers. They incorporate sequencing and pre-reading skills (or reading, for older children) into the experience, and children learn that a lot of food preparation involves recipes. For pre-readers, there should be many illustrations with just a few words. It is possible to use one recipe card listing all the steps (e.g., on a piece of construction paper). For individual portion cooking, a set of recipe cards (one card for each step) makes it easier for children to do one step and then move to the next station.

Tips in making recipe cards:

▶ Cut out pictures or drawings of food, cooking equipment, and utensils used in each step.

▶ Use a dot system rather than numbers to indicate each step, particularly for preschoolers (e.g., one dot on the first card, two dots on the second).

▶ Laminate for durability with repeated use.

As children become more familiar with the printed word, you may want to create recipe cards that combine pictures and words (e.g., have a picture of the apple, and print the word apple, or use the dots and symbol for the number two). For readers, the recipe's steps can be presented in a chart format.

When?

The ideal time is during play time, as one choice among several activities. This way, you may be able to work with smaller groups at a time and repeat the recipe until all

children who want to can do it. With the ideal number of children (or close to it), you are able to focus on each child's questions, reactions, and so on, and each child is truly involved in the process. Your role as facilitator is very important. If children are independently doing a production-line recipe, ensure that other children are not waiting in line. This creates an antisocial climate. Instead, children can sign up and come at their turn.

The worst time is during a circle time or other large group times. It is not realistic to expect a large number of children to work together at something that needs only a few. Passing a bowl around while each child has one stir is not learning—it creates frustration and your role is focused on crowd control rather than on facilitating.

Where?

The ideal place:
In a low-traffic area located close to running water and an electrical outlet, if needed.

The worst place:
In a noisy, busy area.

Why?

Food experiences (or cooking) with children can be positive in many ways:

▶ Everyone needs to eat!
▶ When children are involved in food preparation, they are more likely to try the food.
▶ Cooking is usually an enjoyable experience for children. They are proud of their accomplishments, which builds self-esteem.

Any well-planned food experience has many advantages for children:

1. Cognitive opportunities are made available and facilitated through foods.
   ▷ Children can see similarities and differences (classification).
   ▷ They can experience temporal relations (sense of time and sequence).
   ▷ They can develop a sense of quantity and measurement.
   ▷ They can problem-solve (e.g., What will happen if . . .?).
   ▷ They can take part in matching (one-to-one correspondence).
   ▷ They can learn about growing plants.
   ▷ They can learn about the origins of foods, such as eggs from chickens, milk from cows and goats.
   ▷ They can see the effect of temperature on substances (e.g., freezing fruit juice, frying potato latkes, baking muffins).

2. Caregivers use opportunities to build language skills through food routines and nutritional learning experiences (e.g., by using the correct terms for foods, equipment, cooking processes, discussions about foods, and by following recipe cards).

3. Children regularly have the opportunity to participate in food preparation. This can be integrated into everyday curriculum. In addition to viewing meal and snack preparation as important aspects of everyday life, children build their cooking skills and have opportunities for cooperation and for appreciating a wider repertoire of foods, enhancing their ethno-cultural learning. Refer to Appendix 7.1 (page 541) for a list and some recipes of breads. Most ethno-

cultural groups have particular breads that are either staples or are familiar to them.

4. Food experiences involve both girls and boys, promoting an atmosphere of equity in both food preparation and cleanup.

To enhance the cooking experience, caregivers will

1. prepare for the activity:
   ▷ try out the recipe before using it with the children
   ▷ ensure that all ingredients and equipment are available and in working order
   ▷ check carefully for any food allergies or restrictions

2. promote safety:
   ▷ Have all necessary equipment and ingredients set out in a safe location before beginning the activity. (School-agers are involved in this aspect of cooking.)
   ▷ Explain and/or demonstrate all safety aspects to the children before starting (e.g., using knives) and practise these precautions during the activity.
   ▷ follow food safety tips:

      ✔ The table is cleaned and sanitized before you begin.
      ✔ You and the school-agers wash hands before setting up the ingredients, utensils, and equipment.

✔ All children wash their hands.

✔ Everyone puts on an apron or some type of cover-up.

✔ If the snack is not to be eaten immediately, it is stored safely (e.g., blender drinks in the fridge).

✔ The utensils, equipment, and table are cleaned and sanitized when finished.

3. facilitate the activity:
   ▷ Encourage every child to participate.
   ▷ Be receptive to the questions and feelings of each child.
   ▷ Show interest and enjoyment in the activity through facial expression, tone of voice, body language, flexibility, and positive interactions with children.
   ▷ Ask questions that encourage problem-solving.
   ▷ Use positive guidance throughout the activity.

4. evaluate:
   ▷ Were the expectations appropriate for children's learning?
   ▷ Did each child have opportunities to actively participate?
   ▷ Was the time frame appropriate?
   ▷ What follow-up experiences would be meaningful?

It is important to involve families in your nutritional education curriculum. Some family members may be available to come in and make a favourite recipe with the children; others may send in a recipe or a food that has special meaning in ethno-cultural or religious events. Centres may also find ways to share families' favourite recipes through newsletters, bulletin boards, cookbook projects (possible fundraiser), and potluck events throughout the year.

DENTAL HEALTH EDUCATION

Dental health education is a good example of children learning through a daily routine. Dental care is a lifelong health habit. Caregivers are in an ideal position to take an active role in ensuring that children's teeth are protected and help children to learn good dental health practices. Taking good care of teeth and gums is important in maintaining dental health, and so are regular dental checkups, to respond to problems early. For families who are financially comfortable, professional dental care is usually not a problem. Many of these parents have dental benefits through their employers. Families with a low income, but not on social assistance, are often in a position where they do not have dental benefits, and the family budget may not be able to include the costs of a dentist.

By around age 2, children have 20 primary (or baby) teeth. Between ages 5 and 13, primary teeth start to loosen and fall out as the permanent teeth underneath begin pushing through the gums. Most children start by losing the lower two front teeth and then the top two, creating the classic smile. The back four molars are some of the first permanent teeth to come in, around age 6; special care is needed in brushing and flossing these back teeth.

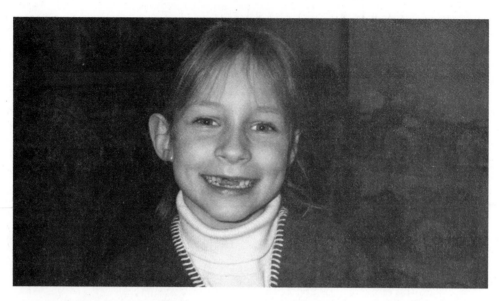

Everyone gets plaque on the teeth. This thick, sticky bacterial layer is constantly on our teeth. The bacteria in the plaque mix with food in our mouth to produce an acid that will begin eroding the enamel layer of our teeth. While saliva helps to neutralize the acid and rinse food out of our mouth, it can't do it all. Brushing and flossing are needed to remove food and plaque; if the plaque stays there, it hardens and causes tartar, which leads to tooth decay. Brushing our teeth before going to bed is a good practice. When we are asleep we don't produce as much saliva, so the bacteria and food left in our mouth produces acid that eats at enamel.

Do not prop baby bottles or put children in bed with a bottle.

▶ These practices allow formula or milk (containing sugar) to pool in the mouth for a long period of time. Babies' teeth are soft and very susceptible to acid and decay. It is shocking to see how quickly nursing bottle syndrome can happen, leading to painful tooth decay of primary teeth. The dull white spots or lines can appear on newly erupted teeth seemingly overnight. Parents are encouraged to see a dentist as soon as possible if this happens.

▶ Children should not be put to bed even with a bottle of water. *This practice increases the child's risk of choking.* Children who need the extra comfort of sucking for sleeping could be offered a soother.

▶ Sucking is a natural and normal developmental need in young children. Although parents and physicians have different opinions about the use of bottles and soothers, dentists are concerned about the child's teeth when usage continues after age 5. If an older child (aged 4 or 5) still derives comfort and security from soothers or thumb-sucking, adults must take care to help the child find a replacement. This is important for children's emotional well-being.

▶ Children's eustachian tubes are shorter and straighter than adults'. When children lie on their back with a bottle in their mouth, the liquid and saliva may run back into the middle ear and cause an ear infection.

How Do We Promote Dental Health? Fluoride is a mineral that strengthens our enamel. People who live in communities in which the drinking water is supplied through a water treatment plant probably haven't given much thought to fluoride. That decision is made by the communities' public health agency. In many communities, fluoride is added to the drinking water before it reaches our homes. Other sources of fluoride are toothpaste, fluoride drops prescribed by physicians, and fluoride treatments by dentists.

Limit the amounts of high-sugar foods offered, particularly sticky ones (e.g., raisins, granola bars, pop, hard candies) or foods with cooked starch (e.g., potato chips, bread, potatoes). Sugars mix with the bacteria to quickly produce acid. Choose nutritious foods, especially fresh fruit and vegetables, plain yogurts, cheese, and milk. Frequent snacking (or grazing) is discouraged because food is in our mouth so often, and acid production is frequent.

Ideally, we should brush our teeth after every meal and snack, and floss at least once a day. When this is not possible, we should at least try to rinse our mouth with water. The Canadian Dental Association recommends that parents thoroughly brush their young children's teeth once a day. This is in addition to the children learning how to brush their teeth themselves. Parents should also floss their child's teeth once a day until the child has the skill to floss his or her own teeth.

In centres, caregivers are encouraged to have children brush their teeth at least once during the day. For many centres, this follows lunch time as children begin the transition for a nap or quiet activity. On field trips, children can rinse their mouth with water. Flossing is difficult in centres because of the extra time and demands involved.

Tips for toothbrushing:

▶ Use a soft toothbrush.
▶ Add toothpaste. Use a small dab for infants and toddlers; preschoolers need an amount only about the size of a pea. Be careful that the tip of the tube doesn't touch the brush. A caregiver will need to help younger children to put on the paste, especially if one tube is used for everyone. Some centres find that it is easier

FIGURE 7.1   TOOTHBRUSHING PATTERN

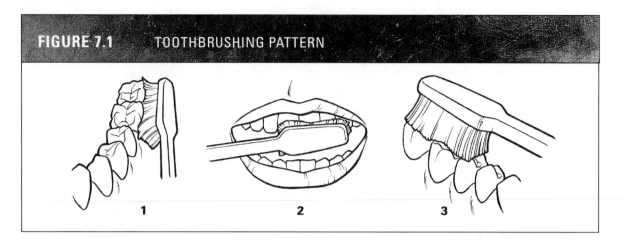

and that it promotes independence if each child has his or her own small tube of toothpaste.

▶ Follow the three-step method (Figure 7.1) and brush or supervise the child's brushing. Start at the far lower-back teeth, using a "wiggling," not a scrubbing motion. Move around the mouth, wiggling the brush on all the surfaces. Don't forget to brush the tongue to fight bacteria and freshen breath.

▶ Teach children not to swallow the toothpaste. Rinse with water and spit.

▶ Rinse the brushes well.

Tips for toothbrushes:

▶ Use a baby toothbrush for infants and toddlers and a child-sized one for children up to 12 years old.

▶ Each child must have his or her own brush and must never share it.

▶ Label each child's toothbrush and store it to dry, where air will circulate around it and where it doesn't touch other toothbrushes. Caregivers often have to be very creative in designing a convenient, hygienic storage method.

▶ Keep out of reach of children to ensure that brushes are not used by different children and as a safety precaution. Children must learn not to run or walk around with a toothbrush in their mouth.

▶ Replace brushes when the bristles begin to flatten, after the child has been ill with a cold/flu, or at least twice a year.

Infants and toddlers:
When toddlers are able to stand at the sink, they are able to participate more in toothbrushing. Standing behind the toddler and facing the mirror tends to be a convenient position. Caregivers may either do the brushing for the child or hold the brush with the toddler. For older toddlers, the caregiver carefully supervises.

Preschoolers and school-agers:
With experience, preschoolers become skilled at toothbrushing, and the caregiver eventually needs only to supervise rather than be actively involved. Most school-

agers are able to brush their teeth without supervision and have gained more responsibility and independence in self-care. Although some children simply don't like brushing their teeth or don't like one more routine, most children appreciate the immediate results: brighter teeth and a clean-tasting mouth. Involve children in planning and preparing dentally healthy snacks. Caregivers can also encourage children to be aware of healthy food choices and explain how some foods promote dental health.

 This centre has the children brush their teeth after lunch. However, for afternoon snack a child's birthday cake is served. Because there is sugar and sticky icing on the cake, the children brush their teeth again after snack that day.

Learning about dental health can be incorporated into all areas of the centre's curriculum:

- ▶ Art—Paint and draw pictures of food; create a big set of teeth with egg cartons.
- ▶ Creative movement—Children can wiggle their bodies like they wiggle the toothbrush, an activity more appropriate for younger preschoolers.
- ▶ Music—Sing songs (e.g., about smiles: Raffi's "You Brush Your Teeth").
- ▶ Science—Place a hard-boiled egg in vinegar, which helps to show how enamel dissolves.
- ▶ Literature—Read books about keeping teeth, losing teeth (e.g., tooth fairy stories such as "Where Do the Fairies Keep All the Teeth?"), and dental health.
- ▶ Numeracy—Count teeth (e.g., how many molars); classify pictures of foods that are good and bad for your teeth.
- ▶ Lunch time/snacks—Discuss the importance of our teeth in crunching carrots and biting into apples.
- ▶ Dramatic play—Set up a dentist's office and provide a rich variety of real props, including flashlight, mirror, and lab coat.
- ▶ Field trips—Tour a dentist's office; invite a dental hygienist to talk about dental health.

HAND-WASHING AND GERMS

Hand-washing is the most important routine that we do every day to prevent infections. It is a health practice that children need to learn in order for it to become a lifelong health habit. Like dental health, education about hand-washing is based on an ongoing routine in the program, and there are many opportunities to reinforce it.

Infants and Toddlers   The hand-washing routine begins in infancy as part of diapering and feeding routines. Caregivers talk with infants about what they are doing as they are doing it, making comments like "The water is warm" or "The cloth feels soft and wet." Infants are aware of their hands being washed, and feel that it is part of caring.

Once toddlers are physically able to stand at the sink, caregivers can help them learn to wash their own hands. It is easier for children to learn the proper way and to make it a habit with practice than it is to change poor habits once they are formed. Caregivers may make the routine enjoyable for children by singing action songs like "This Is The Way We Wash Our Hands."

Preschoolers   Preschool children are ready for basic information about germs and what hand-washing does to germs. During the preschool years, children become skilled at hand-washing when adults provide consistent support built on earlier experience. By the time they are independently washing their hands, with caregivers now only supervising, they can learn some basic information about germs (e.g., germs are on our hands even when they look clean and they hide between fingers and under nails).

How can preschoolers learn about germs when germs can't be seen on hands? As with all aspects of the curriculum, it is essential to encourage active involvement and introduce concepts in a concrete way. Caregivers reinforce that we are trying to prevent as many germs as we can from entering our bodies. Because our hands touch many things, there are a lot of germs on them. Most children don't walk around with facial tissue in a pocket; rather than not covering their mouth when they sneeze, and rather than sneeze into their hands, they can put their arm in front of their mouth. This prevents germs from getting on their hands.

Since we can't see germs, caregivers can show preschoolers something to compare to germs. Use a spray bottle to spray water into the air; the water droplets seem to disappear in the air and fall onto objects. Germs in the water now float in the air, and can land anywhere—including on someone else. When we cough and sneeze, droplets of saliva that carry germs spray out. This helps children to understand why covering their mouth before sneezing is a good way to cut down on germs going from one person to another.

Learning about hand-washing can be incorporated into different curriculum areas:

- ▶ Art—Draw what they think germs would look like if they could see them.
- ▶ Music—Sing songs (e.g., to the tune of "Row, Row, Row Your Boat," "Scrub, scrub, scrub your hands, put the soap between, wash the germs right down the drain, make them nice and clean").
- ▶ Science—Put a piece of bread in a jar, and over the next several days invite the children to watch mould grow.
- ▶ Literature—Read books (e.g., *William! Won't You Wash Your Hands?*).
- ▶ Dramatic play—Use the water table to wash dolls, including the hands.
- ▶ Nutrition—Show how food can be shared without spreading germs (e.g., serving spoons, cutting a sandwich in half rather than taking turns having a bite).

School-Agers School-age children will be hand-washing without supervision, although many need to be reminded. Developmentally, these children are at an age when discussions about germs and the role of hand-washing can be more complex.

Germs are everywhere and some of them help keep us healthy (e.g., penicillin, yogurt). Skin and nose hairs stop some germs from getting into our bodies. Our body has other ways to defend us: tears, saliva, and stomach juices kill some germs when they get into our body.

Activities such as growing moulds on foods (e.g., apple core in a jar) or growing germs from fingers on agar petri dishes are appropriate (contact your local hospital or make agar mixture with the children.) Children in the concrete operational stage can understand that the mouldy apple is the same apple a week later, and the same with the petri dish.

Revisiting the Health Promotion Action Plan

A criticism of *Achieving Health for All*, discussed in Unit 1, is that it does not acknowledge the importance of children's active involvement in promoting their own health (Hart-Zeldin et al. 1990, 196). *Achieving Health for All* holds expectations for individuals to participate in their self-care, mutual aid, and healthy communities. But the skills needed to do so, such as decision-making, coping, and public participation, don't happen overnight; it takes practice and confidence to develop them. These are skills that children can learn only when they are developmentally ready, but they also need ongoing experiences.

In order to fulfill Epp's vision regarding mutual aid and public participation, children need experiences which encourage them to see themselves as participants, helpers or change agents in their communities. They must learn to become empathetic, to create supportive peer environments, and to give and accept help when needed. (Hart-Zeldin et al. 1990, 197)

Children require opportunities to learn to care for themselves and others and to participate in their communities. These experiences serve them well in the vision of *Achieving Health for All*. Caregivers and parents assist children in finding a balance between having confidence in their own abilities and knowing when to depend on adults, the community, and society.

Health promotion is based on the philosophy that individuals can have both personal and public control over their lives, and can improve their own health. Through our awareness, we can effect change from the individual level to the societal level. Using the four components of the Health Promotion Action Plan, let's use the example of reducing the amount of non-reusable paper products going to landfill sites or garbage dumps.

Individual Problem-Solving and Self-Reliance   Caregivers bring their lunches in reusable containers. On coffee breaks they have their own mugs. Caregivers bring in empty food boxes (e.g., crackers, cereal), egg cartons, etc., for children to use in the art, home living centre, and dramatic play areas. Parents too bring these in, providing children with a range of food boxes that reflect the diversity of the centre. Everyone at the centre uses the recycling box and composter.

Collective Self-Help   The centre does not use paper and plastic (picnic-style) dishes and utensils. Three centres have joined together to purchase food in bulk, which reduces the amount of packaging. The centre has a policy that requires parents to bring in litterless meals for children. Caregivers share written materials on the environment with parents and children.

Community Development   Some of the school-agers have become concerned about overpackaging and the number of foam containers used in their neighbourhood fast-food restaurant to serve hamburgers, most of which are carried to a table only a few steps away. With the support of their parents, teachers, and the caregivers, they organize a protest in front of the restaurant.

Societal Change   Growing media attention and public support generated from just that one fast-food restaurant led the company to dramatically change its style of packaging worldwide.

Conclusion

A holistic view of children's health is based on the premise that the whole child must always be considered. This view is particularly important when discussing issues that at first glance seem to relate to only one dimension of well-being, such as stress (emotional) or rest (physical). We quickly realize that there are physical, emotional, and social considerations with all health issues. Health policies and procedures based on the centre's philosophy are written and reviewed regularly to ensure that this holistic view of health is put into practice on an ongoing basis.

Health curriculum is determined by the developmental needs and interests of the children. It is integrated into everyday life at the centre. The relevance of health curriculum to the children's lives is paramount in planning, implementing, and evaluating.

WHAT'S YOUR OPINION?
TO PROVIDE SYRINGES OR NOT?

Caregivers plan to incorporate a doctor/hospital space in the preschool's dramatic play area. One of the parents provides them with two sterile syringes (without needles) for the children to play with. A debate arises about whether providing children with syringes is appropriate. Some caregivers feel that this would help children work through their anxieties about vaccinations.

Others are concerned about discarded syringes and needles frequently picked up in the playground. They regularly tell children that if they find one, leave it on the ground and call a caregiver. These caregivers feel that play syringes give children a mixed message. Which side of the debate would you join?

► A S S E S S   Y O U R   L E A R N I N G

Define terms or describe concepts used in this unit.
* self-regulation
* sexuality
* self-pleasuring
* common, short-term stress factors
* traumatic, long-term stress factors
* coping strategies for stress
* stress-aware environment
* rhythm of the program
* health policies
* children's understanding of health
* health curriculum
* health needs and interests
* 5 W's of cooking with children
* dental health
* nursing bottle syndrome
* bottle-propping
* personal safety

Evaluate your options in each situation.

1. You overhear an ECE student saying to a 3-year-old, "You have to play with Daniel. We are all friends at day care."

2. While you are on a field trip, a 4-year-old boy points to a pregnant woman and asks, "Why is that woman's tummy so big?"

3. A few preschoolers have recently moved to Canada from countries that are much warmer year-round. They are having a difficult time adjusting to winter. The parents have asked you to let them stay inside with another group of children rather than taking them outside to play.

4. A parent of an infant is becoming increasingly frustrated lately with expectations and exclusion guidelines that she feels she had never been informed of.

5. You and a classmate have been asked to plan curriculum to help preschoolers learn about poison prevention. You agree that it would be a good idea to bring in real objects. Next day, your partner arrives with a bag of potentially hazardous products, including oven, window, and toilet cleaners that she uses at home.

6. The centre where you are doing a placement does not promote good nutrition. You are responsible for the weekly after-school cooking club and have submitted your plan to the caregiver. You would like to begin with simple recipes such as "dippidy-doo and vegetables too" and move to more complex recipes such as soups and breads. The caregiver discourages you with the comment, "This will never work. The children only want to make cookies and cakes."

▶ **R E S O U R C E   M A T E R I A L S**

Organizations

Family and Child Health Unit, Health Promotion Directorate, Health Canada, 4th Floor, Jeanne Mance Building, Tunney's Pasture, Ottawa, ON K1A 1B4. Tel. (613) 957-7804, fax (613) 990-7097.

National Multicultural, Racism-Free, Bias-Free Early Childhood Education Network, c/o ECMS, 201–1675 W. 4th Avenue, Vancouver, BC V6J 1L8. Tel. (604) 739-9456.

Printed Matter

Alerta: A Multicultural, Bilingual Approach to Teaching Young Children (1989), by L.R. Williams et al. (Addison-Wesley Publishing).

Anti-Bias Curriculum: Tools for Empowering Young Children (1989), by L. Derman-Sparks and the ABC Task Force (National Association for the Education of Young Children).

Beyond Winning: Sports and Games All Kids Want to Play (1990), by L. Rowen (Fearon Teacher Aids).

The Body Book: How Your Body Gets Built, Learns, Repairs Itself, and Makes You Who You Are (1992), by S. Stein (Workman Publishing).

The Canadian Green Consumer Guide (1989), by Pollution Probe Foundation (McClelland & Stewart).

Caring Spaces, Learning Places: Children's Environments That Work (1988), by J. Greenman (Exchange Press).

The Child in the Family and the Community (1993), by J. Gonzalez-Mena (Maxwell Macmillan Canada).

Children and the AIDS Virus: A Book for Children, Parents & Teachers (1989), by R. Hausherr (Clarion Books).

Come to Your Senses: All Eleven of Them (1993), by M. Tytla (Annick Press).

Co-operative Games: For People Who Love to Play, 2nd ed. (1986), by A.R. Davies (Public Focus).

The Cooperative Indoor & Outdoor Game Book: Easy Classroom and Field Games for Fitness and Fun (1992), by P. Huff (Scholastic Canada).

The Cooperative Sports & Games Book: Challenge without Competition (1978), by T. Orlick, Pantheon Books.

Creative Movement for the Developing Child: A Nursery School Handbook for Non-Musicians, rev. ed. (1971), by C. Cherry (Fearon Teacher Aids).

Dance and Grow: Developmental Dance Activities for Three- through Eight-Year-Olds (1994), by B. Rowen (Princeton Book Company).

Developing Safety Skills with Young Children: A Commonsense, Nonthreatening Approach (1987), by D.E. Comer (Delmar Publishers).

Developmentally Appropriate Television: Putting Children First (1992), by D.E. Levin and N. Carlsson-Paige, *Young Children* (July):38–44. (self-esteem and body image)

Early Childhood Education for a Multicultural Society: A Handbook for Educators (1985), by G. Chud, R. Fahlman, and R. Wedge (Pacific Educational Press).

Feeling Strong, Feeling Free: Movement Exploration for Young Children (1982), by M. Sullivan (National Association for the Education of Young Children).

First Feelings: Milestones in the Emotional Development of Your Baby and Child (1986), by S. Greenspan and N.T. Greenspan (Penguin Books).

First Teeth: A Dental Health Care Booklet for Parents of Children Up to Age 9 (1990), by Canadian Dental Association, 1815 Alta Vista Drive, Ottawa, ON K1G 3Y6; national toll-free (800) 267-6354.

Germ Smart: Children's Activities in Disease Prevention (1990), by J.K. Scheer (Network Publications).

Green Teacher: Education for Planet Earth (for subscriptions: 95 Robert Street, Toronto, ON M5S 2K5. Tel. [416] 960-1244, fax [416] 925-3474). (journal)

A Guide to School Ground Naturalization: Welcoming the Wilderness (1994), by Evergreen Foundation, 24 Mercer Street, Toronto, ON M5V 1H3. Tel. (416) 596-1495 (Prentice-Hall Canada).

Healthy Foundations: Developing Positive Policies and Programs Regarding Young Children's Learning About Sexuality (1993), by P. Brick (Center for Family Life Education, Planned Parenthood of Greater Northern New Jersey, 575 Main Street, Hackensack, NJ 07601. Tel. [201] 489-1265).

Healthy Foundations: The Teacher's Book Responding to Young Children's Questions and Behaviors Regarding Sexuality (1993), by P. Brick (Center for Family Life Education, Planned Parenthood of Greater Northern New Jersey).

Hello Toes! Movement Games for Children (1989), by A.L. Barlin and N. Kalen (Princeton Book Company).

Ideas: The Journal of Emotional Well-Being in Child Care (IDEAS Alliance and George Brown College, Community Services Division, Nightingale Campus, P.O. Box 1015, Station B, Toronto, ON M5T 2T9. Tel. [416] 867-2566).

Infants, Toddlers, and Caregivers (1989), by J. Gonzalez-Mena and D. Widmeyer (Mayfield Publishing).

International Playtime: Classroom Games and Dances from around the World (1992), by W.E. Nelson and H. Glass (Fearon Teacher Aids).

Keepers of Life: Discovering Plants through Native Stories and Earth Activities for Children (1994), by M.J. Caduto and J. Bruchac (Fifth House).

Keepers of the Animals: Native Stories and Wildlife Activities for Children (1991), by M.J. Caduto and J. Bruchac (Fifth House).

Keepers of the Earth: Native Stories and Environmental Activities for Children (1989), by M.J. Caduto and J. Bruchac (Fifth House).

Keepers of the Night: Native Stories and Nocturnal Activities for Children (1994), by M.J. Caduto and J. Bruchac (Fifth House).

The Kid's Around the World Cookbook (1994), by D. Robins (Kingfisher).

Kids in Action: A Community Development Approach to Children's Health (1991), by P. Pollack et al. (Lawrence Heights Community Health Centre Press, 12 Flemington Road, Toronto, ON M6A 2N4. Tel. [416] 787-1672, fax [416] 787-3761).

Kids in the Kitchen (1975), by N. Edge (Peninsula Publishing).

Keeping the Peace: Practicing Cooperation and Conflict Resolution with Preschoolers (1989), by S. Wichert (New Society Publishers).

Learning & Caring about Our World: Activities for Helping Young Children Learn and Care about Their Environment (1990), by G. Bittinger (Warren Publishing House).

Let's Help This Planet: Teachers' Activity Guide (1992), by Kim and Jerry Brody Productions, 178 Wineva Avenue, Toronto, ON M4E 2T4. Tel. (416) 690-8494. (includes CD or cassette)

Looking at Senses (1986), by D. Suzuki (Stoddart Publishing Co.).

Looking at the Body (1987), by D. Suzuki (Stoddart Publishing Co.).

Make It Multicultural—Musical Activities for Early Childhood Education (1989), by P. Fralick (University of Toronto).

A Manual for Parents and Professionals (1979), by M. Gerber (ed.) (Resources for Infant Educarers [RIE], 1550 Murray Circle, Los Angeles, CA 90026).

Model Child Care Health Policies (1993), by S. Aronson and H. Smith (National Association for the Education of Young Children).

Movement Activities for Early Childhood (1992), by C.T. Hammett (Human Kinetics Publishers).

Moving and Growing: Exercises and Activities for Fives and Sixes (1987), by J. Hansen (Fitness Canada and the Canadian Institute of Child Health).

Moving and Growing: Exercises and Activities for the First Two Years (1983), by M. Dalley (Fitness Canada and the Canadian Institute of Child Health).

Moving and Growing: Exercises and Activities for Twos, Threes and Fours (1984), by M. Dalley (Fitness Canada and the Canadian Institute of Child Health).

Multicultural Issues in Child Care (1993), by J. Gonzalez-Mena (Mayfield Publishing).

Nobody's Perfect, by Family and Child Health Unit (Health Promotion Directorate, Health Canada).

Open the Door, Let's Explore: Neighborhood Field Trips for Young Children (1983), by R. Redleaf (Toys 'n Things Press).

Outdoor Action Games for Elementary Children: Active Games & Academic Activities for Fun & Fitness (1994), by J.L. Overholt (Parker Publishing).

The Outrageous Outdoor Games Book: 133 Group Projects, Games, and Activities (1984), by B. Gregson (Fearon Teachers Aids).

The Outside Play and Learning Book: Activities for Young Children (1989), by K. Miller (Gryphon House).

Owl (for school-agers) and *Chickadee* (for preschoolers and younger school-agers), two Canadian magazines on nature and environmental topics. For subscriptions: Owl and Chickadee Magazines, 179 John Street, Suite 500, P.O. Box 15026, Station BRM B, Toronto, ON M7Y 2Y6. Tel. (416) 971-5271; national toll-free (800) 387-4379.

Raising Sexually Healthy Children: A Loving Guide for Parents, Teachers and Care-Givers (1988), by L. Leight (Avon Books).

Reducing Stress in Young Children's Lives (1986), by J. Brown McCracken (ed.) (National Association for the Education of Young Children).

Safe & Happy Personal Safety Kit (1988), by Canadian Institute of Child Health and Outreach Abuse Prevention (Ottawa, ON: Canadian Institute of Child Health).

The Second Cooperative Sports & Games Book: Over Two Hundred Brand-New Noncompetitive Games for Kids and Adults Both (1982), by T. Orlick (Pantheon Books).

Sharing Nature with Children: The Classic Parents' and Teachers' Nature Awareness Guidebook (1979), by J. Cornell (Dawn Publishing).

Starbright: Meditations for Children (1991), by M. Garth (HarperCollins Publishers).

Teaching Snacks: Snacktime Learning Opportunities (1994), by G. Bittinger (Warren Publishing).

Why Do Our Bodies Stop Growing? Questions about Human Anatomy Answered by the Natural History Museum (1988), by P. Whitfield and R. Whitfield (Viking Penguin).

You and Me Tobacco Free: Children's Activities in Tobacco Awareness (1990), by J.K. Scheer (Network Publications).

Zero to Three, National Center for Clinical Infant Programs, 2000 14th Street N., Suite 380, Arlington, VA 22201-2500. (journal)

▶ **B I B L I O G R A P H Y**

American Public Health Association and American Academy of Pediatrics (1992) *Caring for Our Children: National Health and Safety Performance Standards—Guidelines for Out-of-Home Child Care Programs.* Washington, DC: American Public Health Association.

Aronson, S. (1991) *Health and Safety in Child Care.* Toronto: HarperCollins Publishers.

Avery, M. (1994) "Preschool Physical Education: A Practical Approach." *Journal of Physical Education, Research and Development* Aug.: 37–39.

Balaban, N. (1985) *Starting School: From Separation to Independence, A Guide for Early Childhood Teachers.* Toronto: Teachers' College Press.

Barker, G. (1994) "The Facts about Fitness: Why Exercise Is Important for Kids." *Today's Parents* 11(7):25–27.

Bredekamp, S. (ed.) (1989) *Developmentally Appropriate Practice in Early Childhood Programs Serving Children from Birth through Age 8,* expanded ed. Washington, DC: National Association for the Education of Young Children.

Brick, P., et al. (1989) *Bodies, Birth and Babies: Sexuality Education in Early Childhood Programs.* Hackensack, NJ: Center for Family Life Education, Planned Parenthood of Greater Northern New Jersey.

Brown, L. (1994) "When Kids Ask about Homosexuality." *Toronto Star*, 20 September, C1, C3.

Campaign 2000 (1998) *Child Poverty in Canada: Report Card 1998*. Toronto: Family Services Association.

Canadian Association for Health, Physical Education and Recreation (1992a) *Physical Education Report Care*. Gloucester, ON: Canadian Association for Health, Physical Education and Recreation.

——— (1992b) *The Evidence behind Quality Daily Physical Education: Fact Sheets*. Gloucester, ON: Canadian Association for Health, Physical Education and Recreation, 1–5.

Canadian Day Care Advocacy Association and Canadian Child Care Federation (1992) *Caring for a Living: Executive Summary*. Ottawa: Canadian Child Care Federation.

Canadian Dental Association (1990) *First Teeth: A Dental Health Care Booklet for Parents of Children up to Age 9*. Ottawa: Canadian Dental Association.

Canadian Institute of Child Health (1994) *The Health of Canada's Children: A CICH Profile*, 2nd ed. Ottawa: Canadian Institute of Child Health.

Canadian Institute of Child Health and Outreach Abuse Prevention (1988) *Safe & Happy Personal Safety Kit*. Ottawa: Canadian Institute of Child Health.

Canadian Paediatric Society (1992) *Well Beings: A Guide to Promote the Physical Health, Safety and Emotional Well-Being of Children in Child Care Centres and Family Day Care Homes*. Toronto: Creative Premises.

Cech, M. (1990) *Globalchild: Multicultural Resources for Young Children*. Ottawa: Health and Welfare Canada.

Chehrazi, S.S., ed. (1990) *Psychosocial Issues in Day Care*. Washington, DC: American Psychiatric Press.

City of Toronto Department of Public Health (n.d.) *Talk Sex*. Toronto: Information and Communication Services Division, Department of the City Clerk (booklet).

Colgate-Palmolive Company (1991) *Bright Smiles, Bright Futures: Teacher Curriculum Guide—A Cross-Curricular, Multi-Cultural Oral Health Program for First Grade*. New York: Colgate-Palmolive Company.

Corbett, S. (1993) "A Complicated Bias." *Young Children* 48(3):29–31.

Degler, T., and Pollution Probe (1990) *The Canadian Junior Green Guide: How You Can Help Save Our World*. Toronto: McClelland & Stewart.

Gochman, D., and J.F. Saucier (1982) "Perceived Vulnerability in Children and Adolescents." *Health Education Quarterly* 9(2, 3):46–59.

Goulet, M., and R. Schroeder (1998) *How Caring Relationships Support Self-Regulation: Video Guide*. Toronto: Distributed by NAGYC, 1-800-424-2460.

Greenspan, S., and N.T. Greenspan (1986) *First Feelings: Milestones in the Emotional Development of Your Baby and Child*. Markham, ON: Penguin Books.

Greenspan, S.I. (1993) *Playground Politics: Understanding the Emotional Life of Your School-Age Child*. Don Mills, ON: Addison-Wesley Publishing.

Guralnick, K.M., and E. Littmann (1992) *Making Friends: A Guide to Using the Assessment of Peer Relations and Planning Interventions*. Ottawa: Department of National Health and Welfare. (video and guide)

Hart-Zeldin, C., et al. (1990) "Children in the Context of Achieving Health for All: A Framework for Health Promotion." *Canadian Journal of Public Health* 81(3):196–98.

Hendricks, C. (1991) *Here We Go … Watch Me Grow: A Preschool Health Curriculum*. Santa Cruz: Network Publications.

Herr, J., and W. Morse (1982) "Food for Thought: Nutrition Education for Young Children." *Young Children* 38:3–11.

Jewett, C. (1982) *Helping Children Cope with Separation and Loss*. Boston: Harvard Common Press.

Kalmanson, B. (1990) "Understanding Children's Responses to Separation in Psychosocial Issues in Day Care," in *Psychosocial Issues in Day Care*, S.S. Chehrazi (ed.). Washington, DC: American Psychiatric Press.

Kalnins, I., and R. Love (1982) "Children's Concepts of Health and Illness—and Implications for Health Education: An Overview." *Health Education Quarterly* 9(2, 3):104–15.

Kalnins, I., et al. (1992) "Children, Empowerment and Health Promotion: Some New Directions in Research and Practice." *Health Promotion International* 7(1):53–59.

Kalnins, I.V., et al. (1994) "School-Based Community Development as a Health Promotion Strategy for Children." *Health Promotion International* 9(4):269–79.

Kaplan, P.S. (1991) *A Child's Odyssey: Child and Adolescent Development*, 2nd ed. New York: West Publishing.

Labonté, R. (1993) *Health Promotion: Theory and Practice Background Material #1*. Toronto: Centre for Health Promotion, University of Toronto.

La Grange, A., et al. (1994) "Culturally Sensitive Child Care: The Alberta Study." *Interaction* (fall) 8(3):29–32.

Lally, J.R. (1990) *Infant–Toddler Caregiving: A Guide to Social-Emotional Growth and Socialization.* Sacramento: California Department of Education.

Lally, J.R. (ed.) (1990) *Social-Emotional Growth and Socialization.* Berkeley: California Department of Education, Far West Laboratory for Educational Research and Development.

Levin, D.E., and N. Carlsson-Paige (1994) "Developmentally Appropriate Television: Putting Children First." *Young Children* 49(5):38–44.

Lewis-Webber, M. (1993) *Earthcycles: Environmental Education with Preschool Children.* Winnipeg: Mavis Lewis-Webber.

Lowenstein, J. (1992) *A Is for Apple, P Is for Pressure—Preschool Stress Management in Annual Editions: Early Childhood Education.* Connecticut: Dushkin Publishing Group.

Maguire, J. (1993) *Your Child's Emotional Health.* Toronto: Macmillan Canada.

Martin, A.D., and C.S. Houston (1987) "Osteoporosis, Calcium, and Physical Activity." *Canadian Medical Association Journal* 136(6):1–7.

Masi, R., et al., eds. (1993) *Health and Cultures: Exploring the Relationships—Policies, Professional Practice and Education,* vol. 1. Oakville, ON: Mosaic Press.

Mather, P. (1988) "Educating Preschoolers about Health Care." *Childhood Education* 65(2):94–100.

Musson, S. (1994) *School-Age Care: Theory and Practice.* Don Mills, ON: Addison-Wesley Publishers.

Natapoff, N. J. (1982) "A Developmental Analysis of Children's Ideas of Health." *Health Education Quarterly* (summer/fall) 9(2, 3):34–45.

National Clearinghouse on Family Violence (1990) *Information from . . . Child Sexual Abuse.* Ottawa: Health and Welfare Canada.

Nelson, G., and C. Hendricks (1988) "Health Education Needs in Child Care Programs." *Journal of School Health* 58(9):360–64.

Pollack, P., et al. (1991) *Kids in Action: A Community Development Approach to Children's Health.* Toronto: Lawrence Heights Community Health Centre Press.

Prudden, S. (1988) *Starting Right: Suzy Prudden's Fitness Program for Children 5–11*. New York: Doubleday Publishing.

Salkind, N.J. (1990) *Child Development*, 6th ed. Toronto: Holt, Rinehart and Winston.

Santrock, J.W. (1997) *Children*, 5th ed. Dubuque, IA: Wm. C. Brown Publishers.

Sarafino, E.P. (1986) *The Fears of Childhood: A Guide to Recognizing and Reducing Fearful States in Children*. New York: Human Sciences Press.

Sedgwick Galvin, E. (1994) "The Joy of Seasons: With the Children, Discover the Joys of Nature." *Young Children* 49(4):4–9.

Shipley, C.D. (1993) *Empowering Children: Play-Based Curriculum for Lifelong Learning*. Scarborough, ON: Nelson Canada.

Stansbury, K., and M. Gunnar (1994) "Adrenocortical Activity and Emotion Regulation." In N.A. Fox (ed.), *The Development of Emotion Regulation: Biological and Behavioural Considerations*. Monographs of the Society of Research in Child Development, Serial No. 240. vol. 59, nos. 2–3. Chicago: University of Chicago Press.

Sterling Honig, A. (1986) "Stress and Coping in Children," in *Reducing Stress in Young Children's Lives*, J. Brown McCracken (ed.). Washington, DC: National Association for the Education of Young Children.

Sterling Honig, A., and T. Lansburgh (1991) "The Tasks of Early Childhood: The Development of Self-Control Part II." *Day Care and Early Education*, summer:66–71.

Waxler-Morrison, N., et al. (eds.) (1990) *Cross-Cultural Caring: A Handbook for Health Professionals in Western Canada*. Vancouver: University of British Columbia Press.

World Health Organization (1983) *WHO Press Release (Survey of 35 Studies)*. WHO Global Program on AIDS. December.

World Health Organization, Health and Welfare Canada, and Canadian Public Health Association (1986) *Ottawa Charter for Health Promotion*. Ottawa.

Appendix 7.1

Bread

Multicultural snacks need not be exotic and expensive food bought at specialty shops. Start with a very basic food such as bread. Avoid the butter-and-cracker trap and put a variety of breads on your snack plate instead. Slice them, stuff them, spread them, dip them, toast them, or cut them with cookie cutters to make interesting shapes. Some of the breads you may want to use are listed below.

Bagels (Jewish)
Baguette (French)
Bannock bread (early Canadian)
Bran bread
Bread sticks, cheese sticks
Buns
Buttermilk biscuits
Challah (Jewish)
Chapati (Indian)
Christonomo (Italian)
Cornbread
Cornpone (Central American)
Croissants (French)
Datebread
Fry bread (Navajo)
Steamed buns (Chinese)

Croissant

Bagel

Irish soda bread

Roti (Caribbean/East Indian)

Muffin

Pita

Steamed bun

Gingerbread
Injera (Ethiopian)
Irish soda bread
Kamaj (Palestinian)
Klaben (German)
Knackbrod (German)
Laufabrod (Icelandic)
Matzot (Jewish)
Muffins
Nan (Indian)
Pita (Middle Eastern)
Popovers
Potato bread
Pumpernickel
Pumpkin bread
Raisin Bread

(appendix continues on next page)

Taboun (Palestinian)   Rye bread
Whole-wheat bread   Scones

Show the children photographs of people baking bread. Use the book *Bread, Bread, Bread* (published by Lothrop, Lee and Shepard, 1989) to give a photo tour of world cultures and the breads native to each. Then buy the bread or try your hand at making some. Unleavened bread or bread leavened by an agent other than yeast is best to make with young children because it is so quick. Try these recipes, adjusting quantities to suit the group. Each recipe serves about 20 children.

Bannock (early Canadian, originally Scottish)
Ingredients:
    750 mL flour   30 mL water
    dash of salt   10 mL oil
    40 mL baking powder
Method:
1. Use a fork to mix all the dry ingredients.
2. Make a well in the dry ingredients, then pour in the water.
3. Mix the dough by hand, kneading it, then pound it flat.
4. Fry on an oiled griddle until puffy and golden on both sides.

Chapatis (Indian)
Ingredients:
    500 mL whole-wheat flour   175 mL water
    2 mL salt
Method:
1. Mix whole-wheat flour, salt, and water to form a stiff dough. Add more water if necessary.
2. Let the dough rest for 1/2 hour, then roll into small balls.
3. Flatten the balls, then fry them on a very hot griddle until brown spots appear on the dough.
4. Take them off the griddle and brush with butter or serve plain.

Tortillas (Mexican)
Ingredients:
    625 mL corn flour   10 mL oil
    250 mL water   10 mL butter
    rolling pin or tortilla press
Method:
1. Mix corn flour with enough water to make a stiff dough.
2. Roll into small balls, then flatten with a rolling pin or tortilla press.
3. Fry in a lightly oiled pan, turning until cooked.
4. Brush with butter and serve.

Source: Reprinted with permission from M. Cech, *Globalchild: Multicultural Resources for Young Children*, (Ottawa, 1990), 43–44.

Index

To the owner of this book

We hope that you have enjoyed *Healthy Foundations in Child Care*, Second Edition, by Pimento and Kernested (ISBN 0-17-616580-0), and we would like to know as much about your experiences with this text as you would care to offer. Only through your comments and those of others can we learn how to make this a better text for future readers.

School _____ Your instructor's name _____

Course _____ Was the text required? _____ Recommended? _____

1. What did you like the most about *Healthy Foundations in Child Care?*

_____
_____
_____

2. How useful was this text for your course?

_____
_____
_____

3. Do you have any recommendations for ways to improve the next edition of this text?

_____
_____
_____

4. In the space below or in a separate letter, please write any other comments you have about the book. (For example, please feel free to comment on reading level, writing style, terminology, design features, and learning aids.)

_____
_____
_____
_____

Optional

Your name _____ Date
_____

May Nelson Thomson Learning quote you, either in promotion for *Healthy Foundations in Child Care* or in future publishing ventures?

Yes _____ No _____

You can also send your comments to us via e-mail at
college@nelson.com

PLEASE TAPE SHUT. DO NOT STAPLE.

TAPE SHUT

TAPE SHUT

— — — FOLD HERE — — — — —

Nelson
Thomson Learning™

0066102399-M1K5G4-BR01

NELSON, THOMSON LEARNING
HIGHER EDUCATION
PO BOX 60225 STN BRM B
TORONTO ON M7Y 2H1

TAPE SHUT

TAPE SHUT